UNDERSTANDING
ICSE
MATHEMATICS

CLASS IX

In Strict Conformity with the Latest Syllabus prescribed by the Council for Indian School Certificate Examinations, New Delhi for Students appearing for Class IX Examination in 2022 and Class X from 2023 onwards.

by
M.L. AGGARWAL
Former Head of P.G. Department of Mathematics
D.A.V. College, Jalandhar

AVICHAL PUBLISHING COMPANY
Industrial Area, Trilokpur Road, Kala Amb 173 030, Distt. Sirmour (HP)
Delhi Office : 1002 Faiz Road (opp. Hanumanji Murti), Karol Bagh, New Delhi-110 005

Published by:

AVICHAL PUBLISHING COMPANY
Industrial Area, Trilokpur Road
Kala Amb 173 030, Distt. Sirmour (HP)

Delhi Office:
1002 Faiz Road (opp. Hanumanji Murti),
Karol Bagh, New Delhi 110 005 (India)
Phone : 011-28752604, 28752745
Fax : 011-28756921
Email : info@apcbooks.co.in
Website : www.apcbooks.co.in

© Author

ISBN-978-81-7739-554-9

Thoroughly Revised Edition : 2005
Modified Edition : 2006
Thoroughly Revised Edition : 2007
Thoroughly Revised Edition : 2008
Modified Edition : 2009
Revised Edition : 2010
Revised Edition : 2011
Thirteenth Edition : 2012
Reprint with modifications : 2013
Fourteenth Edition : 2014
Fifteenth Edition : 2015
Sixteenth Edition : 2016
Reprint : 2017
Seventeenth Edition: 2018
Reprint : 2019, 20
Reprint : 2021

Price : ₹ 475.00

Laser Typeset at :
Laser Tech Prints

Printed at :
Deepak Offset Printers
Bawana Industrial Area, Delhi

Publication of
Key to this book
is strictly
prohibited.

**Beware of
DUPLICATE BOOKS**

We do not have any policy of selling soiled/badly printed books as rejected lots in the market. Kindly beware of **DUPLICATE BOOKS** sold as so called rejected lots.

Preface

This book was first published in 1994. Sixteen editions and a number of reprints published during these years show its growing popularity among students and teachers. The book has been revised thoroughly again strictly conforming to the latest syllabus issued by the Council for ICSE examinations.

The subject matter contained in this book has been explained in a simple language and includes many examples from real life situations. Emphasis has been laid on basic facts, terms, principles, concepts and on their applications. Carefully selected examples consist of detailed step-by-step solutions so that students get prepared to tackle all the problems given in the exercises.

A new feature *'Multiple Choice Questions'* has been added in each chapter. These questions have been framed in a manner such that they holistically cover all the concepts included in the chapter and also, prepare students for the competitive exams. This is further followed by a **'Chapter Test'** which serves as the brief revision of the entire chapter.

An attempt has been made to make the book user friendly—matter is well spaced out and divided into sections and sub-sections which have been differentiated by using headings of different sizes and colour, thus reducing the strain on the eyes of the students and giving the book a neat and uncluttered look. It has been my sincere endeavour to present the concepts, examples and questions in a coherent and interesting manner so that the students develop interest in 'learning' and 'understanding' mathematics.

I am grateful to my publishers 'M/s Avichal Publishing Company' and 'Laser Tech Prints' and thank them for their friendly cooperation and untiring efforts in bringing out this book in an excellent form. I would highly appreciate if you suggest any improvement you would like to see in the book in its next edition.

—M.L. Aggarwal

www.ilovemaths.com

Log in for Vedic mathematics, Indian mathematicians, Question-answering service and discussion forum moderated by Professor Theta, Classroom material, Model test papers and much more ...

Salient Features of This Book

☆ This book is written strictly according to latest syllabus prescribed by the Council for ICSE examinations.

☆ The subject material has been treated systematically and presented in a coherent and interesting manner.

☆ The theory has been explained in simple language and includes many examples from real life situations. Emphasis has been laid on the basic facts, concepts, terms, principles and on the applications of various concepts.

☆ Carefully selected examples consist of detailed step-by-step solutions. A number of solved examples are included in each section so that students are well prepared to tackle all the problems given in exercises.

☆ Each chapter is followed by a **Chapter Test** which includes problems related to all the topics, so that the students have total understanding of these topics before moving on to next chapter.

☆ An attempt has been made to make the book user friendly—matter is well spaced out and given in a bigger type size. Also, the matter has been divided into sections and sub-sections so that students can learn at their own pace.

☆ Each chapter contains an exercise on **Multiple Choice Questions** which have been framed in a manner such that they holistically cover all the concepts included in the chapter.

☆ This book is sufficient to help the students score cent-percent marks in ICSE examination and also builds a strong foundation for success in any competitive examination.

Contents

Latest Syllabus in Mathematics

CLASS IX

AIMS:

1. To acquire knowledge and understanding of the terms, symbols, concepts, principles, processes, proofs, etc. of mathematics.

2. To develop an understanding of mathematical concepts and their application to further studies in mathematics and science.

3. To develop skills to apply mathematical knowledge to solve real life problems.

4. To develop the necessary skills to work with modern technological devices such as calculators and computers in real life situations.

5. To develop drawing skills, skills of reading tables, charts and graphs.

6. To develop an interest in mathematics.

*There will be one paper of **two and a half** hours duration carrying 80 marks and Internal Assessment of 20 marks.*

The paper will be divided into two sections, Section I (40 marks), Section II (40 marks).

Section I: *Will consist of compulsory short answer questions.*

Section II: *Candidates will be required to answer four out of seven questions.*

The solution of a question may require the knowledge of more than one branch of the syllabus.

1. PURE ARITHMETIC

Rational and Irrational Numbers

Rational, irrational numbers as real numbers, their place in the number system. Surds and rationalization of surds. Simplifying an expression by rationalizing the denominator. Representation of rational and irrational numbers on the number line.

Proofs of irrationality of $\sqrt{2}$, $\sqrt{3}$, $\sqrt{5}$.

2. COMMERCIAL MATHEMATICS

Compound Interest

(a) *Compound interest as a repeated Simple Interest computation with a growing Principal. Use of this in computing Amount over a period of 2 or 3 years.*

(b) *Use of formula $A = P\left(1+\dfrac{r}{100}\right)^n$. Finding CI from the relation CI = A − P.*

- *Interest compounded half-yearly included.*

- *Using the formula to find one quantity given different combinations of A, P, r, n, CI and SI; difference between CI and SI type included.*

- *Rate of growth and depreciation.*

Note: Paying back in equal instalments, being given rate of interest and instalment amount, **not included**.

3. **ALGEBRA**

   (*i*) Expansions

   Recall of concepts learned in earlier classes.

   $(a \pm b)^2$

   $(a \pm b)^3$

   $(x \pm a) (x \pm b)$

   $(a \pm b \pm c)^2$

   (*ii*) Factorisation

   $a^2 - b^2$

   $a^3 \pm b^3$

   $ax^2 + bx + c$, *by splitting the middle term.*

   (*iii*) Simultaneous Linear Equations in two variables. (With numerical coefficients only)

   - *Solving algebraically by:*
     - *Elimination*
     - *Substitution and*
     - *Cross Multiplication method*
   - *Solving simple problems by framing appropriate equations.*

   (*iv*) Indices/Exponents

   Handling positive, fractional, negative and "zero" indices.

   Simplification of expressions involving various exponents

   $a^m \times a^n = a^{m+n}$, $a^m \div a^n = a^{m-n}$, $(a^m)^n = a^{mn}$ *etc. Use of laws of exponents.*

   (*v*) Logarithms

   (*a*) *Logarithmic form vis-à-vis exponential form : interchanging.*

   (*b*) *Laws of Logarithms and their uses.*

   Expansion of expression with the help of laws of logarithms

   e.g. $y = \dfrac{a^4 \times b^2}{c^3}$

   $log\, y = 4\, log\, a + 2\, log\, b - 3\, log\, c$ *etc.*

4. **GEOMETRY**

   (*i*) Triangles

   (*a*) Congruency : four cases : SSS, SAS, AAS and RHS. Illustration through cutouts. Simple applications.

   (*b*) Problems based on :

   - *Angles opposite equal sides are equal and converse.*
   - *If two sides of a triangle are unequal, then the greater angle is opposite the greater side and converse.*
   - *Sum of any two sides of a triangle is greater than the third side.*
   - *Of all straight lines that can be drawn to a given line from a point outside it, the perpendicular is the shortest.*

   Proofs not required.

(c) Mid-Point Theorem and its converse, equal intercept theorem

    (i) *Proof and simple applications of mid-point theorem and its converse.*

    (ii) *Equal intercept theorem : proof and simple application.*

(d) Pythagoras Theorem

Area based proof and simple applications of Pythagoras Theorem and its converse.

(ii) Rectilinear Figures

(a) Proof and use of theorems on parallelogram.

- *Both pairs of opposite sides equal (without proof).*
- *Both pairs of opposite angles equal.*
- *One pair of opposite sides equal and parallel (without proof).*
- *Diagonals bisect each other and bisect the parallelogram.*
- *Rhombus as a special parallelogram whose diagonals meet at right angles.*
- *In a rectangle, diagonals are equal, in a square they are equal and meet at right angles.*

(b) Constructions of Polygons

Construction of quadrilaterals (including parallelograms and rhombus) and regular hexagon using ruler and compasses only.

(c) Proof and use of Area theorems on parallelograms :

- *Parallelograms on the same base and between the same parallels are equal in area.*
- *The area of a triangle is half that of a parallelogram on the same base and between the same parallels.*
- *Triangles between the same base and between the same parallels are equal in area (without proof).*
- *Triangles with equal areas on the same bases have equal corresponding altitudes.*

(iii) Circle:

(a) Chord properties

- *A straight line drawn from the centre of a circle to bisect a chord which is not a diameter is at right angles to the chord.*
- *The perpendicular to a chord from the centre bisects the chord (without proof).*
- *Equal chords are equidistant from the centre.*
- *Chords equidistant from the centre are equal (without proof).*
- *There is one and only one circle that passes through three given points not in a straight line.*

(b) Arc and chord properties:

- *If two arcs subtend equal angles at the centre, they are equal, and its converse.*
- *If two chords are equal, they cut off equal arcs, and its converse (without proof).*

Note : *Proofs of the theorems given above are to be taught unless specified otherwise.*

5.   STATISTICS

Introduction, collection of data, presentation of data, Graphical representation of data, Mean, Median of ungrouped data.

(i) *Understanding and recognition of raw, arrayed and grouped data.*

(ii) *Tabulation of raw data using tally-marks.*

(iii) *Understanding and recognition of discrete and continuous variables.*

(iv) *Mean, median of ungrouped data.*

(v) *Class intervals, class boundaries and limits, frequency, frequency table, class size for grouped data.*

(vi) *Grouped frequency distributions : the need to and how to convert discontinuous intervals to continuous intervals.*

(vii) *Drawing a frequency polygon.*

6. MENSURATION

Area and perimeter of a triangle and a quadrilateral. Area and circumference of circle. Surface area and volume of Cube and Cuboids.

(a) *Area and perimeter of triangle (including Heron's formula), all types of Quadrilaterals.*

(b) *Circle: Area and Circumference. Direct application problems including Inner and Outer area.*

Areas of sectors of circles other than quarter-circle and semicircle are not inlcuded.

(c) *Surface area and volume of 3-D solids: cube and cuboid including problems of type involving:*

- *Different internal and external dimensions of the solid.*

- *Cost.*

- *Concept of volume being equal to area of cross-section × height.*

- *Open/closed cubes/cuboids.*

7. TRIGONOMETRY

(a) *Trigonometric Ratios : sine, cosine, tangent of an angle and their reciprocals.*

(b) *Trigonometric ratios of standard angles—0, 30, 45, 60, 90 degrees. Evaluation of an expression involving these ratios.*

(c) *Simple 2-D problems involving one right-angled triangle.*

(d) *Concept of trigonometric ratios of complementary angles and their direct application.*

$sin\ A = cos(90 - A),\ cos\ A = sin(90 - A)$

$tan\ A = cot(90 - A),\ cot\ A = tan(90 - A)$

$sec\ A = cosec(90 - A),\ cosec\ A = sec(90 - A)$

8. COORDINATE GEOMETRY

Cartesian System, plotting of points in the plane for given coordinates, solving simultaneous linear equations in 2 variables graphically and finding the distance between two points using distance formula.

(a) *Dependent and independent variables.*

(b) *Ordered pairs, coordinates of points and plotting them in the Cartesian plane.*

(c) *Solution of Simultaneous Linear Equations graphically.*

(d) *Distance formula.*

INTERNAL ASSESSMENT

A minimum of two assignments are to be done during the year as prescribed by the teacher.

SUGGESTED ASSIGNMENTS

- Conduct a survey of a group of students and represent it graphically - height, weight, number of family members, pocket money, etc.
- Planning delivery routes for a postman/milkman.
- Running a tuck shop/canteen.
- Study ways of raising a loan to buy a car or house, e.g. bank loan or purchase a refrigerator or a television set through hire purchase.
- Cutting a circle into equal sections of a small central angle to find the area of a circle by using the formula $A = \pi r^2$.
- To use flat cutouts to form cube, cuboids and pyramids to obtain formulae for volume and total surface area.
- Draw a circle of radius r on a $\frac{1}{2}$ cm graph paper, and then on a 2 mm graph paper. Estimate the area enclosed in each case by actually counting the squares. Now try out with circles of different radii. Establish the pattern, if any, between the two observed values and the theoretical value (area = πr^2). Any modifications?

S.I. units, symbols and abbreviations

Agreed Conventions

(a) Units may be written in full or using the agreed symbols, but no other abbreviation may be used.

(b) The letter 's' is never added to symbols to indicate the plural form.

(c) A full stop is not written after symbols for units unless it occurs at the end of a sentence.

(d) When unit symbols are combined as a quotient, e.g. metre per second, it is recommended that they may be written as m/s or better still as $m\,s^{-1}$.

(e) Three decimal signs are in common international use : the full point, the mid-point and the comma. Since the full point is sometimes used for multiplication and comma for spacing digits in large numbers, we shall be on the safe side if we use the mid-point for decimals.

S.I. UNITS (International System of Units)

Basic S.I. Units

Quantity	Unit of Measure	Symbol
Length	metre	m
Mass/Weight	kilogram	kg
Capacity	litre	L
Time	second	s

Measures of Length

	Symbols
10 millimetres = 1 centimetre	10 mm = 1 cm
100 centimetres = 1 metre	100 cm = 1 m
1000 metres = 1 kilometre	1000 m = 1 km

Measures of Mass/Weight

10 milligrams = 1 centigram	10 mg = 1 cg
100 centigrams = 1 gram	100 cg = 1 g
1000 grams = 1 kilogram	1000 g = 1 kg
100 kilograms = 1 quintal	
10 quintals = 1 metric tonne	

Measures of Capacity

10 millilitres = 1 centilitre	10 mL = 1 cL
100 centilitres = 1 litre	100 cL = 1 L
1000 litres = 1 kilolitre	1000 L = 1 kL

Square and Cubic Units

$1 \text{ cm}^2 = 100 \text{ mm}^2$ $1 \text{ cm}^3 = 1000 \text{ mm}^3$

$1 \text{ m}^2 = 10000 \text{ cm}^2$ $1 \text{ m}^3 = 1000000 \text{ cm}^3$

Commonly Used Equivalents

$1 \text{ litre} = 1000 \text{ cm}^3$

$1 \text{ m}^3 = 1000 \text{ litres}$

$1 \text{ hectare} = 10000 \text{ m}^2$

Measures of Time

60 seconds = 1 minute   60 s = 1 min

60 minutes = 1 hour   60 min = 1 h

24 hours = 1 day   24 h = 1 dy

7 days = 1 week

30 days = 1 month

365 days = 1 year   (366 days = 1 leap year)

SYMBOLS AND ABBREVIATIONS

Implies that	$\Rightarrow$	logically equivalent to	$\Leftrightarrow$
identically equal to	$\equiv$	approximately equal to	$\approx$
belongs to	$\in$	does not belong to	$\notin$
is equivalent to	$\leftrightarrow$	is not equivalent to	$\nleftrightarrow$
union	$\cup$	intersection	$\cap$
contains	$\supset$	is contained in	$\subset$
universal set	$\cdot\ \xi$	the empty set	ϕ
natural numbers	N	whole numbers	W
integers	I or Z	real numbers	R
is parallel to	$\parallel$	is perpendicular to	$\perp$
is congruent to	$\cong$		

Rational and Irrational Numbers

1

INTRODUCTION

You are already familiar with the system of natural numbers, whole numbers, integers, rational numbers and their representation on the number line. You also know the four fundamental operations of arithmetic on them—addition, subtraction, multiplication and division. In this chapter, we shall extend our study to irrational numbers and real numbers. We shall learn the decimal expansions of real numbers as terminating/non-terminating decimal numbers and shall explain that every real number can be represented by a unique point on the number line and conversely corresponding to every point on the number line there is a unique real number. We shall also learn the surds and rationalisation of surds; simplifying expressions by rationalising the denominator.

1.1 RATIONAL NUMBERS

Recall the definition of a rational number.

*Any number that can be expressed in the form $\frac{p}{q}$, where p and q are both integers and $q \neq 0$ is called a **rational number**.*

The word 'rational' comes from the word 'ratio'. Thus, every rational number can be written as the ratio of two integers.

Note that every integer (positive, negative or zero) can be written in the form $\frac{p}{q}$ where $q = 1$. For example,

$$5 = \frac{5}{1}, -7 = \frac{-7}{1}, 0 = \frac{0}{1}.$$

Hence, every integer is a rational number.

We know that the rational numbers do not have a unique representation in the form $\frac{p}{q}$, where p and q are both integers and $q \neq 0$. For example, $\frac{1}{2} = \frac{2}{4} = \frac{3}{6} = \frac{7}{14} = \frac{53}{106}$, etc. In fact, these are equivalent rational numbers. However, if we write a rational number in the form $\frac{p}{q}$, where p and q are both integers and $q \neq 0$ and p and q have no common factors except 1, then among the infinitely many rational numbers equivalent to $\frac{1}{2}$, we choose $\frac{1}{2}$ to represent all of them on the number line.

Thus, a rational number can be uniquely expressed as $\frac{p}{q}$ where p and q are both integers, $q \neq 0$ and p and q have no common factors except 1 i.e. p and q are co-prime.

It is called in the **lowest terms** or **simplest form** or **irreducible form**.

Remarks

❑ Since the division by zero is not allowed, $\frac{1}{0}$ is not a rational number *i.e.* the reciprocal of zero is not allowed.

❑ When we write a rational number in the form $\frac{p}{q}$, $p, q \in I$ and $q \neq 0$, usually we take $q > 0$, while p may be positive, negative or zero.

❑ Two rational numbers $\frac{a}{b}$ and $\frac{c}{d}$ are called **equal**, written as $\frac{a}{b} = \frac{c}{d}$, if and only if $ad = bc$.

1.1.1 Representation of rational numbers

Recall the representation of natural numbers, whole numbers, integers and rational numbers on the number line.

Let l be a straight line which extends endlessly on both sides. Mark the positive direction to the right by an arrowhead. Take a point O on l and label it 0 (zero). Next choose another point, say A, on l towards the right of O and label it 1 (one). Thus the points O and A represent the numbers 0 and 1 respectively. The length of the segment OA represents unit length. Now mark points on l to the right of A at unit length intervals and label these 2, 3, 4, ... Similarly, mark points on l to the left of O at unit length intervals and label them $-1, -2, -3, -4, \ldots$, shown in fig. 1.1. *Thus, every integer has been represented by one and only one point on the line l.*

Next, we consider the representation of rational numbers on the line l. Take one-half of the unit length and mark points on l on both sides of O; these points will represent the numbers $\frac{1}{2}, \frac{2}{2}, \frac{3}{2}$ and $-\frac{1}{2}, -\frac{2}{2}, -\frac{3}{2}, \ldots$, shown in fig. 1.1.

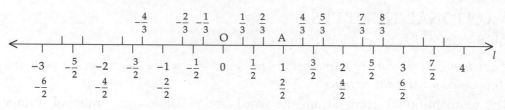

Fig. 1.1

Similarly, take one-third of the unit length and mark points on l on both sides of O; these points will represent the numbers $\frac{1}{3}, \frac{2}{3}, \frac{3}{3}, \frac{4}{3}, \ldots$ and $-\frac{1}{3}, -\frac{2}{3}, -\frac{3}{3}, -\frac{4}{3}, \ldots$ and so on. *Thus, every rational number has been represented by one and only one point on the line l.*

1.1.2 Properties of rational numbers

The following results hold for the system (collection) of rational numbers:

(1) If a, b are any two rational numbers, then $a + b$ is also a rational number.

For example, $\frac{1}{3} + \frac{2}{7} = \frac{7+6}{21} = \frac{13}{21}$, which is a rational number.

(2) If a, b are any two rational numbers, then $a - b$ is also a rational number.

For example, $\frac{1}{3} - \frac{2}{7} = \frac{7-6}{21} = \frac{1}{21}$, which is a rational number.

(3) If a, b are any two rational numbers, then $a \times b$ is also a rational number.

For example, $\frac{1}{3} \times \frac{2}{7} = \frac{2}{21}$, which is a rational number.

(4) If $a, b \, (\neq 0)$ are any two rational numbers, then $\frac{a}{b}$ is also a rational number.

For example, $\frac{1}{3} \div \frac{2}{7} = \frac{1}{3} \times \frac{7}{2} = \frac{7}{6}$, which is a rational number.

Thus, the system (collection) of rational numbers is closed under all the four fundamental operations of arithmetic (except division by zero).

(5) The collection of rational numbers is ordered *i.e.* if a, b are any two rational numbers, then either $a < b$ or $a > b$ or $a = b$.

(6) If a, b are any two different rational numbers, then $\dfrac{a+b}{2}$ is a rational number and it lies between them *i.e.* if $a < b$ then $a < \dfrac{a+b}{2} < b$. Continuing this process, we find that there are *infinitely many* rational numbers between two different rational numbers.

For example, $\dfrac{\frac{1}{3}+\frac{2}{7}}{2} = \dfrac{13}{42}$ is a rational number which lies between $\dfrac{1}{3}$ and $\dfrac{2}{7}$.

Illustrative Examples

Example 1 Insert one rational number between $\dfrac{5}{7}$ and $\dfrac{4}{9}$ and arrange in ascending order.

Solution. The L.C.M. of 7 and 9 is 63.

$$\frac{5}{7} = \frac{5\times9}{7\times9} = \frac{45}{63},\ \frac{4}{9} = \frac{4\times7}{9\times7} = \frac{28}{63}.$$

Since $28 < 45$, $\dfrac{4}{9} < \dfrac{5}{7}$.

A rational number between $\dfrac{4}{9}$ and $\dfrac{5}{7} = \dfrac{\frac{4}{9}+\frac{5}{7}}{2} = \dfrac{\frac{28+45}{63}}{2} = \dfrac{73}{126}$, and the numbers in ascending order are $\dfrac{4}{9}, \dfrac{73}{126}, \dfrac{5}{7}$.

> **Note** Since infinitely many rational numbers lie between two rational numbers, $\dfrac{73}{126}$ is not the only rational number between $\dfrac{4}{9}$ and $\dfrac{5}{7}$.

Example 2 Insert three rational numbers between 3 and 3·5.

Solution. A rational number between 3 and 3·5 $= \dfrac{3+3\cdot5}{2} = \dfrac{6\cdot5}{2} = 3\cdot25$.

A rational number between 3 and 3·25 $= \dfrac{3+3\cdot25}{2} = \dfrac{6\cdot5}{2} = 3\cdot125$.

A rational number between 3 and 3·125 $= \dfrac{3+3\cdot125}{2} = \dfrac{6\cdot125}{2} = 3\cdot0625$.

We note that $3 < 3\cdot0625 < 3\cdot125 < 3\cdot25 < 3\cdot5$, therefore, three rational numbers between 3 and 3·5 are 3·0625, 3·125, 3·25.

Example 3 Find five rational numbers between 2 and 3.

Solution. We shall approach the problem in two ways.

Method I. A rational number between 2 and 3 $= \dfrac{2+3}{2} = \dfrac{5}{2}$.

A rational number between 2 and $\dfrac{5}{2} = \dfrac{2+\frac{5}{2}}{2} = \dfrac{9}{4}$.

A rational number between 2 and $\dfrac{9}{4} = \dfrac{2+\frac{9}{4}}{2} = \dfrac{17}{8}$.

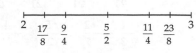

Fig. 1.2

A rational number between $\frac{5}{2}$ and $3 = \dfrac{\frac{5}{2}+3}{2} = \frac{11}{4}$.

A rational number between $\frac{11}{4}$ and $3 = \dfrac{\frac{11}{4}+3}{2} = \frac{23}{8}$.

Thus, five rational numbers between 2 and 3 are $\frac{17}{8}, \frac{9}{4}, \frac{5}{2}, \frac{11}{4}, \frac{23}{8}$.

Method II. The other way is to find all the five rational numbers in one step.

The given numbers 2 and 3 can be written as $2 = \frac{2}{1}$ and $3 = \frac{3}{1}$.

Since we want to find five rational numbers between the given numbers, multiplying the numerator and denominator of each of the above numbers by 5 + 1 *i.e.* by 6, we get $\frac{12}{6}$ and $\frac{18}{6}$, which are equivalent to the given numbers.

As 12 < 13 < 14 < 15 < 16 < 17 < 18,

$$\frac{12}{6} < \frac{13}{6} < \frac{14}{6} < \frac{15}{6} < \frac{16}{6} < \frac{17}{6} < \frac{18}{6}$$

$$\Rightarrow \quad 2 < \frac{13}{6} < \frac{7}{3} < \frac{5}{2} < \frac{8}{3} < \frac{17}{6} < 3.$$

Therefore, five rational numbers between 2 and 3 are:

$$\frac{13}{6}, \frac{7}{3}, \frac{5}{2}, \frac{8}{3}, \frac{17}{6}.$$

Example 4 Find six rational numbers between $\frac{3}{5}$ and $\frac{4}{5}$.

Solution. Since we want to find six rational numbers between $\frac{3}{5}$ and $\frac{4}{5}$, multiplying the numerator and denominator of each of the given numbers by 6 + 1 *i.e.* by 7, we get $\frac{21}{35}$ and $\frac{28}{35}$, which are equivalent to the given numbers.

As   21 < 22 < 23 < 24 < 25 < 26 < 27 < 28,

$$\frac{21}{35} < \frac{22}{35} < \frac{23}{35} < \frac{24}{35} < \frac{25}{35} < \frac{26}{35} < \frac{27}{35} < \frac{28}{35}$$

$$\Rightarrow \quad \frac{3}{5} < \frac{22}{35} < \frac{23}{35} < \frac{24}{35} < \frac{5}{7} < \frac{26}{35} < \frac{27}{35} < \frac{4}{5}.$$

Therefore, six rational numbers between $\frac{3}{5}$ and $\frac{4}{5}$ are:

$$\frac{22}{35}, \frac{23}{35}, \frac{24}{35}, \frac{5}{7}, \frac{26}{35}, \frac{27}{35}.$$

Example 5 Insert eight rational numbers between $-\frac{1}{3}$ and $\frac{2}{7}$.

Solution. Writing the given numbers with same denominator 21 (L.C.M. of 3 and 7), we get $-\frac{1}{3} = \frac{-7}{21}$ and $\frac{2}{7} = \frac{6}{21}$.

As $-7 < -6 < -5 < -4 < -3 < -2 < -1 < 0 < 1 < 6$,

$$-\frac{7}{21} < -\frac{6}{21} < -\frac{5}{21} < -\frac{4}{21} < -\frac{3}{21} < -\frac{2}{21} < -\frac{1}{21} < 0 < \frac{1}{21} < \frac{6}{21}$$

$$\Rightarrow \quad -\frac{1}{3} < -\frac{2}{7} < -\frac{5}{21} < -\frac{4}{21} < -\frac{1}{7} < -\frac{2}{21} < -\frac{1}{21} < 0 < \frac{1}{21} < \frac{2}{7}.$$

Therefore, eight rational numbers between $-\dfrac{1}{3}$ and $\dfrac{2}{7}$ are:

$$-\dfrac{2}{7}, -\dfrac{5}{21}, -\dfrac{4}{21}, -\dfrac{1}{7}, -\dfrac{2}{21}, -\dfrac{1}{21}, 0, \dfrac{1}{21}.$$

Example 6 Find four rational numbers between $\dfrac{3}{4}$ and $\dfrac{5}{6}$.

Solution. Writing the given numbers with same denominator 12 (L.C.M. of 4 and 6), we get $\dfrac{3}{4} = \dfrac{9}{12}$ and $\dfrac{5}{6} = \dfrac{10}{12}$.

Since we want to find four rational numbers between the given numbers, multiplying the numerator and denominator of the above numbers by $4 + 1$ *i.e.* by 5, we get $\dfrac{45}{60}$ and $\dfrac{50}{60}$, which are equivalent to the given numbers.

As $45 < 46 < 47 < 48 < 49 < 50$,

$$\dfrac{45}{60} < \dfrac{46}{60} < \dfrac{47}{60} < \dfrac{48}{60} < \dfrac{49}{60} < \dfrac{50}{60}$$

$\Rightarrow \quad \dfrac{3}{4} < \dfrac{23}{30} < \dfrac{47}{60} < \dfrac{4}{5} < \dfrac{49}{60} < \dfrac{5}{6}.$

Therefore, four rational numbers between $\dfrac{3}{4}$ and $\dfrac{5}{6}$ are: $\dfrac{23}{30}, \dfrac{47}{60}, \dfrac{4}{5}, \dfrac{49}{60}.$

EXERCISE 1.1

1 Insert a rational number between $\dfrac{2}{9}$ and $\dfrac{3}{8}$, and arrange in descending order.

2 Insert two rational numbers between $\dfrac{1}{3}$ and $\dfrac{1}{4}$, and arrange in ascending order.

3 Insert two rational numbers between $-\dfrac{1}{3}$ and $-\dfrac{1}{2}$ and arrange in ascending order.

4 Insert three rational numbers between $\dfrac{1}{3}$ and $\dfrac{4}{5}$, and arrange in descending order.

5 Insert three rational numbers between 4 and 4·5.

6 Find six rational numbers between 3 and 4.

7 Find five rational numbers between $\dfrac{3}{5}$ and $\dfrac{4}{5}$.

8 Find ten rational numbers between $-\dfrac{2}{5}$ and $\dfrac{1}{7}$.

9 Find six rational numbers between $\dfrac{1}{2}$ and $\dfrac{2}{3}$.

1.2 IRRATIONAL NUMBERS

Look at the number line l (shown in fig. 1.1) again and think of the situation in another way. As far as you can imagine, there are infinitely many numbers on the number line.

You may start collecting only natural numbers *i.e.* the numbers 1, 2, 3, 4, …. You know that this list of natural numbers is endless *i.e.* there are infinitely many natural numbers. The system of **natural numbers** is denoted by **N**.

If you put the number zero (0) in the above list, then you have the system of **whole numbers** which is denoted by **W**.

Further, if you put all the negative integers in the set of whole numbers then you get the system of **all integers** which is denoted by **I** (or **Z**).

Are there still more numbers left on the number line? Yes! There are numbers like $\frac{1}{2}, \frac{2}{3}, \frac{6}{7}, -\frac{5}{11}, \frac{231}{14}, \frac{3331}{112}$, etc. If you put all these numbers in the set of all integers, you get the system of **rational numbers** which is denoted by **Q**.

The question arises: Have you collected all the numbers on the number line? Not, as yet! In fact, there are infinitely many more numbers left on the number line. There are gaps in between the places of the numbers you have collected and not just a few gaps but infinitely many gaps. You will be surprised to realise that there are infinitely many more numbers (other than rational numbers) in these gaps.

Pythagoreans (followers of great mathematician Pythagoras), were the first to discover such numbers. These numbers are called **irrational numbers**, because these numbers cannot be written in the form of ratio of two integers.

Formally, we define these numbers as:

A number that cannot be expressed in the form $\frac{p}{q}$*, where p and q are both integers and q ≠ 0, p and q have no common factors (except 1), is called an **irrational number**.*

There are infinitely many irrational numbers. Some examples of these numbers are:

$$\sqrt{2}, \sqrt{3}, \sqrt{7}, -\sqrt{6}, \sqrt{20}, \frac{1}{\sqrt{5}}, 2 + \sqrt{3}, \text{ etc.}$$

Next, to represent irrational numbers on the line l, we use a result from geometry, known as Pythagoras theorem.

The square of the hypotenuse of a right angled triangle is equal to the sum of squares of the other two sides.

Construct a right angled triangle OAC, right angle at A, such that OA = AC = 1, then by Pythagoras theorem,

$$OC^2 = OA^2 + AC^2 \Rightarrow OC^2 = 1^2 + 1^2 = 2 \Rightarrow OC = \sqrt{2}.$$

Now mark a point, say P, on l on the right of O such that OP = OC = $\sqrt{2}$, then the point P represents the irrational number $\sqrt{2}$ (shown in fig. 1.3).

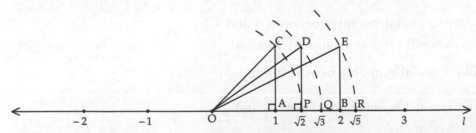

Fig. 1.3

To represent the irrational number $\sqrt{3}$ on the line l, construct a right angled triangle OPD, right angled at P such that DP = 1, then by Pythagoras theorem,

$$OD^2 = OP^2 + DP^2 = (\sqrt{2})^2 + 1^2 = 2 + 1 = 3 \Rightarrow OD = \sqrt{3}.$$

Now mark a point, say Q, on l to the right of O such that OQ = OD = $\sqrt{3}$, then the point Q represents the irrational number $\sqrt{3}$ (shown in fig. 1.3).

Next, to represent the irrational number $\sqrt{5}$ on the line l, construct a right angled triangle OBE, right angled at B such that BE = 1. Then by Pythagoras theorem,

$$OE^2 = OB^2 + BE^2 = 2^2 + 1^2 = 4 + 1 = 5 \Rightarrow OE = \sqrt{5}.$$

Now mark a point, say R, on l to the right of O such that OR = OE = $\sqrt{5}$, then the point R represents the irrational number $\sqrt{5}$ (shown in fig. 1.3).

Thus, geometrical constructions can be devised to identify the points on the number line l which correspond to the irrational numbers $\sqrt{2}, \sqrt{3}, \sqrt{5}$, etc. and so on.

Hence, corresponding to every real number (rational or irrational) there exists one and only one point on the line l and conversely corresponding to every point on the line l there exists one and only one real number.

*The line l is called the **real axis** or the **number line**.*

Remark

When we use the symbol $\sqrt{}$, we assume that it is the positive square root of a number. Thus $\sqrt{4} = 2$, $\sqrt{\dfrac{9}{16}} = \dfrac{3}{4}$, etc. You are already familiar with the number π which is the ratio of the circumference of a circle to its diameter. The number π is irrational (which we accept without proof at this stage).

Theorem 1. *If a is any natural number and p is a prime number such that p divides a^2, then p divides a.*

The generalisation of the above theorem is:

If a, n are any natural numbers and p is a prime number such that p divides a^n, then p divides a.

Theorem 2. *If a and b are any natural numbers and p is a prime number such that p divides ab then p divides a or p divides b or p divides both.*

In proving the numbers $\sqrt{2}, \sqrt{3}, \sqrt{5}, \ldots$ to be irrational, we shall use theorems 1 and 2 stated above.

Illustrative Examples

Example 1 Prove that $\sqrt{2}$ is an irrational number.

Solution. Let $\sqrt{2}$ be a rational number, then

$\sqrt{2} = \dfrac{p}{q}$, where p, q are integers, $q \neq 0$ and p, q have no common factors (except 1)

$$\Rightarrow \quad 2 = \frac{p^2}{q^2} \Rightarrow p^2 = 2q^2 \qquad\qquad \ldots(i)$$

As 2 divides $2q^2$, so 2 divides p^2 but 2 is prime

$\Rightarrow \quad$ 2 divides p $\hfill$ (Theorem 1)

Let $p = 2m$, where m is an integer.

Substituting this value of p in (i), we get

$\qquad (2m)^2 = 2q^2 \Rightarrow 4m^2 = 2q^2 \Rightarrow 2m^2 = q^2$.

As 2 divides $2m^2$, so 2 divides q^2 but 2 is prime

$\Rightarrow \quad$ 2 divides q. $\hfill$ (Theorem 1)

Thus, p and q have a common factor 2. This contradicts that p and q have no common factors (except 1).

Hence, $\sqrt{2}$ is not a rational number. So, we conclude that $\sqrt{2}$ is an irrational number.

Example 2 Prove that $\sqrt{3}$ is an irrational number.

Solution. Let $\sqrt{3}$ be a rational number, then

$\sqrt{3} = \dfrac{p}{q}$, where p, q are integers, $q \neq 0$ and p, q have no common factors (except 1)

$\Rightarrow \quad 3 = \dfrac{p^2}{q^2} \Rightarrow p^2 = 3q^2$ \hfill ...(i)

As 3 divides $3q^2$, so 3 divides p^2 but 3 is prime

$\Rightarrow \quad$ 3 divides p \hfill (Theorem 1)

Let $p = 3m$, where m is an integer.

Substituting this value of p in (i), we get

$\quad (3m)^2 = 3q^2 \Rightarrow 9m^2 = 3q^2 \Rightarrow 3m^2 = q^2$.

As 3 divides $3q^2$, so 3 divides q^2 but 3 is prime

$\Rightarrow \quad$ 3 divides q \hfill (Theorem 1)

Thus, p and q have a common factor 3. This contradicts that p and q have no common factors (except 1).

Hence, $\sqrt{3}$ is not a rational number. So, we conclude that $\sqrt{3}$ is an irrational number.

Example 3 Prove that $\sqrt{p}$ is an irrational number, where p is prime.

Solution. Let $\sqrt{p}$ be a rational number, then

$\sqrt{p} = \dfrac{m}{n}$, where m, n are integers, $n \neq 0$ and m, n have no common factors (except 1)

$\Rightarrow \quad p = \dfrac{m^2}{n^2} \Rightarrow m^2 = pn^2$ \hfill ...(i)

As p divides pn^2, so p divides m^2 but p is prime

$\Rightarrow \quad p$ divides m \hfill (Theorem 1)

$\Rightarrow \quad m = pk$, where k is an integer.

Substituting this value of m in (i), we get

$\quad (pk)^2 = pn^2 \Rightarrow p^2k^2 = pn^2 \Rightarrow pk^2 = n^2$.

As p divides pk^2, so p divides n^2 but p is prime

$\Rightarrow \quad p$ divides n \hfill (Theorem 1)

Thus, m and n have a common factor p. This contradicts that m and n have no common factors (except 1).

Hence, $\sqrt{p}$ is not a rational number. So, we conclude that $\sqrt{p}$ is an irrational number.

Example 4 Show that $\dfrac{1}{\sqrt{2}}$ is an irrational number.

Solution. Let $\dfrac{1}{\sqrt{2}}$ be a rational number, then

$\dfrac{1}{\sqrt{2}} = \dfrac{p}{q}$, where p, q are integers, $q \neq 0$ and p, q have no common factors (except 1)

$\Rightarrow \quad \dfrac{1}{2} = \dfrac{p^2}{q^2} \Rightarrow q^2 = 2p^2$ \hfill ...(i)

As 2 divides $2p^2$, so 2 divides q^2 but 2 is prime

$\Rightarrow$ 2 divides q (Theorem 1)

$\Rightarrow$ $q = 2m$, where m is an integer.

Substituting this value of q in (i), we get

$(2m)^2 = 2p^2 \Rightarrow 4m^2 = 2p^2 \Rightarrow 2m^2 = p^2$.

As 2 divides $2m^2$, so 2 divides p^2 but 2 is prime

$\Rightarrow$ 2 divides p (Theorem 1)

Thus, p and q have a common factor 2. This contradicts that p and q have no common factors (except 1).

Hence, $\dfrac{1}{\sqrt{2}}$ is not a rational number.

So, we conclude that $\dfrac{1}{\sqrt{2}}$ is an irrational number.

Example 5 Prove that $\sqrt{10}$ is an irrational number.

Solution. Suppose that $\sqrt{10}$ is a rational number, then $\sqrt{10} = \dfrac{p}{q}$, where p, q are integers, $q \neq 0$, p and q have no common factors (except 1)

$\Rightarrow$ $10 = \dfrac{p^2}{q^2} \Rightarrow p^2 = 10q^2$ ...(i)

As 2 divides $10q^2$, 2 divides p^2 and 2 is a prime number

$\Rightarrow$ 2 divides p (using theorem 1)

Let $p = 2k$, where k is some integer.

Substituting this value of k in (i), we get

$(2k)^2 = 10q^2 \Rightarrow 2k^2 = 5q^2$.

As 2 divides $2k^2$, 2 divides $5q^2$

$\Rightarrow$ 2 divides 5 or 2 divides q^2 (using theorem 2)

But 2 does not divide 5, therefore, 2 divides q^2

$\Rightarrow$ 2 divides q (using theorem 1)

Thus, p and q have a common factor 2. This contradicts that p and q have no common factors (except 1).

Hence, our supposition is wrong. Therefore, $\sqrt{10}$ is an irrational number.

Example 6 Show that the number $7 - 2\sqrt{3}$ is an irrational number.

Solution. Let us assume that $7 - 2\sqrt{3}$ is a rational number, say r.

Then, $7 - 2\sqrt{3} = r \Rightarrow 2\sqrt{3} = 7 - r \Rightarrow \sqrt{3} = \dfrac{7-r}{2}$.

As r is rational, $7 - r$ is rational $\Rightarrow \dfrac{7-r}{2}$ is rational $\Rightarrow \sqrt{3}$ is rational.

But this contradicts the fact that $\sqrt{3}$ is irrational.

Hence, our assumption is wrong. Therefore, $7 - 2\sqrt{3}$ is an irrational number.

Example 7 Show that $7\sqrt{5}$ is an irrational number.

Solution. Let us assume that $7\sqrt{5}$ is rational, say r.

Then, $7\sqrt{5} = r \Rightarrow \sqrt{5} = \dfrac{r}{7}$.

As r is rational, $\dfrac{r}{7}$ is rational $\Rightarrow \sqrt{5}$ is rational.

But this contradicts that $\sqrt{5}$ is irrational.

Hence, our assumption is wrong. Therefore, $7\sqrt{5}$ is an irrational number.

Example 8 Prove that $\sqrt{3} + \sqrt{5}$ is an irrational number.

Solution. Suppose that $\sqrt{3} + \sqrt{5}$ is rational, say r.

Then, $\sqrt{3} + \sqrt{5} = r$ (note that $r \neq 0$)

$\Rightarrow \quad \sqrt{5} = r - \sqrt{3} \Rightarrow (\sqrt{5})^2 = (r - \sqrt{3})^2$

$\Rightarrow \quad 5 = r^2 + 3 - 2\sqrt{3}\,r \Rightarrow 2\sqrt{3}\,r = r^2 - 2$

$\Rightarrow \quad \sqrt{3} = \dfrac{r^2 - 2}{2r}.$

As r is rational and $r \neq 0$, so $\dfrac{r^2-2}{2r}$ is rational

$\Rightarrow \sqrt{3}$ is rational.

But this contradicts that $\sqrt{3}$ is irrational.

Hence, our supposition is wrong.

Therefore, $\sqrt{3} + \sqrt{5}$ is an irrational number.

Example 9 Prove that $\sqrt{p} + \sqrt{q}$ is irrational, where p, q are primes.

Solution. Suppose that $\sqrt{p} + \sqrt{q}$ is rational, say r.

Then, $\sqrt{p} + \sqrt{q} = r$ (note that $r \neq 0$)

$\Rightarrow \quad \sqrt{q} = r - \sqrt{p} \Rightarrow (\sqrt{q})^2 = (r - \sqrt{p})^2$

$\Rightarrow \quad q = r^2 + p - 2r\sqrt{p} \Rightarrow 2r\sqrt{p} = r^2 + p - q$

$\Rightarrow \quad \sqrt{p} = \dfrac{r^2 + p - q}{2r}.$

As r is rational and $r \neq 0$, so $\dfrac{r^2+p-q}{2r}$ is rational

$\Rightarrow \sqrt{p}$ is rational.

But this contradicts that $\sqrt{p}$ is irrational   ($\because p$ is prime)
Hence, our supposition is wrong.

Therefore, $\sqrt{p} + \sqrt{q}$ is an irrational number.

Example 10 Prove the following:

    (i) the negative of an irrational number is irrational.

    (ii) the sum of a rational and an irrational number is irrational.

    (iii) the product of a non-zero rational number and an irrational number is an irrational number.

Solution. (i) Let x be any irrational number.

      If possible, let $-x$ be rational

      $\Rightarrow \quad -(-x)$ is rational   ($\because$ negative of a rational number is rational)

$\Rightarrow$ x is rational, which is wrong.

Hence, the negative of an irrational number is an irrational number.

Thus, $-\sqrt{2}$, $-\sqrt{3}$, $-\sqrt{6}$, etc. are irrational numbers.

(ii) Let x be a rational number and y be an irrational number.

We have to prove that $x + y$ is irrational.

If possible, let $x + y$ be rational.

As $x + y$ and x are both rational, it follows that $(x + y) - x$ is rational.

$(\because$ difference of two rational numbers is rational$)$

$\Rightarrow$ y is rational, which is wrong.

Hence, the sum of a rational and an irrational number is irrational.

Thus, $3 + \sqrt{2}$, $-2 + \sqrt{3}$, $\frac{1}{2} + \sqrt{6}$, $5 - \sqrt{7}$ etc. are irrational.

(iii) Let x be any non-zero rational number and y be an irrational number.

We have to prove that xy is irrational.

If possible, let xy be rational.

As xy is rational and x is non-zero rational, it follows that $\frac{xy}{x}$ is rational

$\Rightarrow$ y is rational, which is wrong.

Hence, the product of a non-zero rational number and an irrational number is irrational.

Thus, $5\sqrt{2}$, $\frac{-7}{2}\sqrt{5}$, $\frac{3}{8}\sqrt{7}$ etc. are all irrational.

Example 11 Give examples to show that:

(i) the sum of two irrational numbers may not be irrational.

(ii) the difference of two irrational numbers may not be irrational.

(iii) the product of two irrational numbers may not be irrational.

Solution. (i) Let $a = 5 + \sqrt{2}$ and $b = 3 - \sqrt{2}$, then a and b both being the sum of rational and irrational numbers are irrational.

Their sum $= a + b = (5 + \sqrt{2}) + (3 - \sqrt{2}) = 8$, which is rational.

Hence, the sum of two irrational numbers may not be irrational.

(ii) Let $a = 3 + \sqrt{5}$ and $b = 7 + \sqrt{5}$, then a and b are both irrational.

Their difference $= a - b = (3 + \sqrt{5}) - (7 + \sqrt{5}) = -4$, which is rational.

Hence, the difference of two irrational numbers may not be irrational.

(iii) Let $a = 5 - \sqrt{6}$ and $b = 5 + \sqrt{6}$, then a and b are both irrational.

Their product $= ab = (5 - \sqrt{6})(5 + \sqrt{6}) = 25 - 6 = 19$, which is rational.

Hence, the product of two irrational numbers may not be irrational.

Example 12 Check whether the following numbers are irrational numbers or not:

(i) $\frac{1}{\sqrt{3}}$ (ii) $\frac{7}{\sqrt{5}}$ (iii) $\pi - 2$

Solution. (i) $\frac{1}{\sqrt{3}} = \frac{1}{\sqrt{3}} \times \frac{\sqrt{3}}{\sqrt{3}} = \frac{1}{3} \times \sqrt{3}$.

We know that $\frac{1}{3}$ is a (non-zero) rational number and $\sqrt{3}$ is an irrational number, so their product i.e. $\frac{1}{3} \times \sqrt{3}$ is an irrational number. Hence, $\frac{1}{\sqrt{3}}$ is an irrational number.

(*ii*) $\dfrac{7}{\sqrt{5}} = \dfrac{7}{\sqrt{5}} \times \dfrac{\sqrt{5}}{\sqrt{5}} = \dfrac{7}{5} \times \sqrt{5}$.

We know that $\dfrac{7}{5}$ is a (non-zero) rational number and $\sqrt{5}$ is an irrational number, so their product *i.e.* $\dfrac{7}{5} \times \sqrt{5}$ is an irrational number. Hence, $\dfrac{7}{\sqrt{5}}$ is an irrational number.

(*iii*) We know that π is an irrational number and 2 is a rational number, therefore, their difference is an irrational number.

Hence, $\pi - 2$ is an irrational number.

EXERCISE 1.2

1 Prove that $\sqrt{5}$ is an irrational number.

2 Prove that $\sqrt{7}$ is an irrational number.

3 Prove that $\sqrt{6}$ is an irrational number.

4 Prove that $\dfrac{1}{\sqrt{11}}$ is an irrational number.

5 Prove that $\sqrt{2}$ is an irrational number. Hence, show that $3 - \sqrt{2}$ is an irrational number.

6 Prove that $\sqrt{3}$ is an irrational number. Hence, show that $\dfrac{2}{5}\sqrt{3}$ is an irrational number.

7 Prove that $\sqrt{5}$ is an irrational number. Hence, show that $-3 + 2\sqrt{5}$ is an irrational number.

8 Prove that the following numbers are irrational:

$\quad$ (*i*) $5 + \sqrt{2}$ $\qquad$ (*ii*) $3 - 5\sqrt{3}$ $\qquad$ (*iii*) $2\sqrt{3} - 7$ $\qquad$ (*iv*) $\sqrt{2} + \sqrt{5}$

1.3 REAL NUMBERS

The collection of all rational numbers together with all irrational numbers forms the collection of real numbers. This collection is denoted by **R**.

Every real number is either a rational number or an irrational number. Thus, a real number which is not rational is an irrational number.

Look at the adjoining diagram to know the various number systems.

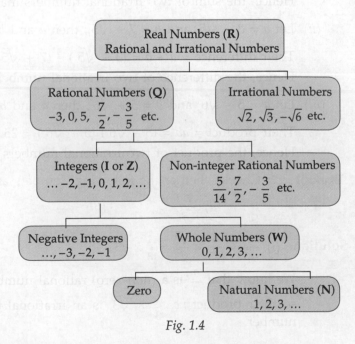

Fig. 1.4

1.3.1 Properties of real numbers

The following results hold for the system (collection) of real numbers (**R**):

(1) If a, b are any two real numbers, then $a + b$ is also a real number.

(2) If a, b are any two real numbers, then $a - b$ is also a real number.

(3) If a, b are any two real numbers, then $a \times b$ is also a real number.

(4) If a, b ($\neq 0$) are any two real numbers, then $\dfrac{a}{b}$ is also a real number.

Thus, the system of real numbers is closed under all the four fundamental operations of arithmetic (except division by zero).

(5) The set of real numbers is ordered *i.e.* if a, b are any two real numbers, then either $a > b$ or $a < b$ or $a = b$. This is called **tricotomy law**.

(6) If a, b are any two real numbers, then $\dfrac{a+b}{2}$ is a real number and it lies between them *i.e.* if $a < b$ then $a < \dfrac{a+b}{2} < b$. Continuing this process, we find that there are *infinitely many real numbers between two different real numbers.*

For example, $\dfrac{\sqrt{2} + \sqrt{3}}{2}$ is a real number which lies between $\sqrt{2}$ and $\sqrt{3}$.

1.4 DECIMAL EXPANSIONS OF REAL NUMBERS

In this section, we shall find the expansions of real numbers and see if we can use these expansions to distinguish between rational and irrational numbers.

As we are more familiar with rational numbers, we begin with the expansions of rational numbers and shall pay special attention to the remainders and see if they follow any pattern.

For example, let us find the decimal expansions of the following rational numbers:

(i) $\dfrac{13}{50}$ (ii) $\dfrac{25}{16}$ (iii) $\dfrac{10}{3}$ (iv) $\dfrac{15}{11}$ (v) $\dfrac{1}{7}$ (vi) $\dfrac{67}{13}$

By actual division, we get

(i)
```
        0·26
  50 | 13·0
       100
       300
       300
         0
```
Remainders: 30, 0

Divisor: 50

(ii)
```
        1·5625
  16 | 25
       16
       90
       80
      100
       96
       40
       32
       80
       80
        0
```
Remainders: 9, 10, 4, 8, 0

Divisor: 16

(iii)
```
        3·333...
   3 | 10
        9
       10
        9
       10
        9
       10
        9
       10
        9
        1  ←——— Repeated
```
Remainders: 1, 1, 1, 1, ...

Divisor: 3

(iv)

```
            1·3636...
    11 | 15
         11
         ──
         40
         33
         ──
         70
         66
         ──
         40
         33
         ──
         70
         66
         ──
          4  ←──── Repeated
```

Remainders: 4, 7, 4, 7, 4, 7, ...
Divisor: 11

(v)

```
           0·142857...
    7 | 1·0
        7
        ──
        30
        28
        ──
        20
        14
        ──
        60
        56
        ──
        40
        35
        ──
        50
        49
        ──
         1  ←──── Repeated
```

Remainders: 3, 2, 6, 4, 5, 1, ...
Divisor: 7

(vi)

```
           5·153846...
    13 | 67
         65
         ──
         20
         13
         ──
         70
         65
         ──
         50
         39
         ──
        110
        104
        ───
         60
         52
         ──
         80
         78
         ──
          2  ←──── Repeated
```

Remainders: 2, 7, 5, 11, 6, 8, ...
Divisor: 13

What have you observed? Have you obtained some patterns? Yes! You must have observed the following things:

(i) In all cases, each remainder is smaller than the divisor, which must be true for all divisors.

(ii) The remainders either become zero after a certain stage or start repeating.

(iii) The number of items in the repeating chain of remainders is less than the divisor.

In case of $\dfrac{10}{3}$, there is just one entry, namely 1, which repeats itself and the divisor is 3.

In case of $\dfrac{15}{11}$, there are two entries, namely 4 and 7, which repeat themselves and the divisor is 11.

In case of $\dfrac{1}{7}$, there are six entries, namely 3, 2, 6, 4, 5 and 1, which repeat themselves and the divisor is 7.

In case of $\dfrac{67}{13}$, there are six entries, namely 2, 7, 5, 11, 6 and 8, which repeat themselves and the divisor is 13.

(*iv*) If the remainders repeat, we get a repeating block of digits in the quotient.

For $\dfrac{10}{3}$, 3 repeats in the quotient; for $\dfrac{15}{11}$, the repeating block of digits is 36; for $\dfrac{1}{7}$, the repeating block of digits is 142857 and for $\dfrac{67}{13}$, the repeating block of digits is 153846.

So far, we have observed these patterns only for the above examples, however, it is true for all rational numbers.

If we consider any positive rational number $\dfrac{p}{q}$, where p and q are both positive integers, on dividing p by q, two things happen — either the remainder becomes zero after a certain stage or it never becomes zero and we get a repeating chain of remainders. We shall discuss the two cases separately.

Case I. *When the remainder becomes zero.*

In case of $\dfrac{13}{50}$, we find that the remainder becomes zero after some steps and $\dfrac{13}{50} = 0.26$; in case of $\dfrac{25}{16}$, the remainder becomes zero after some steps and $\dfrac{25}{16} = 1.5625$. In these cases, the decimal expansions terminate after a finite number of steps.

Such decimal expansions are called **terminating**.

Thus, the rational numbers $\dfrac{13}{50}$ and $\dfrac{25}{16}$ have terminating decimal expansions.
Some other examples are:

$\dfrac{1}{2} = 0.5$, $\dfrac{7}{5} = 1.4$, $\dfrac{253}{4} = 63.25$, $\dfrac{7}{8} = 0.875$, $\dfrac{9}{80} = 0.1125$.

The decimal numbers 0.26, 1.5625, 0.5, 1.4, 63.25, 0.875 and 0.1125 are called **terminating decimals**.

Case II. *When the remainder never becomes zero.*

In case of $\dfrac{10}{3}$, $\dfrac{15}{11}$, $\dfrac{1}{7}$ and $\dfrac{67}{13}$, we find that the remainder never becomes zero and they repeat after a certain stage which force the decimal expansions to go forever. In these cases, we get a repeating block of digits in the quotient.

In the above example, we obtained

$\dfrac{10}{3} = 3.3333...$, $\dfrac{15}{11} = 1.363636...$

$\dfrac{1}{7} = 0.142857142857...$ and $\dfrac{67}{13} = 5.153846153846...$

Such decimal expansions are called **non-terminating recurring**.

The decimal numbers 3.3333..., 1.363636..., 0.142857142857... and 5.153846153846... are called **non-terminating recurring decimals** or simply **recurring (repeating) decimals**.

Notation for non-terminating recurring decimals:

(*i*) If the recurring decimal contains only one repeating digit, put a *dot* or *line* (called *vinculum*) above the repeating digit. For example,

$\dfrac{10}{3} = 3.3333 ... = 3.\dot{3}$ or $3.\overline{3}$.

(*ii*) If the recurring decimal contains two repeating digits, put a dot above each repeating digit or a line above both the repeating digits. For example,

$\frac{15}{11} = 1.363636 \ldots = 1.\dot{3}\dot{6}$ or $1.\overline{36}$.

(*iii*) If the recurring decimal contains more than two repeating digits, put a dot on the first repeating digit and another on the last digit or draw a line covering the entire block of the repeating digits. For example,

$\frac{1}{7} = 0.142857142857 \ldots = 0.\dot{1}4285\dot{7}$ or $0.\overline{142857}$,

$\frac{67}{13} = 5.153846153846 \ldots = 5.\dot{1}5384\dot{6}$ or $5.\overline{153846}$.

In the above example, we have seen that a rational number has either a terminating or a non-terminating recurring (repeating) decimal expansion. The question arises, can a rational number have a non-terminating non-repeating decimal expansion? No! Since each successive remainder is less than the divisor, there comes a stage when a remainder repeats and the digits in the quotient start repeating. Therefore, the decimal expansion of a rational number has only two choices—either it is terminating or it is non-terminating recurring (repeating).

Remarks

❏ All integers (positive, zero or negative) are terminating decimals.

❏ The decimal expansion of a rational number $\frac{p}{q}$, where p, q are integers, $q > 0$, p, q have no common factors (except 1) is:

    (*i*) terminating if q can be expressed as $q = 2^m\, 5^n$, where m, n are whole numbers.

    (*ii*) non-terminating recurring if q has a prime factor other than 2 or 5.

Conversely, can every terminating decimal or a non-terminating recurring (repeating) decimal is a rational number? Yes!

Let us explain it through some examples.

Example 1 Show that the following terminating decimals are rational numbers:

    (*i*) 0·075   (*ii*) 23·7812   (*iii*) 3·142678

Solution. We know that any number which can be expressed in the form $\frac{p}{q}$ where p and q are both integers and $q \neq 0$ is a rational number. So, we are to show that the given numbers can be expressed in this form.

    (*i*) $0.075 = \frac{75}{1000}$, which is a rational number.

    (*ii*) $23.7812 = \frac{237812}{10000}$, which is a rational number.

    (*iii*) $3.142678 = \frac{3142678}{1000000}$, which is a rational number.

Example 2 Show that the following repeating decimals are rational numbers:

    (*i*) $0.\overline{6}$ (*ii*) $1.\overline{27}$ (*iii*) $0.2\overline{35}$ (*iv*) $0.\overline{123}$ (*v*) $0.00\overline{32}$

Solution. (*i*) Let $x = 0.\overline{6} = 0.66666\ldots$ ...(1)

    As there is one repeating digit after the decimal point, so multiplying both sides of (1) by 10, we get

        $10x = 6.66666\ldots$ ...(2)

Subtracting (1) from (2), we get

$9x = 6 \Rightarrow x = \dfrac{2}{3}$, which is a rational number.

(ii) Let $x = 1.\overline{27} = 1.272727...$ ...(1)

As there are two repeating digits after the decimal point, so multiplying both sides of (1) by 100, we get

$100x = 127.2727...$ ...(2)

Subtracting (1) from (2), we get

$99x = 126 \Rightarrow x = \dfrac{14}{11}$, which is a rational number.

(iii) Let $x = 0.2\overline{35} = 0.2353535...$ ...(1)

There is one non-repeating digit after the decimal, multiplying both sides of (1) by 10, we get

$10x = 2.353535$ ...(2)

As there are two repeating digits after the decimal, multiplying both sides of (2) by 100, we get

$1000x = 235.3535...$ ...(3)

Subtracting (2) from (3), we get

$990x = 233 \Rightarrow x = \dfrac{233}{990}$, which is a rational number.

(iv) Let $x = 0.12\overline{3} = 0.123333...$ ...(1)

There are two non-repeating digits after the decimal, multiplying both sides of (1) by 100, we get

$100x = 12.3333...$ ...(2)

As there is one repeating digit after the decimal, multiplying both sides of (2) by 10, we get

$1000x = 123.333...$ ...(3)

Subtracting (2) from (3), we get

$900x = 111 \Rightarrow x = \dfrac{37}{300}$, which is a rational number.

(v) Let $x = 0.00\overline{32} = 0.00323232...$ ...(1)

There are two non-repeating digits after the decimal, multiplying both sides of (1) by 100, we get

$100x = 0.323232...$ ...(2)

As there are two repeating digits after the decimal, so multiplying both sides of (2) by 100, we get

$10000x = 32.3232...$ ...(3)

Subtracting (2) from (3), we get

$9900x = 32 \Rightarrow x = \dfrac{8}{2475}$, which is a rational number.

From the above examples, we see that every terminating decimal or non-terminating recurring (repeating) decimal number is a rational number. This is true in general. We have already seen that every rational number has either a terminating or a non-terminating recurring (repeating) decimal expansion. We summarise these results as:

The decimal expansion of every rational number is either terminating or non-terminating recurring (repeating) and conversely, any number with terminating or non-terminating recurring (repeating) decimal expansion is a rational number.

So, you know what the decimal expansion of a rational number can be. What can you say about the decimal expansion of an irrational number? Because of the above result we can say that the decimal expansion of an irrational number is non-terminating non-recurring and conversely, every non-terminating non-recurring decimal number is an irrational number. We state these results as:

The decimal expansion of every irrational number is non-terminating non-recurring and conversely, any number with non-terminating non-recurring decimal expansion is an irrational number.

Consider the decimal number

$$29{\cdot}101001000100001\ldots \qquad \ldots(i)$$

Observe that in (*i*) above, on the right of the decimal point, there are either 1's or 0's and 1's are separated by one zero, then by two zeros, then by three zeros and so on. Thus, the number of zeros separating two successive 1's goes on increasing successively by one. As we can go on writing this endlessly, this decimal number is non-terminating. Moreover, as no group of integers repeats, so it is non-recurring. Thus, the above decimal number is an irrational number.

In fact, you can obtain different such numbers by replacing the number 1 in (*i*) by any natural number of your choice. Since these are infinitely many, you have infinitely many non-terminating non-recurring decimals *i.e.* irrational numbers. Some other examples of irrational numbers are

$$0{\cdot}0101101110\ldots, \quad 3{\cdot}212112111211112\ldots$$

Let us examine the decimal expansion of $\sqrt{2}$. We find the square root of 2 by division method.

	1·4142135…
1	2·$\overline{00}\,\overline{00}\,\overline{00}\,\overline{00}\,\overline{00}\,\overline{00}\,\overline{00}\,\overline{00}$
	1
24	100
	96
281	400
	281
2824	11900
	11296
28282	60400
	56564
282841	383600
	282841
2828423	10075900
	8485269
28284265	159063100
	141421325
	17641775

So $\sqrt{2} = 1{\cdot}414235\ldots$

You may find some more digits in the decimal expansion of $\sqrt{2}$. You will observe that this expansion will neither terminate nor repeating (recurring). Thus, $\sqrt{2}$ has non-terminating non-recurring decimal expansion and hence, it is an irrational number.

*All decimal numbers (terminating, recurring or non-terminating and non-recurring) are **real numbers.***

Look at the following diagram:

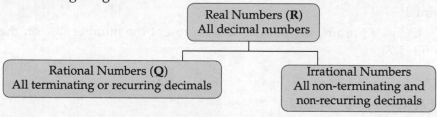

Fig. 1.5

Illustrative Examples

Example 1 Locate $\sqrt{13}$ on the number line.

Solution. We write 13 as the sum of squares of two natural numbers:

$13 = 9 + 4 = 3^2 + 2^2$.

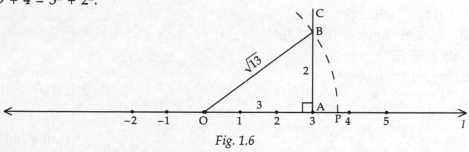

Fig. 1.6

Let l be the number line. If point O represents number 0 and point A represents number 3, then length of line segment OA = 3 units.

At A, draw AC $\perp$ OA. From AC, cut off AB = 2 units.

We observe that OAB is a right angled triangle at A. By Pythagoras theorem, we get

$$OB^2 = OA^2 + AB^2 = 3^2 + 2^2 = 13 \Rightarrow OB = \sqrt{13} \text{ units.}$$

With O as centre and radius = OB, we draw an arc of a circle to meet the number line l at point P.

As OP = OB = $\sqrt{13}$ units, the point P will represent the number $\sqrt{13}$ on the number line (shown in fig. 1.6).

Example 2 Represent $\sqrt{3}$ on the number line.

Solution. Let l be the number line and point O represent number 0 on the number line l. Mark a point A on l such that length of segment OA = 1 unit. At A, draw AE $\perp$ OA. From AE cut off AB = 1 unit. Join AB.

By Pythagoras theorem in ΔOAB, $OB^2 = OA^2 + AB^2 = 1^2 + 1^2 = 2 \Rightarrow OB = \sqrt{2}$ units.

At B, draw BD $\perp$ OB. From BD cut off BC = 1 unit.

By Pythagoras theorem in ΔOBC, $OC^2 = OB^2 + BC^2 = (\sqrt{2})^2 + 1^2 = 3$

$\Rightarrow \quad OC = \sqrt{3}$ units.

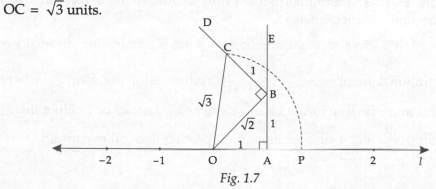

Fig. 1.7

With O as centre and radius = OC, we draw an arc of a circle to meet the number line l at the point P.

As OP = OC = $\sqrt{3}$ units, the point P will represent the number $\sqrt{3}$ on the number line (shown in fig. 1.7).

Example 3 Express $1.3\overline{2}+0.\overline{35}$ in the form $\dfrac{p}{q}$, where p and q are integers, $q \neq 0$.

Solution. Let $x = 1.3\overline{2} = 1.32222 \ldots$ …(i)

Multiplying both sides of (i) by 10, we get

  $10x = 13.2222 \ldots$ …(ii)

Multiplying both sides of (ii) by 10, we get

  $100x = 132.222 \ldots$ …(iii)

Subtracting (ii) from (iii), we get

  $90x = 119 \Rightarrow x = \dfrac{119}{90}$ …(iv)

Let $y = 0.\overline{35} = 0.353535 \ldots$ …(v)

Multiplying both sides of (v) by 100, we get

  $100y = 35.3535 \ldots$ …(vi)

Subtracting (v) from (vi), we get

  $99y = 35 \Rightarrow y = \dfrac{35}{99}$ …(vii)

$\therefore$ $1.3\overline{2} + 0.\overline{35} = \dfrac{119}{90} + \dfrac{35}{99}$ (using (iv) and (vii))

      $= \dfrac{119 \times 11 + 35 \times 10}{990} = \dfrac{1309 + 350}{990} = \dfrac{1659}{990}$.

Example 4 Without performing long division, determine whether the following numbers have a terminating decimal expansion or a non-terminating repeating decimal expansion:

 (i) $\dfrac{11}{50}$ (ii) $\dfrac{6}{1250}$ (iii) $\dfrac{64}{455}$

 (iv) $\dfrac{231}{1260}$ (v) $\dfrac{15}{1600}$ (vi) $\dfrac{7962}{1500}$

Solution. (i) First, we note that the given rational number $\dfrac{11}{50}$ is in its lowest terms.

Denominator of the given rational number $= 50 = 2 \times 25 = 2^1 \times 5^2$, which is of the form $2^m 5^n$, where m and n are whole numbers.

$\therefore$ The given rational number *i.e.* $\dfrac{11}{50}$ is a terminating decimal.

(ii) Given rational number $= \dfrac{6}{1250} = \dfrac{3}{625} = \dfrac{3}{5^4}$.

We note that its denominator has prime factorisation of the form $2^m 5^n$, where m, n are non-negative integers.

Therefore, the given rational number $\dfrac{6}{1250}$ has a terminating decimal expansion.

(iii) Given rational number $= \dfrac{64}{455} = \dfrac{64}{5 \times 7 \times 13}$, which is of the form $\dfrac{p}{q}$ where p, q are co-prime and prime factorisation of q has a prime factor 7 or 13 other than 2 or 5.

Therefore, $\dfrac{64}{455}$ has a non-terminating repeating decimal expansion.

(iv) Given rational number $= \dfrac{231}{1260} = \dfrac{11}{60} = \dfrac{11}{2^2 \times 3 \times 5}$, which is of the form $\dfrac{p}{q}$ where p, q are co-prime and prime factorisation of q has a prime factor 3 other than 2 or 5.

Therefore, $\dfrac{231}{1260}$ has a non-terminating repeating decimal expansion.

(v) Given rational number $= \dfrac{15}{1600} = \dfrac{3}{320} = \dfrac{3}{2^6 \times 5}$.

We note that its denominator has prime factorisation of the form $2^m 5^n$, where m, n are non-negative integers.

Therefore, $\dfrac{15}{1600}$ has a terminating decimal expansion.

(vi) Given rational number $= \dfrac{7962}{1500} = \dfrac{1327}{250} = \dfrac{1327}{2 \times 5^3}$.

We note that its denominator has prime factorisation of the form $2^m 5^n$, where m, n are non-negative integers.

Therefore, $\dfrac{7962}{1500}$ has a terminating decimal expansion.

Example 5 Write the decimal expansions of the following numbers which have terminating decimal expansions:

    (i) $\dfrac{15}{400}$ *(ii)* $\dfrac{1715}{2^3 \times 7^3}$ *(iii)* $\dfrac{31}{243}$ *(iv)* $\dfrac{15}{1600}$

Solution. *(i)* $\dfrac{15}{400} = \dfrac{3}{80} = \dfrac{3}{2^4 \times 5} = \dfrac{3 \times 5^3}{2^4 \times 5^4} = \dfrac{375}{10^4} = 0 \cdot 0375$

(ii) $\dfrac{1715}{2^3 \times 7^3} = \dfrac{5 \times 7^3}{2^3 \times 7^3} = \dfrac{5}{2^3} = \dfrac{5 \times 5^3}{2^3 \times 5^3} = \dfrac{625}{10^3} = 0 \cdot 625$

(iii) $\dfrac{31}{243} = \dfrac{31}{3^5}$, which is of the form $\dfrac{p}{q}$ where p, q are co-prime and prime factorisation of q has a prime factor 3 other than 2 or 5. Therefore, $\dfrac{31}{243}$ has a non-terminating repeating decimal expansion.

(iv) $\dfrac{15}{1600} = \dfrac{3}{320} = \dfrac{3}{2^6 \times 5} = \dfrac{3 \times 5^5}{2^6 \times 5^6} = \dfrac{9375}{10^6} = 0 \cdot 009375$

Example 6 Without using long division, show that the rational number $\dfrac{21}{1120}$ has a terminating decimal expansion. Also find its decimal expansion.

Solution. Given rational number $= \dfrac{21}{1120} = \dfrac{3}{160}$, which is in lowest terms.

Prime factorisation of its denominator 160 is $2^5 \times 5^1$, which is of the form $2^m \times 5^n$ where m, n are non-negative integers. Therefore, the given rational number has terminating decimal expansion.

Also $\dfrac{3}{160} = \dfrac{3}{2^5 \times 5^1} = \dfrac{3}{2^5 \times 5^1} \times \dfrac{5^4}{5^4} = \dfrac{3 \times 625}{2^5 \times 5^5} = \dfrac{1875}{(10)^5} = 0 \cdot 01875$

Example 7 The following real numbers have decimal expansions as given below. In each case, state whether they are rational or not. If they are rational and expressed in the form $\dfrac{p}{q}$ where p, q are integers, $q \neq 0$, p and q are co-prime, then what can you say about the prime factors of q?

(i) 273·0791　　　　　　　　　　　　　(ii) 43·123456789

(iii) 0·120120012000...　　　　　　　　(iv) 43·$\overline{123456789}$

Solution. (i) Given number = 273·0791, which is a terminating decimal. Therefore, the given number is a rational number and the prime factors of q (denominator) will be 2 or 5 or both only.

(ii) Given number = 43·123456789, which is a terminating decimal. Therefore, it is a rational number and the prime factor of its denominator q will be 2 or 5 or both only.

(iii) Given number = 0·120120012000 ..., which is a non-terminating non-repeating decimal number. Therefore, it is an irrational number *i.e.* not a rational number.

(iv) Given number = 43·$\overline{123456789}$, which is a non-terminating repeating decimal number. Therefore, it is a rational number and the prime factor of its denominator q will have a prime factor other than 2 or 5.

Example 8 Insert an irrational number between 3 and 5.

Solution. Consider the squares $3^2 = 9$ and $5^2 = 25$.

Our irrational number can be the square root of any natural number between 9 and 25 except 16. (Why?)

As $9 < 10 < 25 \Rightarrow \sqrt{9} < \sqrt{10} < \sqrt{25} \Rightarrow 3 < \sqrt{10} < 5$.

Hence, the irrational number $\sqrt{10}$ lies between 3 and 5.

> **Note** Since infinitely many irrational numbers lie between two rational numbers, $\sqrt{10}$ is not the only irrational number between 3 and 5.

Example 9 Find an irrational number between $\frac{1}{7}$ and $\frac{2}{7}$.

Solution. The decimal expansions of the given numbers are:

$$\frac{1}{7} = 0·\overline{142857} \text{ (obtain it) and } \frac{2}{7} = 2 \times \frac{1}{7} = 2 \times 0·\overline{142857} = 0·\overline{285714}$$

To find an irrational number between $\frac{1}{7}$ and $\frac{2}{7}$, we find a decimal number which is non-terminating non-recurring and lying between them *i.e.* between $0·\overline{142857}$ and $0·\overline{285714}$. There are infinitely many such numbers.

One such number is 0·202002000200002....

Example 10 Find a rational number between $\sqrt{5}$ and $\sqrt{7}$.

Solution. Consider the squares of $\sqrt{5}$ and $\sqrt{7}$.

$(\sqrt{5})^2 = 5$ and $(\sqrt{7})^2 = 7$.

Take any rational number between 5 and 7 which is a perfect square of a rational number.

One such number is 6·25 and 6·25 = $(2·5)^2$ *i.e.* $\sqrt{6·25} = 2·5$

As　$5 < 6·25 < 7 \Rightarrow \sqrt{5} < \sqrt{6·25} < \sqrt{7}$

$\Rightarrow \quad \sqrt{5} < 2·5 < \sqrt{7}$.

Hence, 2·5 is a rational number between $\sqrt{5}$ and $\sqrt{7}$.

$$\sqrt{5} < \sqrt{5{\cdot}76} < \sqrt{6{\cdot}76} < \sqrt{7} \Rightarrow \sqrt{5} < 2{\cdot}4 < 2{\cdot}6 < \sqrt{7}.$$

So, rational numbers 2·4, 2·6 also lie between $\sqrt{5}$ and $\sqrt{7}$.

In fact, there are many more rational numbers lying between $\sqrt{5}$ and $\sqrt{7}$.

Example 11 Find two irrational numbers between $\sqrt{2}$ and $\sqrt{7}$.

Solution. Consider the squares of $\sqrt{2}$ and $\sqrt{7}$.

$$(\sqrt{2})^2 = 2 \text{ and } (\sqrt{7})^2 = 7.$$

As $2 < 3 < 5 < 7$, it follows that $\sqrt{2} < \sqrt{3} < \sqrt{5} < \sqrt{7}$, therefore $\sqrt{3}$ and $\sqrt{5}$ lie between $\sqrt{2}$ and $\sqrt{7}$.

Hence, two irrational numbers between $\sqrt{2}$ and $\sqrt{7}$ are $\sqrt{3}$ and $\sqrt{5}$.

Note Since infinitely many irrational numbers lie between two distinct irrational numbers, $\sqrt{3}$ and $\sqrt{5}$ are not the only irrational numbers between $\sqrt{2}$ and $\sqrt{7}$.

Example 12 Insert four irrational numbers between $3\sqrt{2}$ and $2\sqrt{3}$.

Solution. Consider the squares of $3\sqrt{2}$ and $2\sqrt{3}$.

$$(3\sqrt{2})^2 = 9 \times 2 = 18 \text{ and } (2\sqrt{3})^2 = 4 \times 3 = 12.$$

As $18 > 17 > 15 > 14 > 13 > 12$, it follows that

$$\sqrt{18} > \sqrt{17} > \sqrt{15} > \sqrt{14} > \sqrt{13} > \sqrt{12}, \text{ therefore}$$

$\sqrt{17}, \sqrt{15}, \sqrt{14}, \sqrt{13}$ lie between $\sqrt{18}$ and $\sqrt{12}$ *i.e.* between $3\sqrt{2}$ and $2\sqrt{3}$.

Hence, four irrational numbers between $3\sqrt{2}$ and $2\sqrt{3}$ are $\sqrt{17}, \sqrt{15}, \sqrt{14}$ and $\sqrt{13}$.

EXERCISE 1.3

1 Locate $\sqrt{10}$ and $\sqrt{17}$ on the number line.

2 Write the decimal expansion of each of the following numbers and say what kind of decimal expansion each has:

(i) $\dfrac{36}{100}$ (ii) $4\dfrac{1}{8}$ (iii) $\dfrac{2}{9}$

(iv) $\dfrac{2}{11}$ (v) $\dfrac{3}{13}$ (vi) $\dfrac{329}{400}$

3 Without actually performing the long division, state whether the following rational numbers will have a terminating decimal expansion or a non-terminating repeating decimal expansion:

(i) $\dfrac{13}{3125}$ (ii) $\dfrac{17}{8}$ (iii) $\dfrac{23}{75}$

(iv) $\dfrac{6}{15}$ (v) $\dfrac{1258}{625}$ (vi) $\dfrac{77}{210}$

4 Without actually performing the long division, find if $\dfrac{987}{10500}$ will have terminating or non-terminating repeating decimal expansion. Give reasons for your answer.

5 Write the decimal expansions of the following numbers which have terminating decimal expansions:

(i) $\dfrac{17}{8}$
(ii) $\dfrac{13}{3125}$
(iii) $\dfrac{7}{80}$

(iv) $\dfrac{6}{15}$
(v) $\dfrac{2^2 \times 7}{5^4}$
(vi) $\dfrac{237}{1500}$

6 Write the denominator of the rational number $\dfrac{257}{5000}$ in the form $2^m \times 5^n$, where m, n are non-negative integers. Hence, write its decimal expansion without actual division.

7 Write the decimal expansion of $\dfrac{1}{7}$. Hence, write the decimal expansions of $\dfrac{2}{7}, \dfrac{3}{7}, \dfrac{4}{7}, \dfrac{5}{7}$ and $\dfrac{6}{7}$.

8 Express the following numbers in the form $\dfrac{p}{q}$, where p and q are both integers and $q \neq 0$:

(i) $0.\overline{3}$
(ii) $5.\overline{2}$
(iii) $0.404040\ldots$

(iv) $0.4\overline{7}$
(v) $0.1\overline{34}$
(vi) $0.\overline{001}$

9 Classify the following numbers as rational or irrational:

(i) $\sqrt{23}$
(ii) $\sqrt{225}$
(iii) 0.3796

(iv) $7.478478\ldots$
(v) $1.101001000100001\ldots$
(vi) $345.0\overline{456}$

10 The following real numbers have decimal expansions as given below. In each case, state whether they are rational or not. If they are rational and expressed in the form $\dfrac{p}{q}$, where p, q are integers, $q \neq 0$ and p, q are co-prime, then what can you say about the prime factors of q?

(i) 37.09158
(ii) $423.\overline{04567}$
(iii) $8.9010010001\ldots$
(iv) $2.3476817681\ldots$

11 Insert an irrational number between the following:

(i) $\dfrac{1}{3}$ and $\dfrac{1}{2}$
(ii) $-\dfrac{2}{5}$ and $\dfrac{1}{2}$
(iii) 0 and 0.1

12 Insert two irrational numbers between 2 and 3.

13 Write two irrational numbers between $\dfrac{4}{9}$ and $\dfrac{7}{11}$.

14 Find a rational number between $\sqrt{2}$ and $\sqrt{3}$.

15 Find two rational numbers between $2\sqrt{3}$ and $\sqrt{15}$.

Hint.

$$2\sqrt{3} = \sqrt{12} \,;\; 12 < 12.25 < 12.96 < 15$$
$$\Rightarrow \sqrt{12} < \sqrt{12.25} < \sqrt{12.96} < \sqrt{15}.$$

16 Insert an irrational number between $\sqrt{5}$ and $\sqrt{7}$.

17 Insert two irrational numbers between $\sqrt{3}$ and $\sqrt{7}$.

1.5 SURDS

We have seen that the numbers of the type $\sqrt{2}, \sqrt{3}, \sqrt{5}, \sqrt{15}$ ... are irrational numbers. In fact, these are special type of irrational numbers. These are square roots of some positive rational numbers, which cannot be written as the squares of any rational numbers. Similarly, $\sqrt[3]{2}, \sqrt[3]{5}, \sqrt[3]{14}$ etc. are numbers which are the cube roots of some positive rational numbers, which cannot be written as the cubes of any rational number. Such numbers are called **surds** or **radicals**.

In general, if a is any positive rational number and n (> 1) is a positive integer and if a cannot be written as the nth power of any rational number, then $\sqrt[n]{a}$ *(or (a)$^{1/n}$) is called a* **surd** *of* **order n.**

In other words, $\sqrt[n]{a}$ is a surd (of order n) if

(i) a is a positive rational number,

(ii) n (> 1) is a positive integer, and

(iii) $\sqrt[n]{a}$ is not a rational number.

For example, $\sqrt{2}, \sqrt{3}, \sqrt{15}$ are surds of order 2

$\qquad\qquad \sqrt[3]{2}, \sqrt[3]{5}, \sqrt[3]{10}$ are surds of order 3

$\qquad\qquad \sqrt[4]{3}, \sqrt[4]{7}, \sqrt[4]{21}$ are surds of order 4 etc.

All surds are irrational numbers.

We state some laws of surds (radicals) without proof:

(i) $(\sqrt[n]{a})^n = a$ $\qquad\qquad\qquad$ (ii) $\sqrt[n]{a}\,\sqrt[n]{b} = \sqrt[n]{ab}$

(iii) $\dfrac{\sqrt[n]{a}}{\sqrt[n]{b}} = \sqrt[n]{\dfrac{a}{b}}$, where a and b are positive rational numbers and $n(> 1)$ is a positive integer.

1.5.1 Some facts about surds of order 2

1. $\sqrt{3} + \sqrt{5} \neq \sqrt{3 + 5}, \sqrt{5} - \sqrt{3} \neq \sqrt{5 - 3}$ etc.

2. $\sqrt{3} + \sqrt{3} \neq \sqrt{6}$ but $\sqrt{3} + \sqrt{3} = 2\sqrt{3}$,

   $5\sqrt{2} - 3\sqrt{2} = (5 - 3)\sqrt{2} = 2\sqrt{2}$ etc.

3. If a and b are positive rational numbers, then

   $\sqrt{a^2} = a, \sqrt{ab} = \sqrt{a}\sqrt{b}$ and $\sqrt{\dfrac{a}{b}} = \dfrac{\sqrt{a}}{\sqrt{b}}$.

   For example, $\sqrt{2^2} = 2, \sqrt{6} = \sqrt{2 \times 3} = \sqrt{2}\sqrt{3}, \sqrt{45} = \sqrt{9 \times 5} = \sqrt{9}\sqrt{5} = 3\sqrt{5}$,

   $\sqrt{\dfrac{5}{9}} = \dfrac{\sqrt{5}}{\sqrt{9}} = \dfrac{\sqrt{5}}{3}, \dfrac{\sqrt{12}}{\sqrt{3}} = \sqrt{\dfrac{12}{3}} = \sqrt{4} = 2,$

   $\sqrt{45} - \sqrt{5} = \sqrt{9 \times 5} - \sqrt{5} = 3\sqrt{5} - \sqrt{5} = 2\sqrt{5}$.

4. If a and b are positive rational numbers, then the following results hold:

   (i) $(\sqrt{a} + \sqrt{b})(\sqrt{a} - \sqrt{b}) = a - b$ $\qquad$ (ii) $(a + \sqrt{b})(a - \sqrt{b}) = a^2 - b$

   (iii) $(\sqrt{a} + \sqrt{b})^2 = a + 2\sqrt{ab} + b$ $\qquad$ (iv) $(\sqrt{a} - \sqrt{b})^2 = a - 2\sqrt{ab} + b$.

5. If a, b, c and d are positive real numbers, then

   $(\sqrt{a} + \sqrt{b})(\sqrt{c} + \sqrt{d}) = \sqrt{ac} + \sqrt{ad} + \sqrt{bc} + \sqrt{bd}$.

6. If a, b, c and d are rational numbers, $\sqrt{p}$ is an irrational number and $a + b\sqrt{p} = c + d\sqrt{p}$, then $a = c$ and $b = d$.

7. If $\sqrt{a}$ and $\sqrt{b}$ are positive irrational numbers, then

   (i) $\sqrt{a} < \sqrt{b}$ if $a < b$ (ii) $\sqrt{a} > \sqrt{b}$ if $a > b$.

8. If a is a positive rational number and $\sqrt{b}$ is an irrational number, then

   (i) $a < \sqrt{b}$ if $a^2 < b$ (ii) $a > \sqrt{b}$ if $a^2 > b$.

Illustrative Examples

Example 1 State with reason which of the following are surds and which are not:

     (i) $\sqrt{45}$ (ii) $\sqrt{20} \times \sqrt{45}$ (iii) $\sqrt[3]{4} \times \sqrt[3]{54}$ (iv) $3\sqrt{12} \div 6\sqrt{27}$.

Solution. (i) $\sqrt{45} = \sqrt{9 \times 5} = \sqrt{9} \times \sqrt{5} = 3\sqrt{5}$, which is not a rational number.

     Therefore, $\sqrt{45}$ is a surd.

(ii) $\sqrt{20} \times \sqrt{45} = \sqrt{20 \times 45} = \sqrt{900}$
           $= 30$, which is a rational number.

     Therefore, $\sqrt{20} \times \sqrt{45}$ is not a surd.

(iii) $\sqrt[3]{4} \times \sqrt[3]{54} = \sqrt[3]{4 \times 54} = \sqrt[3]{216}$

           $= \sqrt[3]{6^3} = 6$, which is a rational number.

     Therefore, $\sqrt[3]{4} \times \sqrt[3]{54}$ is not a surd.

(iv) $3\sqrt{12} \div 6\sqrt{27} = \dfrac{3\sqrt{12}}{6\sqrt{27}} = \dfrac{\sqrt{4 \times 3}}{2\sqrt{9}\sqrt{3}} = \dfrac{\sqrt{4}\sqrt{3}}{2\sqrt{9}\sqrt{3}}$

           $= \dfrac{2\sqrt{3}}{2 \times 3\sqrt{3}} = \dfrac{1}{3}$, which is a rational number.

     Therefore, $3\sqrt{12} \div 6\sqrt{27}$ is not a surd.

Example 2 Simplify the following:

     (i) $(3 + \sqrt{5})(2 + \sqrt{3})$ (ii) $(5 + \sqrt{7})(5 - \sqrt{7})$

     (iii) $(\sqrt{5} - \sqrt{3})^2$ (iv) $(\sqrt{11} + \sqrt{7})(\sqrt{11} - \sqrt{7})$.

Solution. (i) $(3 + \sqrt{5})(2 + \sqrt{3})$ $= 6 + 3\sqrt{3} + 2\sqrt{5} + \sqrt{5}\sqrt{3}$

                             $= 6 + 3\sqrt{3} + 2\sqrt{5} + \sqrt{15}$.

(ii) $(5 + \sqrt{7})(5 - \sqrt{7}) = 5^2 - (\sqrt{7})^2 = 25 - 7 = 18$.

(iii) $(\sqrt{5} - \sqrt{3})^2 = (\sqrt{5})^2 - 2\sqrt{5}\sqrt{3} + (\sqrt{3})^2 = 5 - 2\sqrt{15} + 3$

           $= 8 - 2\sqrt{15}$.

(iv) $(\sqrt{11} + \sqrt{7})(\sqrt{11} - \sqrt{7}) = (\sqrt{11})^2 - (\sqrt{7})^2 = 11 - 7 = 4$.

Example 3 If $\sqrt{3} = 1.732$, then find the value of:

     $\sqrt{27} - 3\sqrt{75} + 5\sqrt{48} + 2\sqrt{108}$

Solution. $\sqrt{27} - 3\sqrt{75} + 5\sqrt{48} + 2\sqrt{108}$

           $= \sqrt{9 \times 3} - 3\sqrt{25 \times 3} + 5\sqrt{16 \times 3} + 2\sqrt{36 \times 3}$

$$= 3\sqrt{3} - 3 \times 5\sqrt{3} + 5 \times 4\sqrt{3} + 2 \times 6\sqrt{3}$$
$$= 3\sqrt{3} - 15\sqrt{3} + 20\sqrt{3} + 12\sqrt{3}$$
$$= (3 - 15 + 20 + 12)\sqrt{3} = 20 \times \sqrt{3}$$
$$= 20 \times 1\cdot732 = 34\cdot64$$

Example 4 Simplify: $\sqrt{5 + 2\sqrt{6}} + \sqrt{8 - 2\sqrt{15}}$.

Solution. $\qquad \sqrt{5 + 2\sqrt{6}} = \sqrt{3 + 2 + 2\sqrt{6}}$ $\qquad\qquad$ (Note this step)

$$= \sqrt{(\sqrt{3} + \sqrt{2})^2} = \sqrt{3} + \sqrt{2}$$

and $\qquad \sqrt{8 - 2\sqrt{15}} = \sqrt{5 + 3 - 2\sqrt{15}}$ $\qquad\qquad$ (Note this step)

$$= \sqrt{(\sqrt{5} - \sqrt{3})^2} = \sqrt{5} - \sqrt{3} .$$

$\therefore \quad \sqrt{5 + 2\sqrt{6}} + \sqrt{8 - 2\sqrt{15}} = (\sqrt{3} + \sqrt{2}) + (\sqrt{5} - \sqrt{3})$

$$= \sqrt{2} + \sqrt{5} .$$

Example 5 Prove that $\sqrt[3]{5}$ is an irrational number.

Solution. Suppose that $\sqrt[3]{5} = \dfrac{p}{q}$, where p, q are integers, $q \neq 0$, p and q have no common factors (except 1)

$\Rightarrow \quad 5 = \left(\dfrac{p}{q}\right)^3 \qquad \Rightarrow p^3 = 5q^3$ $\qquad\qquad\qquad\qquad\qquad$ ...(i)

As 5 divides $5q^3 \quad \Rightarrow$ 5 divides p^3

$\Rightarrow \quad$ 5 divides p $\qquad\qquad\qquad\qquad$ (using generalisation of theorem 1)

Let $\quad p = 5k$, where k is an integer.

Substituting this value of p in (i), we get

$\qquad (5k)^3 = 5q^3 \qquad \Rightarrow \quad 25k^3 = q^3.$

As 5 divides $25k^3 \quad \Rightarrow$ 5 divides q^3

$\Rightarrow \quad$ 5 divides q $\qquad\qquad\qquad\qquad$ (using generalisation of theorem 1)

Thus, p and q have a common factor 5. This contradicts that p and q have no common factors (except 1).

Hence, our supposition is wrong. It follows that $\sqrt[3]{5}$ cannot be expressed as $\dfrac{p}{q}$, where p, q are integers, $q > 0$, p and q have no common factors (except 1). Therefore, $\sqrt[3]{5}$ is an irrational number.

Example 6 Prove that $\sqrt[3]{6}$ is an irrational number.

Solution. Suppose that $\sqrt[3]{6}$ is a rational number, then $\sqrt[3]{6} = \dfrac{p}{q}$, where p, q are both integers, $q \neq 0$ and p, q have no common factors (except 1)

$\Rightarrow \quad 6 = \left(\dfrac{p}{q}\right)^3 \quad \Rightarrow \quad p^3 = 6q^3$ $\qquad\qquad\qquad\qquad$ ...(i)

As 2 divides $6q^3$, so 2 divides p^3 but 2 is prime

$\Rightarrow \quad$ 2 divides p $\qquad\qquad\qquad\qquad$ (using generalisation of theorem 1)

Let $p = 2k$, where k is some integer.

Substituting this value of p in (i), we get

$\qquad (2k)^3 = 6q^3 \quad \Rightarrow \quad 8k^3 = 6q^3 \quad \Rightarrow \quad 4k^3 = 3q^3.$

As 2 divides $4k^3$, so 2 divides $3q^3$ but 2 is prime

$\Rightarrow$ 2 divides 3 or 2 divides q^3 (using theorem 2)

But 2 does not divide 3, therefore, 2 divides q^3 but 2 is prime

$\Rightarrow$ 2 divides q (using generalisation of theorem 1)

Thus, p and q have a common factor 2. This contradicts that p and q have no common factors (except 1).

Hence, our supposition is wrong. Therefore, $\sqrt[3]{6}$ is an irrational number.

Example 7 Write in ascending order: $4\sqrt{5}, 5\sqrt{3}, 10, 3\sqrt{7}, 6\sqrt{2}$.

Solution. Write all the numbers as square roots under one radical.

$$4\sqrt{5} = \sqrt{16} \times \sqrt{5} = \sqrt{80}, 5\sqrt{3} = \sqrt{25} \times \sqrt{3} = \sqrt{75}, 10 = \sqrt{100},$$

$$3\sqrt{7} = \sqrt{9} \times \sqrt{7} = \sqrt{63} \text{ and } 6\sqrt{2} = \sqrt{36} \times \sqrt{2} = \sqrt{72}.$$

Since $63 < 72 < 75 < 80 < 100 \Rightarrow \sqrt{63} < \sqrt{72} < \sqrt{75} < \sqrt{80} < \sqrt{100}$

$\Rightarrow$ $3\sqrt{7} < 6\sqrt{2} < 5\sqrt{3} < 4\sqrt{5} < 10.$

Hence, the given numbers in ascending order are $3\sqrt{7}, 6\sqrt{2}, 5\sqrt{3}, 4\sqrt{5}, 10$.

Example 8 Arrange the following numbers in ascending order: $\sqrt{3}, \sqrt[3]{5}, \sqrt[4]{8}$.

Solution. L.C.M. of 2, 3 and 4 is 12.

$$\sqrt{3} = 3^{\frac{1}{2}} = (3^6)^{\frac{1}{12}} = (729)^{\frac{1}{12}},$$

$$\sqrt[3]{5} = 5^{\frac{1}{3}} = (5^4)^{\frac{1}{12}} = (625)^{\frac{1}{12}},$$

$$\sqrt[4]{8} = 8^{\frac{1}{4}} = (8^3)^{\frac{1}{12}} = (512)^{\frac{1}{12}}.$$

As $512 < 625 < 729, (512)^{\frac{1}{12}} < (625)^{\frac{1}{12}} < (729)^{\frac{1}{12}}$

$\Rightarrow$ $\sqrt[4]{8} < \sqrt[3]{5} < \sqrt{3}$.

Hence, the given numbers in ascending order are $\sqrt[4]{8}, \sqrt[3]{5}, \sqrt{3}$.

EXERCISE 1.4

1 Simplify the following:

   (i) $\sqrt{45} - 3\sqrt{20} + 4\sqrt{5}$ (ii) $3\sqrt{3} + 2\sqrt{27} + \dfrac{7}{\sqrt{3}}$ (iii) $6\sqrt{5} \times 2\sqrt{5}$

   (iv) $8\sqrt{15} \div 2\sqrt{3}$ (v) $\dfrac{\sqrt{24}}{8} + \dfrac{\sqrt{54}}{9}$ (vi) $\dfrac{3}{\sqrt{8}} + \dfrac{1}{\sqrt{2}}$

2 Simplify the following:

   (i) $(5 + \sqrt{7})(2 + \sqrt{5})$ (ii) $(5 + \sqrt{5})(5 - \sqrt{5})$ (iii) $(\sqrt{5} + \sqrt{2})^2$

   (iv) $(\sqrt{3} - \sqrt{7})^2$ (v) $(\sqrt{2} + \sqrt{3})(\sqrt{5} + \sqrt{7})$ (vi) $(4 + \sqrt{5})(\sqrt{3} - \sqrt{7})$

3 If $\sqrt{2} = 1\cdot414$, then find the value of:

   (i) $\sqrt{8} + \sqrt{50} + \sqrt{72} + \sqrt{98}$ (ii) $3\sqrt{32} - 2\sqrt{50} + 4\sqrt{128} - 20\sqrt{18}$.

4 If $\sqrt{3} = 1\cdot732$, then find the value of:

   (i) $\sqrt{27} + \sqrt{75} + \sqrt{108} - \sqrt{243}$ (ii) $5\sqrt{12} - 3\sqrt{48} + 6\sqrt{75} + 7\sqrt{108}$.

5 State which of the following numbers are irrational:

(i) $\sqrt{\dfrac{4}{9}}, -\dfrac{3}{70}, \sqrt{\dfrac{7}{25}}, \sqrt{\dfrac{16}{5}}$

(ii) $-\sqrt{\dfrac{2}{49}}, \dfrac{3}{200}, \sqrt{\dfrac{25}{3}}, -\sqrt{\dfrac{49}{16}}.$

6 State which of the following numbers will change into non-terminating non-recurring decimals:

(i) $-3\sqrt{2}$ (ii) $\sqrt{\dfrac{256}{81}}$ (iii) $\sqrt{27 \times 16}$ (iv) $\sqrt{\dfrac{5}{36}}.$

7 State which of the following numbers are irrational:

(i) $3 - \sqrt{\dfrac{7}{25}}$ (ii) $-\dfrac{2}{3} + \sqrt[3]{2}$ (iii) $\dfrac{3}{\sqrt{3}}$

(iv) $-\dfrac{2}{7}\sqrt[3]{5}$ (v) $(2 - \sqrt{3})(2 + \sqrt{3})$ (vi) $(3 + \sqrt{5})^2$

(vii) $\left(\dfrac{2}{5}\sqrt{7}\right)^2$ (viii) $(3 - \sqrt{6})^2.$

8 Prove that the following numbers are irrational:

(i) $\sqrt[3]{2}$ (ii) $\sqrt[3]{3}$ (iii) $\sqrt[4]{5}.$

9 Find the greatest and the smallest real numbers among the following real numbers:

(i) $2\sqrt{3}, \dfrac{3}{\sqrt{2}}, -\sqrt{7}, \sqrt{15}$ (ii) $-3\sqrt{2}, \dfrac{9}{\sqrt{5}}, -4, \dfrac{4}{3}\sqrt{5}, \dfrac{3}{2}\sqrt{3}.$

10 Write the following numbers in ascending order:

(i) $3\sqrt{2}, 2\sqrt{3}, \sqrt{15}, 4$ (ii) $3\sqrt{2}, 2\sqrt{8}, 4, \sqrt{50}, 4\sqrt{3}.$

11 Write the following real numbers in descending order:

(i) $\dfrac{9}{\sqrt{2}}, \dfrac{3}{2}\sqrt{5}, 4\sqrt{3}, 3\sqrt{\dfrac{6}{5}}$ (ii) $\dfrac{5}{\sqrt{3}}, \dfrac{7}{3}\sqrt{2}, -\sqrt{3}, 3\sqrt{5}, 2\sqrt{7}.$

12 Arrange the following numbers in ascending order: $\sqrt[3]{2}, \sqrt{3}, \sqrt[6]{5}.$

1.6 RATIONALISATION OF SURDS

*The process of multiplying a surd by another surd to get a rational number is called **rationalisation**. Each surd is called **rationalising factor** of the other surd.*

For example:

(i) $(4 + \sqrt{3})(4 - \sqrt{3}) = 4^2 - (\sqrt{3})^2 = 16 - 3 = 13$, therefore, $4 + \sqrt{3}$ and $4 - \sqrt{3}$ are rationalising factors of each other.

(ii) $(\sqrt{5} - \sqrt{7})(\sqrt{5} + \sqrt{7}) = (\sqrt{5})^2 - (\sqrt{7})^2 = -2$, therefore, $\sqrt{5} - \sqrt{7}$ and $\sqrt{5} + \sqrt{7}$ are rationalising factors of each other.

Rule to rationalise the denominator of an expression:

Multiply and divide the numerator and denominator of the given expression by the rationalising factor of its denominator and simplify.

Illustrative Examples

Example 1 Rationalise the denominator of the following:

(i) $\dfrac{2}{3 - \sqrt{5}}$ (ii) $\dfrac{1}{2\sqrt{3} + \sqrt{7}}$

Solution. (*i*) $\dfrac{2}{3-\sqrt{5}} = \dfrac{2}{3-\sqrt{5}} \times \dfrac{3+\sqrt{5}}{3+\sqrt{5}} = \dfrac{2(3+\sqrt{5})}{3^2-(\sqrt{5})^2}$

$$= \dfrac{2(3+\sqrt{5})}{9-5} = \dfrac{2(3+\sqrt{5})}{4} = \dfrac{3+\sqrt{5}}{2}.$$

(*ii*) $\dfrac{1}{2\sqrt{3}+\sqrt{7}} = \dfrac{1}{2\sqrt{3}+\sqrt{7}} \times \dfrac{2\sqrt{3}-\sqrt{7}}{2\sqrt{3}-\sqrt{7}} = \dfrac{2\sqrt{3}-\sqrt{7}}{(2\sqrt{3})^2-(\sqrt{7})^2}$

$$= \dfrac{2\sqrt{3}-\sqrt{7}}{12-7} = \dfrac{2\sqrt{3}-\sqrt{7}}{5}.$$

Example 2 Rationalise the denominator of the following:

(*i*) $\dfrac{4\sqrt{3}+5\sqrt{2}}{\sqrt{48}+\sqrt{18}}$

(*ii*) $\dfrac{2}{\sqrt{5}+\sqrt{3}+2}$

Solution. (*i*) $\dfrac{4\sqrt{3}+5\sqrt{2}}{\sqrt{48}+\sqrt{18}} = \dfrac{4\sqrt{3}+5\sqrt{2}}{\sqrt{48}+\sqrt{18}} \times \dfrac{\sqrt{48}-\sqrt{18}}{\sqrt{48}-\sqrt{18}} = \dfrac{(4\sqrt{3}+5\sqrt{2})(4\sqrt{3}-3\sqrt{2})}{(\sqrt{48})^2-(\sqrt{18})^2}$

$$= \dfrac{16 \times 3 - 12\sqrt{6} + 20\sqrt{6} - 15 \times 2}{48-18} = \dfrac{18+8\sqrt{6}}{30} = \dfrac{9+4\sqrt{6}}{15}.$$

(*ii*) $\dfrac{2}{\sqrt{5}+\sqrt{3}+2} = \dfrac{2}{(\sqrt{5}+\sqrt{3})+2} \times \dfrac{(\sqrt{5}+\sqrt{3})-2}{(\sqrt{5}+\sqrt{3})-2}$

$$= \dfrac{2(\sqrt{5}+\sqrt{3}-2)}{(\sqrt{5}+\sqrt{3})^2-2^2}$$

$$= \dfrac{2(\sqrt{5}+\sqrt{3}-2)}{5+3+2\sqrt{5}\sqrt{3}-4} = \dfrac{2(\sqrt{5}+\sqrt{3}-2)}{4+2\sqrt{15}}$$

$$= \dfrac{\sqrt{5}+\sqrt{3}-2}{2+\sqrt{15}} = \dfrac{\sqrt{5}+\sqrt{3}-2}{2+\sqrt{15}} \times \dfrac{2-\sqrt{15}}{2-\sqrt{15}}$$

$$= \dfrac{2\sqrt{5}+2\sqrt{3}-4-\sqrt{5}\sqrt{15}-\sqrt{3}\sqrt{15}+2\sqrt{15}}{2^2-(\sqrt{15})^2}$$

$$= \dfrac{2\sqrt{5}+2\sqrt{3}-4-5\sqrt{3}-3\sqrt{5}+2\sqrt{15}}{4-15}$$

$$= \dfrac{-\sqrt{5}-3\sqrt{3}-4+2\sqrt{15}}{-11} = \dfrac{\sqrt{5}+3\sqrt{3}-2\sqrt{15}+4}{11}.$$

Example 3 If $\sqrt{2} = 1\cdot414$ and $\sqrt{3} = 1\cdot732$, then find the value of:

$$\dfrac{4}{3\sqrt{3}-2\sqrt{2}} + \dfrac{3}{3\sqrt{3}+2\sqrt{2}}.$$

Solution. $\dfrac{4}{3\sqrt{3}-2\sqrt{2}} + \dfrac{3}{3\sqrt{3}+2\sqrt{2}} = \dfrac{4(3\sqrt{3}+2\sqrt{2})+3(3\sqrt{3}-2\sqrt{2})}{(3\sqrt{3}-2\sqrt{2})(3\sqrt{3}+2\sqrt{2})}$

$$= \dfrac{12\sqrt{3}+8\sqrt{2}+9\sqrt{3}-6\sqrt{2}}{(3\sqrt{3})^2-(2\sqrt{2})^2} = \dfrac{21\sqrt{3}+2\sqrt{2}}{27-8}$$

$$= \dfrac{21 \times 1\cdot732 + 2 \times 1\cdot414}{19} = \dfrac{36\cdot372 + 2\cdot828}{19}$$

$$= \dfrac{39\cdot2}{19} = 2\cdot063 \text{ (approx.)}$$

Example 4 Simplify: $\dfrac{\sqrt{6}}{\sqrt{2}+\sqrt{3}}+\dfrac{3\sqrt{2}}{\sqrt{6}+\sqrt{3}}-\dfrac{4\sqrt{3}}{\sqrt{6}+\sqrt{2}}$.

Solution. $\dfrac{\sqrt{6}}{\sqrt{2}+\sqrt{3}}=\dfrac{\sqrt{6}}{\sqrt{2}+\sqrt{3}}\times\dfrac{\sqrt{2}-\sqrt{3}}{\sqrt{2}-\sqrt{3}}=\dfrac{\sqrt{12}-\sqrt{18}}{2-3}=\dfrac{2\sqrt{3}-3\sqrt{2}}{-1}$

$$=-2\sqrt{3}+3\sqrt{2},$$

$$\dfrac{3\sqrt{2}}{\sqrt{6}+\sqrt{3}}=\dfrac{3\sqrt{2}}{\sqrt{6}+\sqrt{3}}\times\dfrac{\sqrt{6}-\sqrt{3}}{\sqrt{6}-\sqrt{3}}=\dfrac{3(\sqrt{12}-\sqrt{6})}{6-3}=\dfrac{3(2\sqrt{3}-\sqrt{6})}{3}$$

$$=2\sqrt{3}-\sqrt{6}\ \text{ and }$$

$$\dfrac{4\sqrt{3}}{\sqrt{6}+\sqrt{2}}=\dfrac{4\sqrt{3}}{\sqrt{6}+\sqrt{2}}\times\dfrac{\sqrt{6}-\sqrt{2}}{\sqrt{6}-\sqrt{2}}=\dfrac{4(\sqrt{18}-\sqrt{6})}{6-2}=\dfrac{4(3\sqrt{2}-\sqrt{6})}{4}$$

$$=3\sqrt{2}-\sqrt{6}.$$

$\therefore\quad\dfrac{\sqrt{6}}{\sqrt{2}+\sqrt{3}}+\dfrac{3\sqrt{2}}{\sqrt{6}+\sqrt{3}}-\dfrac{4\sqrt{3}}{\sqrt{6}+\sqrt{2}}=-2\sqrt{3}+3\sqrt{2}+2\sqrt{3}-\sqrt{6}-(3\sqrt{2}-\sqrt{6})=0.$

Example 5 Simplify: $\dfrac{1}{3-\sqrt{8}}-\dfrac{1}{\sqrt{8}-\sqrt{7}}+\dfrac{1}{\sqrt{7}-\sqrt{6}}-\dfrac{1}{\sqrt{6}-\sqrt{5}}+\dfrac{1}{\sqrt{5}-2}$.

Solution. $\dfrac{1}{3-\sqrt{8}}-\dfrac{1}{\sqrt{8}-\sqrt{7}}+\dfrac{1}{\sqrt{7}-\sqrt{6}}-\dfrac{1}{\sqrt{6}-\sqrt{5}}+\dfrac{1}{\sqrt{5}-2}$

$$=\dfrac{1}{3-\sqrt{8}}\times\dfrac{3+\sqrt{8}}{3+\sqrt{8}}-\dfrac{1}{\sqrt{8}-\sqrt{7}}\times\dfrac{\sqrt{8}+\sqrt{7}}{\sqrt{8}+\sqrt{7}}+\dfrac{1}{\sqrt{7}-\sqrt{6}}\times\dfrac{\sqrt{7}+\sqrt{6}}{\sqrt{7}+\sqrt{6}}$$

$$-\dfrac{1}{\sqrt{6}-\sqrt{5}}\times\dfrac{\sqrt{6}+\sqrt{5}}{\sqrt{6}-\sqrt{5}}+\dfrac{1}{\sqrt{5}-2}\times\dfrac{\sqrt{5}+2}{\sqrt{5}+2}$$

$$=\dfrac{3+\sqrt{8}}{3^2-(\sqrt{8})^2}-\dfrac{\sqrt{8}+\sqrt{7}}{(\sqrt{8})^2-(\sqrt{7})^2}+\dfrac{\sqrt{7}+\sqrt{6}}{(\sqrt{7})^2-(\sqrt{6})^2}-\dfrac{\sqrt{6}+\sqrt{5}}{(\sqrt{6})^2-(\sqrt{5})^2}+\dfrac{\sqrt{5}+2}{(\sqrt{5})^2-2^2}$$

$$=\dfrac{3+\sqrt{8}}{9-8}-\dfrac{\sqrt{8}+\sqrt{7}}{8-7}+\dfrac{\sqrt{7}+\sqrt{6}}{7-6}-\dfrac{\sqrt{6}+\sqrt{5}}{6-5}+\dfrac{\sqrt{5}+2}{5-4}$$

$$=(3+\sqrt{8})-(\sqrt{8}+\sqrt{7})+(\sqrt{7}+\sqrt{6})-(\sqrt{6}+\sqrt{5})+(\sqrt{5}+2)$$

$$=3+2=5.$$

Example 6 If a and b are rational numbers and $\dfrac{5+2\sqrt{3}}{7+4\sqrt{3}}=a-b\sqrt{3}$, find the values of a and b.

Solution. $\dfrac{5+2\sqrt{3}}{7+4\sqrt{3}}=\dfrac{5+2\sqrt{3}}{7+4\sqrt{3}}\times\dfrac{7-4\sqrt{3}}{7-4\sqrt{3}}=\dfrac{35-20\sqrt{3}+14\sqrt{3}-8\times 3}{7^2-(4\sqrt{3})^2}$

$$=\dfrac{11-6\sqrt{3}}{49-48}=\dfrac{11-6\sqrt{3}}{1}=11-6\sqrt{3}$$

$\therefore\quad a-b\sqrt{3}=11-6\sqrt{3}$

$\Rightarrow\quad a=11$ and $b=6$ \hfill (using fact 6)

Example 7 If a and b are rational numbers and $\dfrac{2\sqrt{5}+\sqrt{3}}{2\sqrt{5}-\sqrt{3}}+\dfrac{2\sqrt{5}-3}{2\sqrt{5}+3}=a+\sqrt{15}\,b$, find the values of a and b.

Solution. $\dfrac{2\sqrt{5}+\sqrt{3}}{2\sqrt{5}-\sqrt{3}}+\dfrac{2\sqrt{5}-\sqrt{3}}{2\sqrt{5}+\sqrt{3}}=\dfrac{(2\sqrt{5}+\sqrt{3})^2+(2\sqrt{5}-\sqrt{3})^2}{(2\sqrt{5}-\sqrt{3})(2\sqrt{5}+\sqrt{3})}$

$$=\dfrac{20+3+2\times 2\sqrt{5}\times\sqrt{3}+20+3-2\times 2\sqrt{5}\times\sqrt{3}}{(2\sqrt{5})^3-(\sqrt{3})^2}$$

$$=\dfrac{46}{20-3}=\dfrac{46}{17}=\dfrac{46}{17}+\sqrt{15}\times 0$$

$\therefore \quad a+\sqrt{15}\,b=\dfrac{46}{17}+\sqrt{15}\times 0$

$\Rightarrow \quad a=\dfrac{46}{17}$ and $b=0$.

Example 8 If $x=2-\sqrt{3}$, find the value of $\left(x-\dfrac{1}{x}\right)^3$.

Solution. Given $x=2-\sqrt{3}$,

$\therefore \quad \dfrac{1}{x}=\dfrac{1}{2-\sqrt{3}}=\dfrac{1}{2-\sqrt{3}}\times\dfrac{2+\sqrt{3}}{2+\sqrt{3}}=\dfrac{2+\sqrt{3}}{2^2-(\sqrt{3})^2}$

$$=\dfrac{2+\sqrt{3}}{4-3}=\dfrac{2+\sqrt{3}}{1}=2+\sqrt{3}.$$

$\therefore \quad x-\dfrac{1}{x}=(2-\sqrt{3})-(2+\sqrt{3})=-2\sqrt{3}.$

$\therefore \quad \left(x-\dfrac{1}{x}\right)^3=(-2\sqrt{3})^3=(-2)^3\,(\sqrt{3})^3=-8\times 3\sqrt{3}=-24\sqrt{3}.$

Example 9 If $a=\dfrac{2-\sqrt{5}}{2+\sqrt{5}}$ and $b=\dfrac{2+\sqrt{5}}{2-\sqrt{5}}$, then find the value of $(a+b)^3$.

Solution. $a+b=\dfrac{2-\sqrt{5}}{2+\sqrt{5}}+\dfrac{2+\sqrt{5}}{2-\sqrt{5}}=\dfrac{(2-\sqrt{5})^2+(2+\sqrt{5})^2}{(2+\sqrt{5})(2-\sqrt{5})}$

$$=\dfrac{(4+5-4\sqrt{5})+(4+5+4\sqrt{5})}{2^2-(\sqrt{5})^2}$$

$$=\dfrac{18}{4-5}=\dfrac{18}{-1}=-18.$$

$\therefore \quad (a+b)^3=(-18)^3=-5832.$

Example 10 If $a=5+2\sqrt{6}$, then find the value of $a^2+\dfrac{1}{a^2}$.

Solution. Given $a=5+2\sqrt{6}$.

$\therefore \quad \dfrac{1}{a}=\dfrac{1}{5+2\sqrt{6}}=\dfrac{1}{5+2\sqrt{6}}\times\dfrac{5-2\sqrt{6}}{5-2\sqrt{6}}=\dfrac{5-2\sqrt{6}}{5^2-(2\sqrt{6})^2}$

$$=\dfrac{5-2\sqrt{6}}{25-24}=\dfrac{5-2\sqrt{6}}{1}=5-2\sqrt{6}$$

$\therefore \quad a+\dfrac{1}{a}=(5+2\sqrt{6})+(5-2\sqrt{6})=10 \hspace{4cm} \ldots(i)$

We know that $\left(a+\dfrac{1}{a}\right)^2=a^2+\dfrac{1}{a^2}+2$

$\Rightarrow \quad a^2+\dfrac{1}{a^2}=\left(a+\dfrac{1}{a}\right)^2-2$

$$\Rightarrow \quad a^2 + \frac{1}{a^2} = (10)^2 - 2 \qquad \text{(using (i))}$$

$$\Rightarrow \quad a^2 + \frac{1}{a^2} = 100 - 2 = 98.$$

Example 11 If $x = 9 + 4\sqrt{5}$, then find the value of $\sqrt{x} - \frac{1}{\sqrt{x}}$.

Solution. $x = 9 + 4\sqrt{5} = 5 + 4 + 4\sqrt{5} = (\sqrt{5} + 2)^2$

$$\Rightarrow \quad \sqrt{x} = \pm(\sqrt{5} + 2) \text{ but } \sqrt{x} > 0$$

$$\Rightarrow \quad \sqrt{x} = \sqrt{5} + 2 \qquad \qquad \ldots(i)$$

$$\therefore \quad \frac{1}{\sqrt{x}} = \frac{1}{\sqrt{5} + 2} = \frac{1}{\sqrt{5} + 2} \times \frac{\sqrt{5} - 2}{\sqrt{5} - 2}$$

$$\Rightarrow \quad \frac{1}{\sqrt{x}} = \frac{\sqrt{5} - 2}{(\sqrt{5})^2 - 2^2} = \frac{\sqrt{5} - 2}{5 - 4}$$

$$\Rightarrow \quad \frac{1}{\sqrt{x}} = \sqrt{5} - 2 \qquad \qquad \ldots(ii)$$

$$\therefore \quad \sqrt{x} - \frac{1}{\sqrt{x}} = (\sqrt{5} + 2) - (\sqrt{5} - 2) \qquad \text{(using (i) and (ii))}$$

$$\Rightarrow \quad \sqrt{x} - \frac{1}{\sqrt{x}} = 4.$$

Example 12 If $x = \frac{3 + \sqrt{7}}{2}$, find the value of $4x^2 + \frac{1}{x^2}$.

Solution. Given $x = \frac{3 + \sqrt{7}}{2} \Rightarrow 2x = 3 + \sqrt{7} \qquad \qquad \ldots(i)$

and $\frac{1}{x} = \frac{2}{3 + \sqrt{7}} = \frac{2}{3 + \sqrt{7}} \times \frac{3 - \sqrt{7}}{3 - \sqrt{7}} = \frac{2(3 - \sqrt{7})}{9 - 7} = \frac{2(3 - \sqrt{7})}{2}$

$$\Rightarrow \quad \frac{1}{x} = 3 - \sqrt{7} \qquad \qquad \ldots(ii)$$

On adding (i) and (ii), we get

$$2x + \frac{1}{x} = 6$$

$$\Rightarrow \quad \left(2x + \frac{1}{x}\right)^2 = (6)^2 \Rightarrow 4x^2 + \frac{1}{x^2} + 2 \times 2x \times \frac{1}{x} = 36$$

$$\Rightarrow \quad 4x^2 + \frac{1}{x^2} + 4 = 36 \Rightarrow 4x^2 + \frac{1}{x^2} = 32.$$

Example 13 If $p = \frac{\sqrt{5} - \sqrt{3}}{\sqrt{5} + \sqrt{3}}$ and $q = \frac{\sqrt{5} + \sqrt{3}}{\sqrt{5} - \sqrt{3}}$, find the value of $p^2 + q^2$.

Solution. Given $p = \frac{\sqrt{5} - \sqrt{3}}{\sqrt{5} + \sqrt{3}}$ and $q = \frac{\sqrt{5} + \sqrt{3}}{\sqrt{5} - \sqrt{3}}$,

$$\therefore \quad p + q = \frac{\sqrt{5} - \sqrt{3}}{\sqrt{5} + \sqrt{3}} + \frac{\sqrt{5} + \sqrt{3}}{\sqrt{5} - \sqrt{3}} = \frac{(\sqrt{5} - \sqrt{3})^2 + (\sqrt{5} + \sqrt{3})^2}{(\sqrt{5})^2 - (\sqrt{3})^2}$$

$$= \frac{(5 + 3 - 2\sqrt{5}\sqrt{3}) + (5 + 3 + 2\sqrt{5}\sqrt{3})}{5 - 3} = \frac{16}{2} = 8 \qquad \ldots(i)$$

Also $pq = \frac{\sqrt{5} - \sqrt{3}}{\sqrt{5} + \sqrt{3}} \times \frac{\sqrt{5} + \sqrt{3}}{\sqrt{5} - \sqrt{3}} = 1 \qquad \qquad \ldots(ii)$

We know that $(p + q)^2 = p^2 + q^2 + 2pq$

$$\Rightarrow \quad p^2 + q^2 = (p + q)^2 - 2pq$$

$\Rightarrow \quad p^2 + q^2 = 8^2 - 2 \times 1$ (using (*i*) and (*ii*))

$\Rightarrow \quad p^2 + q^2 = 64 - 2 = 62.$

Example 14 Prove that $\dfrac{1}{2+\sqrt{3}}$ is an irrational number.

Solution. $\dfrac{1}{2+\sqrt{3}} = \dfrac{1}{2+\sqrt{3}} \times \dfrac{2-\sqrt{3}}{2-\sqrt{3}} = \dfrac{2-\sqrt{3}}{4-3} = \dfrac{2-\sqrt{3}}{1} = 2 - \sqrt{3}$

Suppose that $\dfrac{1}{2+\sqrt{3}}$ is rational $\Rightarrow 2 - \sqrt{3}$ is rational, say r.

Then, $2 - \sqrt{3} = r \Rightarrow \sqrt{3} = 2 - r.$

As r is rational, $2 - r$ is rational $\Rightarrow \sqrt{3}$ is rational.

But this contradicts that $\sqrt{3}$ is irrational.

Hence, our supposition is wrong.

Therefore, $\dfrac{1}{2+\sqrt{3}}$ is an irrational number.

EXERCISE 1.5

1 Rationalise the denominator of the following:

(i) $\dfrac{3}{4\sqrt{5}}$ (ii) $\dfrac{5\sqrt{7}}{\sqrt{3}}$ (iii) $\dfrac{3}{4-\sqrt{7}}$ (iv) $\dfrac{17}{3\sqrt{2}+1}$

(v) $\dfrac{16}{\sqrt{41}-5}$ (vi) $\dfrac{1}{\sqrt{7}-\sqrt{6}}$ (vii) $\dfrac{1}{\sqrt{5}+\sqrt{2}}$ (viii) $\dfrac{\sqrt{2}+\sqrt{3}}{\sqrt{2}-\sqrt{3}}$

2 Simplify each of the following by rationalising the denominator:

(i) $\dfrac{7+3\sqrt{5}}{7-3\sqrt{5}}$ (ii) $\dfrac{3-2\sqrt{2}}{3+2\sqrt{2}}$ (iii) $\dfrac{5-3\sqrt{14}}{7+2\sqrt{14}}$

3 Simplify: $\dfrac{7\sqrt{3}}{\sqrt{10}+\sqrt{3}} - \dfrac{2\sqrt{5}}{\sqrt{6}+\sqrt{5}} - \dfrac{3\sqrt{2}}{\sqrt{15}+3\sqrt{2}}.$

4 Simplify: $\dfrac{1}{\sqrt{4}+\sqrt{5}} + \dfrac{1}{\sqrt{5}+\sqrt{6}} + \dfrac{1}{\sqrt{6}+\sqrt{7}} + \dfrac{1}{\sqrt{7}+\sqrt{8}} + \dfrac{1}{\sqrt{8}+\sqrt{9}}.$

5 Given a and b are rational numbers. Find a and b if:

(i) $\dfrac{3-\sqrt{5}}{3+2\sqrt{5}} = -\dfrac{19}{11} + a\sqrt{5}$ (ii) $\dfrac{\sqrt{2}+\sqrt{3}}{3\sqrt{2}-2\sqrt{3}} = a - b\sqrt{6}$

(iii) $\dfrac{7+\sqrt{5}}{7-\sqrt{5}} - \dfrac{7-\sqrt{5}}{7+\sqrt{5}} = a + \dfrac{7}{11}b\sqrt{5}$

6 If $\dfrac{7+3\sqrt{5}}{3+\sqrt{5}} - \dfrac{7-3\sqrt{5}}{3-\sqrt{5}} = p + q\sqrt{5}$, find the value of p and q where p and q are rational numbers.

7 Rationalise the denominator of the following and hence evaluate by taking $\sqrt{2} = 1.414$ and $\sqrt{3} = 1.732$, upto three places of decimal:

(i) $\dfrac{\sqrt{2}}{2+\sqrt{2}}$ (ii) $\dfrac{1}{\sqrt{3}+\sqrt{2}}$

8 If $a = 2 + \sqrt{3}$, then find the value of $a - \dfrac{1}{a}$.

9 If $x = 1 - \sqrt{2}$, find the value of $\left(x - \dfrac{1}{x}\right)^4$.

10 If $x = 5 - 2\sqrt{6}$, find the value of $x^2 + \dfrac{1}{x^2}$.

11 If $p = \dfrac{2 - \sqrt{5}}{2 + \sqrt{5}}$ and $q = \dfrac{2 + \sqrt{5}}{2 - \sqrt{5}}$, find the values of:

(i) $p + q$ (ii) $p - q$ (iii) $p^2 + q^2$ (iv) $p^2 - q^2$

12 If $x = \dfrac{\sqrt{2} - 1}{\sqrt{2} + 1}$ and $y = \dfrac{\sqrt{2} + 1}{\sqrt{2} - 1}$, then find the value of $x^2 + 5xy + y^2$.

Hint. $x^2 + 5xy + y^2 = (x + y)^2 + 3xy$.

Multiple Choice Questions

Choose the correct answer from the given four options (1 to 21):

1 Choose the correct statement:
  (a) Reciprocal of every rational number is a rational number.
  (b) The square roots of all positive integers are irrational numbers.
  (c) The product of a rational and an irrational number is an irrational number.
  (d) The difference of a rational number and an irrational number is an irrational number.

2 Every rational number is
  (a) a natural number (b) an integer
  (c) a real number (d) a whole number

3 Between two rational numbers
  (a) there is no rational number
  (b) there is exactly one rational number
  (c) there are infinitely many rational numbers
  (d) there are only rational numbers and no irrational numbers.

4 Decimal representation of a rational number cannot be
  (a) terminating (b) non-terminating
  (c) non-terminating repeating (d) non-terminating non-repeating

5 The product of any two irrational numbers is
  (a) always an irrational number (b) always a rational number
  (c) always an integer
  (d) sometimes rational, sometimes irrational

6 The division of two irrational numbers is
  (a) a rational number
  (b) an irrational number
  (c) either a rational number or an irrational number
  (d) neither rational number nor irrational number

7 Which of the following is an irrational number?
  (a) $\sqrt{\dfrac{4}{9}}$ (b) $\dfrac{\sqrt{12}}{\sqrt{3}}$ (c) $\sqrt{7}$ (d) $\sqrt{81}$

8 Which of the following numbers has terminating decimal representation?
  (a) $\dfrac{3}{7}$ (b) $\dfrac{3}{5}$ (c) $\dfrac{1}{3}$ (d) $\dfrac{3}{11}$

9 Which of the following is an irrational number?
  (a) 0.14 (b) $0.14\overline{16}$ (c) $0.\overline{1416}$ (d) $0.4014001400014...$

10 Which of the following numbers has non-terminating repeating decimal expansion?

(a) $\dfrac{11}{80}$ (b) $\dfrac{17}{160}$ (c) $\dfrac{63}{240}$ (d) $\dfrac{93}{420}$

11 A rational number between $\sqrt{2}$ and $\sqrt{3}$ is

(a) $\dfrac{\sqrt{2} + \sqrt{3}}{2}$ (b) $\dfrac{\sqrt{2} \times \sqrt{3}}{2}$ (c) $1 \cdot 5$ (d) $1 \cdot 8$

12 The decimal expansion of $2 - \sqrt{3}$ is

(a) terminating and non-repeating   (b) terminating and repeating

(c) non-terminating and non-repeating   (d) non-terminating and repeating

13 The decimal expansion of the rational number $\dfrac{33}{2^2 \times 5}$ will terminate after

(a) one decimal place   (b) two decimal places

(c) three decimal places   (d) four decimal places

14 $\sqrt{10} \times \sqrt{15}$ is equal to

(a) $6\sqrt{5}$ (b) $5\sqrt{6}$ (c) $\sqrt{25}$ (d) $10\sqrt{5}$

15 $2\sqrt{3} + \sqrt{3}$ is equal to

(a) $2\sqrt{6}$ (b) 6 (c) $3\sqrt{3}$ (d) $4\sqrt{6}$

16 The value of $\sqrt{8} + \sqrt{18}$ is

(a) $\sqrt{26}$ (b) $2(\sqrt{2} + \sqrt{3})$ (c) $5\sqrt{2}$ (d) $6\sqrt{2}$

17 The number $(2 - \sqrt{3})^2$ is

(a) a natural number   (b) an integer

(c) a rational number   (d) an irrational number

18 If x is a positive rational number which is not a perfect square, then $-5\sqrt{x}$ is

(a) a negative integer   (b) an integer

(c) a rational number   (d) an irrational number

19 If x, y are both positive rational numbers, then $(\sqrt{x} + \sqrt{y})(\sqrt{x} - \sqrt{y})$ is

(a) a rational number   (b) an irrational number

(c) neither rational nor irrational number

(d) both rational as well as irrational number

20 After rationalising the denominator of $\dfrac{7}{3\sqrt{3} - 2\sqrt{2}}$, we get the denominator as

(a) 13 (b) 19 (c) 5 (d) 35

21 The number obtained on rationalising the denominator of $\dfrac{1}{\sqrt{7} - 2}$ is

(a) $\dfrac{\sqrt{7} + 2}{3}$ (b) $\dfrac{\sqrt{7} - 2}{3}$ (c) $\dfrac{\sqrt{7} + 2}{5}$ (d) $\dfrac{\sqrt{7} + 2}{45}$

Summary

○ Any number that can be expressed in the form $\dfrac{p}{q}$, where p, q are integers, $q \neq 0$, is called a **rational number.** Usually, we take $q > 0$, while p may be positive, negative or zero. Collection of rational numbers is denoted by **Q**.

Rational numbers do not have unique representation.

For example, $\frac{1}{2} = \frac{2}{4} = \frac{7}{14} = \frac{40}{80}$ etc.

Every rational number can be written in the form $\frac{p}{q}$, where p, q are integers, q ≠ 0, p, q have no common factors (except 1). It is called in the **lowest terms** *or* **simplest form.**

○ A number that cannot be expressed in the form $\frac{p}{q}$, where p, q are integers, q ≠ 0, p, q have no common factors (except 1) is called an **irrational number.**

For example, $\sqrt{2}, \sqrt{3}, \sqrt{6}, -\sqrt{7}, 2 - \sqrt{5}$ are all irrational numbers.

○ The decimal expansion of a rational number is either terminating or non-terminating recurring (repeating). Conversely, a number whose decimal expansion is terminating or non-terminating recurring is rational.

○ The decimal expansion of a rational number $\frac{p}{q}$, where p, q are integers, q > 0, p and q have no common factors except 1 is:

    (i) terminating if prime factors of q are 2 or 5 or both.

    (ii) non-terminating recurring if q has a prime factor other than 2 or 5.

○ The decimal expansion of an irrational number is non-terminating non-recurring. Conversely, a number whose decimal expansion is non-terminating non-recurring is irrational.

○ All rational numbers and all irrational numbers are **real numbers.** The collection of real numbers is denoted by **R.**

○ Every real number (rational or irrational) can be represented by a unique point on the number line. Conversely, every point on the number line represents a unique real number.

○ If x is rational and y is irrational, then x + y, x − y and y − x are irrational numbers.

○ If x is a non-zero rational number and y is an irrational number, then xy, $\frac{x}{y}$ and $\frac{y}{x}$ are irrational numbers.

○ If a is any positive rational number and n(> 1) is a positive integer and if a cannot written

as the nth power of any rational number, then $\sqrt[n]{a}$ (or $a^{\frac{1}{n}}$) is called a **surd of order n.**

○ All surds are irrational numbers.

❏ **Some laws of surds**

If a, b are positive rational numbers and n(> 1) is a positive integer, then

    (i) $(\sqrt[n]{a})^n = a$ (ii) $\sqrt[n]{a}\sqrt[n]{b} = \sqrt[n]{ab}$ (iii) $\frac{\sqrt[n]{a}}{\sqrt[n]{b}} = \sqrt[n]{\frac{a}{b}}$.

❏ **Some facts about surds of order 2**

    1. If a and b are positive rational numbers, then the following results hold:

    (i) $\sqrt{ab} = \sqrt{a}\sqrt{b}$ (ii) $\sqrt{\frac{a}{b}} = \frac{\sqrt{a}}{\sqrt{b}}$

    (iii) $(\sqrt{a} + \sqrt{b})(\sqrt{a} - \sqrt{b}) = a - b$ (iv) $(a + \sqrt{b})(a - \sqrt{b}) = a^2 - b$

    (v) $(\sqrt{a} + \sqrt{b})^2 = a + 2\sqrt{ab} + b$ (vi) $(\sqrt{a} - \sqrt{b})^2 = a - 2\sqrt{ab} + b$

    2. If a, b, c and d are rational numbers, $\sqrt{p}$ is an irrational number and $a + b\sqrt{p} = c + d\sqrt{p}$, then a = c and b = d.

1 Without actual division, find whether the following rational numbers are terminating decimals or recurring decimals:

(i) $\dfrac{13}{45}$ (ii) $-\dfrac{5}{56}$ (iii) $\dfrac{7}{125}$ (iv) $-\dfrac{23}{80}$ (v) $-\dfrac{15}{66}$.

In case of terminating decimals, write their decimal expansions.

2 Express the following recurring decimals as vulgar fractions:

(i) $1 \cdot 3\overline{45}$ (ii) $2 \cdot \overline{357}$.

3 Insert a rational number between $\dfrac{5}{9}$ and $\dfrac{7}{13}$, and arrange in ascending order.

4 Insert four rational numbers between $\dfrac{4}{5}$ and $\dfrac{5}{6}$.

5 Prove that the reciprocal of an irrational number is irrational.

6 Prove that the following numbers are irrational:

(i) $\sqrt{8}$ (ii) $\sqrt{14}$ (iii) $\sqrt[3]{2}$.

7 Prove that $\sqrt{3}$ is an irrational number. Hence show that $5 - \sqrt{3}$ is an irrational number.

8 Prove that the following numbers are irrational:

(i) $3 + \sqrt{5}$ (ii) $15 - 2\sqrt{7}$ (iii) $\dfrac{1}{3 - \sqrt{5}}$

9 Rationalise the denominator of the following:

(i) $\dfrac{10}{2\sqrt{2} + \sqrt{3}}$ (ii) $\dfrac{7\sqrt{3} - 5\sqrt{2}}{\sqrt{48} + \sqrt{18}}$ (iii) $\dfrac{1}{\sqrt{3} - \sqrt{2} + 1}$.

10 If p, q are rational numbers and $p - \sqrt{15}\, q = \dfrac{2\sqrt{3} - \sqrt{5}}{4\sqrt{3} - 3\sqrt{5}}$, find the values of p and q.

11 If $x = \dfrac{1}{3 + 2\sqrt{2}}$, then find the value of $x - \dfrac{1}{x}$.

12   (i) If $x = \dfrac{7 + 3\sqrt{5}}{7 - 3\sqrt{5}}$, find the value of $x^2 + \dfrac{1}{x^2}$.

(ii) If $x = \dfrac{\sqrt{5} - \sqrt{2}}{\sqrt{5} + \sqrt{2}}$ and $y = \dfrac{\sqrt{5} + \sqrt{2}}{\sqrt{5} - \sqrt{2}}$, then find the value of $x^2 + xy + y^2$.

(iii) If $x = \dfrac{\sqrt{3} - \sqrt{2}}{\sqrt{3} + \sqrt{2}}$ and $y = \dfrac{\sqrt{3} + \sqrt{2}}{\sqrt{3} - \sqrt{2}}$, find the value of $x^3 + y^3$.

Hint.

(iii) $x^3 + y^3 = (x + y)^3 - 3xy(x + y)$.

13 Write the following real numbers in descending order:

$\sqrt{2},\ 3 \cdot 5,\ \sqrt{10},\ -\dfrac{5}{\sqrt{2}},\ \dfrac{5}{2}\sqrt{3}$.

14 Find a rational number and an irrational number between $\sqrt{3}$ and $\sqrt{5}$.

15 Insert three irrational numbers between $2\sqrt{3}$ and $2\sqrt{5}$, and arrange in descending order.

16 Give an example each of two different irrational numbers, whose

    (*i*) sum is an irrational number.

    (*ii*) product is an irrational number.

17 Give an example of two different irrational numbers, *a* and *b*, where $\frac{a}{b}$ is a rational number.

18 If 34·0356 is expressed in the form $\frac{p}{q}$, where *p* and *q* are coprime integers, then what can you say about the factorisation of *q*?

19 In each case, state whether the following numbers are rational or irrational. If they are rational and expressed in the form $\frac{p}{q}$, where *p* and *q* are coprime integers, then what can you say about the prime factors of *q*?

    (*i*) 279·034   (*ii*) 76·$\overline{17893}$ (*iii*) 3·010010001...

    (*iv*) 39·546782   (*v*) 2·3476817681...   (*vi*) 59·120120012000...

2 Compound Interest

INTRODUCTION

In the previous classes, you have learnt about simple interest and other related terms. You have also solved many problems on simple interest. In this chapter, we shall learn about compound interest, difference between simple and compound interest, computation of compound interest as a repeated simple interest with a growing principal and also by use of formula.

2.1 INTEREST

It is the additional money besides the original money paid by the borrower to the moneylender (bank, financial agency or individual) in lieu of the money used by him.

Principal. *The money borrowed (or the money lent) is called* **principal.**

Amount. *The sum of the principal and the interest is called* **amount.**

Thus, **amount = principal + interest.**

Rate. *It is the interest paid on ₹100 for a specified period.*

Time. *It is the time for which the money is borrowed.*

Simple Interest. *It is the interest calculated on the original money (principal) for any given time and rate.*

Formula: **Simple Interest** $= \dfrac{\text{Principal} \times \text{Rate} \times \text{Time}}{100}$.

Compound Interest

At the end of the first year (or any other fixed period), if the interest accrued is not paid to the moneylender but is added to the principal, then this amount becomes the principal for the next year (or any other fixed period) and so on. This process is repeated until the amount for the whole time is found.

The difference between the final amount and the (original) principal is called **compound interest.**

Remark

In the case of simple interest, the principal remains constant for the whole time but in the case of compound interest, the principal keeps on changing every year (or any other fixed period).

If the interest is *compounded annually*, the principal changes after every year and if the interest is *compounded half-yearly* (or *any other fixed period*), the principal changes after every six months (or any other fixed period).

Illustrative Examples

Example 1 Find the amount and the compound interest on ₹15000 for 2 years at 8% per annum.

Solution.

Principal for the first year = ₹15000.

Interest for the first year = ₹ $\frac{15000 \times 8 \times 1}{100}$ = ₹1200.

Amount after one year = ₹15000 + ₹1200 = ₹16200.

Principal for the second year = ₹16200.

Interest for the second year = ₹ $\frac{16200 \times 8 \times 1}{100}$ = ₹1296.

Amount after 2 years = ₹16200 + ₹1296 = ₹17496.

Compound interest for 2 years = final amount − (original) principal

= ₹17496 − ₹15000 = ₹2496.

Note The compound interest may also be obtained by adding together the interest of consecutive years.

Thus, in the above example,

compound interest = interest of first year + interest of second year

= ₹1200 + ₹1296 = ₹2496.

Example 2 Find the amount and the compound interest on ₹25000 for 3 years at 12% per annum, compounded annually.

Solution.

Principal for the first year = ₹25000.

Interest for the first year = ₹ $\frac{25000 \times 12 \times 1}{100}$ = ₹3000.

Amount after one year = ₹25000 + ₹3000 = ₹28000.

Principal for the second year = ₹28000.

Interest for the second year = ₹ $\frac{28000 \times 12 \times 1}{100}$ = ₹3360.

Amount after 2 years = ₹28000 + ₹3360

= ₹31360.

Principal for the third year = ₹31360.

Interest for the third year = ₹ $\frac{31360 \times 12 \times 1}{100}$ = ₹3763·20

Amount after 3 years = ₹31360 + ₹3763·20

= ₹35123·20

Compound interest for 3 years = final amount − (original) principal

= ₹35123·20 − ₹25000

= ₹10123·20

Example 3 Find the compound interest to the nearest rupee on ₹7500 for 2 years 4 months at 12% per annum reckoned annually.

Solution. Principal for the first year = ₹7500.

Interest for the first year = ₹ $\frac{7500 \times 12 \times 1}{100}$ = ₹900.

Amount after one year = ₹7500 + ₹900 = ₹8400.

Principal for the second year = ₹8400.

Interest for the second year = ₹$\dfrac{8400 \times 12 \times 1}{100}$ = ₹1008.

Amount after 2 years = ₹8400 + ₹1008 = ₹9408.

Remaining time = 4 months = $\dfrac{4}{12}$ year = $\dfrac{1}{3}$ year.

Principal for the next $\dfrac{1}{3}$ year = ₹9408.

Interest for the next $\dfrac{1}{3}$ year = ₹$\dfrac{9408 \times 12 \times \frac{1}{3}}{100}$ = ₹376·32

Amount after 2 years 4 months = ₹9408 + ₹376·32
$$= ₹9784·32$$

∴ Compound interest for 2 years 4 months

= final amount – (original) principal

= ₹9784·32 – ₹7500 = ₹2284·32

= ₹2284 (to the nearest rupee).

Example 4 Find the amount and the compound interest on ₹16000 for $1\dfrac{1}{2}$ years at 10% per annum, the interest being compounded half-yearly.

Solution. Since the rate of interest is 10% per annum, therefore, the rate of interest half-yearly = $\dfrac{1}{2}$ of 10% = 5%.

Principal for the first half-year = ₹16000.

Interest for the first half-year = ₹$\dfrac{16000 \times 5 \times 1}{100}$ = ₹800.

Amount after the first half-year = ₹16000 + ₹800 = ₹16800.

Principal for the second half-year = ₹16800.

Interest for the second half-year = ₹$\dfrac{16800 \times 5 \times 1}{100}$ = ₹840.

Amount after one year = ₹16800 + ₹840 = ₹17640.

Principal for the third half-year = ₹17640.

Interest for the third half-year = ₹$\dfrac{17640 \times 5 \times 1}{100}$ = ₹882.

Amount after $1\dfrac{1}{2}$ years = ₹17640 + ₹882 = ₹18522.

∴   Compound interest for $1\dfrac{1}{2}$ years = final amount – (original) principal

= ₹18522 – ₹16000 = ₹2522.

Example 5 Nikita invests ₹6000 for two years at a certain rate of interest compounded annually. At the end of first year it amounts to ₹6720. Calculate :

(*i*) the rate of interest.

(*ii*) the amount at the end of the second year.

Solution. Given, principal = ₹6000, amount after one year = ₹6720.

(*i*) Interest for the first year = ₹6720 – ₹6000 = ₹720.

Let the rate of interest be R% p.a., then

$$\text{S.I.} = \dfrac{P \times R \times T}{100} \Rightarrow 720 = \dfrac{6000 \times R \times 1}{100} \Rightarrow R = 12.$$

Hence, the rate of interest = 12% p.a.

(ii) Principal for the second year = ₹6720.

Interest for the second year = ₹$\dfrac{6720 \times 12 \times 1}{100}$ = ₹806·40

∴ The amount at the end of second year = ₹6720 + ₹806·40

= ₹7526·40.

Example 6 Calculate the amount due and the compound interest on ₹7500 in 2 years when the rate of interest on successive years is 8% and 10% respectively.

Solution.   Principal for the first year = ₹7500, rate = 8%.

Interest for the first year = ₹$\dfrac{7500 \times 8 \times 1}{100}$ = ₹600.

Amount after the first year = ₹7500 + ₹600 = ₹8100.

Principal for the second year = ₹8100, rate = 10%.

Interest for the second year = ₹$\dfrac{8100 \times 10 \times 1}{100}$ = ₹810.

∴   Amount due after 2 years = ₹8100 + ₹810 = ₹8910.

Compound interest for 2 years = amount − principal

= ₹8910 − ₹7500 = ₹1410.

Example 7 Calculate the difference between the compound interest and the simple interest on ₹12000 at 9% per annum in 2 years.

Solution. Given   principal = ₹12000, rate = 9% p.a. and time = 2 years

∴   S.I. = ₹$\dfrac{12000 \times 9 \times 2}{100}$ = ₹2160.

For C.I.

Principal for the first year = ₹12000.

Interest for the first year = ₹$\dfrac{12000 \times 9 \times 1}{100}$ = ₹1080.

Amount after one year = ₹12000 + ₹1080 = ₹13080.

Principal for the second year = ₹13080.

Interest for the 2nd year = ₹$\dfrac{13080 \times 9 \times 1}{100}$

= ₹1177·20

∴   C.I. of 2 years = ₹1080 + ₹1177·20 = ₹2257·20.

∴ Difference between compound interest and simple interest in 2 years

= ₹2257·20 − ₹2160

= ₹97·20.

Example 8 The simple interest on a sum of money for 2 years at 4% per annum is ₹340. Find

(i) the sum of money

(ii) the compound interest on this sum for one year payable half-yearly at the same rate.

Solution. Given, S.I. = ₹340, rate = 4% p.a. and time = 2 years

(i) Let the sum of money be P, then

S.I. = $\dfrac{P \times R \times T}{100}$ ⇒ ₹340 = $\dfrac{P \times 4 \times 2}{100}$

⇒   P = ₹$\dfrac{340 \times 100}{4 \times 2}$ = ₹4250.

(ii) Since the rate of interest is 4% per annum, therefore, the rate of interest half-yearly = 2%.

$$\text{Principal for the first half-year} = ₹4250.$$

$$\text{Interest for the first half-year} = ₹\frac{4250 \times 2 \times 1}{100} = ₹85.$$

∴ $$\text{Amount after the first half-year} = ₹4250 + ₹85 = ₹4335.$$

$$\text{Principal for the 2nd half-year} = ₹4335.$$

$$\text{Interest for the 2nd half-year} = ₹\frac{4335 \times 2 \times 1}{100} = ₹86·70$$

∴ Compound interest on the above sum for one year payable half-yearly

$$= ₹85 + ₹86·70 = ₹171·70$$

Example 9 The simple interest on a certain sum of money for 3 years at 5% per annum is ₹1200. Find the amount due and the compound interest on this sum of money at the same rate after 3 years, interest is reckoned annually.

Solution. Given simple interest for 3 years = ₹1200.

∴ $$\text{Simple interest for one year} = \frac{1}{3} \text{ of } ₹1200 = ₹400$$

$$\text{S.I.} = \frac{P \times R \times T}{100} \Rightarrow ₹400 = \frac{P \times 5 \times 1}{100}$$

⇒ $$P = ₹\frac{400 \times 100}{5 \times 1} = ₹8000.$$

∴ $$\text{Amount after one year} = ₹8000 + ₹400 = ₹8400.$$

$$\text{Principal for the second year} = ₹8400.$$

$$\text{Interest for the second year} = ₹\frac{8400 \times 5 \times 1}{100} = ₹420.$$

$$\text{Amount after 2 years} = ₹8400 + ₹420 = ₹8820.$$

$$\text{Interest for the third year} = ₹\frac{8820 \times 5 \times 1}{100} = ₹441.$$

∴ $$\text{Amount due after 3 years} = ₹8820 + ₹441 = ₹9261.$$

$$\text{Compound interest for 3 years} = ₹9261 – ₹8000 = ₹1261.$$

Example 10 Ranbir borrows ₹20000 at 12% per annum compound interest. If he repays ₹8400 at the end of the first year and ₹9680 at the end of the second year, find the amount of the loan outstanding at the beginning of the third year.

Solution. $$\text{Principal for the first year} = ₹20000, \text{ rate} = 12\%.$$

$$\text{Interest for the first year} = ₹\frac{20000 \times 12 \times 1}{100} = ₹2400.$$

$$\text{Amount after the first year} = ₹20000 + ₹2400 = ₹22400.$$

$$\text{Money refunded at the end of first year} = ₹8400.$$

∴ $$\text{Principal for the second year} = ₹22400 – ₹8400 = ₹14000.$$

$$\text{Interest for the second year} = ₹\frac{14000 \times 12 \times 1}{100} = ₹1680.$$

$$\text{Amount after the second year} = ₹14000 + ₹1680 = ₹15680.$$

$$\text{Money refunded at the end of 2nd year} = ₹9680.$$

∴ The loan outstanding at the beginning of the third year

$$= ₹15680 – ₹9680 = ₹6000.$$

Example 11 Mr. Kumar borrowed ₹15000 for two years. The rate of interest for the two successive years are 8% and 10% respectively. If he repays ₹6200 at the end of first year, find the outstanding amount at the end of the second year.

Solution.

Principal for the first year = ₹15000, rate = 8% p.a.

$$\text{Interest for the first year} = ₹\frac{15000 \times 8 \times 1}{100} = ₹1200.$$

Amount after one year = ₹15000 + ₹1200 = ₹16200.

Money repaid at the end of first year = ₹6200.

∴ Principal for the second year = ₹16200 – ₹6200 = ₹10000;

rate of interest for second year = 10% p.a.

$$\text{Interest for the second year} = ₹\frac{10000 \times 10 \times 1}{100} = ₹1000.$$

Amount after second year = ₹10000 + ₹1000 = ₹11000.

∴ The amount outstanding at the end of second year = ₹11000.

Example 12 Sulekha deposits ₹8000 in a bank every year in the beginning of the year, at 10% per annum compound interest. Calculate the amount due to her at the end of three years. Also find her gain in three years.

Solution.

Principal for the first year = ₹8000, rate = 10% p.a.

$$\text{Interest for the first year} = ₹\frac{8000 \times 10 \times 1}{100} = ₹800.$$

Amount after one year = ₹8000 + ₹800 = ₹8800.

Money deposited at the beginning of 2nd year = ₹8000.

Principal for the 2nd year = ₹8800 + ₹8000 = ₹16800.

$$\text{Interest for the 2nd year} = ₹\frac{16800 \times 10 \times 1}{100} = ₹1680.$$

Amount after 2 years = ₹16800 + ₹1680 = ₹18480.

Money deposited at the beginning of 3rd year = ₹8000.

Principal for the 3rd year = ₹18480 + ₹8000 = ₹26480.

$$\text{Interest for the 3rd year} = ₹\frac{26480 \times 10 \times 1}{100} = ₹2648.$$

Amount after 3 years = ₹26480 + ₹2648 = ₹29128.

∴ The amount due to Sulekha at the end of 3 years = ₹29128.

Money deposited by Sulekha in 3 years = ₹8000 + ₹8000 + ₹8000

= ₹24000.

∴ Gain of Sulekha in 3 years = ₹29128 – ₹24000

= ₹5128.

Example 13 A man borrows ₹5000 at 12% compound interest per annum, interest payable after six months. He pays back ₹1800 at the end of every six months. Calculate the third payment he has to make at the end of 18 months in order to clear the entire loan.

Solution. Since the rate of interst is 12% per annum, therefore, rate of interest half-yearly = 6%.

Principal for the first six months = ₹5000.

$$\text{Interest for the first six months} = ₹\frac{5000 \times 6 \times 1}{100} = ₹300.$$

Amount after first six months = ₹5000 + ₹300 = ₹5300.

Money refunded at the end of first six months = ₹1800.

∴ Principal for the second six months = ₹5300 – ₹1800

= ₹3500.

Interest for the second six months = ₹$\frac{3500 \times 6 \times 1}{100}$ = ₹210.

Amount after second six months = ₹3500 + ₹210

= ₹3710.

Money refunded at the end of second six months = ₹1800.

∴ Principal for the third six months = ₹3710 – ₹1800

= ₹1910.

Interest for the third six months = ₹$\frac{1910 \times 6 \times 1}{100}$ = ₹114·60

∴ The payment to be made at the end of 18 months to clear the entire loan

= ₹1910 + ₹114·60

= ₹2024·60

EXERCISE 2.1

1. Find the amount and the compound interest on ₹8000 at 5% per annum for 2 years.

2. A man invests ₹46875 at 4% per annum compound interest for 3 years. Calculate:
   (i) the interest for the first year.
   (ii) the amount standing to his credit at the end of the second year.
   (iii) the interest for the third year.

3. Calculate the compound interest for the second year on ₹8000 invested for 3 years at 10% p.a.

   Also find the sum due at the end of third year.

4. Ramesh invests ₹12800 for three years at the rate of 10% per annum compound interest. Find :
   (i) the sum due to Ramesh at the end of the first year.
   (ii) the interest he earns for the second year.
   (iii) the total amount due to him at the end of three years.

5. The simple interest on a sum of money for 2 years at 12% per annum is ₹1380. Find:
   (i) the sum of money.
   (ii) the compound interest on this sum for one year payable half-yearly at the same rate.

6. A person invests ₹10000 for two years at a certain rate of interest, compounded annually. At the end of one year this sum amounts to ₹11200. Calculate :
   (i) the rate of interest per annum.
   (ii) the amount at the end of second year.

7. Mr. Lalit invested ₹5000 at a certain rate of interest, compounded annually for two years. At the end of first year it amounts to ₹ 5325. Calculate
   (i) the rate of interest.
   (ii) the amount at the end of second year, to the nearest rupee.

8. A man invests ₹5000 for three years at a certain rate of interest, compounded annually. At the end of one year it amounts to ₹5600. Calculate:
   (i) the rate of interest per annum.

(*ii*) the interest accrued in the second year.

(*iii*) the amount at the end of the third year.

9   Find the amount and the compound interest on ₹2000 at 10% p.a. for $2\frac{1}{2}$ years, compounded annually.

10   Find the amount and the compound interest on ₹50000 for $1\frac{1}{2}$ years at 8% per annum, the interest being compounded semi-annually.

11   Calculate the amount and the compound interest on ₹5000 in 2 years when the rate of interest for successive years is 6% and 8% respectively.

12   Calculate the amount and the compound interest on ₹17000 in 3 years when the rate of interest for successive years is 10%, 10% and 14% respectively.

13   A sum of ₹9600 is invested for 3 years at 10% per annum at compound interest.

(*i*)   What is the sum due at the end of the first year?

(*ii*) What is the sum due at the end of the second year?

(*iii*) Find the compound interest earned in 2 years.

(*iv*) Find the difference between the answers in (*ii*) and (*i*) and find the interest on this sum for one year.

(*v*)   Hence, write down the compound interest for the third year.

14   The simple interest on a certain sum of money for 2 years at 10% per annum is ₹1600. Find the amount due and the compound interest on this sum of money at the same rate after 3 years, interest being reckoned annually.

15   Vikram borrowed ₹20000 from a bank at 10% per annum simple interest. He lent it to his friend Venkat at the same rate but compounded annually. Find his gain after $2\frac{1}{2}$ years.

16   A man borrows ₹6000 at 5% compound interest. If he repays ₹1200 at the end of each year, find the amount outstanding at the beginning of the third year.

17   Mr. Dubey borrows ₹100000 from State Bank of India at 11% per annum compound interest. He repays ₹41000 at the end of first year and ₹47700 at the end of second year. Find the amount outstanding at the beginning of the third year.

18   Jaya borrowed ₹50000 for 2 years. The rates of interest for two successive years are 12% and 15% respectively. She repays ₹ 33000 at the end of first year. Find the amount she must pay at the end of second year to clear her debt.

2.2 FORMULA FOR COMPOUND INTEREST

Compound interest (abbreviated C.I.) can be easily calculated by the following formula:

Formula : $A = P\left(1+\dfrac{r}{100}\right)^{n}$

where A is the final amount, P is the principal, r is the rate of interest compounded yearly and n is the number of years.

$$C.I. = A - P = P\left(1+\dfrac{r}{100}\right)^{n} - P = P\left[\left(1+\dfrac{r}{100}\right)^{n} - 1\right].$$

Remark

If the interest is calculated for any other fixed period (like 6 months), then the principal keeps on changing every term of the fixed period (like 6 months).

*The time from one specified interest period to the next period is called a **conversion period**. If this specified period is one year (i.e. the interest is compounded annually), then there is one conversion period in a year; if this period is six months (i.e. the interest is compounded semi-annually), then there are two conversion periods in a year; if this period is three* months (*i.e.* the interest is compounded quarterly), then there are *four conversion periods* in a year. In view of this discussion, we can restate the formula as:

Formula : $A = P\left(1+\dfrac{r}{100}\right)^n$

where A is the final amount, P is the principal, r is the rate of interest per conversion period and n is the number of conversion periods.

> **Note** Obviously, if the rate of interest per annum is 10% and if the interest is compounded semi-annually, then the rate of interest per conversion period is $\dfrac{1}{2}$ of 10% *i.e.* 5%. If the interest is compounded quarterly, then the rate of interest per conversion period is $\dfrac{1}{4}$ of 10% *i.e.* 2·5%.

2.2.1 In solving problems on compound interest, remember the following:

1. $A = P\left(1+\dfrac{r}{100}\right)^n$ and $C.I. = P\left[\left(1+\dfrac{r}{100}\right)^n - 1\right]$

   where A is the amount, P is the principal, r is the rate of interest per conversion period and n is the number of conversions periods.

2. When the rates of interest for the successive fixed periods are r_1%, r_2%, r_3%, ..., then amount A is given by

   $$A = P\left(1+\dfrac{r_1}{100}\right)\left(1+\dfrac{r_2}{100}\right)\left(1+\dfrac{r_3}{100}\right) ....$$

3. S.I. (simple interest) and C.I. are equal for the first conversion period on the same sum and at the same rate.

4. C.I. of 2nd conversion period is more than the C.I. of 1st conversion period and C.I. of 2nd conversion period – C.I. of 1st conversion period = S.I. on the interest of the 1st conversion period.

5. C.I. for the nth conversion period

   = amount after n conversion periods – amount after $(n-1)$ conversion periods.

6. When the total time is not a complete number of conversion periods, we consider simple interest for the last partial period. For example, if time is 2 years 5 months and the interest is r% per annum compounded annually, then

   $$A = P\left(1+\dfrac{r}{100}\right)^2 \times \left(1+\dfrac{\frac{5}{12}r}{100}\right).$$

Illustrative Examples

Example 1 Find the amount and compound interest on ₹16000 for 2 years at 15%, interest being payable annually.

Solution. Using the formula, we get

$$A = ₹16000\left(1+\dfrac{15}{100}\right)^2 \qquad\qquad A = P\left(1+\dfrac{r}{100}\right)^n$$

$$= ₹16000 \times \left(\dfrac{115}{100}\right)^2 = ₹16000 \times \left(\dfrac{23}{20}\right)^2$$

$$= ₹16000 \times \dfrac{23}{20} \times \dfrac{23}{20} = ₹21160.$$

$$C.I. = A - P = ₹21160 - ₹16000 = ₹5160.$$

Example 2 Rohit borrows ₹86000 from Arun for two years at 5% per annum simple interest. He immediately lends out this money to Akshay at 5% compound interest compounded annually for the same period. Calculate Rohit's profit in the transaction at the end of two years.

Solution. Principal = ₹86000, rate = 5% and time = 2 years.

Simple interest paid by Rohit in 2 years :

$$\text{S.I.} = \frac{P \times R \times T}{100} = ₹\frac{86000 \times 5 \times 2}{100} = ₹8600.$$

Compound interest earned by Rohit in 2 years

If A is the amount after 2 years, then

$$A = P\left(1 + \frac{R}{100}\right)^n = ₹86000\left(1 + \frac{5}{100}\right)^2 = ₹86000 \times \left(\frac{21}{20}\right)^2$$

$$= ₹86000 \times \frac{441}{400} = ₹94815.$$

∴ C.I. earned by Rohit in 2 years = amount after 2 years – principal

$$= ₹94815 - ₹86000 = ₹8815$$

∴ Rohit's profit at the end of 2 years = C.I. earned – S.I. paid

$$= ₹8815 - ₹8600 = ₹215.$$

Example 3 Calculate the interest earned and the amount due, if a sum of ₹15000 is invested for $1\frac{1}{2}$ years at 8% per annum compound interest, interest being compounded semi-annually.

Solution. Since rate of interest is 8% per annum, therefore, rate of interest per conversion period (half-yearly) = 4%.

As the money is invested for $1\frac{1}{2}$ years, therefore,

n (the number of conversion periods) = 3.

$$\therefore \qquad A = P\left(1 + \frac{r}{100}\right)^n = ₹15000\left(1 + \frac{4}{100}\right)^3$$

$$= ₹15000 \times \left(\frac{26}{25}\right)^3 = ₹15000 \times \frac{26}{25} \times \frac{26}{25} \times \frac{26}{25}$$

$$= ₹\frac{421824}{25} = ₹16872·96.$$

Interest earned = A – P = ₹16872·96 – ₹15000 = ₹1872·96.

Example 4 How much will ₹25000 amount to in 2 years, at compound interest, if the rates for the successive years are 4% and 5% per year?

Solution.

$$A = P\left(1 + \frac{r_1}{100}\right)\left(1 + \frac{r_2}{100}\right)$$

$$= ₹25000\left(1 + \frac{4}{100}\right)\left(1 + \frac{5}{100}\right) = ₹25000 \times \frac{26}{25} \times \frac{21}{20} = ₹27300.$$

Example 5 Compute the amount and the compound interest on ₹10000 compounded annually for $2\frac{1}{2}$ years at 4% per annum.

Solution. First, we find the amount after 2 years

$$A = P\left(1 + \frac{r}{100}\right)^n = ₹10000\left(1 + \frac{4}{100}\right)^2$$

$$= ₹10000 \times \left(\frac{26}{25}\right)^2 = ₹10000 \times \frac{26}{25} \times \frac{26}{25} = ₹10816.$$

Principal for the third year = ₹10816.

$$\text{Interest for the next } \frac{1}{2} \text{ year} = ₹\frac{10816 \times 4 \times \frac{1}{2}}{100} = ₹216 \cdot 32$$

$$\text{Amount after } 2\frac{1}{2} \text{ years} = ₹10816 + ₹216 \cdot 32$$
$$= ₹11032 \cdot 32$$

$$\therefore \quad \text{Compound interest for } 2\frac{1}{2} \text{ years} = A - P$$
$$= ₹11032 \cdot 32 - ₹10000$$
$$= ₹1032 \cdot 32$$

Alternative method (by using formula)

$$\text{Amount at the end of } 2\frac{1}{2} \text{ years} = ₹10000 \left(1 + \frac{4}{100}\right)^2 \left(1 + \frac{\frac{6}{12} \times 4}{100}\right)$$

$$= ₹\left(10000 \times \frac{26}{25} \times \frac{26}{25} \times \frac{51}{50}\right) = ₹11032 \cdot 32$$

$$\therefore \quad \text{Compound interest for } 2\frac{1}{2} \text{ years} = ₹11032 \cdot 32 - ₹10000$$
$$= ₹1032 \cdot 32$$

Example 6 Rohan borrowed ₹40000 at 10% p.a. simple interest. He immediately invested this money at 10% p.a., the interest compounded half-yearly. Calculate Rohan's gain in 18 months.

Solution. Principal = ₹40000, rate = 10% p.a., time = 18 months = $\frac{18}{12}$ years = $\frac{3}{2}$ years.

Simple interest paid by Rohan in 18 months :

$$\text{S.I.} = \frac{P \times R \times T}{100} = ₹\frac{40000 \times 10 \times \frac{3}{2}}{100} = ₹6000.$$

Compound interest earned by Rohan in 18 months :

Since the rate of interest is 10% p.a., therefore, the rate of interest per conversion period (half-yearly) = 5%.

As the money is invested for 18 months, therefore, n(the number of conversion periods) = 3.

$$A = P\left(1 + \frac{r}{100}\right)^n = ₹40000 \left(1 + \frac{5}{100}\right)^3$$

$$= ₹40000 \times \left(\frac{21}{20}\right)^3 = ₹40000 \times \frac{9261}{8000} = ₹46305.$$

$$\therefore \quad \text{C.I. earned by Rohan in 18 months} = \text{amount after 18 months} - \text{principal}$$
$$= ₹46305 - ₹40000 = ₹6305.$$

$$\therefore \quad \text{Rohan's gain in 18 months} = \text{C.I. earned} - \text{S.I. paid}$$
$$= ₹6305 - ₹6000 = ₹305.$$

Example 7 What sum of money will amount to ₹3630 in two years at 10% per annum compound interest?

Solution. $\quad A = P\left(1 + \frac{r}{100}\right)^n \Rightarrow ₹3630 = P\left(1 + \frac{10}{100}\right)^2$

$$\Rightarrow \quad ₹3630 = P \times \frac{11}{10} \times \frac{11}{10}$$

$$\Rightarrow \quad P = ₹\left(3630 \times \frac{10}{11} \times \frac{10}{11}\right) = ₹3000.$$

Example 8 What sum of money will amount to ₹3704·40 in 3 years at 5% compound interest?

Solution.
$$A = P\left(1+\frac{r}{100}\right)^n \Rightarrow ₹3704·40 = P\left(1+\frac{5}{100}\right)^3$$

$$\Rightarrow ₹\frac{370440}{100} = P \times \frac{21}{20} \times \frac{21}{20} \times \frac{21}{20}$$

$$\Rightarrow P = ₹\frac{37044}{10} \times \frac{20}{21} \times \frac{20}{21} \times \frac{20}{21} = ₹3200.$$

Example 9 On a certain sum, the compound interest for 2 years is ₹2172. If the rates of interest for successive years are 6% and 8% per year, then find the sum.

Solution.
$$A = P\left(1+\frac{r_1}{100}\right)\left(1+\frac{r_2}{100}\right)$$

$$= P\left(1+\frac{6}{100}\right)\left(1+\frac{8}{100}\right) = P \times \frac{53}{50} \times \frac{27}{25}$$

$$= \frac{1431}{1250}P.$$

∴ $$C.I. = A - P = \frac{1431}{1250}P - P = \frac{181}{1250}P.$$

Given, $$C.I. = ₹2172$$

$$\Rightarrow \frac{181}{1250}P = ₹2172 \Rightarrow P = ₹2172 \times \frac{1250}{181} = ₹15000.$$

Hence, the sum = ₹15000.

Example 10 The compound interest on a certain sum of money at 5% per annum for two years is ₹246. Calculate the simple interest on the same sum for three years at 6% per annum.

Solution.
$$C.I. = P\left[\left(1+\frac{r}{100}\right)^n - 1\right]$$

$$\Rightarrow ₹246 = P\left[\left(1+\frac{5}{100}\right)^2 - 1\right]$$

$$\Rightarrow ₹246 = P\left[\frac{21}{20} \times \frac{21}{20} - 1\right] = P \times \frac{41}{400}$$

$$\Rightarrow P = ₹\left(246 \times \frac{400}{41}\right) = ₹2400.$$

∴ Simple interest for the same sum for 3 years at 6% per annum

$$= ₹\frac{2400 \times 6 \times 3}{100} = ₹432.$$

Example 11 At what rate percent per annum compound interest will ₹5000 amount to ₹ 5832 in 2 years?

Solution. $$A = P\left(1+\frac{r}{100}\right)^n \Rightarrow ₹5832 = ₹5000\left(1+\frac{r}{100}\right)^2$$

$$\Rightarrow \left(1+\frac{r}{100}\right)^2 = \frac{5832}{5000} = \frac{729}{625} = \left(\frac{27}{25}\right)^2$$

$\Rightarrow \qquad 1 + \dfrac{r}{100} = \dfrac{27}{25} \Rightarrow \dfrac{r}{100} = \dfrac{27}{25} - 1 = \dfrac{2}{25}$

$\Rightarrow \qquad r = \dfrac{2}{25} \times 100 = 8.$

Hence, rate = 8% per annum.

Example 12 At what rate % p.a. will a sum of ₹4000 yield ₹1324 as compound interest in 3 years?

Solution. Given P = ₹4000, C.I. = ₹1324 and T = 3 years.

A = P + C.I. = ₹4000 + ₹1324 = ₹5324.

Let the rate of interest be r% p.a.

Here, time = 3 years, so $n = 3$.

Using the formula :

$$A = P \left(1 + \dfrac{r}{100}\right)^n, \text{ we get}$$

$$₹5324 = ₹4000 \left(1 + \dfrac{r}{100}\right)^3$$

$\Rightarrow \qquad \left(1 + \dfrac{r}{100}\right)^3 = \dfrac{5324}{4000} = \dfrac{1331}{1000}$

$\Rightarrow \qquad \left(1 + \dfrac{r}{100}\right)^3 = \left(\dfrac{11}{10}\right)^3 \Rightarrow 1 + \dfrac{r}{100} = \dfrac{11}{10}$

$\Rightarrow \qquad \dfrac{r}{100} = \dfrac{11}{10} - 1 \Rightarrow \dfrac{r}{100} = \dfrac{1}{10} \Rightarrow r = 10.$

Hence, the rate of interest = 10% p.a.

Example 13 A sum of ₹16000 earns a compound interest of ₹2522 in 18 months, when the interest is compounded half-yearly. Find the rate of interest.

Solution. Given P = ₹16000, C.I. = ₹2522 and T = 18 months.

Let the rate of interest per conversion period (half-year) be r%.

As the interest is compounded half-yearly *i.e.* after 6 months and the time is 18 months, so n(number of conversion periods) = $\dfrac{18}{3}$ = 3.

$$A = P + C.I. = ₹16000 + ₹2522 = ₹18522.$$

$$A = P \left(1 + \dfrac{r}{100}\right)^n \Rightarrow ₹18522 = ₹16000 \left(1 + \dfrac{r}{100}\right)^3$$

$\Rightarrow \qquad \left(1 + \dfrac{r}{100}\right)^3 = \dfrac{18522}{16000} = \dfrac{9261}{8000}$

$\Rightarrow \qquad \left(1 + \dfrac{r}{100}\right)^3 = \left(\dfrac{21}{20}\right)^3 \Rightarrow 1 + \dfrac{r}{100} = \dfrac{21}{20}$

$\Rightarrow \qquad \dfrac{r}{100} = \dfrac{21}{20} - 1 \Rightarrow \dfrac{r}{100} = \dfrac{1}{20} \Rightarrow r = 5.$

Thus, rate of interest per conversion period (6 months) = 5%.

∴ Rate of interest per annum = 10%.

Example 14 Determine the rate of interest per annum for a sum that becomes $\dfrac{729}{625}$ of itself in one year, compounded half-yearly.

Solution. Let the principal be P and the rate of interest be $r\%$ per conversion period (half-year).

Here, interest is compounded half-yearly.

Total time is one year, so n(the number of conversion periods) = 2.

According to given, $A = \dfrac{729}{625} P$

$$\Rightarrow \qquad \dfrac{729}{625} P = P\left(1 + \dfrac{r}{100}\right)^2 \qquad\qquad \left| A = P\left(1 + \dfrac{r}{100}\right)^n \right.$$

$$\Rightarrow \qquad \left(1 + \dfrac{r}{100}\right)^2 = \dfrac{729}{625} = \left(\dfrac{27}{25}\right)^2$$

$$\Rightarrow \qquad 1 + \dfrac{r}{100} = \dfrac{27}{25} \Rightarrow \dfrac{r}{100} = \dfrac{27}{25} - 1 = \dfrac{2}{25} \Rightarrow r = 8$$

i.e. rate of interest per conversion period (half-year) = 8%.

$\therefore$ Rate of interest per annum = 16%.

Example 15 The compound interest on a sum of money for 2 years is ₹410 and the simple interest on the same sum for the same period and at the same rate is ₹400. Find the sum and the rate of interest.

Solution.

$$\text{S.I. for 2 years} = ₹400$$

$$\therefore \qquad \text{S.I. for 1 year} = \dfrac{₹400}{2} = ₹200$$

$\therefore \qquad$ C.I. for first year = ₹200 $\qquad\qquad$ (∵ for first year, C.I. = S.I.)

Given, $\qquad$ C.I. for 2 years = ₹410

$\therefore \qquad$ C.I. for the second year = ₹410 – ₹200 = ₹210.

$\therefore \qquad$ Difference of interests = ₹210 – ₹200 = ₹10

$\Rightarrow$ ₹10 is the interest on ₹200 for one year.

$$\therefore \qquad \text{Rate of interest} = \dfrac{10 \times 100}{200 \times 1}\% = 5\% \qquad\qquad \left| R = \dfrac{\text{S.I.} \times 100}{P \times T} \right.$$

$$\text{Principal} = ₹\dfrac{200 \times 100}{5 \times 1} = ₹4000. \qquad\qquad \left| P = \dfrac{\text{S.I.} \times 100}{R \times T} \right.$$

Example 16 A certain sum amounts to ₹4840 in 2 years and to ₹5324 in 3 years at compound interest. Find the rate and the sum.

Solution. Let the rate of compound interest be $r\%$ per annum.

The amount after 2 years will be the principal for the third year,

$$₹5324 = ₹4840\left(1 + \dfrac{r}{100}\right) \qquad\qquad \left| A = P\left(1 + \dfrac{r}{100}\right)^n \right.$$

$$\Rightarrow \qquad 1 + \dfrac{r}{100} = \dfrac{5324}{4840}$$

$$\Rightarrow \qquad \dfrac{r}{100} = \dfrac{5324}{4840} - 1 = \dfrac{5324 - 4840}{4840} = \dfrac{484}{4840} = \dfrac{1}{10}$$

$$\Rightarrow \qquad r = \dfrac{1}{10} \times 100 = 10.$$

$\therefore$ The rate of compound interest = 10% per annum.

Let the original sum be P.

$$₹4840 = P\left(1 + \dfrac{10}{110}\right)^2 \qquad\qquad \left| A = P\left(1 + \dfrac{r}{100}\right)^n \right.$$

$$\Rightarrow \qquad ₹4840 = P \times \frac{11}{10} \times \frac{11}{10}$$

$$\Rightarrow \qquad P = ₹4840 \times \frac{10}{11} \times \frac{10}{11} = ₹4000.$$

∴ The original sum is ₹4000.

Example 17 The compound interest, calculated yearly, on a certain sum of money for the second year is ₹1320 and for the third year it is ₹1452. Calculate the rate of interest and the original money.

Solution. C.I. for the third year = ₹1320 and

C.I. for the second year = ₹1452.

∴ S.I. on ₹ 1320 for one year = ₹1452 − ₹1320 = ₹132.

∴ Rate of interest = $\frac{132 \times 100}{1320 \times 1}$ % = 10% $\qquad \left| R = \frac{S.I. \times 100}{P \times T} \right.$

Let the original money be ₹P.

Amount after 2 years − amount after one year = C.I. for second year

$$\Rightarrow \qquad P\left(1 + \frac{10}{100}\right)^2 - P\left(1 + \frac{10}{100}\right) = 1320$$

$$\Rightarrow \qquad P\left[\left(\frac{11}{10}\right)^2 - \frac{11}{10}\right] = 1320 \quad \Rightarrow \quad P\left(\frac{121}{100} - \frac{11}{10}\right) = 1320$$

$$\Rightarrow \qquad P \times \frac{11}{100} = 1320 \qquad \Rightarrow P = 1320 \times \frac{100}{11} = 12000.$$

∴ The rate of interest = 10%, and original money = ₹12000.

Example 18 In how many years will ₹4000 amount to ₹5324 at 10% compound interest?

Solution. Here P = ₹4000, A = ₹5324 and r = 10% p.a.

$$A = P\left(1 + \frac{r}{100}\right)^n \Rightarrow ₹5324 = ₹4000\left(1 + \frac{10}{100}\right)^n$$

$$\Rightarrow \qquad \frac{5324}{4000} = \left(\frac{11}{10}\right)^n \quad \Rightarrow \quad \left(\frac{11}{10}\right)^n = \frac{1331}{1000} = \left(\frac{11}{10}\right)^3$$

$$\Rightarrow \qquad n = 3.$$

∴ The required time = 3 years.

Example 19 In what period of time will ₹12000 yield ₹3972 as compound interest at 10% per annum, if compounded on yearly basis.

Solution. P = ₹12000, C.I. = ₹3972, rate = 10% p.a.

A = P + C.I. = ₹12000 + ₹3972 = ₹15972.

Using $A = P\left(1 + \frac{r}{100}\right)^n$, we get

$$₹15972 = ₹12000 \times \left(1 + \frac{10}{100}\right)^n$$

$$\Rightarrow \qquad \frac{15972}{12000} = \left(\frac{11}{10}\right)^n$$

$$\Rightarrow \qquad \left(\frac{11}{10}\right)^n = \frac{1331}{1000} \Rightarrow \left(\frac{11}{10}\right)^n = \left(\frac{11}{10}\right)^3$$

$$\Rightarrow \qquad n = 3.$$

∴ The required time = 3 years.

Example 20 A sum of ₹25000 invested at 8% p.a. compounded semi-annually amounts to ₹28121·60. Compute the time period of investment.

Solution. Here, P = ₹25000, A = ₹28121·60

As the interest is compounded semi-annually, r (rate of interest per conversion period)

$$= \frac{1}{2} \text{ of } 8\% = 4\%.$$

Let the number of conversion periods be n, then

$$₹28121 \cdot 60 = ₹25000 \left(1 + \frac{4}{100}\right)^n \qquad \qquad \left| A = P\left(1 + \frac{r}{100}\right)^n \right.$$

$$\Rightarrow \qquad \frac{2812160}{100} = 25000 \left(\frac{26}{25}\right)^n$$

$$\Rightarrow \qquad \left(\frac{26}{25}\right)^n = \frac{2812160}{100 \times 25000} = \frac{17576}{15625} = \left(\frac{26}{25}\right)^3$$

$$\Rightarrow \qquad n = 3.$$

∴ Time period of investment is 3 half-years *i.e.* $1\frac{1}{2}$ years.

Example 21 A sum of money invested at compound interest doubles itself in 4 years, interest being payable annually. In how much time will it be eight times?

Solution. Let the principal be ₹P and rate of interest be $r\%$ p.a.

As the money doubles itself in 4 years, we have

$$\Rightarrow \qquad 2P = P\left(1 + \frac{r}{100}\right)^4 \Rightarrow \left(1 + \frac{r}{100}\right)^4 = \frac{2P}{P} = 2$$

$$\Rightarrow \qquad 1 + \frac{r}{100} = 2^{1/4} \qquad \qquad \qquad \qquad \qquad \dots(i)$$

Let the money become eight times in n years, then

$$8P = P\left(1 + \frac{r}{100}\right)^n \Rightarrow \left(1 + \frac{r}{100}\right)^n = \frac{8P}{P} = 8$$

$$\Rightarrow \qquad (2^{1/4})^n = 2^3 \qquad \qquad \qquad \qquad \qquad \qquad \text{(using } (i))$$

$$\Rightarrow \qquad 2^{n/4} = 2^3 \Rightarrow \frac{n}{4} = 3 \Rightarrow n = 12.$$

Hence, the required time = 12 years.

Example 22 The simple interest in 3 years and the compound interest in 2 years on a certain sum at the same rate are ₹1200 and ₹832 respectively. Find :

   (i) the rate of interest   (ii) the principal

  (iii) the difference between the C.I. and S.I. for 3 years.

Solution. (i) Let the principal be ₹P and rate of interest be R% p.a.

According to the first condition of the question,

$$\frac{P \times R \times 3}{100} = 1200 \Rightarrow P \times R = 40000 \qquad \qquad \dots(1)$$

According to the second condition of the question,

$$P \left[\left(1 + \frac{R}{100}\right)^2 - 1\right] = 832$$

$$\Rightarrow \qquad \frac{40000}{R} \left[\frac{(100 + R)^2}{(100)^2} - 1\right] = 832 \qquad \qquad \text{(using (1))}$$

$$\Rightarrow \qquad 40000 \times \frac{(100+R)^2 - (100)^2}{100 \times 100} = 832\, R$$

$$\Rightarrow \qquad 4[(100)^2 + R^2 + 2 \times 100 \times R - (100)^2] = 832\, R$$

$$\Rightarrow \qquad R^2 + 200\, R = 208\, R \;\Rightarrow\; R^2 + 200\, R - 208\, R = 0$$

$$\Rightarrow \qquad R^2 - 8R = 0 \;\Rightarrow\; R(R - 8) = 0$$

$$\Rightarrow \qquad \text{either } R = 0 \text{ or } R - 8 = 0$$

$$\Rightarrow \qquad \text{either } R = 0 \text{ or } R = 8, \text{ but } R \text{ cannot be zero.}$$

$$\therefore \qquad R = 8 \;\Rightarrow\; \text{rate of interest} = 8\% \text{ p.a.}$$

(*ii*) On using (1), we get

$$P \times 8 = 40000 \;\Rightarrow\; P = 5000.$$

$$\therefore \qquad \text{Principal} = ₹5000.$$

(*iii*) Rate of compound interest = 8% p.a. and principal = ₹5000.

$$\text{Amount due after 3 years} = ₹5000\left(1 + \frac{8}{100}\right)^3$$

$$= ₹5000 \times \left(\frac{27}{25}\right)^3 = ₹5000 \times \frac{27}{25} \times \frac{27}{25} \times \frac{27}{25}$$

$$= ₹\frac{157464}{25} = ₹6298 \cdot 56$$

$$\therefore \qquad \text{C.I. for 3 years} = A - P = ₹6298 \cdot 56 - ₹5000$$

$$= ₹1298 \cdot 56$$

∴ The difference between the C.I. and S.I. for 3 years

$$= ₹1298 \cdot 56 - ₹1200 = ₹98 \cdot 56$$

Example 23 A certain sum of money is invested at the rate of 5% per annum compound interest, the interest compounded annually. If the difference between the interests of third year and first year is ₹102·50, find the sum.

Solution. Let the sum of money invested be ₹x.

$$\text{Rate of interest} = 5\% \text{ p.a.}$$

$$\therefore \qquad \text{Interest for the first year} = ₹\frac{x \times 5 \times 1}{100} = ₹\frac{x}{20}.$$

Interest for the 3rd year *i.e.* the compound interest for the 3rd year

$$= \text{amount after 3 years} - \text{amount after 2 years}$$

$$= ₹x\left(1 + \frac{5}{100}\right)^3 - ₹x\left(1 + \frac{5}{100}\right)^2$$

$$= ₹x\left[\left(\frac{21}{20}\right)^3 - \left(\frac{21}{20}\right)^2\right] = ₹\left[x \times \left(\frac{21}{20}\right)^2\left(\frac{21}{20} - 1\right)\right]$$

$$= ₹\left(x \times \frac{441}{400} \times \frac{1}{20}\right) = ₹\frac{441x}{8000}.$$

Given, difference between interests of third year and first year is ₹102·50

$$\Rightarrow \qquad \frac{441x}{8000} - \frac{x}{20} = \frac{205}{2}$$

$$\Rightarrow \qquad \frac{(441 - 400)x}{8000} = \frac{205}{2} \;\Rightarrow\; \frac{41}{8000}x = \frac{205}{2}$$

$$\Rightarrow \qquad x = \frac{205}{2} \times \frac{8000}{41} = 20000.$$

∴ The sum of money invested = ₹20000.

Example 24 On a certain sum of money, the difference between the compound interest for a year, payable half-yearly, and the simple interest for a year is ₹180. Find the sum lent out, if the rate of interest in both the cases is 10%.

Solution. Let the principal be ₹x.

S.I. for 1 year at 10% per annum = ₹$\dfrac{x \times 10 \times 1}{100}$ = ₹$\dfrac{x}{10}$.

Rate of interest per conversion period (half-year) = $\dfrac{1}{2}$ of 10% = 5%

and n(the number of conversion periods) = 2.

$$\text{C.I.} = ₹x\left[\left(1+\frac{5}{100}\right)^2 - 1\right] \qquad \left| \text{C.I.} = P\left[\left(1+\frac{r}{100}\right)^n - 1\right] \right.$$

$$= ₹x\left(\frac{21}{20} \times \frac{21}{20} - 1\right) = ₹x\left(\frac{441}{400} - 1\right) = ₹\frac{41}{400}x.$$

$\therefore \qquad$ C.I. − S.I. = ₹$\dfrac{41}{400}x$ − ₹$\dfrac{x}{10}$ = ₹$\left(\dfrac{41}{400} - \dfrac{1}{10}\right)x$ = ₹$\dfrac{x}{400}$.

According to the given information, $\dfrac{x}{400} = 180 \Rightarrow x = 72000$.

$\therefore$ The sum lent out = ₹72000.

Example 25 The difference between the compound interest and the simple interest on ₹42000 for two years is ₹105 at the same rate of interest per annum. Find :

    (*i*) the rate of interest

    (*ii*) the compound interest earned in the second year.

Solution. (*i*) Let the rate of interest be r% per annum.

Here P (principal) = ₹42000 and T (time) = 2 years.

$$\text{S.I.} = ₹\frac{42000 \times r \times 2}{100}.$$

$$\text{C.I.} = ₹42000\left[\left(1+\frac{r}{100}\right)^2 - 1\right] = ₹42000\left[\left(\frac{r}{100}\right)^2 + \frac{2r}{100}\right]$$

$\therefore \qquad$ C.I. − S.I. = ₹$42000\left[\left(\dfrac{r}{100}\right)^2 + \dfrac{2r}{100}\right] - ₹42000 \times \dfrac{2r}{100}$

$$= ₹42000 \times \left(\frac{r}{100}\right)^2 = ₹\frac{21}{5}r^2.$$

According to given, $\dfrac{21}{5}r^2 = 105$

$\Rightarrow \qquad r^2 = 25 \Rightarrow r = 5, -5$, but r cannot be negative

$\Rightarrow \qquad r = 5$.

Hence, the rate of interest = 5% per annum.

(*ii*)   C.I. earned in two years = ₹$42000\left[\left(1+\dfrac{5}{100}\right)^2 - 1\right]$

$$= ₹42000\left[\left(\frac{21}{20}\right)^2 - 1\right] = ₹42000 \times \frac{41}{400}$$

$$= ₹4305.$$

Interest earned in one year $= ₹\dfrac{42000 \times 5 \times 1}{100} = ₹2100.$

∴   C.I. earned in the second year $= ₹4305 - ₹2100 = ₹2205.$

Example 26 A man borrowed a sum of money and agrees to pay off by paying ₹ 3150 at the end of the first year and ₹ 4410 at the end of the second year. If the rate of compound interest is 5% per annum, find the sum borrowed.

Solution. Let the money borrowed be ₹x.

$$\text{Amount after one year} = ₹x\left(1+\dfrac{5}{100}\right) = ₹\dfrac{21}{20}x.$$

Money refunded at the end of first year $= ₹3150.$

∴   Principal for the 2nd year $= ₹\left(\dfrac{21}{20}x - 3150\right).$

$$\text{Amount at the end of 2nd year} = ₹\left(\dfrac{21}{20}x - 3150\right) \times \left(1+\dfrac{5}{100}\right)$$

$$= ₹\left(\dfrac{21}{20}x - 3150\right) \times \dfrac{21}{20}.$$

But the money paid at the end of the 2nd year $= ₹4410,$

∴ $\left(\dfrac{21}{20}x - 3150\right) \times \dfrac{21}{20} = 4410$

$\Rightarrow$ $\dfrac{21}{20}x - 3150 = 4410 \times \dfrac{20}{21} = 4200$

$\Rightarrow$ $\dfrac{21}{20}x = 4200 + 3150 = 7350$

$\Rightarrow$ $x = 7350 \times \dfrac{20}{21} = 7000.$

∴ The sum borrowed $= ₹7000.$

EXERCISE 2.2

1   Find the amount and the compound interest on ₹5000 for 2 years at 6% per annum, interest payable yearly.

2   Find the amount and the compound interest on ₹8000 for 4 years at 10% per annum, interest reckoned yearly.

3   If the interest is compounded half yearly, calculate the amount when the principal is ₹7400, the rate of interest is 5% and the duration is one year.

4   Find the amount and the compound interest on ₹5000 at 10% p.a. for $1\dfrac{1}{2}$ years, compound interest reckoned semi-annually.

5   Find the amount and the compound interest on ₹100000 compounded quarterly for 9 months at the rate of 4% p.a.

     Hint. $r = \dfrac{1}{4}$ of 4% = 1% and $n = \dfrac{9}{3} = 3.$

6   Find the difference between C.I. and S.I. on sum of ₹4800 for 2 years at 5% per annum payable yearly.

7 Find the difference between the simple interest and compound interest on ₹2500 for 2 years at 4% per annum, compound interest being reckoned semi-annually.

8 Find the amount and the compound interest on ₹2000 in 2 years if the rate is 4% for the first year and 3% for the second year.

9 Find the compound interest on ₹3125 for 3 years if the rates of interest for the first, second and third year are respectively 4%, 5% and 6% per annum.

10 What sum of money will amount to ₹9261 in 3 years at 5% per annum compound interest?

11 What sum invested at 4% per annum compounded semi-annually amounts to ₹7803 at the end of one year?

12 What sum invested for $1\frac{1}{2}$ years compounded half-yearly at the rate of 4% p.a. will amount to ₹132651?

13 On what sum will the compound interest for 2 years at 4% per annum be ₹5712?

14 A man invests ₹1200 for two years at compound interest. After one year the money amounts to ₹1275. Find the interest for the second year correct to the nearest rupee.

15 At what rate percent per annum compound interest will ₹2304 amount to ₹2500 in 2 years?

16 A sum compounded annually becomes $\frac{25}{16}$ times of itself in two years. Determine the rate of interest per annum.

17 At what rate percent will ₹2000 amount to ₹2315·25 in 3 years at compound interest?

18 If ₹40000 amounts to ₹48620·25 in 2 years, compound interest payable half-yearly, find the rate of interest per annum.

19 Determine the rate of interest for a sum that becomes $\frac{216}{125}$ times of itself in $1\frac{1}{2}$ years, compounded semi-annually.

20 At what rate percent p.a. compound interest would ₹80000 amount to ₹88200 in two years, interest being compounded yearly. Also find the amount after 3 years at the above rate of compound interest.

21 A certain sum amounts to ₹5292 in 2 years and to ₹5556·60 in 3 years at compound interest. Find the rate and the sum.

22 A certain sum amounts to ₹798·60 after 3 years and ₹878·46 after 4 years. Find the interest rate and the sum.

23 In what time will ₹15625 amount to ₹17576 at 4% per annum compound interest?

24   (i) In what time will ₹ 1500 yield ₹ 496·50 as compound interest at 10% per annum compounded annually?

   (ii) Find the time (in years) in which ₹12500 will produce ₹3246·40 as compound interest at 8% per annum, interest compounded annually.

25 ₹16000 invested at 10% p.a., compounded semi-annually, amounts to ₹18522. Find the time period of investment.

26 What sum will amount to ₹2782·50 in 2 years at compound interest, if the rates are 5% and 6% for the successive years?

27 A sum of money is invested at compound interest payable annually. The interest in two successive years is ₹225 and ₹240. Find :

   (i) the rate of interest.

   (ii) the original sum.

   (iii) the interest earned in the third year.

28 On what sum of money will the difference between the compound interest and simple interest for 2 years be equal to ₹25 if the rate of interest charged for both is 5% p.a.?

29 The difference between the compound interest for a year payable half-yearly and the simple interest on a certain sum of money lent out at 10% for a year is ₹15. Find the sum of money lent out.

30 The amount at compound interest which is calculated yearly on a certain sum of money is ₹1250 in one year and ₹1375 in two years. Calculate the rate of interest.

31 The simple interest on a certain sum for 3 years is ₹225 and the compound interest on the same sum at the same rate for 2 years is ₹153. Find the rate of interest and the principal.

32 Find the difference between compound interest on ₹8000 for $1\frac{1}{2}$ years at 10% p.a. when compounded annually and semi-annually.

33 A sum of money is lent out at compound interest for two years at 20% p.a., C.I. being reckoned yearly. If the same sum of money is lent out at compound interest at the same rate percent per annum, C.I. being reckoned half-yearly, it would have fetched ₹482 more by way of interest. Calculate the sum of money lent out.

34 A sum of money amounts to ₹13230 in one year and to ₹13891·50 in $1\frac{1}{2}$ years at compound interest, compounded semi-annually. Find the sum and the rate of interest per annum.

2.3 GROWTH AND DEPRECIATION

Growth. We know certain things grow (increase, appreciate). For example, India's population, Delhi's pollution level, height of a plant, weight of a child, cost of goods etc.

*The growth per year (or unit of time) is called **rate of growth**.*

If the rate of growth is constant, then

$$V = V_0 \left(1 + \frac{r}{100}\right)^n$$

where $r\%$ is the rate of growth per year, n is the number of years, V_0 is the present measure of the quantity and V is the measure of the quantity after n years.

Similarly, if V_0 is the measure of the quantity n years ago and V is the present measure of the quantity, then

$$V = V_0 \left(1 + \frac{r}{100}\right)^n$$

Remark

If the rate of growth is $r_1\%$ during the first year (or unit of time) and $r_2\%$ during the second year (or unit of time), then

$$V = V_0 \left(1 + \frac{r_1}{100}\right)\left(1 + \frac{r_2}{100}\right)$$

where V_0 is the present measure of the quantity and V is the measure of the quantity after two years (or units of time).

This formula can be extended for more than 2 years (or units of time).

Depreciation. The value of a machine or vehicle etc. decreases with time due to wear and tear.

*The decrease of the value per year (or unit of time) is called **rate of depreciation**.*

If the rate of depreciation is constant, then

$$V = V_0 \left(1 - \frac{r}{100}\right)^n$$

where $r\%$ is the rate of depreciation per year, n is the number of years, V_0 is the present value and V is the value after n years.

Similarly, if V_0 is the value n years ago and V is the present value, then

$$V = V_0 \left(1 - \frac{r}{100}\right)^n$$

*The number of years a machine can be effectively used is called its lifespan, after which it is sold as **waste** or **scrap**.*

Illustrative Examples

Example 1 The present population of a town is 48000. It is increasing at the rate of 5% every year. What will be the increase in population in next 3 years?

Solution. Population after 3 years = (present population) $\times \left(1 + \frac{5}{100}\right)^3$

$$\left| V = V_0 \left(1 + \frac{r}{100}\right)^n \right.$$

$$= 48000 \times \frac{21}{20} \times \frac{21}{20} \times \frac{21}{20} = 55566.$$

∴   Increase in population in 3 years = 55566 − 48000 = 7566.

Example 2 The present population of a village is 5408. If it has increased at the rate of 4% every year, what was its population two years ago?

Solution.   Present population = (population 2 years ago) $\times \left(1 + \frac{4}{100}\right)^2$

$$\Rightarrow \qquad 5408 = \text{(population 2 years ago)} \times \frac{26}{25} \times \frac{26}{25}$$

$$\Rightarrow \text{ population 2 years ago} = 5408 \times \frac{25}{26} \times \frac{25}{26} = 5000.$$

Example 3 The value of a machine, purchased two years ago, depreciates at the annual rate of 10%. If its present value is ₹97200, find :

  (i) its value after 3 years   (ii) its value when it was purchased.

Solution. (i) Value after 3 years = (present value) $\times \left(1 - \frac{10}{100}\right)^3$ $\left| V = V_0 \left(1 - \frac{r}{100}\right)^n \right.$

$$= ₹\left(97200 \times \frac{9}{10} \times \frac{9}{10} \times \frac{9}{10}\right) = ₹\frac{708588}{10}$$

$$= ₹70858 \cdot 80$$

(ii)   Present value = (value 2 years ago) $\times \left(1 - \frac{10}{100}\right)^2$

$$\Rightarrow \qquad ₹97200 = \text{(value 2 years ago)} \times \frac{9}{10} \times \frac{9}{10}$$

$$\Rightarrow \text{ value 2 years ago} = ₹\left(97200 \times \frac{10}{9} \times \frac{10}{9}\right) = ₹120000.$$

Example 4 The population of a village 2 years ago was 6250. Due to migration to cities, it decreases at the rate of 8% every year. Find the decrease in its population in the last 2 years.

Solution. Present population = (population 2 years ago) $\times \left(1 - \frac{8}{100}\right)^2$

$$= 6250 \times \frac{23}{25} \times \frac{23}{25} = 5290.$$

$\therefore$ The decrease in the population in 2 years = $6250 - 5290 = 960$.

Example 5 The value of a car depreciates by 12·5 % every year. By what percent will the value of the car decrease after 3 years?

Solution. Let the present value of the car be $₹V_0$.

Value of the car after 3 years = (present value) $\times \left(1 - \frac{12·5}{100}\right)^3$

$$= ₹V_0 \times \left(1 - \frac{1}{8}\right)^3 = ₹V_0 \times \left(\frac{7}{8}\right)^3$$

$\therefore$ Decrease in the value of car = $₹V_0 - ₹V_0 \times \left(\frac{7}{8}\right)^3$

$$= ₹V_0 \left[1 - \left(\frac{7}{8}\right)^3\right] = ₹V_0 \times \frac{512 - 343}{512}$$

$$= ₹\left(V_0 \times \frac{169}{512}\right).$$

$\therefore$ Percentage decrease in the value of the car after 3 years

$$= \left(\frac{\text{decrease}}{\text{present value}} \times 100\right)\% = \left(\frac{V_0 \times \frac{169}{512}}{V_0} \times 100\right)\%$$

$$= \left(\frac{169}{512} \times 100\right)\% = \frac{169 \times 25}{128}\% = \frac{4225}{128}\%$$

$$= 33\frac{1}{128}\%.$$

Example 6 6000 workers were employed to construct a river bridge in four years. At the end of first year, 20% workers were retrenched. At the end of second year, 5% of the workers at that time were retrenched. However, to complete the project in time, the number of workers was increased by 15% at the end of third year. How many workers were working during the fourth year?

Solution. The number of workers who were working during the fourth year

$$= 6000 \left(1 - \frac{20}{100}\right)\left(1 - \frac{5}{100}\right)\left(1 + \frac{15}{100}\right) \qquad \left| V = V_0 \left(1 - \frac{r_1}{100}\right)\left(1 - \frac{r_2}{100}\right)\left(1 + \frac{r_3}{100}\right) \right.$$

$$= 6000 \times \frac{4}{5} \times \frac{19}{20} \times \frac{23}{20} = 5244.$$

Example 7 24000 blood donors were registered with 'red cross' at Kolkata. The number of donors increased at the rate of 5% every six months. Find the time period at the end of which the total number of blood donors becomes 27783.

Solution. Here rate of increase of the number of blood donors per unit time (six months) = 5%. Let the number of units of time (six months) be n.

Using $V = V_0 \left(1 + \frac{r}{100}\right)^n$, we get

$$27783 = 24000 \left(1 + \frac{5}{100}\right)^n$$

$$\Rightarrow \qquad \left(\frac{21}{20}\right)^n = \frac{27783}{24000} = \frac{9261}{8000} = \left(\frac{21}{20}\right)^3$$

$$\Rightarrow \qquad n = 3.$$

$\therefore$ The time period $= 3 \times$ (six months) $= 1\frac{1}{2}$ years.

Example 8 In a factory, the production of motorbikes rose to 23328 from 20000 in 2 years. Find the rate of growth of the production of motorbikes.

Solution. Let the rate of growth of the production of motorbikes be $r\%$ per annum.

Here, present production $V = 23328$ motorbikes and production 2 years earlier $V_0 = 20000$ motorbikes.

Using the formula, $V = V_0\left(1 + \frac{r}{100}\right)^n$, we get

$$23328 = 20000\left(1 + \frac{r}{100}\right)^2$$

$$\Rightarrow \quad \left(1 + \frac{r}{100}\right)^2 = \frac{23328}{20000} = \frac{729}{625}$$

$$\Rightarrow \quad \left(1 + \frac{r}{100}\right)^2 = \left(\frac{27}{25}\right)^2$$

$$\Rightarrow \quad 1 + \frac{r}{100} = \frac{27}{25} \Rightarrow \frac{r}{100} = \frac{27}{25} - 1$$

$$\Rightarrow \quad \frac{r}{100} = \frac{2}{25} \Rightarrow r = 8.$$

Hence, the rate of growth of the production of motorbikes is 8% p.a.

Example 9 The cost of a washing machine depreciates by ₹720 during the second year and by ₹648 during the third year. Calculate :

  (i) the rate of depreciation per annum

  (ii) the original cost of the machine

  (iii) the value of the machine at the end of third year.

Solution. (i) Let the original cost of the washing machine be ₹ P and the rate of depreciation of its value be $r\%$ p.a. Then, the value of the machine (in ₹) after one year, two years

and 3 years are $P\left(1 - \frac{r}{100}\right)$, $P\left(1 - \frac{r}{100}\right)^2$ and $\left(1 - \frac{r}{100}\right)^3$ respectively.

Given that the cost of the machine depreciates by ₹ 720 during the second year and by ₹ 648 during the third year,

$$\therefore \quad P\left(1 - \frac{r}{100}\right) - P\left(1 - \frac{r}{100}\right)^2 = 720 \text{ and}$$

$$P\left(1 - \frac{r}{100}\right)^2 - P\left(1 - \frac{r}{100}\right)^3 = 648$$

$$\Rightarrow \quad P\left(1 - \frac{r}{100}\right)\left(1 - \left(1 - \frac{r}{100}\right)\right) = 720 \text{ and}$$

$$P\left(1 - \frac{r}{100}\right)^2\left(1 - \left(1 - \frac{r}{100}\right)\right) = 648$$

$$\Rightarrow \quad P\left(1 - \frac{r}{100}\right) \times \frac{r}{100} = 720 \qquad \qquad \text{...(1)}$$

and $P\left(1 - \dfrac{r}{100}\right)^2 \times \dfrac{r}{100} = 648$ ...(2)

Dividing (2) by (1), we get

$$1 - \dfrac{r}{100} = \dfrac{648}{720} \Rightarrow 1 - \dfrac{r}{100} = \dfrac{9}{10}$$

$$\Rightarrow \quad \dfrac{r}{100} = \dfrac{1}{10} \Rightarrow r = 10$$

Hence, the rate of depreciation of the value of machine = 10% p.a.

(ii) Putting $r = 10$ in (1), we get

$$P\left(1 - \dfrac{1}{10}\right) \times \dfrac{1}{10} = 720 \Rightarrow P \times \dfrac{9}{100} = 720 \Rightarrow P = 8000.$$

Hence, the original cost of the machine = ₹ 8000.

(iii) The value of the machine at the end of third year = ₹ $P\left(1 - \dfrac{r}{100}\right)^3$

$$= ₹\ 8000\left(1 - \dfrac{1}{10}\right)^3 \qquad (\because r = 10)$$

$$= ₹\ 8000 \times \left(\dfrac{9}{10}\right)^3 = ₹\ 5832.$$

EXERCISE 2.3

1 ▶ The present population of a town is 200000. Its population increases by 10% in the first year and 15% in the second year. Find the population of the town at the end of the two years.

2 ▶ The present population of a town is 15625. If the population increases at the rate of 4% every year, what will be the increase in the population in next 3 years?

3 ▶ The population of a city increases each year by 4% of what it had been at the beginning of each year. If its present population is 6760000, find :

(i) its population 2 years hence   (ii) its population 2 years ago.

4 ▶ The cost of a refrigerator is ₹9000. Its value depreciates at the rate of 5% every year. Find the total depreciation in its value at the end of 2 years.

5 ▶ Dinesh purchased a scooter for ₹24000. The value of the scooter is depreciating at the rate of 5% per annum. Calculate its value after 3 years.

6 ▶ A farmer increases his output of wheat in his farm every year by 8%. This year he produced 2187 quintals of wheat. What was the yearly produce of wheat two years ago?

7 ▶ The value of a property decreases every year at the rate of 5%. If its present value is ₹411540, what was its value three years ago?

8 ▶ Ahmed purchased an old scooter for ₹16000. If the cost of the scooter after 2 years depreciates to ₹14440, find the rate of depreciation.

9 ▶ A factory increased its production of cars from 80000 in the year 2011-2012 to 92610 in 2014-2015. Find the annual rate of growth of production of cars.

10 ▶ The value of a machine worth ₹500000 is depreciating at the rate of 10% every year. In how many years will its value be reduced to ₹364500?

11 ▶ Afzal purchased an old motorbike for ₹ 16000. If the value of the motorbike after 2 years is ₹ 14440, find the rate of depreciation.

12 Mahindra set up a factory by investing ₹2500000. During the first two years, his profits were 5% and 10% respectively. If each year the profit was on previous year's capital, calculate his total profit.

13 The value of a property is increasing at the rate of 25% every year. By what percent will the value of the property increase after 3 years?

14 Mr. Durani bought a plot of land for ₹180000 and a car for ₹320000 at the same time. The value of the plot of land grows uniformly at the rate of 30% p.a., while the value of the car depreciates by 20% in the first year and by 15% p.a. thereafter. If he sells the plot of land as well as the car after 3 years, what will be his profit or loss?

Multiple Choice Questions

Choose the correct answer from the given four options (1 to 7):

1 The compound interest on ₹ 1000 at 10% p.a. compounded annually for 2 years is
(a) ₹ 190   (b) ₹ 200   (c) ₹ 210   (d) ₹ 1210

2 If Sukriti borrows ₹ 8000 for two years at the rate of 10% per annum compound interest, then the amount to be paid by her at the end of two years to clear the debt is
(a) ₹ 8800   (b) ₹ 9600   (c) ₹ 9680   (d) ₹ 102400

3 If a man invests ₹ 12000 for two years at the rate of 10% per annum compound interest, then the compound interest earned by him at the end of two years is
(a) ₹ 2400   (b) ₹ 2520   (c) ₹ 2000   (d) ₹ 1800

4 Mr. Rao bought 1-year, ₹ 10000 certificate of deposit that paid interest at an annual rate of 8% compounded semi-annually. The interest received by him on maturity is
(a) ₹ 816   (b) ₹ 864   (c) ₹ 800   (d) ₹ 10816

5 The compound interest on ₹ 5000 at 20% per annum for $1\frac{1}{2}$ years compounded half-yearly is
(a) ₹ 6655   (b) ₹ 1655   (c) ₹ 1500   (d) ₹ 1565

6 If the number of conversion periods ≥ 2, then the compound interest is
(a) less than simple interest   (b) equal to simple interest
(c) greater than or equal to simple interest (d) greater than simple interest

7 The present population of a city is 12,00,000. If it increases at the rate of 8% every year, then the population of the city after 2 years is
(a) 199680   (b) 1399680   (c) 1500000   (d) 1299680

Summary

○ Simple interest is the interest calculated on the original money (principal) at the given rate of interest for any given period.

○ In the simple interest, the principal remains constant for the whole loan period.

○ Amount = Principal + Interest.

○ Simple interest = $\dfrac{\text{Principal} \times \text{Rate} \times \text{Time}}{100}$

○ In compound interest, the principal goes on changing every year (or any other fixed period).

○ $A = P\left(1+\dfrac{r}{100}\right)^n$, where A = amount, P = principal, r = rate of interest per year (or conversion period) and n = number of years (or conversion periods).

○ C.I. = A – P, where C.I. = compound interest.

○ C.I. = $P\left\{\left(1+\dfrac{r}{100}\right)^n - 1\right\}$

○ S.I. (simple interest) and C.I. are equal for the first conversion period on the same sum and at the same rate.

○ C.I. of 2nd conversion period is more than the C.I. of Ist conversion period.

○ C.I. of 2nd conversion period – C.I. of Ist conversion period
    = S.I. on the interest of Ist conversion period.

○ The growth per year (or unit of time) is called the **rate of growth**.

○ If the rate of growth is constant, then

$$V = V_0 \left(1+\dfrac{r}{100}\right)^n$$

where $r\%$ is the rate of growth per year, n is the number of years, V_0 is the present measure of the quantity and V is the measure of the quantity after n years.

If V_0 is the measure of the quantity n years ago and V is the present measure of the quantity, then

$$V = V_0 \left(1+\dfrac{r}{100}\right)^n$$

○ The decrease of the value per year (or unit of time) is called **rate of depreciation.**

○ If the rate of depreciation is constant, then

$$V = V_0 \left(1-\dfrac{r}{100}\right)^n$$

where $r\%$ is the rate of depreciation per year, n is the number of years, V_0 is the present value and V is the value after n years.

If V_0 is the value n years ago and V is the present value, then

$$V = V_0 \left(1-\dfrac{r}{100}\right)^n$$

○ The number of years a machine can be effectively used is called its **lifespan**, after which it is sold as **waste** or **scrap**.

1. ₹10000 was lent for one year at 10% per annum. By how much more will the interest be, if the sum was lent at 10% per annum, interest being compounded half-yearly?

2. A man invests ₹3072 for two years at compound interest. After one year the money amounts to ₹3264. Find the rate of interest and the amount due at the end of 2nd year.

3. What sum will amount to ₹28090 in two years at 6% per annum compound interest? Also find the compound interest.

4. Two equal sums were lent at 5% and 6% per annum compound interest for 2 years. If the difference in the compound interest was ₹422, find:

   (i) the equal sums   (ii) compound interest for each sum.

5. The compound interest on a sum of money for 2 years is ₹1331·20 and the simple interest on the same sum for the same period and at the same rate is ₹1280. Find the sum and the rate of interest per annum.

6. On what sum will the difference between the simple and compound interest for 3 years at 10% p.a. is ₹232·50?

7. The simple interest on a certain sum for 3 years is ₹1080 and the compound interest on the same sum at the same rate for 2 years is ₹741·60. Find:

   (i) the rate of interest   (ii) the principal.

8. In what time will ₹2400 amount to ₹2646 at 10% p.a. compounded semi-annually?

9. Sudarshan invested ₹60000 in a finance company and received ₹79860 after $1\frac{1}{2}$ years. Find the rate of interest per annum compounded half-yearly.

10. The population of a city is 320000. If the annual birth rate is 9·2% and the annual death rate is 1·7%, calculate the population of the town after 3 years.

    Hint. Net growth rate = 9·2% – 1·7% = 7·5%.

11. The cost of a car, purchased 2 years ago, depreciates at the rate of 20% every year. If its present worth is ₹315600, find :

    (i) its purchase price   (ii) its value after 3 years.

12. Amar Singh started a business with an initial investment of ₹400000. In the first year, he incurred a loss of 4%. However, during the second year, he earned a profit of 5% which in the third year rose to 10%. Calculate his net profit for the entire period of 3 years.

3 Expansions

INTRODUCTION

In the previous classes, you have studied about algebraic expressions and the basic operations on them *i.e.* their addition, subtraction, multiplication and division. You have also studied some special products and expansions. In this chapter, we shall study some more special products and expansions, and will learn their applications.

3.1 SPECIAL PRODUCTS

The following products occur frequently in algebra, and the students are advised to memorize them (without resorting to actual multiplication) until they can recognise each, both the product from the factors and the factors from the product.

1. $(a + b)^2 = a^2 + 2ab + b^2$.

2. $(a - b)^2 = a^2 - 2ab + b^2$.

3. $(a + b)(a - b) = a^2 - b^2$.

4. $\left(a + \dfrac{1}{a}\right)^2 = a^2 + \dfrac{1}{a^2} + 2$.

5. $\left(a - \dfrac{1}{a}\right)^2 = a^2 + \dfrac{1}{a^2} - 2$.

6. $\left(a + \dfrac{1}{a}\right)\left(a - \dfrac{1}{a}\right) = a^2 - \dfrac{1}{a^2}$.

7. (i) $(x + a)(x + b) = x^2 + (a + b)x + ab$.

   (ii) $(x + a)(x - b) = x^2 + (a - b)x - ab$.

   (iii) $(x - a)(x + b) = x^2 - (a - b)x - ab$.

   (iv) $(x - a)(x - b) = x^2 - (a + b)x + ab$.

8. $(a + b + c)^2 = a^2 + b^2 + c^2 + 2(ab + bc + ca)$.

9. $(a + b)^3 = a^3 + b^3 + 3ab(a + b) = a^3 + 3a^2b + 3ab^2 + b^3$.

10. $(a - b)^3 = a^3 - b^3 - 3ab(a - b) = a^3 - 3a^2b + 3ab^2 - b^3$.

11. $(a + b)(a^2 - ab + b^2) = a^3 + b^3$.

12. $(a - b)(a^2 + ab + b^2) = a^3 - b^3$.

13. $(a + b + c)(a^2 + b^2 + c^2 - ab - bc - ca) = a^3 + b^3 + c^3 - 3abc$.

14. $(x + a)(x + b)(x + c) = x^3 + (a + b + c)x^2 + (ab + bc + ca)x + abc$.

15. If $a + b + c = 0$, then $a^3 + b^3 + c^3 = 3abc$.

Remarks

❏ The expression $a^2 + 2ab + b^2$ is called the **expansion** of $(a + b)^2$, $a^2 - 2ab + b^2$ is the expansion of $(a - b)^2$ and $a^3 + b^3 + 3ab(a + b)$ is the expansion of $(a + b)^3$ and so on.

❑ The above results 1 to 3 and 7 to 14 are true for all values of the variables involved, and the results 4 to 6 are true for all values of a except 0. *An equation which is true for all values of the variables involved is called an **identity.*** Thus, the above results 1 to 14 are all identities; of course, $a \neq 0$ in the results 4 to 6.

3.2 APPLICATIONS OF THE SPECIAL PRODUCTS

We learn the applications of the special products with the help of the following examples:

Illustrative Examples

Example 1 Find the expansions of the following:

(i) $(2a + 3b)^2$ (ii) $(3x - 4y)^2$ (iii) $(2a + 3b - 4c)^2$.

Solution. (i) $(2a + 3b)^2 = (2a)^2 + 2(2a)(3b) + (3b)^2$

$$= 4a^2 + 12ab + 9b^2.$$

(ii) $(3x - 4y)^2 = (3x)^2 - 2(3x)(4y) + (4y)^2$

$$= 9x^2 - 24xy + 16y^2.$$

(iii) $(2a + 3b - 4c)^2 = [2a + 3b + (-4c)]^2$

$$= (2a)^2 + (3b)^2 + (-4c)^2 + 2\,[(2a)(3b)$$
$$+ (3b)(-4c) + (-4c)(2a)]$$

$$= 4a^2 + 9b^2 + 16c^2 + 2\,(6ab - 12bc - 8ca)$$

$$= 4a^2 + 9b^2 + 16c^2 + 12ab - 24bc - 16ca.$$

Example 2 Find the expansions of the following:

(i) $\left(\dfrac{2}{3}x + \dfrac{5}{7}y\right)^2$ (ii) $\left(\dfrac{3a}{2} - \dfrac{2}{3b}\right)^2$ (iii) $\left(\dfrac{1}{2}x - \dfrac{2}{3}y - \dfrac{4}{5}z\right)^2$.

Solution. (i) $\left(\dfrac{2}{3}x + \dfrac{5}{7}y\right)^2 = \left(\dfrac{2}{3}x\right)^2 + 2\left(\dfrac{2}{3}x\right)\left(\dfrac{5}{7}y\right) + \left(\dfrac{5}{7}y\right)^2$

$$= \dfrac{4}{9}x^2 + \dfrac{20}{21}xy + \dfrac{25}{49}y^2.$$

(ii) $\left(\dfrac{3a}{2} - \dfrac{2}{3b}\right)^2 = \left(\dfrac{3a}{2}\right)^2 - 2\left(\dfrac{3a}{2}\right)\left(\dfrac{2}{3b}\right) + \left(\dfrac{2}{3b}\right)^2$

$$= \dfrac{9}{4}a^2 - 2\dfrac{a}{b} + \dfrac{4}{9b^2}.$$

(iii) $\left(\dfrac{1}{2}x - \dfrac{2}{3}y - \dfrac{4}{5}z\right)^2 = \left(\dfrac{1}{2}x + \left(-\dfrac{2}{3}y\right) + \left(-\dfrac{4}{5}z\right)\right)^2$

$$= \left(\dfrac{1}{2}x\right)^2 + \left(-\dfrac{2}{3}y\right)^2 + \left(-\dfrac{4}{5}z\right)^2$$

$$+ 2\left[\left(\dfrac{1}{2}x\right)\left(-\dfrac{2}{3}y\right) + \left(-\dfrac{2}{3}y\right)\left(-\dfrac{4}{5}z\right) + \left(-\dfrac{4}{5}z\right)\left(\dfrac{1}{2}x\right)\right]$$

$$= \dfrac{1}{4}x^2 + \dfrac{4}{9}y^2 + \dfrac{16}{25}z^2 + 2\left[-\dfrac{1}{3}xy + \dfrac{8}{15}yz - \dfrac{2}{5}zx\right]$$

$$= \dfrac{1}{4}x^2 + \dfrac{4}{9}y^2 + \dfrac{16}{25}z^2 - \dfrac{2}{3}xy + \dfrac{16}{15}yz - \dfrac{4}{5}zx.$$

Example 3 Simplify the following:

    (i) $(2x - 3y + 5)(2x - 3y - 5)$
                        (ii) $\left(2x - \dfrac{3}{x} + 1\right)\left(2x + \dfrac{3}{x} + 1\right)$.

Solution. (i) Given expression $= (2x - 3y + 5)(2x - 3y - 5)$.

        Let $2x - 3y = a$, then

        given expression $= (a + 5)(a - 5) = a^2 - 5^2 = a^2 - 25$

$$= (2x - 3y)^2 - 25$$
$$= (2x)^2 - 2\,(2x)\,(3y) + (3y)^2 - 25$$
$$= 4x^2 - 12xy + 9y^2 - 25.$$

    (ii) Given expression $= \left\{(2x + 1) - \dfrac{3}{x}\right\}\left\{(2x + 1) + \dfrac{3}{x}\right\}$.

        Let $2x + 1 = a$, then

        given expression $= \left(a - \dfrac{3}{x}\right)\left(a + \dfrac{3}{x}\right) = a^2 - \left(\dfrac{3}{x}\right)^2$

$$= (2x + 1)^2 - \dfrac{9}{x^2}$$
$$= (2x)^2 + 2\,(2x)\,(1) + (1)^2 - \dfrac{9}{x^2}$$
$$= 4x^2 + 4x + 1 - \dfrac{9}{x^2}.$$

Example 4 Simplify the following:

    (i) $\left(2p - \dfrac{q}{5} - 3\right)\left(2p + \dfrac{q}{5} + 3\right)$
             (ii) $(3x - 2y)(3x + 2y)(9x^2 + 4y^2)$.

Solution. (i) Given expression $= \left(2p - \dfrac{q}{5} - 3\right)\left(2p + \dfrac{q}{5} + 3\right)$

$$= \left\{2p - \left(\dfrac{q}{5} + 3\right)\right\}\left(2p + \left(\dfrac{q}{5} + 3\right)\right)$$
$$= (2p)^2 - \left(\dfrac{q}{5} + 3\right)^2$$
$$= 4p^2 - \left\{\left(\dfrac{q}{5}\right)^2 + 2\left(\dfrac{q}{5}\right)(3) + (3)^2\right\}$$
$$= 4p^2 - \dfrac{q^2}{25} - \dfrac{6q}{5} - 9.$$

    (ii) Given expression $= (3x - 2y)(3x + 2y)(9x^2 + 4y^2)$

$$= ((3x - 2y)(3x + 2y))(9x^2 + 4y^2)$$
$$= ((3x)^2 - (2y)^2)(9x^2 + 4y^2)$$
$$= (9x^2 - 4y^2)(9x^2 + 4y^2)$$
$$= (9x^2)^2 - (4y^2)^2$$
$$= 81x^4 - 16y^4.$$

Example 5 Find the expansions of the following:

    (i) $(2a + 3b)^3$
        (ii) $(3x - 4y)^3$
        (iii) $(x + y - 1)^3$.

Solution. (i) $(2a + 3b)^3 = (2a)^3 + (3b)^3 + 3(2a)(3b)(2a + 3b)$

$$= 8a^3 + 27b^3 + 18ab\,(2a + 3b)$$
$$= 8a^3 + 27b^3 + 36a^2b + 54ab^2.$$

(ii) $(3x - 4y)^3 = (3x)^3 - (4y)^3 - 3(3x)(4y)(3x - 4y)$

$$= 27x^3 - 64y^3 - 36xy(3x - 4y)$$

$$= 27x^3 - 64y^3 - 108x^2y + 144xy^2.$$

(iii) $(x + y - 1)^3 = (\overline{x + y} - 1)^3$ [consider $x + y$ as one term]

$$= (x + y)^3 - (1)^3 - 3(x + y)(1)(\overline{x + y} - 1)$$

$$= (x + y)^3 - 1 - 3(x + y)(\overline{x + y} - 1)$$

$$= [x^3 + y^3 + 3xy(x + y)] - 1 - 3(x + y)^2 + 3(x + y)$$

$$= x^3 + y^3 + 3x^2y + 3xy^2 - 1 - 3(x^2 + 2xy + y^2) + 3x + 3y$$

$$= x^3 + y^3 + 3x^2y + 3xy^2 - 3x^2 - 6xy - 3y^2 + 3x + 3y - 1.$$

Example 6   Find the product of the following (using standard results):

(i) $(2x + 5y + 3)(2x + 5y + 4)$ (ii) $(3x - y - 4)(3x - y + 5)$.

Solution. (i) Given expression $= (2x + 5y + 3)(2x + 5y + 4)$.

Let $2x + 5y = a$, then

given expression $= (a + 3)(a + 4)$

$$= a^2 + (3 + 4)a + 3 \times 4$$

$$[\because (x + a)(x + b) = x^2 + (a + b)x + ab]$$

$$= a^2 + 7a + 12$$

$$= (2x + 5y)^2 + 7(2x + 5y) + 12$$

$$= (2x)^2 + 2(2x)(5y) + (5y)^2 + 14x + 35y + 12$$

$$= 4x^2 + 20xy + 25y^2 + 14x + 35y + 12$$

(ii)   Given expression $= (3x - y - 4)(3x - y + 5)$

Let $3x - y = a$, then

given expression $= (a - 4)(a + 5)$

$$= a^2 - (4 - 5)a - 4 \times 5 \qquad [\because (x - a)(x + b) = x^2 - (a - b)x - ab]$$

$$= a^2 + a - 20$$

$$= (3x - y)^2 + (3x - y) - 20$$

$$= (3x)^2 - 2(3x)(y) + (y)^2 + 3x - y - 20$$

$$= 9x^2 - 6xy + y^2 + 3x - y - 20.$$

Example 7   Simplify the following:

(i) $(3x + 5y)(9x^2 - 15xy + 25y^2)$ (ii) $\left(x - \dfrac{2}{x}\right)\left(x^2 + 2 + \dfrac{4}{x^2}\right)$.

Solution. (i) We know that $(a + b)(a^2 - ab + b^2) = a^3 + b^3$,

$\therefore$ given expression $= (3x + 5y)[(3x)^2 - (3x)(5y) + (5y)^2]$

$$= (3x)^3 + (5y)^3$$

$$= 27x^3 + 125y^3.$$

(ii) We know that $(a - b)(a^2 + ab + b^2) = a^3 - b^3$,

$\therefore$ given expression $= \left(x - \dfrac{2}{x}\right)\left[x^2 + x . \dfrac{2}{x} + \left(\dfrac{2}{x}\right)^2\right]$

$$= (x)^3 - \left(\dfrac{2}{x}\right)^3$$

$$= x^3 - \dfrac{8}{x^3}.$$

Example 8 Simplify: $(3a - 2b)(9a^2 + 6ab + 4b^2) - (2a + 3b)(4a^2 - 6ab + 9b^2)$.

Solution. $(3a - 2b)(9a^2 + 6ab + 4b^2) - (2a + 3b)(4a^2 - 6ab + 9b^2)$

$= (3a - 2b)((3a)^2 + (3a)(2b) + (2b)^2) - (2a + 3b)((2a)^2 - (2a)(3b) + (3b)^2)$

$= ((3a)^3 - (2b)^3) - ((2a)^3 + (3b)^3)$ (using identities 11 and 12)

$= (27a^3 - 8b^3) - (8a^3 + 27b^3)$

$= 19a^3 - 35b^3$.

Example 9 Simplify: $(2a + 3b)^3 - (2a - 3b)^3$.

Solution. Let $2a + 3b = x$ and $2a - 3b = y$, then

$(2a + 3b)^3 - (2a - 3b)^3 = x^3 - y^3$

$= (x - y)(x^2 + xy + y^2)$ (identity 12)

$= (\overline{2a + 3b} - \overline{2a - 3b})((2a + 3b)^2 + (2a + 3b)(2a - 3b) + (2a - 3b)^2)$

$= 6b(4a^2 + 12ab + 9b^2 + 4a^2 - 9b^2 + 4a^2 - 12ab + 9b^2)$

$= 6b(12a^2 + 9b^2) = 18b(4a^2 + 3b^2)$.

Example 10 Simplify: $(x + 3y + 5z)(x^2 + 9y^2 + 25z^2 - 3xy - 15yz - 5zx)$.

Solution. We know that

$(a + b + c)(a^2 + b^2 + c^2 - ab - bc - ca) = a^3 + b^3 + c^3 - 3abc$.

$\therefore$ Given expression $= (x + 3y + 5z)[(x)^2 + (3y)^2 + (5z)^2 - (x)(3y) - (3y)(5z) - (5z)(x)]$

$= (x)^3 + (3y)^3 + (5z)^3 - 3(x)(3y)(5z)$

$= x^3 + 27y^3 + 125z^3 - 45xyz$.

Example 11 Multiply $(9x^2 + 25y^2 + 15xy + 12x - 20y + 16)$ by $(3x - 5y - 4)$, using a suitable identity.

Solution. We know that

$(a + b + c)(a^2 + b^2 + c^2 - ab - bc - ca) = a^3 + b^3 + c^3 - 3abc$.

$\therefore$ $(3x - 5y - 4)(9x^2 + 25y^2 + 15xy + 12x - 20y + 16)$

$= (3x - 5y - 4)[(3x)^2 + (-5y)^2 + (-4)^2 - (3x)(-5y) - (-5y)(-4) - (-4)(3x)]$

$= (3x)^3 + (-5y)^3 + (-4)^3 - 3(3x)(-5y)(-4)$

$= 27x^3 - 125y^3 - 64 - 180xy$

$= 27x^3 - 125y^3 - 180xy - 64$.

Example 12 Using proper identity, prove that:

$(x + y)^3 + (y + z)^3 + (z + x)^3 - 3(x + y)(y + z)(z + x) = 2(x^3 + y^3 + z^3)$.

Solution. We know that

$a^3 + b^3 + c^3 - 3abc = (a + b + c)(a^2 + b^2 + c^2 - ab - bc - ca)$ (identity 13)

$\therefore (x + y)^3 + (y + z)^3 + (z + x)^3 - 3(x + y)(y + z)(z + x)$

$= (\overline{x + y} + \overline{y + z} + \overline{z + x})[(x + y)^2 + (y + z)^2 + (z + x)^2 - (x + y)(y + z)$

$- (y + z)(z + x) - (z + x)(x + y)]$

$= (2x + 2y + 2z)[x^2 + 2xy + y^2 + y^2 + 2yz + z^2 + z^2 + 2zx + x^2$

$- (y^2 + xy + yz + zx) - (z^2 + xy + yz + zx) - (x^2 + xy + yz + zx)]$

$= 2(x + y + z)(x^2 + y^2 + z^2 - xy - yz - zx)$

$= 2(x^3 + y^3 + z^3)$.

Example 13 Find the products of:

(i) $(x + 2)(x + 3)(x + 5)$ (ii) $(x + 1)(x - 3)(x - 4)$.

Solution. We know that

$$(x + a)(x + b)(x + c) = x^3 + (a + b + c)x^2 + (ab + bc + ca)x + abc.$$

(i) Compare $(x + 2)(x + 3)(x + 5)$ with $(x + a)(x + b)(x + c)$.

Here $a = 2$, $b = 3$, $c = 5$.

$\therefore$ Given product $= x^3 + (2 + 3 + 5)x^2 + (2 \times 3 + 3 \times 5 + 5 \times 2)x + 2 \times 3 \times 5$

$$= x^3 + 10x^2 + 31x + 30.$$

(ii) Compare $(x + 1)(x - 3)(x - 4)$ with $(x + a)(x + b)(x + c)$.

Here $a = 1$, $b = -3$ and $c = -4$.

$\therefore$ Given product $= x^3 + (1 + (-3) + (-4))x^2 + [1.(-3) + (-3)(-4) + (-4).1]x$

$$+ 1.(-3)(-4)$$

$$= x^3 - 6x^2 + 5x + 12.$$

Example 14 Find the coefficient of x^2 and x in the product of $(x - 5)(x + 3)(x + 7)$.

Solution. We know that

$$(x + a)(x + b)(x + c) = x^3 + (a + b + c)x^2 + (ab + bc + ca)x + abc.$$

Compare $(x - 5)(x + 3)(x + 7)$ with $(x + a)(x + b)(x + c)$.

Here $a = -5$, $b = 3$ and $c = 7$.

$\therefore$ Coefficient of $x^2 = a + b + c = (-5) + 3 + 7 = 5$ and

coefficient of $x = ab + bc + ca = (-5) \times 3 + 3 \times 7 + 7 \times (-5) = -29$.

Example 15 Find the coefficient of x^2 in the expansion of $(x^2 + 2x + 3)^2 + (x^2 - 2x + 3)^2$.

Solution. Given expression $= (x^2 + 2x + 3)^2 + (x^2 - 2x + 3)^2$

$$= ((x^2 + 3) + (2x))^2 + ((x^2 + 3) - (2x))^2.$$

Let $x^2 + 3 = a$ and $2x = b$, then

given expression $= (a + b)^2 + (a - b)^2$

$$= (a^2 + 2ab + b^2) + (a^2 - 2ab + b^2) = 2(a^2 + b^2)$$

$$= 2[(x^2 + 3)^2 + (2x)^2]$$

$$= 2[(x^2)^2 + 2(x^2)(3) + (3)^2 + 4x^2]$$

$$= 2(x^4 + 6x^2 + 9 + 4x^2)$$

$$= 2x^4 + 20x^2 + 18.$$

$\therefore$ Coefficient of $x^2 = 20$.

Example 16 By using $(a + b)^2 = a^2 + 2ab + b^2$, find the value of $(10.3)^2$.

Solution. $(10.3)^2 = (10 + 0.3)^2$

$$= (10)^2 + 2 \times 10 \times 0.3 + (0.3)^2$$

$$= 100 + 6 + .09 = 106.09$$

Example 17 Using a suitable identity, find the value of $(98)^3$.

Solution. We know that $(a - b)^3 = a^3 - 3a^2b + 3ab^2 - b^3$.

Now $(98)^3 = (100 - 2)^3$ (take $a = 100$ and $b = 2$)

$$= (100)^3 - 3 \times (100)^2 \times 2 + 3 \times 100 \times (2)^2 - (2)^3$$

$$= 1000000 - 60000 + 1200 - 8$$

$$= 1001200 - 60008 = 941192.$$

Example 18 If $a + b + c = 0$, prove that $a^3 + b^3 + c^3 = 3abc$.

Solution. Given $a + b + c = 0 \Rightarrow a + b = -c$.

On cubing both sides, we get $(a + b)^3 = (-c)^3$

$\Rightarrow \quad a^3 + b^3 + 3ab\,(a + b) = -c^3$ but $a + b = -c$

$\Rightarrow \quad a^3 + b^3 + 3ab\,(-c) = -c^3$

$\Rightarrow \quad a^3 + b^3 + c^3 - 3abc = 0$

$\Rightarrow \quad a^3 + b^3 + c^3 = 3abc.$

Example 19 Without actually calculating the cubes, find the values of:

   (i) $(-23)^3 + 15^3 + 8^3$ (ii) $\left(\dfrac{1}{4}\right)^3 + \left(\dfrac{1}{3}\right)^3 - \left(\dfrac{7}{12}\right)^3.$

Solution. (i) Let $a = -23$, $b = 15$ and $c = 8$, then

$$a + b + c = -23 + 15 + 8 = 0$$

$\therefore \qquad\qquad a^3 + b^3 + c^3 = 3abc$ (See example 18)

$\Rightarrow \qquad (-23)^3 + 15^3 + 8^3 = 3(-23) \times 15 \times 8 = -8280.$

(ii) Let $a = \dfrac{1}{4}$, $b = \dfrac{1}{3}$ and $c = -\dfrac{7}{12}$, then

$$a + b + c = \frac{1}{4} + \frac{1}{3} - \frac{7}{12} = \frac{3 + 4 - 7}{12} = \frac{0}{12} = 0.$$

$\therefore \qquad a^3 + b^3 + c^3 = 3abc$ (See example 18)

$\Rightarrow \quad \left(\dfrac{1}{4}\right)^3 + \left(\dfrac{1}{3}\right)^3 - \left(\dfrac{7}{12}\right)^3 = \left(\dfrac{1}{4}\right)^3 + \left(\dfrac{1}{3}\right)^3 + \left(-\dfrac{7}{12}\right)^3$

$$= 3\left(\dfrac{1}{4}\right)\left(\dfrac{1}{3}\right)\left(-\dfrac{7}{12}\right) = -\dfrac{7}{48}.$$

Example 20 If $x = 2y + 6$, then find the value of $x^3 - 8y^3 - 36xy - 216$.

Solution. Given $x = 2y + 6 \Rightarrow x - 2y - 6 = 0$

$\Rightarrow \quad x + (-2y) + (-6) = 0$

$\Rightarrow \quad (x)^3 + (-2y)^3 + (-6)^3 = 3(x)(-2y)(-6)$ ($\because$ if $a + b + c = 0$, then $a^3 + b^3 + c^3 = 3abc$)

$\Rightarrow \quad x^3 - 8y^3 - 216 = 36xy$

$\Rightarrow \quad x^3 - 8y^3 - 36xy - 216 = 0.$

Example 21 If $a = 1$, $b = -2$ and $c = -3$, find the value of

$$\frac{a^3 + b^3 + c^3 - 3abc}{ab + bc + ca - (a^2 + b^2 + c^2)}.$$

Solution. We know that $(a + b + c)(a^2 + b^2 + c^2 - ab - bc - ca) = a^3 + b^3 + c^3 - 3abc$,

$\therefore \qquad \dfrac{a^3 + b^3 + c^3 - 3abc}{ab + bc + ca - (a^2 + b^2 + c^2)} = \dfrac{(a + b + c)(a^2 + b^2 + c^2 - ab - bc - ca)}{-(a^2 + b^2 + c^2 - ab - bc - ca)}$

$$= -(a + b + c)$$

$$= -(1 - 2 - 3) = -(-4) = 4.$$

Example 22 Using suitable identity, find the value of:

$$\frac{0{\cdot}75 \times 0{\cdot}75 \times 0{\cdot}75 + 0{\cdot}25 \times 0{\cdot}25 \times 0{\cdot}25}{0{\cdot}75 \times 0{\cdot}75 - 0{\cdot}75 \times 0{\cdot}25 + 0{\cdot}25 \times 0{\cdot}25}.$$

Solution. We know that $a^3 + b^3 = (a + b)(a^2 - ab + b^2)$

$\Rightarrow \qquad \dfrac{a^3 + b^3}{a^2 - ab + b^2} = a + b.$

Putting $a = 0.75$ and $b = 0.25$ in this result, we get

$$\frac{0.75 \times 0.75 \times 0.75 + 0.25 \times 0.25 \times 0.25}{0.75 \times 0.75 - 0.75 \times 0.25 + 0.25 \times 0.25} = \frac{a^3 + b^3}{a^2 - ab + b^2}$$

$$= a + b = 0.75 + 0.25 = 1.$$

Example 23 If $a + b + c = 0$, find the value of $\dfrac{(b+c)^2}{bc} + \dfrac{(c+a)^2}{ca} + \dfrac{(a+b)^2}{ab}$.

Solution. Given $a + b + c = 0 \Rightarrow a^3 + b^3 + c^3 = 3abc$ ...(i)

(See example 18)

Also $a + b + c = 0 \Rightarrow b + c = -a, c + a = -b, a + b = -c$.

$$\therefore \quad \frac{(b+c)^2}{bc} + \frac{(c+a)^2}{ca} + \frac{(a+b)^2}{ab} = \frac{(-a)^2}{bc} + \frac{(-b)^2}{ca} + \frac{(-c)^2}{ab}$$

$$= \frac{a^2}{bc} + \frac{b^2}{ca} + \frac{c^2}{ab}$$

$$= \frac{a^3 + b^3 + c^3}{abc} = \frac{3abc}{abc} \qquad \text{(using } (i))$$

$$= 3.$$

Example 24 Simplify: $\dfrac{(a^2 - b^2)^3 + (b^2 - c^2)^3 + (c^2 - a^2)^3}{(a - b)^3 + (b - c)^3 + (c - a)^3}$.

Solution. We know that if $x + y + z = 0$, then $x^3 + y^3 + z^3 = 3xyz$.

Here, $(a^2 - b^2) + (b^2 - c^2) + (c^2 - a^2) = 0$,

$\therefore \quad (a^2 - b^2)^3 + (b^2 - c^2)^3 + (c^2 - a^2)^3 = 3(a^2 - b^2)(b^2 - c^2)(c^2 - a^2)$.

Also, $(a - b) + (b - c) + (c - a) = 0$,

$\therefore \quad (a - b)^3 + (b - c)^3 + (c - a)^3 = 3(a - b)(b - c)(c - a)$.

$$\therefore \quad \frac{(a^2 - b^2)^3 + (b^2 - c^2)^3 + (c^2 - a^2)^3}{(a - b)^3 + (b - c)^3 + (c - a)^3} = \frac{3(a^2 - b^2)(b^2 - c^2)(c^2 - a^2)}{3(a - b)(b - c)(c - a)}$$

$$= \frac{(a - b)(a + b)(b - c)(b + c)(c - a)(c + a)}{(a - b)(b - c)(c - a)}$$

$$= (a + b)(b + c)(c + a).$$

Example 25 If $ab + bc + ca = 0$, then find the value of:

$$\frac{1}{a^2 - bc} + \frac{1}{b^2 - ca} + \frac{1}{c^2 - ab}.$$

Solution. Given $ab + bc + ca = 0$ ...(i)

$\Rightarrow \quad -bc = ab + ca, -ca = ab + bc, -ab = bc + ca$.

$$\therefore \quad \frac{1}{a^2 - bc} + \frac{1}{b^2 - ca} + \frac{1}{c^2 - ab}$$

$$= \frac{1}{a^2 + ab + ca} + \frac{1}{b^2 + ab + bc} + \frac{1}{c^2 + bc + ca}$$

$$= \frac{1}{a(a + b + c)} + \frac{1}{b(a + b + c)} + \frac{1}{c(a + b + c)}$$

$$= \frac{bc + ca + ab}{abc(a + b + c)} = \frac{0}{abc(a + b + c)} \qquad \text{(using } (i))$$

$$= 0.$$

EXERCISE 3.1

By using standard formulae, expand the following (1 to 9):

1 (i) $(2x + 7y)^2$ (ii) $\left(\dfrac{1}{2}x + \dfrac{2}{3}y\right)^2$.

2 (i) $\left(3x + \dfrac{1}{2x}\right)^2$ (ii) $(3x^2y + 5z)^2$.

3 (i) $\left(3x - \dfrac{1}{2x}\right)^2$ (ii) $\left(\dfrac{1}{2}x - \dfrac{3}{2}y\right)^2$.

4 (i) $(x + 3)(x + 5)$ (ii) $(x + 3)(x - 5)$
  (iii) $(x - 7)(x + 9)$ (iv) $(x - 2y)(x - 3y)$.

5 (i) $(x - 2y - z)^2$ (ii) $(2x - 3y + 4z)^2$.

6 (i) $\left(2x + \dfrac{3}{x} - 1\right)^2$ (ii) $\left(\dfrac{2}{3}x - \dfrac{3}{2x} - 1\right)^2$.

7 (i) $(x + 2)^3$ (ii) $(2a + b)^3$.

8 (i) $\left(3x + \dfrac{1}{x}\right)^3$ (ii) $(2x - 1)^3$.

9 (i) $(5x - 3y)^3$ (ii) $\left(2x - \dfrac{1}{3y}\right)^3$.

Simplify the following (10 to 19):

10 (i) $(a + b)^2 + (a - b)^2$ (ii) $(a + b)^2 - (a - b)^2$.

11 (i) $\left(a + \dfrac{1}{a}\right)^2 + \left(a - \dfrac{1}{a}\right)^2$ (ii) $\left(a + \dfrac{1}{a}\right)^2 - \left(a - \dfrac{1}{a}\right)^2$.

12 (i) $(3x - 1)^2 - (3x - 2)(3x + 1)$ (ii) $(4x + 3y)^2 - (4x - 3y)^2 - 48xy$.

13 (i) $(7p + 9q)(7p - 9q)$ (ii) $\left(2x - \dfrac{3}{x}\right)\left(2x + \dfrac{3}{x}\right)$.

14 (i) $(2x - y + 3)(2x - y - 3)$ (ii) $(3x + y - 5)(3x - y - 5)$.

15 (i) $\left(x + \dfrac{2}{x} - 3\right)\left(x - \dfrac{2}{x} - 3\right)$ (ii) $(5 - 2x)(5 + 2x)(25 + 4x^2)$.

16 (i) $(x + 2y + 3)(x + 2y + 7)$ (ii) $(2x + y + 5)(2x + y - 9)$
  (iii) $(x - 2y - 5)(x - 2y + 3)$ (iv) $(3x - 4y - 2)(3x - 4y - 6)$.

17 (i) $(2p + 3q)(4p^2 - 6pq + 9q^2)$ (ii) $\left(x + \dfrac{1}{x}\right)\left(x^2 - 1 + \dfrac{1}{x^2}\right)$.

18 (i) $(3p - 4q)(9p^2 + 12pq + 16q^2)$ (ii) $\left(x - \dfrac{3}{x}\right)\left(x^2 + 3 + \dfrac{9}{x^2}\right)$.

19 $(2x + 3y + 4z)(4x^2 + 9y^2 + 16z^2 - 6xy - 12yz - 8zx)$.

20 Find the product of the following:
  (i) $(x + 1)(x + 2)(x + 3)$ (ii) $(x - 2)(x - 3)(x + 4)$.

21 Find the coefficient of x^2 and x in the product of $(x - 3)(x + 7)(x - 4)$.

22 If $a^2 + 4a + x = (a + 2)^2$, find the value of x.

23 Use $(a + b)^2 = a^2 + 2ab + b^2$ to evaluate the following:
  (i) $(101)^2$ (ii) $(1003)^2$ (iii) $(10\cdot2)^2$.

24 Use $(a - b)^2 = a^2 - 2ab + b^2$ to evaluate the following:

    (i) $(99)^2$ (ii) $(997)^2$ (iii) $(9 \cdot 8)^2$.

25 By using suitable identities, evaluate the following:

    (i) $(103)^3$ (ii) $(99)^3$ (iii) $(10 \cdot 1)^3$.

26 If $2a - b + c = 0$, prove that $4a^2 - b^2 + c^2 + 4ac = 0$.

    Hint. $2a - b + c = 0 \Rightarrow 2a + c = b \Rightarrow (2a + c)^2 = b^2$.

27 If $a + b + 2c = 0$, prove that $a^3 + b^3 + 8c^3 = 6abc$.

28 If $a + b + c = 0$, then find the value of $\dfrac{a^2}{bc} + \dfrac{b^2}{ca} + \dfrac{c^2}{ab}$.

29 If $x + y = 4$, then find the value of $x^3 + y^3 + 12xy - 64$.

30 Without actually calculating the cubes, find the values of:

    (i) $(27)^3 + (-17)^3 + (-10)^3$ (ii) $(-28)^3 + (15)^3 + (13)^3$.

31 Using suitable identity, find the value of:

$$\frac{86 \times 86 \times 86 + 14 \times 14 \times 14}{86 \times 86 - 86 \times 14 + 14 \times 14}.$$

3.3 MORE APPLICATIONS OF SPECIAL PRODUCTS

Illustrative Examples

Example 1 If $a + b = 3$ and $ab = 2$, find the values of:

    (i) $a^2 + b^2$ (ii) $a - b$ (iii) $a^2 - b^2$ (iv) $a^3 + b^3$.

Solution. (i) We know that $(a + b)^2 = a^2 + b^2 + 2ab$

    $\Rightarrow a^2 + b^2 = (a + b)^2 - 2ab$ but $a + b = 3$ and $ab = 2$

    $\Rightarrow a^2 + b^2 = (3)^2 - 2 \times 2 = 9 - 4 = 5$.

    (ii) $(a - b)^2 = a^2 + b^2 - 2ab = 5 - 2 \times 2 = 5 - 4 = 1$

    $\Rightarrow$ $a - b = \pm\sqrt{1} = \pm 1$.

    (iii) $a^2 - b^2 = (a + b)(a - b) = 3 \times (\pm 1) = \pm 3$.

    (iv) We know that $(a + b)^3 = a^3 + b^3 + 3ab(a + b)$

    $\Rightarrow a^3 + b^3 = (a + b)^3 - 3ab(a + b)$

    $\Rightarrow a^3 + b^3 = (3)^3 - 3 \times 2 \times 3 = 27 - 18 = 9$.

Example 2 If $x - \dfrac{1}{x} = 5$, find the values of:

    (i) $x^2 + \dfrac{1}{x^2}$ (ii) $x^4 + \dfrac{1}{x^4}$ (iii) $x^3 - \dfrac{1}{x^3}$.

Solution. (i) We know that $\left(x - \dfrac{1}{x}\right)^2 = x^2 + \dfrac{1}{x^2} - 2$

    $\Rightarrow$ $x^2 + \dfrac{1}{x^2} = \left(x - \dfrac{1}{x}\right)^2 + 2$

    $\Rightarrow$ $x^2 + \dfrac{1}{x^2} = (5)^2 + 2 = 25 + 2 = 27$.

(ii)

$$\left(x^2 + \frac{1}{x^2}\right)^2 = x^4 + \frac{1}{x^4} + 2$$

$$\Rightarrow \quad x^4 + \frac{1}{x^4} = \left(x^2 + \frac{1}{x^2}\right)^2 - 2$$

$$\Rightarrow \quad x^4 + \frac{1}{x^4} = (27)^2 - 2 = 729 - 2 = 727.$$

(iii) We know that $\left(x - \frac{1}{x}\right)^3 = x^3 - \frac{1}{x^3} - 3.x.\frac{1}{x}\left(x - \frac{1}{x}\right)$

$$\Rightarrow \quad x^3 - \frac{1}{x^3} = \left(x - \frac{1}{x}\right)^3 + 3\left(x - \frac{1}{x}\right)$$

$$\Rightarrow \quad x^3 - \frac{1}{x^3} = (5)^3 + 3 \times 5 = 125 + 15 = 140.$$

Example 3 If $x^2 + \frac{1}{x^2} = 7$, find the values of:

    (i) $x + \frac{1}{x}$ *(ii)* $x - \frac{1}{x}$ *(iii)* $2x^2 - \frac{2}{x^2}$.

Solution. *(i)* $\left(x + \frac{1}{x}\right)^2 = x^2 + \frac{1}{x^2} + 2 = 7 + 2 = 9$

$$\Rightarrow \quad x + \frac{1}{x} = \pm\sqrt{9} = \pm 3.$$

(ii) $\left(x - \frac{1}{x}\right)^2 = x^2 + \frac{1}{x^2} - 2 = 7 - 2 = 5$

$$\Rightarrow \quad x - \frac{1}{x} = \pm\sqrt{5}.$$

(iii) $2x^2 - \frac{2}{x^2} = 2\left(x^2 - \frac{1}{x^2}\right) = 2\left(x + \frac{1}{x}\right)\left(x - \frac{1}{x}\right)$

$$= 2 \times (\pm 3)(\pm\sqrt{5}) = \pm 6\sqrt{5}.$$

Example 4 If $a^2 - 3a - 1 = 0$, find the value of $a^2 + \frac{1}{a^2}$.

Solution. Given $a^2 - 3a - 1 = 0$, dividing each term by a, we get

$$a - 3 - \frac{1}{a} = 0 \Rightarrow a - \frac{1}{a} = 3.$$

Now $\left(a - \frac{1}{a}\right)^2 = a^2 + \frac{1}{a^2} - 2$

$$\Rightarrow \quad a^2 + \frac{1}{a^2} = \left(a - \frac{1}{a}\right)^2 + 2$$

$$\Rightarrow \quad a^2 + \frac{1}{a^2} = (3)^2 + 2 = 9 + 2 = 11.$$

Example 5 If $\frac{x^2 + 1}{x} = 2\frac{1}{2}$, find the values of:

    (i) $x - \frac{1}{x}$ *(ii)* $x^3 - \frac{1}{x^3}$.

Solution. Given $\frac{x^2 + 1}{x} = 2\frac{1}{2} \Rightarrow x + \frac{1}{x} = \frac{5}{2}.$

(i) Now $\left(x-\dfrac{1}{x}\right)^2 = \left(x^2+\dfrac{1}{x^2}\right)-2$

$$= \left(\left(x+\dfrac{1}{x}\right)^2-2\right)-2 = \left(x+\dfrac{1}{x}\right)^2-4$$

$$= \left(\dfrac{5}{2}\right)^2-4 = \dfrac{25}{4}-4 = \dfrac{9}{4}$$

$\Rightarrow \qquad x-\dfrac{1}{x} = \pm\sqrt{\dfrac{9}{4}} = \pm\dfrac{3}{2}.$

(ii) $\left(x-\dfrac{1}{x}\right)^3 = x^3-\dfrac{1}{x^3}-3\cdot x\cdot\dfrac{1}{x}\left(x-\dfrac{1}{x}\right) = x^3-\dfrac{1}{x^3}-3\left(x-\dfrac{1}{x}\right)$

$\Rightarrow \qquad x^3-\dfrac{1}{x^3} = \left(x-\dfrac{1}{x}\right)^3+3\left(x-\dfrac{1}{x}\right).$

Two cases arise:

Case I. When $x-\dfrac{1}{x} = \dfrac{3}{2}$,

$$x^3-\dfrac{1}{x^3} = \left(\dfrac{3}{2}\right)^3+3\cdot\dfrac{3}{2} = \dfrac{27}{8}+\dfrac{9}{2} = \dfrac{63}{8} = 7\dfrac{7}{8}.$$

Case II. When $x-\dfrac{1}{x} = -\dfrac{3}{2}$,

$$x^3-\dfrac{1}{x^3} = \left(-\dfrac{3}{2}\right)^3+3\left(-\dfrac{3}{2}\right) = -\dfrac{27}{8}-\dfrac{9}{2} = -\dfrac{63}{8} = -7\dfrac{7}{8}.$$

Example 6 If $x^2+\dfrac{1}{25x^2} = 8\dfrac{3}{5}$, find the value of $x^3+\dfrac{1}{125x^3}$.

Solution. Given $\quad x^2+\dfrac{1}{25x^2} = 8\dfrac{3}{5} = \dfrac{43}{5}$.

We know that $\quad \left(x+\dfrac{1}{5x}\right)^2 = x^2+\dfrac{1}{25x^2}+2\cdot x\cdot\dfrac{1}{5x}$

$$= \dfrac{43}{5}+\dfrac{2}{5} = \dfrac{45}{5} = 9$$

$\Rightarrow \qquad x+\dfrac{1}{5x} = \pm\sqrt{9} = \pm 3.$

Now $\quad \left(x+\dfrac{1}{5x}\right)^3 = x^3+\dfrac{1}{125x^3}+3\cdot x\cdot\dfrac{1}{5x}\left(x+\dfrac{1}{5x}\right)$

$\Rightarrow \qquad x^3+\dfrac{1}{125x^3} = \left(x+\dfrac{1}{5x}\right)^3-\dfrac{3}{5}\left(x+\dfrac{1}{5x}\right).$

Two cases arise:

Case I. When $x+\dfrac{1}{5x} = 3$,

$$x^3+\dfrac{1}{125x^3} = (3)^3-\dfrac{3}{5}\cdot 3 = 27-\dfrac{9}{5} = \dfrac{126}{5} = 25\dfrac{1}{5}.$$

Case II. When $x+\dfrac{1}{5x} = -3$,

$$x^3+\dfrac{1}{125x^3} = (-3)^3-\dfrac{3}{5}(-3) = -27+\dfrac{9}{5} = -\dfrac{126}{5} = -25\dfrac{1}{5}.$$

Example 7 If $x^4 + \dfrac{1}{x^4} = 194$, find the values of:

(i) $x^2 + \dfrac{1}{x^2}$ (ii) $x + \dfrac{1}{x}$ (iii) $x^3 + \dfrac{1}{x^3}$.

Solution. (i) $\left(x^2 + \dfrac{1}{x^2} \right)^2 = x^4 + \dfrac{1}{x^4} + 2 = 194 + 2 = 196$

$\Rightarrow \quad x^2 + \dfrac{1}{x^2} = \pm 14$ but $x^2 + \dfrac{1}{x^2}$ is always positive,

$\therefore \quad x^2 + \dfrac{1}{x^2} = 14.$

(ii) $\left(x + \dfrac{1}{x} \right)^2 = x^2 + \dfrac{1}{x^2} + 2 = 14 + 2$ (using part (i))

$\Rightarrow \quad \left(x + \dfrac{1}{x} \right)^2 = 16$

$\Rightarrow \quad x + \dfrac{1}{x} = \pm 4.$

(iii) $\left(x + \dfrac{1}{x} \right)^3 = x^3 + \dfrac{1}{x^3} + 3 \cdot x \cdot \dfrac{1}{x} \left(x + \dfrac{1}{x} \right)$

$\qquad\qquad\quad = x^3 + \dfrac{1}{x^3} + 3 \left(x + \dfrac{1}{x} \right)$

$\Rightarrow \quad x^3 + \dfrac{1}{x^3} = \left(x + \dfrac{1}{x} \right)^3 - 3 \left(x + \dfrac{1}{x} \right).$

Two cases arise:

Case I. When $x + \dfrac{1}{x} = 4$,

$\qquad x^3 + \dfrac{1}{x^3} = (4)^3 - 3 \cdot 4 = 64 - 12 = 52.$

Case II. When $x + \dfrac{1}{x} = -4$,

$\qquad x^3 + \dfrac{1}{x^3} = (-4)^3 - 3 \cdot (-4) = -64 + 12 = -52.$

Example 8 If $x = 7 - 4\sqrt{3}$, find the value of $\sqrt{x} + \dfrac{1}{\sqrt{x}}$.

Solution. Given $x = 7 - 4\sqrt{3}$ ...(i)

$\therefore \qquad \dfrac{1}{x} = \dfrac{1}{7 - 4\sqrt{3}} = \dfrac{1}{7 - 4\sqrt{3}} \times \dfrac{7 + 4\sqrt{3}}{7 + 4\sqrt{3}} = \dfrac{7 + 4\sqrt{3}}{7^2 - (4\sqrt{3})^2}$

$\qquad\qquad = \dfrac{7 + 4\sqrt{3}}{49 - 48} = \dfrac{7 + 4\sqrt{3}}{1}$

$\Rightarrow \qquad \dfrac{1}{x} = 7 + 4\sqrt{3}$ ...(ii)

On adding (i) and (ii), we get

$\qquad\qquad x + \dfrac{1}{x} = 14$ ...(iii)

Now $\left(\sqrt{x} + \dfrac{1}{\sqrt{x}} \right)^2 = x + \dfrac{1}{x} + 2 \cdot \sqrt{x} \cdot \dfrac{1}{\sqrt{x}} = x + \dfrac{1}{x} + 2$

$\qquad\qquad\qquad\qquad = 14 + 2$ (using (iii))

$$\Rightarrow \quad \left(\sqrt{x}+\frac{1}{\sqrt{x}}\right)^2 = 16 \Rightarrow \sqrt{x}+\frac{1}{\sqrt{x}} = \pm\sqrt{16} = \pm 4.$$

As $\quad \sqrt{x} > 0$, $\sqrt{x}+\frac{1}{\sqrt{x}} > 0$. So, we reject -4.

$$\therefore \quad \sqrt{x}+\frac{1}{\sqrt{x}} = 4.$$

Example 9 If $x = 3 + 2\sqrt{2}$, find the value of $x^3 - \frac{1}{x^3}$.

Solution. Given $x = 3 + 2\sqrt{2}$ $\hspace{4cm}$ ...(i)

$$\therefore \quad \frac{1}{x} = \frac{1}{3+2\sqrt{2}} = \frac{1}{3+2\sqrt{2}} \times \frac{3-2\sqrt{2}}{3-2\sqrt{2}} = \frac{3-2\sqrt{2}}{(3)^2-(2\sqrt{2})^2}$$

$$= \frac{3-2\sqrt{2}}{9-8} = \frac{3-2\sqrt{2}}{1}$$

$$\Rightarrow \quad \frac{1}{x} = 3 - 2\sqrt{2} \hspace{4cm} ...(ii)$$

On subtracting (ii) from (i), we get

$$x - \frac{1}{x} = 4\sqrt{2} \hspace{4cm} ...(iii)$$

Now $\quad \left(x-\frac{1}{x}\right)^3 = x^3 - \frac{1}{x^3} - 3.x.\frac{1}{x}\left(x-\frac{1}{x}\right)$

$$= x^3 - \frac{1}{x^3} - 3\left(x-\frac{1}{x}\right)$$

$$\Rightarrow \quad x^3 - \frac{1}{x^3} = \left(x-\frac{1}{x}\right)^3 + 3\left(x-\frac{1}{x}\right)$$

$$\Rightarrow \quad x^3 - \frac{1}{x^3} = (4\sqrt{2})^3 + 3 \times 4\sqrt{2} \hspace{2cm} \text{(using (iii))}$$

$$= 128\sqrt{2} + 12\sqrt{2}$$

$$\Rightarrow \quad x^3 - \frac{1}{x^3} = 140\sqrt{2}.$$

Example 10 If $a = 5 + 2\sqrt{6}$ and $b = \frac{1}{a}$, then find the values of:

(i) $a^2 + b^2$ $\quad$ (ii) $a^3 + b^3$.

Solution. $b = \frac{1}{a} = \frac{1}{5+2\sqrt{6}} = \frac{1}{5+2\sqrt{6}} \times \frac{5-2\sqrt{6}}{5-2\sqrt{6}}$

$$= \frac{5-2\sqrt{6}}{(5)^2-(2\sqrt{6})^2} = \frac{5-2\sqrt{6}}{25-24} = 5 - 2\sqrt{6}$$

$\therefore \quad a + b = (5 + 2\sqrt{6}) + (5 - 2\sqrt{6}) = 10.$

Also $b = \frac{1}{a} \Rightarrow ab = 1.$

(i) $(a+b)^2 = a^2 + b^2 + 2ab$

$\Rightarrow \quad (10)^2 = a^2 + b^2 + 2 \times 1 \Rightarrow 100 = a^2 + b^2 + 2$

$\Rightarrow \quad a^2 + b^2 = 98.$

(ii) $(a+b)^3 = a^3 + b^3 + 3ab(a+b)$

$\Rightarrow \quad (10)^3 = a^3 + b^3 + 3 \times 1 \times 10 \Rightarrow 1000 = a^3 + b^3 + 30$

$\Rightarrow \quad a^3 + b^3 = 970.$

Example 11 If $a^2 + b^2 + c^2 = 50$ and $ab + bc + ca = 47$, find $a + b + c$.

Solution. $(a + b + c)^2 = a^2 + b^2 + c^2 + 2(ab + bc + ca)$

$$= 50 + 2 \times 47 = 50 + 94 = 144$$

$\Rightarrow \qquad a + b + c = \pm \sqrt{144} = \pm 12.$

Example 12 If $x + y - z = 4$ and $x^2 + y^2 + z^2 = 38$, then find the value of $xy - yz - zx$.

Solution. We know that

$$(a + b + c)^2 = a^2 + b^2 + c^2 + 2(ab + bc + ca).$$

$\therefore \qquad (x + y - z)^2 = x^2 + y^2 + (-z)^2 + 2[xy + y(-z) + (-z)x]$

$$= x^2 + y^2 + z^2 + 2(xy - yz - zx)$$

$\Rightarrow \quad 4^2 = 38 + 2(xy - yz - zx)$

$\Rightarrow \quad 16 = 38 + 2(xy - yz - zx)$

$\Rightarrow \quad 2(xy - yz - zx) = 16 - 38 = -22$

$\Rightarrow \quad xy - yz - zx = -11.$

Example 13 If $a + b + c = 2$, $ab + bc + ca = -1$ and $abc = -2$, find the value of $a^3 + b^3 + c^3$.

Solution. We know that

$a^3 + b^3 + c^3 - 3abc = (a + b + c)(a^2 + b^2 + c^2 - ab - bc - ca)$

$$= (a + b + c)(a^2 + b^2 + c^2 + 2ab + 2bc + 2ca - 3ab - 3bc - 3ca)$$

$$= (a + b + c)[(a + b + c)^2 - 3(ab + bc + ca)]$$

$$= 2[(2)^2 - 3(-1)] = 2(4 + 3) = 14$$

$\Rightarrow \quad a^3 + b^3 + c^3 - 3(-2) = 14$

$\Rightarrow \quad a^3 + b^3 + c^3 + 6 = 14$

$\Rightarrow \quad a^3 + b^3 + c^3 = 8.$

Example 14 If $a^2 + b^2 + c^2 = 280$ and $ab + bc + ca = \dfrac{9}{2}$, then find the value of $(a + b + c)^3$.

Solution. $(a + b + c)^2 = a^2 + b^2 + c^2 + 2(ab + bc + ca)$

$$= 280 + 2 \times \frac{9}{2} = 280 + 9 = 289$$

$\Rightarrow \quad a + b + c = 17, -17$

Two cases arise:

Case I. If $a + b + c = 17$, then

$(a + b + c)^3 = (17)^3 = 4913.$

Case II. If $a + b + c = -17$, then

$(a + b + c)^3 = (-17)^3 = -4913.$

Example 15 If $a + b = 10$ and $a^2 + b^2 = 58$, find the value of $a^3 + b^3$.

Solution. Given $a + b = 10$ $\quad$ ...(i) $\qquad$ and $\qquad$ $a^2 + b^2 = 58$ $\qquad$ ...(ii)

Now $(a + b)^2 = a^2 + b^2 + 2ab$

$\Rightarrow \quad 10^2 = 58 + 2ab$ $\hfill$ (using (i) and (ii))

$\Rightarrow \quad 100 - 58 = 2ab \Rightarrow 42 = 2ab$

$\Rightarrow \quad ab = 21$ $\hfill$ ...(iii)

We know that $(a + b)^3 = a^3 + b^3 + 3ab(a + b)$

$\Rightarrow \quad 10^3 = a^3 + b^3 + 3 \times 21 \times 10$ $\hfill$ (using (i), (ii) and (iii))

$\Rightarrow \quad 1000 = a^3 + b^3 + 630$

$\Rightarrow \quad a^3 + b^3 = 370.$

Example 16 If $\dfrac{a}{b} = \dfrac{b}{c}$, prove that $(a + b + c)(a - b + c) = a^2 + b^2 + c^2$.

Solution. Let $\dfrac{a}{b} = \dfrac{b}{c} = k$ (say)

$\Rightarrow \quad a = bk$ and $b = ck$

$\Rightarrow \quad a = ck.k$ and $b = ck$

$\Rightarrow \quad a = ck^2$ ...(i)

and $b = ck$ ...(ii)

Now, L.H.S. of the given result $= (a + b + c)(a - b + c)$

$\qquad = (ck^2 + ck + c)(ck^2 - ck + c)$ (using (i) and (ii))

$\qquad = c(k^2 + k + 1)\, c(k^2 - k + 1)$

$\qquad = c^2\, \overline{(k^2 + 1 + k)}(\overline{k^2 + 1} - k)$

$\qquad = c^2\, [(k^2 + 1)^2 - k^2]$

$\qquad = c^2\, (k^4 + 2k^2 + 1 - k^2)$

$\qquad = c^2\, (k^4 + k^2 + 1)$ ...(iii)

And R.H.S. of the given result $= a^2 + b^2 + c^2$

$\qquad = (ck^2)^2 + (ck)^2 + c^2$

$\qquad = c^2k^4 + c^2k^2 + c^2$

$\qquad = c^2\, (k^4 + k^2 + 1)$ ...(iv)

From (iii) and (iv), it follows that $(a + b + c)(a - b + c) = a^2 + b^2 + c^2$.

Example 17 If the number p is 7 more than the number q and the sum of the squares of p and q is 85, find the product of p and q.

Solution. Given $p = q + 7$ and $p^2 + q^2 = 85$.

Now $p = q + 7 \Rightarrow p - q = 7$

$\Rightarrow \qquad (p - q)^2 = 7^2 \Rightarrow p^2 + q^2 - 2pq = 49$

$\Rightarrow \qquad 85 - 2pq = 49$ $(\because p^2 + q^2 = 85)$

$\Rightarrow \qquad 85 - 49 = 2pq$

$\Rightarrow \qquad 2pq = 36 \Rightarrow pq = 18.$

Example 18 If the sum of two numbers is 7 and the sum of their cubes is 133, find the sum of their squares.

Solution. Let the two numbers be a and b, then

$\qquad a + b = 7$ and $a^3 + b^3 = 133$.

Now $a + b = 7 \Rightarrow (a + b)^3 = 7^3$

$\Rightarrow \qquad a^3 + b^3 + 3ab\,(a + b) = 343$

$\Rightarrow \qquad 133 + 3ab \times 7 = 343$

$\Rightarrow \qquad 21ab = 343 - 133 = 210$

$\Rightarrow \qquad ab = 10.$

We know that $(a + b)^2 = a^2 + b^2 + 2ab$

$\Rightarrow \qquad 7^2 = a^2 + b^2 + 2 \times 10$

$\Rightarrow \qquad 49 = a^2 + b^2 + 20$

$\Rightarrow \qquad a^2 + b^2 = 49 - 20 = 29.$

Hence, the sum of the squares of the numbers is 29.

EXERCISE 3.2

1. If $x - y = 8$ and $xy = 5$, find $x^2 + y^2$.

2. If $x + y = 10$ and $xy = 21$, find $2(x^2 + y^2)$.

3. If $2a + 3b = 7$ and $ab = 2$, find $4a^2 + 9b^2$.

4. If $3x - 4y = 16$ and $xy = 4$, find the value of $9x^2 + 16y^2$.

5. If $x + y = 8$ and $x - y = 2$, find the value of $2x^2 + 2y^2$.

   Hint. $2(x^2 + y^2) = (x + y)^2 + (x - y)^2$.

6. If $a^2 + b^2 = 13$ and $ab = 6$, find (i) $a + b$ (ii) $a - b$.

7. If $a + b = 4$ and $ab = -12$, find (i) $a - b$ (ii) $a^2 - b^2$.

8. If $p - q = 9$ and $pq = 36$, evaluate

   (i) $p + q$ (ii) $p^2 - q^2$.

9. If $x + y = 6$ and $x - y = 4$, find (i) $x^2 + y^2$ (ii) xy.

   Hint. (ii) $4xy = (x + y)^2 - (x - y)^2$.

10. If $x - 3 = \dfrac{1}{x}$, find the value of $x^2 + \dfrac{1}{x^2}$.

    Hint. $x - 3 = \dfrac{1}{x} \Rightarrow x - \dfrac{1}{x} = 3$.

11. If $x + y = 8$ and $xy = 3\dfrac{3}{4}$, find the values of

    (i) $x - y$ (ii) $3(x^2 + y^2)$ (iii) $5(x^2 + y^2) + 4(x - y)$.

12. If $x^2 + y^2 = 34$ and $xy = 10\dfrac{1}{2}$, find the value of $2(x + y)^2 + (x - y)^2$.

13. If $a - b = 3$ and $ab = 4$, find $a^3 - b^3$.

14. If $2a - 3b = 3$ and $ab = 2$, find the value of $8a^3 - 27b^3$.

15. If $x + \dfrac{1}{x} = 4$, find the values of

    (i) $x^2 + \dfrac{1}{x^2}$ (ii) $x^4 + \dfrac{1}{x^4}$ (iii) $x^3 + \dfrac{1}{x^3}$ (iv) $x - \dfrac{1}{x}$.

16. If $x - \dfrac{1}{x} = 5$, find the value of $x^4 + \dfrac{1}{x^4}$.

17. If $x - \dfrac{1}{x} = \sqrt{5}$, find the values of

    (i) $x^2 + \dfrac{1}{x^2}$ (ii) $x + \dfrac{1}{x}$ (iii) $x^3 + \dfrac{1}{x^3}$.

18. If $x + \dfrac{1}{x} = 6$, find (i) $x - \dfrac{1}{x}$ (ii) $x^2 - \dfrac{1}{x^2}$.

19. If $x + \dfrac{1}{x} = 2$, prove that $x^2 + \dfrac{1}{x^2} = x^3 + \dfrac{1}{x^3} = x^4 + \dfrac{1}{x^4}$.

20. If $x - \dfrac{2}{x} = 3$, find the value of $x^3 - \dfrac{8}{x^3}$.

21. If $a + 2b = 5$, prove that $a^3 + 8b^3 + 30ab = 125$.

22 If $a + \dfrac{1}{a} = p$, prove that $a^3 + \dfrac{1}{a^3} = p\,(p^2 - 3)$.

23 If $x^2 + \dfrac{1}{x^2} = 27$, find the value of $x - \dfrac{1}{x}$.

24 If $x^2 + \dfrac{1}{x^2} = 27$, find the value of $3x^3 + 5x - \dfrac{3}{x^3} - \dfrac{5}{x}$.

25 If $x^2 + \dfrac{1}{25x^2} = 8\dfrac{3}{5}$, find $x + \dfrac{1}{5x}$.

26 If $x^2 + \dfrac{1}{4x^2} = 8$, find $x^3 + \dfrac{1}{8x^3}$.

27 If $a^2 - 3a + 1 = 0$, find (i) $a^2 + \dfrac{1}{a^2}$ (ii) $a^3 + \dfrac{1}{a^3}$.

28 If $a = \dfrac{1}{a-5}$, find (i) $a - \dfrac{1}{a}$ (ii) $a + \dfrac{1}{a}$ (iii) $a^2 - \dfrac{1}{a^2}$.

Hint. $a = \dfrac{1}{a-5} \Rightarrow a^2 - 5a - 1 = 0.$

29 If $\left(x + \dfrac{1}{x}\right)^2 = 3$, find $x^3 + \dfrac{1}{x^3}$.

30 If $x = 5 - 2\sqrt{6}$, find the value of $\sqrt{x} + \dfrac{1}{\sqrt{x}}$.

31 If $a + b + c = 12$ and $ab + bc + ca = 22$, find $a^2 + b^2 + c^2$.

32 If $a + b + c = 12$ and $a^2 + b^2 + c^2 = 100$, find $ab + bc + ca$.

33 If $a^2 + b^2 + c^2 = 125$ and $ab + bc + ca = 50$, find $a + b + c$.

34 If $a + b - c = 5$ and $a^2 + b^2 + c^2 = 29$, find the value of $ab - bc - ca$.

35 If $a - b = 7$ and $a^2 + b^2 = 85$, then find the value of $a^3 - b^3$.

36 If the number x is 3 less than the number y and the sum of the squares of x and y is 29, find the product of x and y.

37 If the sum and the product of two numbers are 8 and 15 respectively, find the sum of their cubes.

Multiple Choice Questions

Choose the correct answer from the given four options (1 to 10):

1 If $x + \dfrac{1}{x} = 2$, then $x^2 + \dfrac{1}{x^2}$ is equal to

   (a) 4   (b) 2   (c) 0   (d) none of these

2 If $x^2 + y^2 = 9$ and $xy = 8$, then $x + y$ is equal to

   (a) 25   (b) 5   (c) −5   (d) ±5

3 $(102)^2 - (98)^2$ is equal to

   (a) 200   (b) 400   (c) 600   (d) 800

4 96×104 is equal to

   (a) 9984   (b) 9974   (c) 9964   (d) none of these

5 $\dfrac{103^2 - 97^2}{200}$ is equal to

    (a) 3   (b) 4   (c) 5   (d) 6

6 If $x + y = 11$ and $xy = 24$, then $x^2 + y^2$ is equal to

    (a) 121   (b) 73   (c) 48   (d) 169

7 The value of $249^2 - 248^2$ is

    (a) 1^2 (b) 477   (c) 487   (d) 497

8 If $\dfrac{x}{y} + \dfrac{y}{x} = -1$ $(x, y \neq 0)$, then the value of $x^3 - y^3$ is

    (a) 1   (b) −1   (c) 0   (d) $\dfrac{1}{2}$

9 If $a + b + c = 0$, then the value of $a^3 + b^3 + c^3$ is

    (a) 0   (b) abc (c) $2abc$ (d) $3abc$

10 If $x - \dfrac{2}{x} = 3$, then $x^3 - \dfrac{8}{x^3}$ is equal to

    (a) 27   (b) 36   (c) 45   (d) 54

S ummary

1. $(a + b)^2 = a^2 + 2ab + b^2$.

2. $(a - b)^2 = a^2 - 2ab + b^2$.

3. $(a + b)(a - b) = a^2 - b^2$.

4. $\left(a + \dfrac{1}{a}\right)^2 = a^2 + \dfrac{1}{a^2} + 2, a \neq 0$.

5. $\left(a - \dfrac{1}{a}\right)^2 = a^2 + \dfrac{1}{a^2} - 2, a \neq 0$.

6. $\left(a + \dfrac{1}{a}\right)\left(a - \dfrac{1}{a}\right) = a^2 - \dfrac{1}{a^2}, a \neq 0$.

7.   (i) $(x + a)(x + b) = x^2 + (a + b)x + ab$.

    (ii) $(x + a)(x - b) = x^2 + (a - b)x - ab$.

    (iii) $(x - a)(x + b) = x^2 - (a - b)x - ab$.

    (iv) $(x - a)(x - b) = x^2 - (a + b)x + ab$.

8. $(a + b + c)^2 = a^2 + b^2 + c^2 + 2(ab + bc + ca)$.

9. $(a + b)^3 = a^3 + b^3 + 3ab(a + b) = a^3 + 3a^2b + 3ab^2 + b^3$.

10. $(a - b)^3 = a^3 - b^3 - 3ab(a - b) = a^3 - 3a^2b + 3ab^2 - b^3$.

11. $a^3 + b^3 = (a + b)(a^2 - ab + b^2)$.

12. $a^3 - b^3 = (a - b)(a^2 + ab + b^2)$.

13. $a^3 + b^3 + c^3 - 3abc = (a + b + c)(a^2 + b^2 + c^2 - ab - bc - ca)$.

14. $(x + a)(x + b)(x + c) = x^3 + (a + b + c)x^2 + (ab + bc + ca)x + abc$.

15. If $a + b + c = 0$, then $a^3 + b^3 + c^3 = 3abc$.

- An equation which is true for all values of the variables involved is called an **identity**. The above results 1 to 14 are all **identities**; of course, $a \neq 0$ in the results 4 to 6.

1 Find the expansions of the following:

   (i) $(2x + 3y + 5)(2x + 3y - 5)$ (ii) $(6 - 4a - 7b)^2$

   (iii) $(7 - 3xy)^3$ (iv) $(x + y + 2)^3$.

2 Simplify $(x - 2)(x + 2)(x^2 + 4)(x^4 + 16)$.

3 Evaluate 1002×998 by using a special product.

4 If $a + 2b + 3c = 0$, prove that $a^3 + 8b^3 + 27c^3 = 18abc$.

5 If $2x = 3y - 5$, then find the value of $8x^3 - 27y^3 - 90xy + 125$.

6 If $a^2 - \dfrac{1}{a^2} = 5$, evaluate $a^4 + \dfrac{1}{a^4}$.

7 If $a + \dfrac{1}{a} = p$ and $a - \dfrac{1}{a} = q$, find the relation between p and q.

8 If $\dfrac{a^2 + 1}{a} = 4$, find the value of $2a^3 + \dfrac{2}{a^3}$.

9 If $x = \dfrac{1}{4 - x}$, find the values of

   (i) $x + \dfrac{1}{x}$ (ii) $x^3 + \dfrac{1}{x^3}$ (iii) $x^6 + \dfrac{1}{x^6}$.

10 If $x - \dfrac{1}{x} = 3 + 2\sqrt{2}$, find the value of $\dfrac{1}{4}\left(x^3 - \dfrac{1}{x^3}\right)$.

11 If $x + \dfrac{1}{x} = 3\dfrac{1}{3}$, find the value of $x^3 - \dfrac{1}{x^3}$.

12 If $x = 2 - \sqrt{3}$, then find the value of $x^3 - \dfrac{1}{x^3}$.

13 If the sum of two numbers is 11 and sum of their cubes is 737, find the sum of their squares.

14 If $a - b = 7$ and $a^3 - b^3 = 133$, find (i) ab (ii) $a^2 + b^2$.

15 Find the coefficient of x^2 in the expansion of

   $(x^2 + x + 1)^2 + (x^2 - x + 1)^2$.

   Hint. Given expression $= \{(x^2 + 1) + x\}^2 + \{(x^2 + 1) - x\}^2$

   $\qquad\qquad\qquad = 2\{(x^2 + 1)^2 + x^2\}$.

4 Factorisation

INTRODUCTION

In previous classes, you have learnt that composite numbers can be expressed as the product of prime numbers.

For example:

$$42 = 2 \times 3 \times 7$$

Here, 2, 3 and 7 are prime factors of 42.

Similarly, algebraic expressions can also be expressed as the product of irreducible factors. By an irreducible factor, we mean a factor which cannot be expressed further as the product of factors.

We know that the product of $3x + 7$ and $3x - 7 = (3x + 7)(3x - 7) = 9x^2 - 49$; we say that $3x + 7$ and $3x - 7$ are factors of $9x^2 - 49$. We write it as

$$9x^2 - 49 = (3x + 7)(3x - 7).$$

Similarly, the product of $2x + 1$ and $x - 3 = (2x + 1)(x - 3) = 2x^2 - 5x - 3$; we say that $2x + 1$ and $x - 3$ are factors of $2x^2 - 5x - 3$. We write it as

$$2x^2 - 5x - 3 = (2x + 1)(x - 3).$$

*Thus, when an algebraic expression can be written as the product of two or more algebraic expressions, then each of these expression is called a **factor** of the given expression.*

To find the factors of a given algebraic expression means to obtain two or more expressions whose product is the given expression.

*The process of finding two or more expressions whose product is the given expression is called **factorisation**.*

Thus, factorisation is the reverse process of multiplication.

For example:

Product	Factors
(i) $(2x + 5)(2x - 5) = 4x^2 - 25$	$4x^2 - 25 = (2x + 5)(2x - 5)$
(ii) $(p + 3)(p - 7) = p^2 - 4p - 21$	$p^2 - 4p - 21 = (p + 3)(p - 7)$
(iii) $(2y + 3)(3y - 5) = 6y^2 - y - 15$	$6y^2 - y - 15 = (2y + 3)(3y - 5).$

However, in this book, we shall deal only with some special types of expressions.

4.1 FACTORISING BY TAKING OUT COMMON FACTORS

If the different terms of a given polynomial have common factors, then the given polynomial can be factorised by the following procedure:

(i) Find the H.C.F. of all the terms of the given polynomial.

(ii) Divide each term of the given polynomial by H.C.F. Enclose the quotient within the brackets and keep the common factor outside the bracket.

Illustrative Examples

Example 1 Factorise the following:

(i) $24x^3 - 32x^2$

(ii) $15ab^2 - 21a^2b$

(iii) $6xy^2 + 9x^2y - 21xy$

(iv) $14x^2y^2 - 10x^2y + 8xy^2$.

Solution. (i) H.C.F. of $24x^3$ and $32x^2$ is $8x^2$.

$$\therefore \quad 24x^3 - 32x^2 = 8x^2(3x - 4).$$

> Divide each term by $8x^2$ and keep $8x^2$ outside the bracket.

(ii) H.C.F. of $15ab^2$ and $21a^2b$ is $3ab$.

$$\therefore \quad 15ab^2 - 21a^2b = 3ab(5b - 7a).$$

(iii) H.C.F. of $6xy^2$, $9x^2y$ and $21xy$ is $3xy$.

$$\therefore \quad 6xy^2 + 9x^2y - 21xy = 3xy(2y + 3x - 7).$$

(iv) H.C.F. of $14x^2y^2$, $10x^2y$ and $8xy^2$ is $2xy$.

$$\therefore \quad 14x^2y^2 - 10x^2y + 8xy^2 = 2xy(7xy - 5x + 4y).$$

Example 2 Factorise the following:

(i) $3x(y + 2z) + 5a(y + 2z)$

(ii) $10(p - 2q)^3 + 6(p - 2q)^2 - 20(p - 2q)$.

Solution. (i) H.C.F. of the expressions $3x(y + 2z)$ and

$5a(y + 2z)$ is $y + 2z$.

$$\therefore \quad 3x(y + 2z) + 5a(y + 2z) = (y + 2z)(3x + 5a).$$

> Divide each term by $y + 2z$ and keep $y + 2z$ outside the bracket.

(ii) H.C.F. of the expressions

$10(p - 2q)^3$, $6(p - 2q)^2$ and $20(p - 2q)$ is $2(p - 2q)$

$$\therefore \quad 10(p - 2q)^3 + 6(p - 2q)^2 - 20(p - 2q) = 2(p - 2q)[5(p - 2q)^2 + 3(p - 2q) - 10].$$

EXERCISE 4.1

Factorise the following (1 to 9):

1 (i) $8xy^3 + 12x^2y^2$ (ii) $15ax^3 - 9ax^2$.

2 (i) $21py^2 - 56py$ (ii) $4x^3 - 6x^2$.

3 (i) $2\pi r^2 - 4\pi r$ (ii) $18m + 16n$.

4 (i) $25abc^2 - 15a^2b^2c$ (ii) $28p^2q^2r - 42pq^2r^2$.

5 (i) $8x^3 - 6x^2 + 10x$ (ii) $14mn + 22m - 62p$.

6 (i) $18p^2q^2 - 24pq^2 + 30p^2q$ (ii) $27a^3b^3 - 18a^2b^3 + 75a^3b^2$.

7 (i) $15a(2p - 3q) - 10b(2p - 3q)$ (ii) $3a(x^2 + y^2) + 6b(x^2 + y^2)$.

8 (i) $6(x + 2y)^3 + 8(x + 2y)^2$ (ii) $14(a - 3b)^3 - 21p(a - 3b)$.

9 (i) $10a(2p + q)^3 - 15b(2p + q)^2 + 35(2p + q)$

(ii) $x(x^2 + y^2 - z^2) + y(-x^2 - y^2 + z^2) - z(x^2 + y^2 - z^2)$.

4.2 FACTORISING BY GROUPING OF TERMS

When the grouping of terms of the given polynomial gives rise to common factor, then the given polynomial can be factorised by the following procedure:

   (*i*) Arrange the terms of the given polynomial in groups in such a way that each group has a common factor.

   (*ii*) Factorise each group.

   (*iii*) Take out the factor which is common to each group.

Illustrative Examples

Example 1 Factorise the following:

   (*i*) $ax - ay + bx - by$ (*ii*) $4x^2 - 10xy - 6xz + 15yz$.

Solution. (*i*) $ax - ay + bx - by = (ax - ay) + (bx - by)$

$$= a(x - y) + b(x - y)$$
$$= (x - y)(a + b).$$

   (*ii*) $4x^2 - 10xy - 6xz + 15yz = (4x^2 - 10xy) - (6xz - 15yz)$

$$= 2x(2x - 5y) - 3z(2x - 5y)$$
$$= (2x - 5y)(2x - 3z).$$

Example 2 Factorise the following:

   (*i*) $x^3 + 2x^2 + x + 2$ (*ii*) $1 + p + pq + p^2q$.

Solution. (*i*) $x^3 + 2x^2 + x + 2 = (x^3 + 2x^2) + (x + 2)$

$$= x^2(x + 2) + 1(x + 2)$$
$$= (x + 2)(x^2 + 1).$$

   (*ii*) $1 + p + pq + p^2q = (1 + p) + (pq + p^2q)$

$$= 1(1 + p) + pq(1 + p)$$
$$= (1 + p)(1 + pq).$$

Example 3 Factorise the following:

   (*i*) $xy - pq + qy - px$ (*ii*) $ab(x^2 + y^2) + xy(a^2 + b^2)$.

Solution. (*i*) Since xy and pq have nothing in common, we do not group the terms in pairs in order in which the given expression is written. Hence, we interchange $-pq$ and $-px$

$$\therefore \quad xy - pq + qy - px = (xy - px) + (qy - pq)$$
$$= x(y - p) + q(y - p)$$
$$= (y - p)(x + q)$$

   (*ii*) $ab(x^2 + y^2) + xy(a^2 + b^2) = abx^2 + aby^2 + a^2xy + b^2xy$

$$= (abx^2 + a^2xy) + (aby^2 + b^2xy)$$
$$= ax(bx + ay) + by(ay + bx)$$
$$= (bx + ay)(ax + by)$$

Example 4 Factorise the following:

   (*i*) $a(a + b - c) - bc$ (*ii*) $a^2x^2 + (ax^2 + 1)x + a$.

Solution. (*i*) $a(a + b - c) - bc = a^2 + ab - ac - bc$

$$= (a^2 + ab) - (ac + bc)$$
$$= a(a + b) - c(a + b)$$
$$= (a + b)(a - c).$$

(ii) $a^2x^2 + (ax^2 + 1)x + a = a^2x^2 + ax^3 + x + a$

$$= (ax^3 + a^2x^2) + (x + a) = ax^2(x + a) + 1(x + a)$$

$$= (x + a)(ax^2 + 1).$$

Example 5 Factorise the following:

(i) $ax + by + bx + az + ay + bz$ (ii) $x^3 - x^2 + ax + x - a - 1$.

Solution. (i) $ax + by + bx + az + ay + bz$

$$= (ax + ay + az) + (bx + by + bz)$$

$$= a(x + y + z) + b(x + y + z)$$

$$= (x + y + z)(a + b).$$

(ii) $x^3 - x^2 + ax + x - a - 1 = (x^3 - x^2) + (ax - a) + (x - 1)$

$$= x^2(x - 1) + a(x - 1) + 1(x - 1)$$

$$= (x - 1)(x^2 + a + 1).$$

Example 6 Factorise the following:

(i) $p(x - y)^2 - qy + qx + 3x - 3y$ (ii) $ax - (ax + by)^2 + a^2x + aby + by$.

Solution. (i) $p(x - y)^2 - qy + qx + 3x - 3y$

$$= p(x - y)^2 + (qx - qy) + (3x - 3y)$$

$$= p(x - y)^2 + q(x - y) + 3(x - y)$$

$$= (x - y)[p(x - y) + q + 3].$$

(ii) $ax - (ax + by)^2 + a^2x + aby + by$

$$= (ax + a^2x) + (aby + by) - (ax + by)^2$$

$$= ax(1 + a) + by(a + 1) - (ax + by)^2$$

$$= (1 + a)(ax + by) - (ax + by)^2$$

$$= (ax + by)[1 + a - (ax + by)]$$

$$= (ax + by)(1 + a - ax - by).$$

Example 7 Factorise the following:

(i) $a^3x + a^2(x - y) - a(y + z) - z$ (ii) $(x^2 - 2x)^2 - 5(x^2 - 2x) - y(x^2 - 2x) + 5y$.

Solution. (i) $a^3x + a^2(x - y) - a(y + z) - z$

$$= a^3x + a^2x - a^2y - ay - az - z$$

$$= (a^3x + a^2x) - (a^2y + ay) - (az + z)$$

$$= a^2x(a + 1) - ay(a + 1) - z(a + 1)$$

$$= (a + 1)(a^2x - ay - z).$$

(ii) $(x^2 - 2x)^2 - 5(x^2 - 2x) - y(x^2 - 2x) + 5y$

$$= ((x^2 - 2x)^2 - 5(x^2 - 2x)) - (y(x^2 - 2x) - 5y)$$

$$= (x^2 - 2x)(x^2 - 2x - 5) - y(x^2 - 2x - 5)$$

$$= (x^2 - 2x - 5)(x^2 - 2x - y).$$

Example 8 Factorise: $a^2 + b^2 - 2(ab - ac + bc)$.

Solution. $a^2 + b^2 - 2(ab - ac + bc) = (a^2 + b^2 - 2ab) - 2(-ac + bc)$

$$= (a - b)^2 - 2(-c)(a - b) = (a - b)[(a - b) + 2c]$$

$$= (a - b)(a - b + 2c).$$

EXERCISE 4.2

Factorise the following (1 to 13):

1.   (i) $x^2 + xy - x - y$ (ii) $y^2 - yz - 5y + 5z$.

2.   (i) $5xy + 7y - 5y^2 - 7x$ (ii) $5p^2 - 8pq - 10p + 16q$.

3.   (i) $a^2b - ab^2 + 3a - 3b$ (ii) $x^3 - 3x^2 + x - 3$.

4.   (i) $6xy^2 - 3xy - 10y + 5$ (ii) $3ax - 6ay - 8by + 4bx$.

5.   (i) $1 - a - b + ab$ (ii) $a(a - 2b - c) + 2bc$.

6.   (i) $x^2 + xy(1 + y) + y^3$ (ii) $y^2 - xy(1 - x) - x^3$.

7.   (i) $ab^2 + (a - 1)b - 1$ (ii) $2a - 4b - xa + 2bx$.

8.   (i) $5ph - 10qk + 2rph - 4qrk$ (ii) $x^2 - x(a + 2b) + 2ab$.

9.   (i) $ab(x^2 + y^2) - xy(a^2 + b^2)$ (ii) $(ax + by)^2 + (bx - ay)^2$.

10.   (i) $a^3 + ab(1 - 2a) - 2b^2$ (ii) $3x^2y - 3xy + 12x - 12$.

Hint. (ii) 3 is a common factor. First take 3 outside.

11. $a^2b + ab^2 - abc - b^2c + axy + bxy$.

12. $ax^2 - bx^2 + ay^2 - by^2 + az^2 - bz^2$.

13. $x - 1 - (x - 1)^2 + ax - a$.

4.3 DIFFERENCE OF TWO SQUARES

We shall use the identity $a^2 - b^2 = (a + b)(a - b)$.

Illustrative Examples

Example 1   Factorise the following:

    (i) $4x^2 - 169y^2$ (ii) $1 - (b - c)^2$

    (iii) $x^2 - 2y + xy - 4$ (iv) $a(a - 3) - b(b - 3)$.

Solution. (i) $4x^2 - 169y^2 = (2x)^2 - (13y)^2$

$$= (2x + 13y)(2x - 13y).$$

$$\begin{aligned}
(ii) \quad 1 - (b - c)^2 &= (1)^2 - (b - c)^2 \\
&= (1 + \overline{b - c})(1 - \overline{b - c}) \\
&= (1 + b - c)(1 - b + c).
\end{aligned}$$

$$\begin{aligned}
(iii) \quad x^2 - 2y + xy - 4 &= (x^2 - 4) + (xy - 2y) \\
&= (x + 2)(x - 2) + y(x - 2) \\
&= (x - 2)(\overline{x + 2} + y) \\
&= (x - 2)(x + y + 2).
\end{aligned}$$

$$\begin{aligned}
(iv) \quad a(a - 3) - b(b - 3) &= a^2 - 3a - b^2 + 3b \\
&= (a^2 - b^2) - 3a + 3b
\end{aligned}$$

$$= (a - b)\ (a + b) - 3(a - b)$$
$$= (a - b)\ (a + b - 3).$$

Example 2 Factorise the following:

(i) $16y^3 - 4y$ (ii) $9x^2 - 4a^2 + 4ay - y^2$ (iii) $x^3 - 3x^2 - x + 3$.

Solution. (i) $16y^3 - 4y = 4y(4y^2 - 1)$
$$= 4y[(2y)^2 - (1)^2]$$
$$= 4y(2y + 1)\ (2y - 1).$$

(ii) $9x^2 - 4a^2 + 4ay - y^2 = 9x^2 - (4a^2 - 4ay + y^2)$
$$= (3x)^2 - (2a - y)^2$$
$$= (3x + \overline{2a - y})\ (3x - \overline{2a - y})$$
$$= (3x - y + 2a)\ (3x + y - 2a).$$

(iii) $x^3 - 3x^2 - x + 3 = (x^3 - 3x^2) + (-x + 3)$
$$= x^2(x - 3) - 1\ (x - 3)$$
$$= (x - 3)\ (x^2 - 1)$$
$$= (x - 3)\ (x^2 - 1^2)$$
$$= (x - 3)\ (x + 1)\ (x - 1).$$

Example 3 Factorise the following:

(i) $3 - 12(a - b)^2$ (ii) $4a^2 - 9b^2 - 2a - 3b$

(iii) $(a + b + c)^2 - (a - b - c)^2 + 4b^2 - 4c^2$.

Solution. (i) $3 - 12(a - b)^2 = 3[1 - 4(a - b)^2]$
$$= 3[1^2 - (2(a - b))^2]$$
$$= 3(1 + 2(a - b))\ (1 - 2(a - b))$$
$$= 3(1 + 2a - 2b)\ (1 - 2a - 2b).$$

(ii) $4a^2 - 9b^2 - 2a - 3b = ((2a)^2 - (3b)^2) - 2a - 3b$
$$= (2a + 3b)\ (2a - 3b) - 1(2a + 3b)$$
$$= (2a + 3b)\ (2a - 3b - 1).$$

(iii) $(a + b + c)^2 - (a - b - c)^2 + 4b^2 - 4c^2$
$$= ((a + b + c) + (a - b - c))\ ((a + b + c) - (a - b - c)) + 4(b^2 - c^2)$$
$$= 2a(2b + 2c) + 4(b + c)\ (b - c)$$
$$= 4a(b + c) + 4(b + c)\ (b - c)$$
$$= 4(b + c)\ (a + b - c).$$

Example 4 Factorise the following:

(i) $3x^5 - 48x$ (ii) $2(ab + cd) - a^2 - b^2 + c^2 + d^2$

(iii) $(1 - x^2)\ (1 - y^2) + 4xy$ (iv) $x^4 + y^4 - 11x^2y^2$.

Solution. (i) $3x^5 - 48x = 3x\ (x^4 - 16) = 3x\ [(x^2)^2 - (4)^2]$
$$= 3x\ (x^2 + 4)\ (x^2 - 4)$$
$$= 3x\ (x^2 + 4)\ (x + 2)\ (x - 2).$$

(ii) $2(ab + cd) - a^2 - b^2 + c^2 + d^2 = 2ab + 2cd - a^2 - b^2 + c^2 + d^2$
$$= (c^2 + 2cd + d^2) - (a^2 - 2ab + b^2)$$
$$= (c + d)^2 - (a - b)^2$$

$$= \overline{(c+d} + \overline{a-b})\overline{(c+d} - \overline{a-b})$$
$$= (c + d + a - b)\,(c + d - a + b).$$

(iii) $(1 - x^2)\,(1 - y^2) + 4xy = 1 - x^2 - y^2 + x^2y^2 + 4xy$

$$= x^2y^2 + 1 + 2xy - x^2 - y^2 + 2xy$$
$$= (x^2y^2 + 2xy + 1) - (x^2 - 2xy + y^2)$$
$$= (xy + 1)^2 - (x - y)^2$$
$$= \overline{(xy + 1} + \overline{x - y})\overline{(xy + 1} - \overline{x - y})$$
$$= (xy + x - y + 1)\,(xy - x + y + 1).$$

(iv) $\quad x^4 + y^4 - 11\,x^2y^2 = (x^4 + y^4 - 2\,x^2y^2) - 9\,x^2y^2$

$$= (x^2 - y^2)^2 - (3xy)^2$$
$$= (x^2 - y^2 + 3xy)\,(x^2 - y^2 - 3xy).$$

Example 5 Factorise the following:

(i) $x^4 + 4$ \qquad (ii) $x^4 + x^2 + 1$ \qquad (iii) $x^4 + x^2y^2 + y^4$.

Solution. (i) $\quad x^4 + 4 = x^4 + 4x^2 + 4 - 4x^2$ \qquad\qquad (Adding and subtracting $4x^2$)

$$= (x^2 + 2)^2 - (2x)^2$$
$$= (x^2 + 2 + 2x)\,(x^2 + 2 - 2x)$$
$$= (x^2 + 2x + 2)\,(x^2 - 2x + 2).$$

(ii) $\quad x^4 + x^2 + 1 = x^4 + 2x^2 + 1 - x^2$ \qquad\qquad (Adding and subtracting x^2)

$$= (x^2 + 1)^2 - x^2$$
$$= (x^2 + 1 + x)\,(x^2 + 1 - x)$$
$$= (x^2 + x + 1)\,(x^2 - x + 1).$$

(iii) $x^4 + x^2y^2 + y^4 = x^4 + 2x^2y^2 + y^4 - x^2y^2$ \qquad (Adding and subtracting x^2y^2)

$$= (x^2 + y^2)^2 - (xy)^2$$
$$= (x^2 + y^2 + xy)\,(x^2 + y^2 - xy).$$

Example 6 Factorise completely $(x^2 + y^2 - z^2)^2 - 4x^2y^2$.

Solution. $\quad (x^2 + y^2 - z^2)^2 - 4x^2y^2 = (x^2 + y^2 - z^2)^2 - (2xy)^2$

$$= (x^2 + y^2 - z^2 + 2xy)\,(x^2 + y^2 - z^2 - 2xy)$$
$$= \overline{(x^2 + 2xy + y^2} - z^2)\overline{(x^2 - 2xy + y^2} - z^2)$$
$$= [(x + y)^2 - z^2]\,[(x - y)^2 - z^2]$$
$$= (x + y + z)\,(x + y - z)\,(x - y + z)\,(x - y - z).$$

Example 7 Express $(x^2 - 4x + 9)\,(x^2 + 4x - 9)$ as a difference of two squares.

Solution. $(x^2 - 4x + 9)\,(x^2 + 4x - 9) = (x^2 - \overline{4x - 9})(x^2 + \overline{4x - 9})$

(Expressing as $(a - b)\,(a + b)$)

$$= (x^2)^2 - (4x - 9)^2.$$

EXERCISE 4.3

Factorise the following (1 to 17):

1 \quad (i) $4x^2 - 25y^2$ \hfill (ii) $9x^2 - 1$.

2   (i) $150 - 6a^2$ (ii) $32x^2 - 18y^2$.

3   (i) $(x - y)^2 - 9$ (ii) $9(x + y)^2 - x^2$.

4   (i) $20x^2 - 45y^2$ (ii) $9x^2 - 4(y + 2x)^2$.

5   (i) $2(x - 2y)^2 - 50y^2$ (ii) $32 - 2(x - 4)^2$.

6   (i) $108a^2 - 3(b - c)^2$ (ii) $\pi a^5 - \pi^3 ab^2$.

7   (i) $50x^2 - 2(x - 2)^2$ (ii) $(x - 2)(x + 2) + 3$.

       Hint.   (ii) $(x - 2)(x + 2) + 3 = (x^2 - 4) + 3 = x^2 - 1$.

8   (i) $x - 2y - x^2 + 4y^2$ (ii) $4a^2 - b^2 + 2a + b$.

9   (i) $a(a - 2) - b(b - 2)$ (ii) $a(a - 1) - b(b - 1)$.

10   (i) $9 - x^2 + 2xy - y^2$ (ii) $9x^4 - (x^2 + 2x + 1)$.

11   (i) $9x^4 - x^2 - 12x - 36$ (ii) $x^3 - 5x^2 - x + 5$.

12   (i) $a^4 - b^4 + 2b^2 - 1$ (ii) $x^3 - 25x$.

13   (i) $2x^4 - 32$ (ii) $a^2(b + c) - (b + c)^3$.

14   (i) $(a + b)^3 - a - b$ (ii) $x^2 - 2xy + y^2 - a^2 - 2ab - b^2$.

15   (i) $(a^2 - b^2)(c^2 - d^2) - 4abcd$ (ii) $4x^2 - y^2 - 3xy + 2x - 2y$.

       Hint.   (i) Given expression $= (ac - bd)^2 - (bc + ad)^2$.

                  (ii) Given expression $= (x^2 - y^2) + (3x^2 - 3xy) + (2x - 2y)$.

16   (i) $x^2 + \dfrac{1}{x^2} - 11$ (ii) $x^4 + 5x^2 + 9$.

17   (i) $a^4 + b^4 - 7a^2b^2$ (ii) $x^4 - 14x^2 + 1$.

18   Express each of the following as the difference of two squares:

       (i) $(x^2 - 5x + 7)(x^2 + 5x + 7)$ (ii) $(x^2 - 5x + 7)(x^2 - 5x - 7)$

       (iii) $(x^2 + 5x - 7)(x^2 - 5x + 7)$.

19   Evaluate the following by using factors:

       (i) $(979)^2 - (21)^2$ (ii) $(99 \cdot 9)^2 - (0 \cdot 1)^2$.

4.4 FACTORISATION OF TRINOMIALS

In this section, we shall learn the factorisation of trinomials of the form $ax^2 + bx + c$, where a, b and c are real numbers.

    Rule to factorise trinomial $ax^2 + bx + c$, where a, b and c are real numbers:

    Split b (the coefficient of x) into two real numbers such that the algebraic sum of these two numbers is b and their product is ac, then factorise by grouping method.

Remark

    It is not always possible to factorise a trinomial $ax^2 + bx + c$ (*i.e.* a quadratic expression); the following rule can save lot of time:

    For the expression $ax^2 + bx + c$, work out $b^2 - 4ac$. If it is a perfect square, then the given expression will factorise; otherwise, not.

Illustrative Examples

Example 1 Factorise the following trinomials:

(i) $x^2 + 9x + 18$ (ii) $y^2 - 3y - 54$.

Solution. (i) To factorise $x^2 + 9x + 18$, we want to find two real numbers whose sum is 9 and product is 18. By trial, we see that $3 + 6 = 9$ and $3 \times 6 = 18$.

$$\therefore \quad x^2 + 9x + 18 = x^2 + 3x + 6x + 18$$
$$= x(x + 3) + 6(x + 3)$$
$$= (x + 3)\,(x + 6).$$

(ii) To factorise $y^2 - 3y - 54$, we want to find two real numbers whose sum is -3 and product is -54. By trial, we see that $(-9) + 6 = -3$ and $(-9) \times 6 = -54$.

$$\therefore \quad y^2 - 3y - 54 = y^2 - 9y + 6y - 54$$
$$= y(y - 9) + 6(y - 9)$$
$$= (y - 9)\,(y + 6).$$

Example 2 Factorise the following trinomials:

(i) $6x^2 + 17x + 5$ (ii) $12x^2 - 7x + 1$

(iii) $2x^2 - 7x - 15$ (iv) $84 - 2r - 2r^2$.

Solution. (i) To factorise $6x^2 + 17x + 5$, we want to find two real numbers whose sum is 17 and product is 6×5 *i.e.* 30. By trial, we see that $2 + 15 = 17$ and $2 \times 15 = 30$.

$$\therefore \quad 6x^2 + 17x + 5 = 6x^2 + 2x + 15x + 5$$
$$= 2x(3x + 1) + 5(3x + 1)$$
$$= (3x + 1)\,(2x + 5).$$

(ii) To factorise $12x^2 - 7x + 1$, we want to find two real numbers whose sum is -7 and product is 12×1 *i.e.* 12. By trial, we see that $(-3) + (-4) = -7$ and $(-3) \times (-4) = 12$.

$$\therefore \quad 12x^2 - 7x + 1 = 12x^2 - 3x - 4x + 1$$
$$= 3x(4x - 1) - 1(4x - 1)$$
$$= (4x - 1)\,(3x - 1).$$

(iii) To factorise $2x^2 - 7x - 15$, we want to find two real numbers whose sum is -7 and product is $2 \times (-15)$ *i.e.* -30. By trial, we see that $(-10) + 3 = -7$ and $(-10) \times 3 = -30$.

$$\therefore \quad 2x^2 - 7x - 15 = 2x^2 - 10x + 3x - 15$$
$$= 2x(x - 5) + 3(x - 5)$$
$$= (x - 5)\,(2x + 3).$$

(iv) We note that $84 - 2r - 2r^2 = 2(42 - r - r^2)$.

To factorise $42 - r - r^2$, we want to find two real numbers whose sum $= -1$ and product is $42 \times (-1)$ *i.e.* -42. By trial, we see that $(-7) + 6 = -1$ and $(-7) \times 6 = -42$.

$$\therefore \quad 84 - 2r - 2r^2 = 2(42 - r - r^2)$$
$$= 2(42 - 7r + 6r - r^2)$$
$$= 2[7(6 - r) + r(6 - r)]$$
$$= 2(6 - r)\,(7 + r).$$

Example 3 Factorise the following:

(i) $7\sqrt{2}\,x^2 - 10x - 4\sqrt{2}$

(ii) $x^2 + \dfrac{1}{4}x - \dfrac{1}{8}$.

Solution. (i) To factorise $7\sqrt{2}\,x^2 - 10x - 4\sqrt{2}$, we want to find two real numbers whose sum is -10 and product is $(7\sqrt{2}) \times (-4\sqrt{2})$ i.e. -56. By trial, we see that $(-14) + 4 = -10$ and $(-14) \times 4 = -56$.

$$\therefore \quad 7\sqrt{2}\,x^2 - 10x - 4\sqrt{2} = 7\sqrt{2}\,x^2 - 14x + 4x - 4\sqrt{2}$$
$$= 7\sqrt{2}\,x(x - \sqrt{2}) + 4(x - \sqrt{2})$$
$$= (x - \sqrt{2})\,(7\sqrt{2}\,x + 4).$$

(ii) Since $\dfrac{1}{2} - \dfrac{1}{4} = \dfrac{1}{4}$ and $\dfrac{1}{2}\left(-\dfrac{1}{4}\right) = -\dfrac{1}{8}$,

$$\therefore \quad x^2 + \dfrac{1}{4}x - \dfrac{1}{8} = x^2 + \dfrac{1}{2}x - \dfrac{1}{4}x - \dfrac{1}{8}$$
$$= x\left(x + \dfrac{1}{2}\right) - \dfrac{1}{4}\left(x + \dfrac{1}{2}\right)$$
$$= \left(x + \dfrac{1}{2}\right)\left(x - \dfrac{1}{4}\right).$$

Example 4 Factorise the following:

(i) $3x^2 - 5xy - 12y^2$

(ii) $2x^3 + 5x^2y - 12xy^2$

(iii) $8(a - 2b)^2 - 2a + 4b - 1$

(iv) $9x^2 - (x^2 - 4)^2$.

Solution. (i) Since $\quad -9 + 4 = -5$ and $(-9).4 = -36$,

$$\therefore \quad 3x^2 - 5xy - 12y^2 = 3x^2 - 9xy + 4xy - 12y^2$$
$$= 3x(x - 3y) + 4y\,(x - 3y)$$
$$= (x - 3y)\,(3x + 4y).$$

(ii) $\quad 2x^3 + 5x^2y - 12xy^2 = x(2x^2 + 5xy - 12y^2)$
$$= x(2x^2 + 8xy - 3xy - 12y^2)$$
$$[\because 8 + (-3) = 5 \text{ and } 8.(-3) = -24]$$
$$= x\,[2x\,(x + 4y) - 3y\,(x + 4y)]$$
$$= x\,(x + 4y)\,(2x - 3y).$$

(iii) $8(a - 2b)^2 - 2a + 4b - 1 = 8(a - 2b)^2 - 2(a - 2b) - 1$
$$= 8x^2 - 2x - 1 \quad \text{where} \quad x = a - 2b$$
$$= 8x^2 - 4x + 2x - 1 \quad [\because -4 + 2 = -2 \text{ and } (-4).2 = -8]$$
$$= 4x(2x - 1) + 1\,(2x - 1)$$
$$= (2x - 1)\,(4x + 1)$$
$$= (2.\overline{a - 2b} - 1)\,(4.\overline{a - 2b} + 1)$$

[replacing back the value of x]

$$= (2a - 4b - 1)\,(4a - 8b + 1).$$

(iv) $\quad 9x^2 - (x^2 - 4)^2 = (3x)^2 - (x^2 - 4)^2$
$$= (3x + \overline{x^2 - 4})\,(3x - \overline{x^2 - 4})$$
$$= (x^2 + 3x - 4)\,(4 + 3x - x^2)$$
$$= (x^2 + 4x - x - 4)\,(4 + 4x - x - x^2)$$
$$= [x\,(x + 4) - 1\,(x + 4)]\,[4(1 + x) - x\,(1 + x)]$$
$$= (x + 4)\,(x - 1)\,(1 + x)\,(4 - x).$$

Example 5 Factorise the following:

    (*i*) $(x^2 - 4x)(x^2 - 4x - 1) - 20$ (*ii*) $(x - y)^2 - 7(x^2 - y^2) + 12(x + y)^2$.

Solution. (*i*) Let $x^2 - 4x = p$, then

$$(x^2 - 4x)(x^2 - 4x - 1) - 20 = p(p - 1) - 20$$
$$= p^2 - p - 20 = p^2 - 5p + 4p - 20$$
$$= p(p - 5) + 4(p - 5) = (p - 5)(p + 4)$$
$$= (x^2 - 4x - 5)(x^2 - 4x + 4).$$

Now $x^2 - 4x - 5 = x^2 - 5x + x - 5$
$$= x(x - 5) + 1(x - 5) = (x - 5)(x + 1)$$

and $x^2 - 4x + 4 = (x - 2)^2$.

∴ $(x^2 - 4x)(x^2 - 4x - 1) - 20 = (x - 5)(x + 1)(x - 2)^2$.

(*ii*) $(x - y)^2 - 7(x^2 - y^2) + 12(x + y)^2$
$$= (x - y)^2 - 7(x - y)(x + y) + 12(x + y)^2.$$

Let $x - y = p$ and $x + y = q$, then

$$(x - y)^2 - 7(x^2 - y^2) + 12(x + y)^2 = p^2 - 7pq + 12q^2$$
$$= p^2 - 4pq - 3pq + 12q^2$$
$$= p(p - 4q) - 3q(p - 4q)$$
$$= (p - 4q)(p - 3q)$$
$$= ((x - y) - 4(x + y))((x - y) - 3(x + y))$$
$$= (-3x - 5y)(-2x - 4y)$$
$$= 2(3x + 5y)(x + 2y).$$

Example 6 Factorise: $(x^2 - 3x)^2 - 8(x^2 - 3x) - 20$.

Solution. Let $x^2 - 3x = y$, then

$$(x^2 - 3x)^2 - 8(x^2 - 3x) - 20 = y^2 - 8y - 20$$
$$= y^2 - 10y + 2y - 20$$
$$= y(y - 10) + 2(y - 10)$$
$$= (y - 10)(y + 2)$$
$$= (x^2 - 3x - 10)(x^2 - 3x + 2)$$
$$= (x^2 - 5x + 2x - 10)(x^2 - 2x - x + 2)$$
$$= [x(x - 5) + 2(x - 5)][x(x - 2) - 1(x - 2)]$$
$$= (x - 5)(x + 2)(x - 2)(x - 1).$$

Example 7 Factorise: $5 - (3x^2 - 2x)(6 - 3x^2 + 2x)$.

Solution. $5 - (3x^2 - 2x)(6 - 3x^2 + 2x) = 5 - (3x^2 - 2x)(6 - \overline{3x^2 - 2x})$
$$= 5 - y(6 - y) \text{ where } y = 3x^2 - 2x$$
$$= 5 - 6y + y^2 = 5 - 5y - y + y^2$$
$$= 5(1 - y) - y(1 - y) = (1 - y)(5 - y)$$
$$= (1 - 3x^2 + 2x)(5 - 3x^2 + 2x)$$
$$= (1 + 3x - x - 3x^2)(5 + 5x - 3x - 3x^2)$$
$$= [1(1 + 3x) - x(1 + 3x)][5(1 + x) - 3x(1 + x)]$$
$$= (1 + 3x)(1 - x)(1 + x)(5 - 3x).$$

Example 8 Factorise the following:

    (*i*) $x^4 - 14x^2y^2 - 51y^4$ (*ii*) $(x^2 + x)^2 + 4(x^2 + x) - 12$.

Solution. (*i*) Since $-17 + 3 = -14$ and $(-17) \cdot 3 = -51$,

$$\therefore \quad x^4 - 14x^2y^2 - 51y^2 = x^4 - 17x^2y^2 + 3x^2y^2 - 51y^4$$
$$= x^2(x^2 - 17y^2) + 3y^2(x^2 - 17y^2)$$
$$= (x^2 - 17y^2)(x^2 + 3y^2)$$
$$= (x^2 - (\sqrt{17}\,y)^2)(x^2 + 3y^2)$$
$$= (x - \sqrt{17}\,y)(x + \sqrt{17}\,y)(x^2 + 3y^2).$$

(*ii*) $(x^2 + x)^2 + 4(x^2 + x) - 12 = y^2 + 4y - 12$ where $y = x^2 + x$

$$= y^2 + 6y - 2y - 12$$
$$= y(y + 6) - 2(y + 6)$$
$$= (y + 6)(y - 2)$$
$$= (x^2 + x + 6)(x^2 + x - 2)$$
$$= (x^2 + x + 6)(x^2 + 2x - x - 2)$$
$$= (x^2 + x + 6)[x(x + 2) - 1(x + 2)]$$
$$= (x^2 + x + 6)(x + 2)(x - 1).$$

Now compare $x^2 + x + 6$ with $ax^2 + bx + c$.

Here $a = 1$, $b = 1$ and $c = 6$.

$\therefore \quad b^2 - 4ac = 1^2 - 4 \cdot 1 \cdot 6 = -23$, which is not a perfect square.

Therefore, $x^2 + x + 6$ cannot be factorised. (See remark)

Hence $(x^2 + x)^2 + 4(x^2 + x) - 12 = (x^2 + x + 6)(x + 2)(x - 1)$.

Example 9 Factorise the following:

$$12(x^2 + 7)^2 - 8(x^2 + 7)(2x - 1) - 15(2x - 1)^2.$$

Solution. Let $x^2 + 7 = p$ and $2x - 1 = q$, then

$$12(x^2 + 7)^2 - 8(x^2 + 7)(2x - 1) - 15(2x - 1)^2$$
$$= 12p^2 - 8pq - 15q^2$$
$$= 12p^2 - 18pq + 10pq - 15q^2$$
$$= 6p(2p - 3q) + 5q(2p - 3q)$$
$$= (2p - 3q)(6p + 5q)$$
$$= (2(x^2 + 7) - 3(2x - 1))(6(x^2 + 7) + 5(2x - 1))$$
$$= (2x^2 - 6x + 17)(6x^2 + 10x + 37)$$

Note that $2x^2 - 6x + 7$ and $6x^2 + 10x + 37$ can not be factorised.

Example 10 Factorise the following:

(*i*) $125a^3 - 27b^3 + 75a^2b - 45ab^2$ (*ii*) $x^4 + 2x^3y - 2xy^3 - y^4$.

Solution. (*i*) $125a^3 - 27b^3 + 75a^2b - 45ab^2$

$$= (125a^3 + 75a^2b) - (45ab^2 + 27b^3)$$
$$= 25a^2(5a + 3b) - 9b^2(5a + 3b)$$
$$= (5a + 3b)(25a^2 - 9b^2)$$
$$= (5a + 3b)((5a)^2 - (3b)^2)$$
$$= (5a + 3b)(5a + 3b)(5a - 3b).$$

(*ii*) $x^4 + 2x^3y - 2xy^3 - y^4 = ((x^2)^2 - (y^2)^2) + 2x^3y - 2xy^3$

$$= (x^2 - y^2)(x^2 + y^2) + 2xy(x^2 - y^2)$$
$$= (x^2 - y^2)(x^2 + y^2 + 2xy)$$
$$= (x - y)(x + y)(x + y)^2$$
$$= (x - y)(x + y)(x + y)(x + y).$$

EXERCISE 4.4

Factorise the following (1 to 18):

1   (i) $x^2 + 5x + 6$ (ii) $x^2 - 8x + 7$.

2   (i) $x^2 + 6x - 7$ (ii) $y^2 + 7y - 18$.

3   (i) $y^2 - 7y - 18$ (ii) $a^2 - 3a - 54$.

4   (i) $2x^2 - 7x + 6$ (ii) $6x^2 + 13x - 5$.

5   (i) $6x^2 + 11x - 10$ (ii) $6x^2 - 7x - 3$.

6   (i) $2x^2 - x - 6$ (ii) $1 - 18y - 63y^2$.

7   (i) $2y^2 + y - 45$ (ii) $5 - 4x - 12x^2$.

8   (i) $x(12x + 7) - 10$ (ii) $(4 - x)^2 - 2x$.

     Hint.   (i) $x(12x + 7) - 10 = 12x^2 + 7x - 10$.

               (ii) $(4 - x)^2 - 2x = x^2 - 10x + 16$.

9   (i) $60x^2 - 70x - 30$ (ii) $x^2 - 6xy - 7y^2$.

10   (i) $2x^2 + 13xy - 24y^2$ (ii) $6x^2 - 5xy - 6y^2$.

11   (i) $5x^2 + 17xy - 12y^2$ (ii) $x^2y^2 - 8xy - 48$.

12   (i) $2a^2b^2 - 7ab - 30$ (ii) $a(2a - b) - b^2$.

13   (i) $(x - y)^2 - 6(x - y) + 5$ (ii) $(2x - y)^2 - 11(2x - y) + 28$.

14   (i) $4(a - 1)^2 - 4(a - 1) - 3$ (ii) $1 - 2a - 2b - 3(a + b)^2$.

15   (i) $3 - 5a - 5b - 12(a + b)^2$ (ii) $a^4 - 11a^2 + 10$.

16   (i) $(x + 4)^2 - 5xy - 20y - 6y^2$ (ii) $(x^2 - 2x)^2 - 23(x^2 - 2x) + 120$.

     Hint.   (i) $(x + 4)^2 - 5xy - 20y - 6y^2 = (x + 4)^2 - 5y(x + 4) - 6y^2$

                       $= z^2 - 5yz - 6y^2$ where $z = x + 4$

                       $= (z + y)(z - 6y)$.

17 $4(2a - 3)^2 - 3(2a - 3)(a - 1) - 7(a - 1)^2$.

     Hint.   Let $2a - 3 = x$ and $a - 1 = y$,

             then given expression $= 4x^2 - 3xy - 7y^2 = (x + y)(4x - 7y)$.

18 $(2x^2 + 5x)(2x^2 + 5x - 19) + 84$

     Hint.   Let $2x^2 + 5x = y$, then

             $(2x^2 + 5x)(2x^2 + 5x - 19) + 84 = y(y - 19) + 84$

                         $= y^2 - 19y + 84 = (y - 7)(y - 12)$.

4.5 SUM OR DIFFERENCE OF TWO CUBES

We shall use the following identities:

     $a^3 + b^3 = (a + b)(a^2 - ab + b^2)$,

     $a^3 - b^3 = (a - b)(a^2 + ab + b^2)$.

Illustrative Examples

Example 1 Resolve the following into factors:

(i) $8x^3 + 125y^3$ (ii) $27x^3 - \dfrac{343}{x^3}$ (iii) $27x^4 - 8x$.

Solution. (i) $8x^3 + 125y^3 = (2x)^3 + (5y)^3$

$$= (2x + 5y)\,[(2x)^2 - 2x.5y + (5y)^2]$$
$$= (2x + 5y)\,(4x^2 - 10xy + 25y^2).$$

(ii) $27x^3 - \dfrac{343}{x^3} = (3x)^3 - \left(\dfrac{7}{x}\right)^3$

$$= \left(3x - \dfrac{7}{x}\right)\left[(3x)^2 + 3x.\dfrac{7}{x} + \left(\dfrac{7}{x}\right)^2\right]$$

$$= \left(3x - \dfrac{7}{x}\right)\left(9x^2 + \dfrac{49}{x^2} + 21\right).$$

(iii) $27x^4 - 8x = x(27x^3 - 8) = x\,[(3x)^3 - (2)^3]$

$$= x(3x - 2)\,[(3x)^2 + 3x.2 + (2)^2]$$
$$= x(3x - 2)\,(9x^2 + 6x + 4).$$

Example 2 Factorise the following:

(i) $x^4 - 125xy^3$ (ii) $8x^3 - (2x - y)^3$.

Solution. (i) $x^4 - 125xy^3 = x(x^3 - 125y^3) = x(x^3 - (5y)^3)$

$$= x(x - 5y)\,(x^2 + x \times 5y + (5y)^2)$$
$$= x(x - 5y)\,(x^2 + 5xy + 25y^2).$$

(ii) $8x^3 - (2x - y)^3 = (2x)^3 - (2x - y)^3$

$$= (2x - \overline{2x - y})\,((2x)^2 + 2x(2x - y) + (2x - y)^2)$$
$$= y(4x^2 + 4x^2 - 2xy + 4x^2 - 4xy + y^2)$$
$$= y(12x^2 - 6xy + y^2).$$

Example 3 Factorise the following:

(i) $64 - a^3b^3 + 8 - 2ab$ (ii) $64a^6 - b^6$.

Solution. (i) $64 - a^3b^3 + 8 - 2ab = [(4)^3 - (ab)^3] + 2(4 - ab)$

$$= (4 - ab)\,(16 + 4.ab + a^2b^2) + 2\,(4 - ab)$$
$$= (4 - ab)\,(16 + 4ab + a^2b^2 + 2)$$
$$= (4 - ab)\,(18 + 4ab + a^2b^2).$$

(ii) $64a^6 - b^6 = (8a^3)^2 - (b^3)^2$

$$= (8a^3 + b^3)\,(8a^3 - b^3)$$
$$= [(2a)^3 + b^3]\,[(2a)^3 - b^3]$$
$$= (2a + b)\,(4a^2 - 2a.b + b^2)\,(2a - b)\,(4a^2 + 2a.b + b^2)$$
$$= (2a + b)\,(2a - b)\,(4a^2 - 2ab + b^2)\,(4a^2 + 2ab + b^2).$$

Example 4 Factorise the following:

(i) $a^7 - ab^6$ (ii) $27(x + y)^3 - 8(x - y)^3$.

Solution. (i) $a^7 - ab^6 = a(a^6 - b^6) = a((a^3)^2 - (b^3)^2)$

$$= a(a^3 + b^3)\,(a^3 - b^3)$$
$$= a(a + b)\,(a^2 - ab + b^2)\,(a - b)\,(a^2 + ab + b^2).$$

(ii) $27(x + y)^3 - 8(x - y)^3 = (3(x + y))^3 - (2(x - y))^3$

$$= (3(x + y) - 2(x - y)) [(3(x + y))^2$$
$$+ 3(x + y).2(x - y) + (2(x - y))^2]$$
$$= (x + 5y) [9(x^2 + 2xy + y^2) + 6(x^2 - y^2) + 4(x^2 - 2xy + y^2)]$$
$$= (x + 5y) (19x^2 + 10xy + 7y^2)$$

Example 5 Factorise the following:

(*i*) $x^3p^2 - 8y^3p^2 - 4x^3q^2 + 32y^3q^2$ (*ii*) $x^3 + 3x^2y + 3xy^2 + 2y^3$.

Solution. (*i*) $x^3p^2 - 8y^3p^2 - 4x^3q^2 + 32y^3q^2 = p^2 (x^3 - 8y^3) - 4q^2 (x^3 - 8y^3)$

$$= (x^3 - 8y^3) (p^2 - 4q^2)$$
$$= [x^3 - (2y)^3] [p^2 - (2q)^2]$$
$$= (x - 2y) (x^2 + 2xy + 4y^2) (p + 2q) (p - 2q).$$

(*ii*) $x^3 + 3x^2y + 3xy^2 + 2y^3 = (x^3 + 3x^2y + 3xy^2 + y^3) + y^3$ (Note this step)

$$= (x + y)^3 + y^3$$
$$= p^3 + y^3, \text{ where } p = x + y$$
$$= (p + y) (p^2 - py + y^2)$$
$$= (\overline{x + y} + y) [(x + y)^2 - (x + y) y + y^2]$$
$$= (x + 2y) (x^2 + 2xy + y^2 - xy - y^2 + y^2)$$
$$= (x + 2y) (x^2 + xy + y^2).$$

Example 6 Factorise the following:

(*i*) $x^3 + 3x^2 + 3x - 7$ (*ii*) $x^3 - 3x^2 + 3x + 7$.

Solution. (*i*) $x^3 + 3x^2 + 3x - 7 = (x^3 + 3x^2 + 3x + 1) - 8$ (Note this step)

$$= (x + 1)^3 - (2)^3$$
$$= \{(x + 1) - 2\} \{(x + 1)^2 + 2(x + 1) + 2^2\}$$
$$= (x - 1) (x^2 + 2x + 1 + 2x + 2 + 4)$$
$$= (x - 1) (x^2 + 4x + 7).$$

(*ii*) $x^3 - 3x^2 + 3x + 7 = (x^3 - 3x^2 + 3x - 1) + 8$ (Note this step)

$$= (x^3 - 3x^2 + 3x - 1) + 8$$
$$= (x - 1)^3 + (2)^3$$
$$= \{(x - 1) + 2\} \{(x - 1)^2 - 2(x - 1) + 2^2\}$$
$$= (x + 1) (x^2 - 2x + 1 - 2x + 2 + 4)$$
$$= (x + 1) (x^2 - 4x + 7).$$

Example 7 Factorise: $x^6 - 26x^3 - 27$.

Solution. $x^6 - 26x^3 - 27 = y^2 - 26y - 27$ where $y = x^3$

$$= y^2 - 27y + y - 27$$
$$= y (y - 27) + 1 (y - 27)$$
$$= (y - 27) (y + 1)$$
$$= (x^3 - 27) (x^3 + 1)$$
$$= [x^3 - (3)^3] [x^3 + 1^3]$$
$$= (x - 3) (x^2 + 3x + 9) (x + 1) (x^2 - x + 1).$$

EXERCISE 4.5

Factorise the following (1 to 13):

1   (i) $8x^3 + y^3$ (ii) $64x^3 - 125y^3$.

2   (i) $64x^3 + 1$ (ii) $7a^3 + 56b^3$.

3   (i) $\dfrac{x^6}{343} + \dfrac{343}{x^6}$ (ii) $8x^3 - \dfrac{1}{27y^3}$.

4   (i) $x^2 + x^5$ (ii) $32x^4 - 500x$.

5   (i) $27x^3y^3 - 8$ (ii) $27(x + y)^3 + 8(2x - y)^3$.

     Hint.   (ii) Given expression = $[3(x + y) + 2(2x - y)] [9(x + y)^2$

$$- 3(x + y).2(2x - y) + 4(2x - y)^2).$$

6   (i) $a^3 + b^3 + a + b$ (ii) $a^3 - b^3 - a + b$.

7   (i) $x^3 + x + 2$ (ii) $a^3 - a - 120$.

     Hint.   (i) $x^3 + x + 2 = (x^3 + 1) + (x + 1)$

               (ii) $a^3 - a - 120 = (a^3 - 125) - (a - 5)$.

8   (i) $x^3 + 6x^2 + 12x + 16$ (ii) $a^3 - 3a^2b + 3ab^2 - 2b^3$.

9   (i) $2a^3 + 16b^3 - 5a - 10b$ (ii) $a^3 - \dfrac{1}{a^3} - 2a + \dfrac{2}{a}$.

10   (i) $a^6 - b^6$ (ii) $x^6 - 1$.

11   (i) $64x^6 - 729y^6$ (ii) $x^2 - \dfrac{8}{x}$.

12   (i) $250 (a - b)^3 + 2$ (ii) $32a^2x^3 - 8b^2x^3 - 4a^2y^3 + b^2y^3$.

13   (i) $x^9 + y^9$ (ii) $x^6 - 7x^3 - 8$.

Multiple Choice Questions

Choose the correct answer from the given four options (1 to 14):

1   Factorisation of $12a^2b + 15ab^2$ is

     (a) $3a(4ab + 5b^2)$ (b) $3b(4a^2 + 5ab)$ (c) $3ab(4a + 5b)$ (d) none of these

2   Factorisation of $6xy - 4y + 6 - 9x$ is

     (a) $(3y - 2)(2x - 3)$ (b) $(3x - 2)(2y - 3)$ (c) $(2y - 3)(2 - 3x)$ (d) none of these

3   Factorisation of $49p^3q - 36pq$ is

     (a) $p(7p + 6q)(7p - 6q)$ (b) $q(7p - 6)(7p + 6)$

     (c) $pq(7p + 6)(7p - 6)$ (d) none of these

4   Factorisation of $y(y - z) + 9(z - y)$ is

     (a) $(y - z)(y + 9)$ (b) $(y - z)(y - 9)$ (c) $(z - y)(y + 9)$ (d) none of these

5   Factorisation of $(lm + l) + m + 1$ is

     (a) $(lm + 1)(m + l)$ (b) $(lm + m)(l + 1)$ (c) $l(m + 1)$ (d) $(l + 1)(m + 1)$

6   Factorisation of $63x^2 - 112y^2$ is

     (a) $63(x - 2y)(x + 2y)$ (b) $7(3x + 2y)(3x - 2y)$

     (c) $7(3x + 4y)(3x - 4y)$ (d) none of these

7 Factorisation of $p^4 - 81$ is

    (a) $(p^2 - 9)(p^2 + 9)$ (b) $(p - 3)(p + 3)(p^2 + 9)$

    (c) $(p - 3)^2 (p + 3)^2$ (d) none of these

8 One of the factors of $(25x^2 - 1) + (1 + 5x)^2$ is

    (a) $5 + x$ (b) $5 - x$ (c) $5x - 1$ (d) $10x$

9 Factorisation of $x^2 - 4x - 12$ is

    (a) $(x + 6)(x - 2)$ (b) $(x - 6)(x + 2)$ (c) $(x - 6)(x - 2)$ (d) $(x + 6)(x + 2)$

10 Factorisation of $3x^2 + 7x - 6$ is

    (a) $(3x - 2)(x + 3)$ (b) $(3x + 2)(x - 3)$ (c) $(3x - 2)(x - 3)$ (d) $(3x + 2)(x + 3)$

11 The factorisation of $4x^2 + 8x + 3$ is

    (a) $(x + 1)(x + 3)$ (b) $(2x + 1)(2x + 3)$

    (c) $(2x + 2)(2x + 5)$ (d) $(2x - 1)(2x - 3)$

12 Factorisation of $16x^2 + 40x + 25$ is

    (a) $(4x + 5)(4x + 5)$ (b) $(4x + 5)(4x - 5)$ (c) $(4x - 5)(4x - 5)$ (d) $(4x + 5)(4x + 7)$

13 Factorisation of $x^2 - 4xy + 4y^2$ is

    (a) $(x + 2y)(x - 2y)$ (b) $(x + 2y)(x + 2y)$ (c) $(x - 2y)(x - 2y)$ (d) $(2x - y)(2x + y)$

14 Which of the following is a factor of $(x + y)^3 - (x^3 + y^3)$?

    (a) $x^2 + xy + 2xy$ (b) $x^2 + y^2 - xy$ (c) xy^2 (d) $3xy$

Summary

○ Algebraic expressions can be expressed as the product of irreducible factors.

○ When an algebraic expression is written as the product of two or more algebraic expressions, then each of these expression is called a **factor** of the given expression.

○ The process of finding two or more algebraic expressions whose product is the given expression is called **factorisation**.

○ Factorisation is the reverse process of multiplication.

❑ Different methods of factorisation are:

    (i) Factorisation by taking out common factors.

    (ii) Factorisation by grouping of terms.

    (iii) Factorisation by using identities:

        • $a^2 - b^2 = (a + b)(a - b)$

        • $a^2 + 2ab + b^2 = (a + b)(a + b)$

        • $a^2 - 2ab + b^2 = (a - b)(a - b)$

    (iv) Factorisation of trinomials.

    (v) Factorisation by using the identities:

        $a^3 + b^3 = (a + b)(a^2 - ab + b^2)$

        $a^3 - b^3 = (a - b)(a^2 + ab + b^2).$

Factorise the following (1 to 12):

1 (i) $15(2x - 3)^3 - 10(2x - 3)$ (ii) $a(b - c)(b + c) - d(c - b)$.

2 (i) $2a^2x - bx + 2a^2 - b$ (ii) $p^2 - (a + 2b)p + 2ab$.

3 (i) $(x^2 - y^2)z + (y^2 - z^2)x$ (ii) $5a^4 - 5a^3 + 30a^2 - 30a$.

4 (i) $b(c - d)^2 + a(d - c) + 3c - 3d$ (ii) $x^3 - x^2 - xy + x + y - 1$.

5 (i) $x(x + z) - y(y + z)$ (ii) $a^{12}x^4 - a^4x^{12}$.

6 (i) $9x^2 + 12x + 4 - 16y^2$ (ii) $x^4 + 3x^2 + 4$.

Hint. (ii) $x^4 + 3x^2 + 4 = (x^2 + 2)^2 - x^2$.

7 (i) $21x^2 - 59xy + 40y^2$ (ii) $4x^3y - 44x^2y + 112xy$.

8 (i) $x^2y^2 - xy - 72$ (ii) $9x^3y + 41x^2y + 20xy^3$.

9 (i) $(3a - 2b)^2 + 3(3a - 2b) - 10$ (ii) $(x^2 - 3x)(x^2 - 3x + 7) + 10$.

Hint. (ii) Given expression $= y(y + 7) + 10$ where $y = x^2 - 3x$

$$= y^2 + 7y + 10 = (y + 5)(y + 2).$$

10 (i) $(x^2 - x)(4x^2 - 4x - 5) - 6$ (ii) $x^4 + 9x^2y^2 + 81y^4$.

Hint. (ii) $x^4 + 9x^2y^2 + 81y^4 = (x^4 + 18x^2y^2 + 81y^4) - 9x^2y^2$

$$= (x^2 + 9y^2)^2 - (3xy)^2.$$

11 (i) $\dfrac{8}{27}x^3 - \dfrac{1}{8}y^3$ (ii) $x^6 + 63x^3 - 64$.

12 (i) $x^3 + x^2 - \dfrac{1}{x^2} + \dfrac{1}{x^3}$ (ii) $(x + 1)^6 - (x - 1)^6$.

Hint. (ii) Let $x + 1 = a$, $x - 1 = b$.

Given expression $= a^6 - b^6 = (a^3 - b^3)(a^3 + b^3)$

$$= (a - b)(a^2 + ab + b^2)(a + b)(a^2 - ab + b^2).$$

13 Show that $97^3 + 14^3$ is divisible by 111.

14 If $a + b = 8$ and $ab = 15$, find the value of $a^4 + a^2b^2 + b^4$.

Hint. $a^4 + a^2b^2 + b^4 = (a^2 + b^2)^2 - a^2b^2$.

5 Simultaneous Linear Equations

INTRODUCTION

In previous classes, we have read that an equation of the form $ax + b = 0$, where a, b are real numbers and $a \neq 0$, is called a linear equation in one variable. We have also learnt that every linear equation in one variable has a unique solution.

In this chapter, we shall extend our knowledge of linear equations in one variable to linear equations in two variables and we shall also learn the various methods of solving a pair or a system of two linear equations in two variables.

5.1 SIMULTANEOUS LINEAR EQUATIONS

Linear equation in two variables

*An equation of the form $ax + by + c = 0$, where a, b and c are real numbers and a and b are non-zero, is called a **general linear equation** in the two variables x and y.*

For example, $x + y - 3 = 0$ is a linear equation in the two variables (unknowns) x and y.

Solution of a linear equation in two variables

$x = \alpha$ and $y = \beta$ is a solution of the linear equation $ax + by + c = 0$ if and only if $a\alpha + b\beta + c = 0$, where α, β are real numbers.

Every linear equation in two variables has an unlimited number of solutions.

For example, $x = 0$, $y = 3$; $x = 1$, $y = 2$; $x = 2$, $y = 1$; $x = 3$, $y = 0$ and $x = 7$, $y = -4$ etc. are *all solutions* of the equation $x + y - 3 = 0$.

System of simultaneous linear equations

Let us consider two linear equations in two variables,

$$a_1x + b_1y + c_1 = 0$$
$$a_2x + b_2y + c_2 = 0.$$

These two equations are said to form a **system of simultaneous linear equations.**

For example,

$$x + y - 3 = 0$$
$$2x - 5y + 1 = 0$$

is a system of two simultaneous linear equations in the two variables x and y.

*A **solution** to a system of two simultaneous linear equations in two variables is an ordered pair of numbers which satisfy both the equations.*

For the above example, $x = 2$, $y = 1$ is a solution to the system of simultaneous linear equations. We can check this by substituting $x = 2$, $y = 1$ into each of these two equations.

If there is *only one* such solution, then the system of linear equations is said to be **consistent** and **independent.** In this book, we shall be dealing only with such a system of simultaneous linear equations.

The various methods of solving a pair or a system of linear equations are:

  (*i*) Substitution method.

  (*ii*) Elimination method.

  (*iii*) Cross-multiplication method.

We shall discuss these methods one by one.

5.2 SUBSTITUTION METHOD

Procedure:

  (*i*) Solve one of the given equations for one of the variables, whichever is convenient.

  (*ii*) Substitute that value of the variable in the *other* equation.

  (*iii*) Solve the resulting single variable equation. Substitute this value into either of the two *original* equations, and solve it to find the value of the second variable.

Remark

The solution may be checked by substituting in both the original equations.

Illustrative Examples

Example 1 Solve the following system of linear equations:
$$4x - 3y = 8$$
$$x - 2y = -3.$$

Solution. The given equations are

$$4x - 3y = 8 \qquad \qquad \dots(i)$$
$$x - 2y = -3 \qquad \qquad \dots(ii)$$

We can solve either equation for either variable. But to avoid fractions, we solve the second equation for x,

$$x = 2y - 3 \qquad \qquad \dots(iii)$$

Substituting this value of x in equation (*i*), we get

$$4(2y - 3) - 3y = 8$$
$$\Rightarrow \quad 8y - 12 - 3y = 8$$
$$\Rightarrow \quad 5y = 20 \quad \Rightarrow \quad y = 4.$$

Substituting this value of y in (*ii*), we get

$$x - 2 \times 4 = -3 \quad \Rightarrow \quad x - 8 = -3 \quad \Rightarrow \quad x = 5.$$

Hence, the solution is $x = 5$, $y = 4$.

Example 2 Solve the following system of linear equations:
$$8x + 5y = 9$$
$$3x + 2y = 4.$$

Solution. The given system of simultaneous linear equations is

$$8x + 5y = 9 \qquad \qquad \dots(i)$$
$$3x + 2y = 4 \qquad \qquad \dots(ii)$$

From equation (*ii*), we get

$$2y = 4 - 3x \Rightarrow y = \frac{4 - 3x}{2}.$$

Substituting this value of y in equation (*i*), we get

$$8x + 5 \cdot \frac{4 - 3x}{2} = 9$$

$$\Rightarrow \quad 16x + 20 - 15x = 18 \Rightarrow x + 20 = 18$$

$$\Rightarrow \quad x = -2.$$

Substituting this value of x in equation (*ii*), we get

$$3 \times (-2) + 2y = 4$$

$$\Rightarrow \quad -6 + 2y = 4 \Rightarrow 2y = 10 \Rightarrow y = 5.$$

Hence, the solution is $x = -2$, $y = 5$.

Example 3 Solve the following pair of linear equations:

$$\frac{3x}{2} - \frac{5y}{3} = -2$$

$$\frac{x}{3} + \frac{y}{2} = \frac{13}{6}.$$

Solution. The given equations are:

$$\frac{3x}{2} - \frac{5y}{3} = -2 \quad \dots(i) \qquad \text{and} \qquad \frac{x}{3} + \frac{y}{2} = \frac{13}{6} \qquad \dots(ii)$$

Multiplying both sides of the equations (*i*) and (*ii*) by 6, we get

$$9x - 10y = -12 \quad \dots(iii) \qquad \text{and} \qquad 2x + 3y = 13 \qquad \dots(iv)$$

From equation (*iv*), we get $y = \dfrac{13 - 2x}{3}$ $\qquad \dots(v)$

Substituting this value of y in equation (*iii*), we get

$$9x - 10 \left(\frac{13 - 2x}{3} \right) = -12$$

$$\Rightarrow \quad 27x - 130 + 20x = -36 \qquad \text{(Multiplying both sides by 3)}$$

$$\Rightarrow \quad 47x = 94 \Rightarrow x = 2.$$

Substituting this value of x in equation (*v*), we get

$$y = \frac{13 - 2 \times 2}{3} = \frac{13 - 4}{3} = \frac{9}{3} = 3.$$

Hence, the solution is $x = 2$ and $y = 3$.

Example 4 Solve the following pairs of linear equations by substitution method:

(*i*) $0.2x + 0.3y = 1.3$ $\qquad\qquad$ (*ii*) $\sqrt{2}x + \sqrt{3}y = 0$

 $0.4x + 0.5y = 2.3$ $\qquad\qquad\qquad$ $\sqrt{3}x - \sqrt{8}y = 0$

Solution. (*i*) The given equations are:

$$0.2x + 0.3y = 1.3 \quad \dots(1) \qquad \text{and} \qquad 0.4x + 0.5y = 2.3 \qquad \dots(2)$$

Multiplying both sides of equations (1) and (2) by 10, we get

$$2x + 3y = 13 \quad \dots(3) \qquad\qquad 4x + 5y = 23 \qquad \dots(4)$$

From equation (3), we get $x = \dfrac{13 - 3y}{2}$ $\qquad \dots(5)$

Substituting this value of x in equation (4), we get

$$4 \left(\frac{13 - 3y}{2} \right) + 5y = 23$$

$\Rightarrow \quad 26 - 6y + 5y = 23$

$\Rightarrow \quad -y = -3 \Rightarrow y = 3.$

Substituting this value of y in equation (5), we get

$$x = \frac{13 - 3 \times 3}{2} = \frac{13 - 9}{2} = \frac{4}{2} = 2.$$

Hence, the solution is $x = 2$ and $y = 3$.

(ii) The given equations are:

$$\sqrt{2}x + \sqrt{3}y = 0 \qquad \dots(1) \qquad \text{and} \qquad \sqrt{3}x - \sqrt{8}y = 0 \qquad \dots(2)$$

From equation (2), $x = \dfrac{\sqrt{8}}{\sqrt{3}}y$ $\qquad \dots(3)$

Substituting this value of x in equation (1), we get

$$\sqrt{2} \cdot \frac{\sqrt{8}}{\sqrt{3}}y + \sqrt{3}y = 0$$

$\Rightarrow \quad \sqrt{16}y + 3y = 0 \qquad\qquad\qquad$ (Multiplying both sides by $\sqrt{3}$)

$\Rightarrow \quad 4y + 3y = 0 \Rightarrow 7y = 0 \Rightarrow y = 0$

Substituting this value of y in equation (3), we get

$$x = \frac{\sqrt{8}}{\sqrt{3}} \times 0 \Rightarrow x = 0$$

Hence, the solution is $x = 0, y = 0$.

Example 5 Solve the following pair of linear equations for x and y:

$\dfrac{b}{a}x + \dfrac{a}{b}y = a^2 + b^2$ and $x + y = 2ab$.

Solution. The given pair of linear equations is

$$\frac{b}{a}x + \frac{a}{b}y = a^2 + b^2 \quad \dots(i) \qquad \text{and} \qquad x + y = 2ab \qquad \dots(ii)$$

From (ii), $y = 2ab - x$ $\qquad \dots(iii)$

Substituting this value of y in (i), we get

$$\frac{b}{a}x + \frac{a}{b}(2ab - x) = a^2 + b^2$$

$\Rightarrow \quad b^2x + a^2(2ab - x) = ab(a^2 + b^2) \qquad$ (Multiplying both sides by ab)

$\Rightarrow \quad b^2x + 2a^3b - a^2x = a^3b + ab^3$

$\Rightarrow \quad (b^2 - a^2)x = ab^3 - a^3b$

$\Rightarrow \quad (b^2 - a^2)\, x = ab(b^2 - a^2) \Rightarrow x = ab$

From (iii), $y = 2ab - ab = ab$

Hence, the solution is $x = ab$ and $y = ab$.

Example 6 Solve $2x + 3y = 11$ and $2x - 4y = -24$. Hence, find the value of 'm' for which $y = mx + 3$.

Solution. The given equations are

$$2x + 3y = 11 \qquad \dots(i) \qquad \text{and} \qquad 2x - 4y = -24 \qquad \dots(ii)$$

From equation (ii), we get $x = \dfrac{4y - 24}{2}$

$\Rightarrow \quad x = 2y - 12$ $\qquad \dots(iii)$

Substituting this value of x in equation (i), we get

$$2(2y - 12) + 3y = 11$$

$\Rightarrow \quad 4y + 3y - 24 = 11 \Rightarrow 7y = 35 \Rightarrow y = 5.$

Substituting this value of y in equation (iii), we get

$x = 2 \times 5 - 12 = 10 - 12 = -2$.

Hence, the solution is $x = -2$ and $y = 5$.

Now, $y = mx + 3$ ...(iv)

Putting $x = -2$ and $y = 5$ in (iv), we get

$5 = m(-2) + 3 \Rightarrow 2m = 3 - 5$

$\Rightarrow \quad 2m = -2 \Rightarrow m = -1$.

Hence, the value of m is -1.

EXERCISE 5.1

Solve the following systems of simultaneous linear equations by the substitution method (1 to 4):

1 (i) $x + y = 14$

$x - y = 4$

     (ii) $s - t = 3$

$\dfrac{s}{3} + \dfrac{t}{2} = 6$

   (iii) $2x + 3y = 9$

$3x + 4y = 5$

     (iv) $3x - 5y = 4$

$9x - 2y = 7$.

2 (i) $a + 3b = 5$

$7a - 8b = 6$

     (ii) $5x + 4y - 4 = 0$

$x - 20 = 12y$.

3 (i) $2x - \dfrac{3y}{4} = 3$

$5x - 2y - 7 = 0$

     (ii) $2x + 3y = 23$

$5x - 20 = 8y$.

4 (i) $mx - ny = m^2 + n^2$

$x + y = 2m$

     (ii) $\dfrac{2x}{a} + \dfrac{y}{b} = 2$

$\dfrac{x}{a} - \dfrac{y}{b} = 4$.

5   Solve $2x + y = 35$, $3x + 4y = 65$. Hence, find the value of $\dfrac{x}{y}$.

6   Solve the simultaneous equations $3x - y = 5$, $4x - 3y = -1$. Hence, find p, if $y = px - 3$.

5.3 ELIMINATION METHOD

Now let us consider another method of eliminating (removing) one variable. This method is sometimes more convenient than substitution method.

Procedure:

(i) Multiply one or both equations (if necessary) by a suitable number(s) to transform them so that addition or subtraction will eliminate one variable.

(ii) Solve the resulting single variable equation and substitute this value into either of the two original equations, and solve it to find the value of the second variable.

Remark

In particular, if the coefficient of x in the first equation is numerically equal to the coefficient of y in the second equation and the coefficient of y in the first equation is numerically equal to the coefficient of x in the second equation, then add and subtract the given equations. This gives the values of $x + y$ and $x - y$. Then find the values of x and y. (See example 5)

Illustrative Examples

Example 1 Solve the following system of simultaneous linear equations:

(i) $x + y = 5$
$2x - 3y = 4$

(ii) $\dfrac{x}{2} + \dfrac{2y}{3} = -1$
$x - \dfrac{y}{3} = 3.$

Solution. (i) The given equations are:

$$x + y = 5 \qquad \ldots(1) \qquad\qquad 2x - 3y = 4 \qquad \ldots(2)$$

Multiplying both sides of equation (1) by 3, we get

$$3x + 3y = 15 \qquad \ldots(3)$$

On adding equations (2) and (3), we get

$$5x = 19 \implies x = \frac{19}{5}.$$

Substituting this value of x in (1), we get

$$\frac{19}{5} + y = 5 \implies y = 5 - \frac{19}{5} \implies y = \frac{6}{5}.$$

Hence, the solution is $x = \dfrac{19}{5}$ and $y = \dfrac{6}{5}$.

(ii) The given equations are:

$$\frac{x}{2} + \frac{2y}{3} = -1 \qquad \ldots(1) \qquad \text{and} \qquad x - \frac{y}{3} = 3 \qquad \ldots(2)$$

Multiplying both sides of equation (2) by 2, we get

$$2x - \frac{2y}{3} = 6 \qquad \ldots(3)$$

On adding equations (1) and (3), we get

$$\frac{x}{2} + 2x = 5 \implies \frac{5}{2}x = 5 \implies x = 2.$$

Substituting this value of x in (2), we get

$$2 - \frac{y}{3} = 3 \implies -\frac{y}{3} = 1 \implies y = -3.$$

Hence, the solution is $x = 2$ and $y = -3$.

Example 2 Solve the following system of simultaneous linear equations:

(i) $\dfrac{x}{3} + \dfrac{y}{4} = 4$
$\dfrac{5x}{6} - \dfrac{y}{8} = 4$

(ii) $4x + \dfrac{6}{y} = 15$
$6x - \dfrac{8}{y} = 14, \ y \neq 0.$

Solution. (i) The given equations are:

$$\frac{x}{3} + \frac{y}{4} = 4 \qquad \ldots(1) \qquad \text{and} \qquad \frac{5x}{6} - \frac{y}{8} = 4 \qquad \ldots(2)$$

Multiplying equation (1) by 12 and equation (2) by 24, we get

$$4x + 3y = 48 \qquad \ldots(3) \qquad \text{and} \qquad 20x - 3y = 96 \qquad \ldots(4)$$

On adding equations (3) and (4), we get

$$24x = 144 \implies x = 6.$$

Substituting this value of x in (3), we get

$$4 \times 6 + 3y = 48 \implies 3y = 24 \implies y = 8.$$

Hence, the solution is $x = 6$ and $y = 8$.

(*ii*) The given equation are:

$$4x + \frac{6}{y} = 15 \qquad ...(1) \qquad \text{and} \qquad 6x - \frac{8}{y} = 14 \qquad ...(2)$$

Multiplying equation (1) by 4 and equation (2) by 3, we get

$$16x + \frac{24}{y} = 60 \qquad ...(3) \qquad \text{and} \qquad 18x - \frac{24}{y} = 42 \qquad ...(4)$$

On adding equations (3) and (4), we get

$$34x = 102 \Rightarrow x = 3.$$

Substituting this value of x in equation (1), we get

$$4 \times 3 + \frac{6}{y} = 15 \Rightarrow \frac{6}{y} = 15 - 12$$

$$\Rightarrow \quad \frac{6}{y} = 3 \Rightarrow 3y = 6 \Rightarrow y = 2.$$

Hence, the solution is $x = 3$ and $y = 2$.

Example 3 Solve the following pairs of linear equations:

(*i*) $x + y = 3 \cdot 3$

$$\frac{0 \cdot 6}{3x - 2y} = -1, \ 3x - 2y \neq 0$$

(*ii*) $\frac{x}{a} + \frac{y}{b} = a + b$

$$\frac{x}{a^2} + \frac{y}{b^2} = 2, \ a \neq 0, \ b \neq 0.$$

Solution. (*i*) The given equations are:

$$x + y = 3 \cdot 3 \qquad ...(1) \qquad \frac{0 \cdot 6}{3x - 2y} = -1 \qquad ...(2)$$

The equation (2) can be written as

$$3x - 2y = -0 \cdot 6 \qquad \qquad ...(3)$$

Multiplying equation (1) by 2, we get

$$2x + 2y = 6 \cdot 6 \qquad \qquad ...(4)$$

On adding equations (3) and (4), we get

$$5x = 6 \Rightarrow \ x = \frac{6}{5} \ \Rightarrow \ x = 1 \cdot 2$$

Substituting this value of x in equation (1), we get

$$1 \cdot 2 + y = 3 \cdot 3 \ \Rightarrow y = 2 \cdot 1$$

Hence, the solution is $x = 1 \cdot 2$ and $y = 2 \cdot 1$

(*ii*) The given equations are:

$$\frac{x}{a} + \frac{y}{b} = a + b \qquad ...(1) \qquad \text{and} \qquad \frac{x}{a^2} + \frac{y}{b^2} = 2 \qquad ...(2)$$

On multiplying equation (2) by b, we get

$$\frac{bx}{a^2} + \frac{y}{b} = 2b \qquad \qquad ...(3)$$

On subtracting equation (3) from (1), we get

$$\left(\frac{1}{a} - \frac{b}{a^2} \right) x = a - b$$

$$\Rightarrow \quad \frac{a - b}{a^2} x = a - b \ \Rightarrow x = a^2$$

Substituting this value of x in equation (2), we get

$$\frac{a^2}{a^2} + \frac{y}{b^2} = 2 \Rightarrow 1 + \frac{y^2}{b^2} = 2 \Rightarrow \frac{y^2}{b^2} = 1 \Rightarrow y = b^2.$$

Hence, the solution is $x = a^2$ and $y = b^2$

Example 4 Solve the following pairs of linear equations:

$(a - b)x + (a + b)y = a^2 - 2ab - b^2$

$(a + b) (x + y) = a^2 + b^2$

Solution. The given equations are:

$$(a - b)x + (a + b)y = a^2 - 2ab - b^2 \qquad \ldots(i)$$

$$(a + b) (x + y) = a^2 + b^2 \qquad \ldots(ii)$$

Equation (ii) can be written as

$$(a + b)x + (a + b)y = a^2 + b^2 \qquad \ldots(iii)$$

Subtracting equation (i) from equation (iii), we get

$$2bx = 2ab + 2b^2 \Rightarrow x = a + b$$

Substituting $x = a + b$ in equation (iii), we get

$$(a + b) (a + b) + (a + b)y = a^2 + b^2$$

$$\Rightarrow \quad a^2 + b^2 + 2ab + (a + b)y = a^2 + b^2$$

$$\Rightarrow \quad (a + b) y = -2ab \Rightarrow y = -\frac{2ab}{a+b}$$

Hence, the solution is $x = a + b$ and $y = -\frac{2ab}{a+b}$.

Example 5 Solve: $83x - 67y = 383$

$67x - 83y = 367.$

Solution. Given $\quad 83x - 67y = 383 \qquad \ldots(i)$

$$67x - 83y = 367 \qquad \ldots(ii)$$

Adding (i) and (ii), we get

$$150x - 150y = 750$$

$$\Rightarrow \qquad x - y = 5 \qquad \ldots(iii)$$

Subtracting (ii) from (i), we get

$$16x + 16y = 16$$

$$\Rightarrow \qquad x + y = 1 \qquad \ldots(iv)$$

On adding (iii) and (iv), we get

$$2x = 6 \quad \Rightarrow \quad x = 3.$$

Substituting $x = 3$ in equation (iv), we get

$$3 + y = 1 \quad \Rightarrow \quad y = -2.$$

Hence, the solution is $x = 3$, $y = -2$.

Example 6 Solve : $\dfrac{3x - 7}{2} - \dfrac{2y - 8}{3} = -1,\ \dfrac{5 - x}{3} - \dfrac{3 - 2y}{7} = 1.$

Solution. Given $\quad \dfrac{3x - 7}{2} - \dfrac{2y - 8}{3} = -1 \qquad \ldots(i)$

$$\dfrac{5 - x}{3} - \dfrac{3 - 2y}{7} = 1 \qquad \ldots(ii)$$

To clear fractions, multiplying equation (i) by 6 and equation (ii) by 21, we get

$$3(3x - 7) - 2(2y - 8) = -6 \Rightarrow -9x - 4y + 1 = 0 \qquad \ldots(iii)$$

$$7(5 - x) - 3(3 - 2y) = 21 \Rightarrow -7x + 6y + 5 = 0 \qquad \ldots(iv)$$

On multiplying equation (iii) by 3 and equation (iv) by 2, we get

$$27x - 12y + 3 = 0 \qquad \ldots(v)$$

$$-14x + 12y + 10 = 0 \qquad \ldots(vi)$$

On adding (v) and (vi), we get
$$13x + 13 = 0 \Rightarrow 13x = -13 \Rightarrow x = -1.$$
Substituting $x = -1$ in (iv), we get
$$-7(-1) + 6y + 5 = 0 \Rightarrow 6y = -12 \Rightarrow y = -2.$$
Hence, the solution is $x = -1$, $y = -2$.

Example 7 Can the following equations hold simultaneously?
$$\frac{x}{2} + \frac{5y}{3} = 12, \frac{5x}{4} - \frac{y}{6} = 4 \text{ and } 7x - 3y = 10.$$
If so, find x and y.

Solution. The given equations are

$$\frac{x}{2} + \frac{5y}{3} = 12 \qquad \text{...(i)} \qquad\qquad \frac{5x}{4} - \frac{y}{6} = 4 \qquad\qquad \text{...(ii)}$$

$$7x - 3y = 10 \qquad \text{...(iii)}$$

Let us solve the first two equations simultaneously. To clear fractions, multiplying equation (i) by 6 and equation (ii) by 12, we get

$$3x + 10y = 72 \qquad\qquad\qquad \text{...(iv)}$$
$$15x - 2y = 48 \qquad\qquad\qquad \text{...(v)}$$

On multiplying equation (v) by 5, we get
$$75x - 10y = 240 \qquad\qquad\qquad \text{...(vi)}$$
On adding (iv) and (vi), we get
$$78x = 312 \Rightarrow x = 4.$$
Substituting $x = 4$ in (iv), we get
$$3 \times 4 + 10y = 72 \Rightarrow 10y = 60 \Rightarrow y = 6.$$
Thus $x = 4$ and $y = 6$ is the solution of (i) and (ii).

Putting $x = 4$ and $y = 6$ in equation (iii), we get
$$7 \times 4 - 3 \times 6 = 10 \Rightarrow 28 - 18 = 10 \Rightarrow 10 = 10, \text{ which is true.}$$
Therefore, the three given equations can hold simultaneously *i.e.* they are **consistent** and the solution is $x = 4$ and $y = 6$.

Note If the values of x and y obtained from two equations do not satisfy the third, then the three equations cannot hold simultaneously and we conclude that the three equations are **inconsistent**.

EXERCISE 5.2

Solve the following systems of simultaneous linear equations by the elimination method (1 to 9):

1   (i) $3x + 4y = 10$ (ii) $2x = 5y + 4$

              $2x - 2y = 2$ $3x - 2y + 16 = 0.$

2   (i) $\frac{3}{4}x - \frac{2}{3}y = 1$ (ii) $2x - 3y - 3 = 0$

              $\frac{3}{8}x - \frac{1}{6}y = 1$ $\frac{2x}{3} + 4y + \frac{1}{2} = 0.$

3   (i) $15x - 14y = 117$ (ii) $41x + 53y = 135$

              $14x - 15y = 115$ $53x + 41y = 147.$

4   (i) $\dfrac{x}{6} = y - 6$

   $\dfrac{3x}{4} = 1 + y$

   (ii) $x - \dfrac{2}{3}y = \dfrac{8}{3}$

   $\dfrac{2x}{5} - y = \dfrac{7}{5}$.

5   (i) $9 - (x - 4) = y + 7$

   $2(x + y) = 4 - 3y$

   (ii) $2x + \dfrac{x - y}{6} = 2$

   $x - \dfrac{2x + y}{3} = 1$.

6 $x - 3y = 3x - 1 = 2x - y$.

   Hint. $x - 3y = 3x - 1 = 2x - y$

   $\Rightarrow$ $x - 3y = 3x - 1,\ 3x - 1 = 2x - y$.

7   (i) $4x + \dfrac{x - y}{8} = 17$

   $2y + x - \dfrac{5y + 2}{3} = 2$

   (ii) $\dfrac{x + 1}{2} + \dfrac{y - 1}{3} = 8$

   $\dfrac{x - 1}{3} + \dfrac{y + 1}{2} = 9$.

8   (i) $\dfrac{3}{x} + 4y = 7$

   $\dfrac{5}{x} + 6y = 13$

   (ii) $5x - 9 = \dfrac{1}{y}$

   $x + \dfrac{1}{y} = 3$.

9   (i) $px + qy = p - q$

   $qx - py = p + q$

   (ii) $\dfrac{x}{a} - \dfrac{y}{b} = 0$

   $ax + by = a^2 + b^2$.

10 Solve $2x + y = 23$, $4x - y = 19$. Hence, find the values of $x - 3y$ and $5y - 2x$.

11 The expression $ax + by$ has value 7 when $x = 2$, $y = 1$. When $x = -1$, $y = 1$, it has value 1, find a and b.

12 Can the following equations hold simultaneously?

   $3x - 7y = 7$

   $11x + 5y = 87$

   $5x + 4y = 43$.

   If so, find x and y.

5.4 CROSS-MULTIPLICATION METHOD

Let the system of simultaneous linear equations be

   $a_1x + b_1y + c_1 = 0$

   $a_2x + b_2y + c_2 = 0$.

To solve this system of linear equation by cross-multiplication method:

Write the coefficients of the pair of linear equations

   $a_1x + b_1y + c_1 = 0$

   $a_2x + b_2y + c_2 = 0$

as

The arrows between the two numbers indicate that they are to be multiplied. The down arrows ($\searrow$) show the term with a plus sign and up arrows ($\nearrow$) show the term with a negative sign.

The solution is given by

$$\frac{x}{b_1c_2 - b_2c_1} = \frac{y}{c_1a_2 - c_2a_1} = \frac{1}{a_1b_2 - a_2b_1}$$

$$\Rightarrow \quad x = \frac{b_1c_2 - b_2c_1}{a_1b_2 - a_2b_1}, y = \frac{c_1a_2 - c_2a_1}{a_1b_2 - a_2b_1}.$$

Illustrative Examples

Example 1 Solve the following pairs of linear equations by cross-multiplication method:

(i) $2x + y = 5$
    $3x + 2y = 8$

(ii) $x - 3y - 7 = 0$
    $3x - 3y = 15.$

Solution. (i) The given equations can be written as

$2x + y - 5 = 0$ and $3x + 2y - 8 = 0$

To solve the given pair of equations by cross-multiplication method, write the coefficients of the pair of these linear equations as

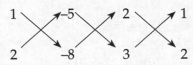

$\therefore \quad \dfrac{x}{1 \times (-8) - 2 \times (-5)} = \dfrac{y}{(-5) \times 3 - (-8) \times 2} = \dfrac{1}{2 \times 2 - 3 \times 1}$

$\Rightarrow \quad \dfrac{x}{-8 + 10} = \dfrac{y}{-15 + 16} = \dfrac{1}{4 - 3}$

$\Rightarrow \quad \dfrac{x}{2} = \dfrac{y}{1} = \dfrac{1}{1} \Rightarrow x = 2$ and $y = 1.$

Hence, the solution is $x = 2$ and $y = 1.$

(ii) The given equations can be written as

$x - 3y - 7 = 0$ and $3x - 3y - 15 = 0.$

To solve the given pair of linear equations by cross-multiplication method, write the coefficients of these equations as

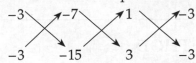

$\therefore \quad \dfrac{x}{(-3)(-15) - (-3)(-7)} = \dfrac{y}{(-7) \times 3 - (-15) \times 1} = \dfrac{1}{1 \times (-3) - 3 \times (-3)}$

$\Rightarrow \quad \dfrac{x}{45 - 21} = \dfrac{y}{-21 + 15} = \dfrac{1}{-3 + 9}$

$\Rightarrow \quad \dfrac{x}{24} = \dfrac{y}{-6} = \dfrac{1}{6}$

$\Rightarrow \quad x = \dfrac{24}{6} = 4$ and $y = \dfrac{-6}{6} = -1.$

Hence, the solution is $x = 4$ and $y = -1.$

Example 2 Solve the following system of linear equations by cross-multiplication method:

$$2(ax - by) + (a + 4b) = 0$$
$$2(bx + ay) + (b - 4a) = 0, a^2 + b^2 \neq 0.$$

Solution. The given linear equations are

$$2ax - 2by + (a + 4b) = 0$$
$$2bx + 2ay + (b - 4a) = 0.$$

Write the coefficients of the pair of these linear equations as

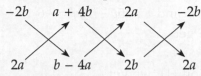

$$\begin{array}{cccc} -2b & a + 4b & 2a & -2b \\ 2a & b - 4a & 2b & 2a \end{array}$$

By cross-multiplication method, the solution is given by

$$\frac{x}{-2b(b-4a) - 2a(a+4b)} = \frac{y}{(a+4b)2b - (b-4a)2a} = \frac{1}{2a.2a - 2b.(-2b)}$$

$$\Rightarrow \quad \frac{x}{-2b^2 - 2a^2} = \frac{y}{8b^2 + 8a^2} = \frac{1}{4a^2 + 4b^2}$$

$$\Rightarrow \quad \frac{x}{-2(a^2 + b^2)} = \frac{y}{8(a^2 + b^2)} = \frac{1}{4(a^2 + b^2)}$$

$$\Rightarrow \quad \frac{x}{-2} = \frac{y}{8} = \frac{1}{4}$$

$$\Rightarrow \quad x = -\frac{2}{4} \text{ and } y = \frac{8}{4} \Rightarrow x = -\frac{1}{2} \text{ and } y = 2.$$

Hence, the solution is $x = -\dfrac{1}{2}$, $y = 2$.

EXERCISE 5.3

1 Solve the following systems of simultaneous linear equations by cross-multiplication method:

    (i) $3x + 2y = 4$
        $8x + 5y = 9$

    (ii) $3x - 7y + 10 = 0$
          $y - 2x = 3.$

2 Solve the following pairs of linear equations by cross-multiplication method:

    (i) $x - y = a + b$
        $ax + by = a^2 - b^2$

    (ii) $2bx + ay = 2ab$
          $bx - ay = 4ab.$

5.5 EQUATIONS REDUCIBLE TO PAIR OF LINEAR EQUATIONS

In this section, we shall find solutions of such pairs of equations in two variables which are not linear but can be reduced to linear equations in two variables by making some suitable substitutions. We shall explain the process with the help of some examples.

Illustrative Examples

Example 1 Solve the following pairs of equations by reducing them to pairs of linear equations:

    (i) $\dfrac{2}{x} + \dfrac{3}{y} = 13$

        $\dfrac{5}{x} - \dfrac{4}{y} = -2$

    (ii) $\dfrac{1}{2x} + \dfrac{1}{3y} = 2$

        $\dfrac{1}{3x} + \dfrac{1}{2y} = \dfrac{13}{6}.$

Solution. (*i*) Substituting $\frac{1}{x} = p$ and $\frac{1}{y} = q$ in the given equations, we get

$$2p + 3q = 13 \qquad \ldots(1) \qquad \text{and} \qquad 5p - 4q = -2 \qquad \ldots(2)$$

Multiplying equation (1) by 4 and equation (2) by 3, we get

$$8p + 12q = 52 \qquad \ldots(3) \qquad \text{and} \qquad 15p - 12q = -6 \qquad \ldots(4)$$

On adding equations (3) and (4), we get

$$23p = 46 \implies p = 2.$$

Substituting this value of p in equation (1), we get

$$2 \times 2 + 3q = 13 \implies 3q = 9 \implies q = 3.$$

$$\therefore \quad \frac{1}{x} = 2 \text{ and } \frac{1}{y} = 3 \implies x = \frac{1}{2} \text{ and } y = \frac{1}{3}.$$

Hence, the solution of the given pair of equations is

$$x = \frac{1}{2} \text{ and } y = \frac{1}{3}.$$

(*ii*) Substituting $\frac{1}{x} = u$ and $\frac{1}{y} = v$ in the given equations, we get

$$\frac{1}{2}u + \frac{1}{3}v = 2 \text{ i.e. } 3u + 2v = 12 \qquad \ldots(1)$$

and $\quad \frac{1}{3}u + \frac{1}{2}v = \frac{13}{6} \text{ i.e. } 2u + 3v = 13 \qquad \ldots(2)$

On adding equations (3) and (4), we get

$$5u + 5v = 25 \implies u + v = 5 \qquad \ldots(3)$$

On subtracting equation (2) from equation (1), we get

$$u - v = -1 \qquad \ldots(4)$$

On adding equations (3) and (4), we get

$$2u = 4 \implies u = 2.$$

On substituting this value of u in (3), we get

$$2 + v = 5 \implies v = 3.$$

$$\therefore \quad \frac{1}{x} = 2 \text{ and } \frac{1}{y} = 3 \implies x = \frac{1}{2} \text{ and } y = \frac{1}{3}.$$

Hence, the solution of the given pair of equations is $x = \frac{1}{2}$ and $y = \frac{1}{3}$.

Example 2 Solve: $\frac{2}{x} + \frac{5}{y} = 1$, $\frac{60}{x} - \frac{20}{y} = 13$. Hence, find the value of k if $y = kx - 2$.

Solution. Given $\qquad \frac{2}{x} + \frac{5}{y} = 1 \qquad \qquad \ldots(i)$

$$\frac{60}{x} - \frac{20}{y} = 13 \qquad \qquad \ldots(ii)$$

Let $\quad \frac{1}{x} = a$ and $\frac{1}{y} = b$, then the given equations become

$$2a + 5b = 1 \qquad \qquad \ldots(iii)$$
$$60a - 20b = 13 \qquad \qquad \ldots(iv)$$

Multiplying (*iii*) by 4, we get

$$8a + 20b = 4 \qquad \qquad \ldots(v)$$

Adding (*iv*) and (*v*), we get

$$68a = 17 \implies a = \frac{1}{4}.$$

Substituting this value of a in (iii), we get

$$2 \times \frac{1}{4} + 5b = 1 \Rightarrow \frac{1}{2} + 5b = 1 \Rightarrow 5b = 1 - \frac{1}{2}$$

$$\Rightarrow \quad 5b = \frac{1}{2} \Rightarrow b = \frac{1}{10}.$$

$$\therefore \quad \frac{1}{x} = \frac{1}{4} \text{ and } \frac{1}{y} = \frac{1}{10} \Rightarrow x = 4 \text{ and } y = 10.$$

Hence, the solution is $x = 4$, $y = 10$.

To find k

Putting $x = 4$ and $y = 10$ in $y = kx - 2$, we get

$10 = 4k - 2 \Rightarrow 4k = 12 \Rightarrow k = 3$.

Example 3 Solve the following pairs of equations:

(i) $\dfrac{2}{\sqrt{x}} + \dfrac{3}{\sqrt{y}} = 2$

$\dfrac{4}{\sqrt{x}} - \dfrac{9}{\sqrt{y}} = -1$

(ii) $\dfrac{5}{x-1} + \dfrac{1}{y-2} = 2$

$\dfrac{6}{x-1} - \dfrac{3}{y-2} = 1$.

Solution. (i) Substituting $\dfrac{1}{\sqrt{x}} = a$ and $\dfrac{1}{\sqrt{y}} = b$, in the given pair of equations, we get

$\qquad 2a + 3b = 2 \qquad ...(1) \qquad$ and $\qquad 4a - 9b = -1 \qquad ...(2)$

Multiplying (1) by 3, we get

$\qquad 6a + 9b = 6 \qquad ...(3)$

On adding (2) and (3), we get

$$10a = 5 \Rightarrow a = \frac{1}{2}.$$

Putting $a = \dfrac{1}{2}$ in (1), we get

$$2 \cdot \frac{1}{2} + 3b = 2 \Rightarrow 3b = 1 \Rightarrow b = \frac{1}{3}.$$

$$\therefore \quad \frac{1}{\sqrt{x}} = \frac{1}{2} \text{ and } \frac{1}{\sqrt{y}} = \frac{1}{3} \Rightarrow x = 4 \text{ and } y = 9.$$

Hence, the solution of the given pair of equations is $x = 4$, $y = 9$.

(ii) Substituting $\dfrac{1}{x-1} = p$ and $\dfrac{1}{y-2} = q$ in the given equations, we get

$\qquad 5p + q = 2 \qquad ...(1) \qquad$ and $\qquad 6p - 3q = 1 \qquad ...(2)$

From (1), $q = 2 - 5p \qquad ...(3)$

Substituting this value of q in equation (2), we get

$\qquad 6p - 3(2 - 5p) = 1$

$\Rightarrow \quad 6p - 6 + 15p = 1 \Rightarrow 21p = 7 \Rightarrow p = \dfrac{1}{3}.$

From (3), $q = 2 - 5 \times \dfrac{1}{3} = 2 - \dfrac{5}{3} = \dfrac{1}{3}$

$\therefore \quad \dfrac{1}{x-1} = \dfrac{1}{3}$ and $\dfrac{1}{y-2} = \dfrac{1}{3}$

$\Rightarrow \quad x - 1 = 3$ and $y - 2 = 3$

$\Rightarrow \quad x = 4$ and $y = 5$.

Hence, the solution of the given pair of equations is $x = 4$ and $y = 5$.

Example 4 Solve: $4x + 9y = 30xy$, $5y - 3x = xy$.

Solution. The given system of simultaneous equations is

$$4x + 9y = 30xy \qquad \qquad \text{...}(i)$$
$$5x - 3y = xy \qquad \qquad \text{...}(ii)$$

First, we note that $x = 0$, $y = 0$ is a solution of the given system of equations.

Now, when $x \neq 0$, $y \neq 0$, then dividing both sides of each equation by xy, we get

$$\frac{4}{y} + \frac{9}{x} = 30 \qquad \qquad \text{...}(iii)$$

$$\frac{5}{x} - \frac{3}{y} = 1 \qquad \qquad \text{...}(iv)$$

Let $\frac{1}{x} = a$ and $\frac{1}{y} = b$, then equations (iii) and (iv) become

$$9a + 4b = 30 \qquad \qquad \text{...}(v)$$
$$5a - 3b = 1 \qquad \qquad \text{...}(vi)$$

On multiplying (v) by 3 and (vi) by 4, we get

$$27a + 12b = 90 \qquad \qquad \text{...}(vii)$$
$$20a - 12b = 4 \qquad \qquad \text{...}(viii)$$

Adding (vii) and (viii), we get

$$47a = 94 \Rightarrow a = 2.$$

Substituting $a = 2$ in (v), we get

$$9 \times 2 + 4b = 30 \Rightarrow 4b = 12 \Rightarrow b = 3.$$

$$\therefore \qquad \frac{1}{x} = 2 \text{ and } \frac{1}{y} = 3 \Rightarrow x = \frac{1}{2} \text{ and } y = \frac{1}{3}.$$

Hence, the solutions of the given system of equations are

$$x = 0, y = 0; \ x = \frac{1}{2}, y = \frac{1}{3}.$$

Example 5 Solve: $\dfrac{20}{x+y} + \dfrac{3}{x-y} = 7$, $\dfrac{8}{x-y} - \dfrac{15}{x+y} = 5$.

Solution. Let $\dfrac{1}{x+y} = a$ and $\dfrac{1}{x-y} = b$, then the given equations become

$$20a + 3b = 7 \qquad \text{...}(i) \qquad \text{and} \qquad 8b - 15a = 5 \qquad \text{...}(ii)$$

Multiplying (i) by 3 and (ii) by 4, we get

$$60a + 9b = 21 \qquad \text{...}(iii) \qquad \text{and} \qquad -60a + 32b = 20 \qquad \text{...}(iv)$$

Adding (iii) and (iv), we get

$$41b = 41 \Rightarrow b = 1.$$

Substituting $b = 1$ in (i), we get

$$20a + 3 \times 1 = 7 \Rightarrow 20a = 4 \Rightarrow a = \frac{1}{5}.$$

$$\therefore \qquad \frac{1}{x+y} = \frac{1}{5} \text{ and } \frac{1}{x-y} = 1$$

$$\Rightarrow \qquad x + y = 5, \ x - y = 1.$$

Adding these equations, we get

$$2x = 6 \Rightarrow x = 3.$$

$$\therefore \qquad 3 + y = 5 \Rightarrow y = 2.$$

Hence, the solution of the given linear equations is $x = 3$, $y = 2$.

Example 6 Solve the following pairs of equations:

$$\frac{1}{3x+y} + \frac{1}{3x-y} = \frac{3}{4}, \quad \frac{1}{2(3x+y)} - \frac{1}{2(3x-y)} = -\frac{1}{8}.$$

Solution. Substituting $\frac{1}{3x+y} = p$ and $\frac{1}{3x-y} = q$ in the given equations, we get

$$p + q = \frac{3}{4} \qquad \text{...(i)} \qquad\qquad \frac{p}{2} - \frac{q}{2} = -\frac{1}{8} \text{ i.e. } p - q = -\frac{1}{4} \qquad \text{...(ii)}$$

On adding equations (i) and (ii), we get

$$2p = \frac{3}{4} - \frac{1}{4} \Rightarrow 2p = \frac{1}{2} \Rightarrow p = \frac{1}{4}$$

Substituting this value of p in equation (i), we get

$$\frac{1}{4} + q = \frac{3}{4} \Rightarrow q = \frac{3}{4} - \frac{1}{4} \Rightarrow q = \frac{1}{2}$$

$$\therefore \quad \frac{1}{3x+y} = \frac{1}{4} \text{ and } \frac{1}{3x-y} = \frac{1}{2}$$

$$\Rightarrow \quad 3x + y = 4 \qquad \text{...(iii)} \qquad \text{and} \qquad 3x - y = 2 \qquad\qquad \text{...(iv)}$$

On adding equations (iii) and (iv), we get

$$6x = 6 \Rightarrow x = 1$$

Substituting this value of x in equation (iii), we get

$$3 \times 1 + y = 4 \Rightarrow y = 1.$$

Hence, the solution is $x = 1$ and $y = 1$.

EXERCISE 5.4

Solve the following pairs of linear equations (1 to 5):

1 (i) $\dfrac{2}{x} + \dfrac{2}{3y} = \dfrac{1}{6}$

   $\dfrac{2}{x} - \dfrac{1}{y} = 1$

(ii) $\dfrac{3}{2x} + \dfrac{2}{3y} = 5$

   $\dfrac{5}{x} - \dfrac{3}{y} = 1.$

2 (i) $\dfrac{7x - 2y}{xy} = 5$

   $\dfrac{8x + 7y}{xy} = 15$

(ii) $99x + 101y = 499xy$

   $101x + 99y = 501xy.$

3 (i) $3x + 14y = 5xy$

   $21y - x = 2xy$

(ii) $3x + 5y = 4xy$

   $2y - x = xy.$

4 (i) $\dfrac{20}{x+1} + \dfrac{4}{y-1} = 5$

   $\dfrac{10}{x+1} - \dfrac{4}{y-1} = 1$

(ii) $\dfrac{3}{x+y} + \dfrac{2}{x-y} = 3$

   $\dfrac{2}{x+y} + \dfrac{3}{x-y} = \dfrac{11}{3}.$

5 (i) $\dfrac{1}{2(2x+3y)} + \dfrac{12}{7(3x-2y)} = \dfrac{1}{2}$

   $\dfrac{7}{2x+3y} + \dfrac{4}{3x-2y} = 2$

(ii) $\dfrac{1}{2(x+2y)} + \dfrac{5}{3(3x-2y)} = -\dfrac{3}{2}$

   $\dfrac{5}{4(x+2y)} - \dfrac{3}{5(3x-2y)} = \dfrac{61}{60}.$

Multiple Choice Questions

Choose the correct answer from the given four options (1 to 5):

1. If $x = 3$, $y = k$ is a solution of the equation $3x - 4y + 7 = 0$, then the value of k is

   (a) 16 (b) -16 (c) 4 (d) -4

2. The solution of the pair of linear equations $2x - y = 5$ and $5x - y = 11$ is

   (a) $x = -1, y = 2$ (b) $x = 2, y = -1$ (c) $x = 0, y = -5$ (d) $x = \dfrac{5}{2}, y = 0$

3. If $x = a$, $y = b$ is the solution of the equations $x - y = 2$ and $x + y = 4$, then the values of a and b are, respectively

   (a) 3 and 5 (b) 5 and 3 (c) 3 and 1 (d) -1 and -3

4. The solution of the system of equations $\dfrac{4}{x} + 5y = 7$ and $\dfrac{3}{x} + 4y = 5$ is

   (a) $x = \dfrac{1}{3}, y = -1$ (b) $x = -\dfrac{1}{3}, y = 1$ (c) $x = 3, y = -1$ (d) $x = -3, y = 1$

5. A pair of linear equations which has a unique solution $x = 2$, $y = -3$ is

   (a) $x + y = -1$
   $2x - 3y = -5$

   (b) $2x + 5y = -11$
   $4x + 10y = -22$

   (c) $2x - y = 1$
   $3x + 2y = 0$

   (d) $x - 4y - 14 = 0$
   $5x - y - 13 = 0$

Summary

- An equation of the form $ax + by + c = 0$, where a, b and c are real numbers and a, b are non-zero is called a general linear equation in the two variables x and y.
- $x = \alpha$ and $y = \beta$ is a solution of the linear equation $ax + by + c = 0$ if and only if $a\alpha + b\beta + c = 0$.
- Every linear equation in two variables has infinitely many solutions.
- **Algebraic methods**

  The various methods of solving a pair of linear equations in two variables are:

  (i) *Substitution method*

  (ii) *Elimination method*

  (iii) *Cross-multiplication method.*

Solve the following simultaneous linear equations (1 to 4):

1   (*i*) $2x - \dfrac{3}{4}y = 3$

           $5x - 2y = 7$

       (*ii*) $2(x - 4) = 9y + 2$

            $x - 6y = 2.$

2   (*i*) $97x + 53y = 177$

           $53x + 97y = 573$

       (*ii*) $x + y = 5 \cdot 5$

            $x - y = 0 \cdot 9$

3   (*i*) $x + y = 7xy$

           $2x - 3y + xy = 0$

       (*ii*) $\dfrac{30}{x - y} + \dfrac{44}{x + y} = 10$

            $\dfrac{40}{x - y} + \dfrac{55}{x + y} = 13.$

4   (*i*) $ax + by = a - b$

           $bx - ay = a + b$

       (*ii*) $3x + 2y = 2xy$

            $\dfrac{1}{x} + \dfrac{2}{y} = 1\dfrac{1}{6}.$

5   Solve $2x - \dfrac{3}{y} = 9$, $3x + \dfrac{7}{y} = 2$. Hence, find the value of k if $x = ky + 5$.

6   Solve $\dfrac{1}{x + y} - \dfrac{1}{2x} = \dfrac{1}{30}$, $\dfrac{5}{x + y} + \dfrac{1}{x} = \dfrac{4}{3}$. Hence, find the value of $2x^2 - y^2$.

7   Can x, y be found to satisfy the following equations simultaneously?

       $\dfrac{2}{y} + \dfrac{5}{x} = 19$, $\dfrac{5}{y} - \dfrac{3}{x} = 1$, $3x + 8y = 5.$

       If so, find them.

6 Problems on Simultaneous Linear Equations

INTRODUCTION

In day-to-day life, we come across many situations where we have to solve a pair of linear equations in two variables. In the previous chapter, we read about linear equations in two variables and also learnt the various methods of solving a pair of linear equations in two variables. In this chapter, we shall learn the applications of a pair of linear equations in two variables in solving word problems.

6.1 WORD PROBLEMS

*Problems stated in words are called **word** or **applied problems.***

Success with word (or applied) problems comes with practice and knowing some simple techniques of translating. Solving word problems involves two steps. First, translating the words of the problem into algebraic equations. Second, solving the resulting equations.

6.1.1 Solving word problems

Due to the wide variety of word (or applied) problems, there is no single technique that works in all cases. However, the following general suggestions should prove helpful:

   (*i*) Read and reread the statement of the problem carefully, and determine what quantities must be found.
   (*ii*) Represent the unknown quantities by letters.
   (*iii*) Determine which expressions are equal and write equations.
   (*iv*) Solve the resulting equations.

Remark

Check the answer (or answers) obtained, by determining whether or not they fulfil the condition(s) of the original problem.

6.2 PROBLEMS ON SIMULTANEOUS LINEAR EQUATIONS

Illustrative Examples

Example 1 Twice one number minus three times a second is equal to 2, and the sum of these numbers is 11. Find the numbers.

Solution. Let the two numbers be x, y.

According to the problem,

$$2x - 3y = 2 \qquad \qquad \qquad …(i)$$

and $\qquad \qquad x + y = 11 \qquad \qquad \qquad …(ii)$

Multiplying both sides of (ii) by 3, we get

$$3x + 3y = 33 \qquad \qquad \ldots(iii)$$

On adding (i) and (iii), we get

$$5x = 35 \implies x = 7.$$

Substituting this value of x in (ii), we get

$$7 + y = 11 \implies y = 11 - 7 \implies y = 4.$$

Hence, the required numbers are 7 and 4.

Example 2 Once a mule and a donkey were talking. The mule said, "I am carrying more sacks than you. In fact, if you give me one of your sacks, then I would have twice as many as you. If I give you a sack, our loads would be equal." How many sacks was each animal carrying?

Solution. Let mule and donkey carry x sacks and y sacks respectively. Then the two statements mean:

If you give me one of your sacks, then I would have twice as many as you (i.e. if the mule had one more and the donkey one less, the mule would have twice as many as donkey).

$$\therefore \qquad x + 1 = 2(y - 1) \implies x - 2y + 3 = 0 \qquad \qquad \ldots(i)$$

If I give you a sack, our loads would be equal (i.e. if the mule had one less and the donkey one more, they would have the same number of sacks).

$$\therefore \qquad x - 1 = y + 1 \implies x - y - 2 = 0 \qquad \qquad \ldots(ii)$$

Subtracting (i) from (ii), we get

$$y - 5 = 0 \implies y = 5.$$

Substituting $y = 5$ in (ii), we get

$$x - 5 - 2 = 0 \implies x = 7.$$

Hence, the mule was carrying 7 sacks and the donkey 5 sacks.

Example 3 A man buys postage stamps of denominations 25 paise and 50 paise for ₹10. He buys 28 stamps in all. Find the number of 25 paise stamps bought by him.

Solution. Let the number of 25 paise stamps be x and the number of 50 paise stamps be y.

According to the problem,

$$x + y = 28 \qquad \qquad \ldots(i)$$

and $\qquad 25x + 50y = 1000 \qquad \qquad$ (∵ ₹10 = 1000 paise)

i.e. $\qquad x + 2y = 40 \qquad \qquad \ldots(ii)$

Subtracting (i) from (ii), we get, $y = 12$.

Substituting this value of y in (i), we get

$$x + 12 = 28 \implies x = 28 - 12 \implies x = 16.$$

Hence, the number of 25 paise stamps = 16.

Example 4 The sum of the digits of a two digit number is 5. The digit obtained by increasing the digit in ten's place by unity is one-eighth of the number. Find the number.

Solution. Let x be the digit at ten's place and y be the digit at unit's place.

∴ The digit by increasing the digit in ten's place by unity = $x + 1$.

The number is $10x + y$.

According to the problem, $x + y = 5 \qquad \qquad \ldots(i)$

and
$$x + 1 = \frac{1}{8}(10x + y)$$
$$\Rightarrow \qquad 8(x + 1) = 10x + y$$
$$\Rightarrow \qquad 8x + 8 = 10x + y$$
$$\Rightarrow \qquad 2x + y = 8 \qquad \qquad \qquad \text{...(ii)}$$

Subtracting (i) from (ii), we get, $x = 3$.

On substituting this value of x in (i), we get
$$3 + y = 5 \Rightarrow y = 5 - 3 \Rightarrow y = 2.$$

Hence, the required number is 32.

Example 5 A two digit number is seven times the sum of its digits. The number formed by reversing the digits is 18 less than the original number. Find the number.

Solution. Let x be the digit at ten's place and y be the digit at unit's place.

Then the number is $10x + y$.

According to the first condition of the problem,
$$10x + y = 7(x + y)$$
$$\Rightarrow \qquad 10x + y = 7x + 7y$$
$$\Rightarrow \qquad 3x = 6y$$
$$\Rightarrow \qquad x = 2y \qquad \qquad \qquad \text{...(i)}$$

The number formed by reversing the digits is $10y + x$.

According to the second condition of the problem,
$$10y + x = (10x + y) - 18$$
$$\Rightarrow \qquad 10y - y = 10x - x - 18$$
$$\Rightarrow \qquad 9y = 9x - 18$$
$$\Rightarrow \qquad y = x - 2$$
$$\Rightarrow \qquad y = 2y - 2 \qquad \qquad \qquad \text{(using (i))}$$
$$\Rightarrow \qquad y = 2.$$

From (i), $\qquad x = 2 \times 2 = 4.$

Hence, the required number is 42.

Example 6 The sum of a two digit number and the number obtained by interchanging the digits is 132. If the two digits differ by 2, find the number(s).

Solution. Let the ten's and unit's digits in the number be x and y respectively. Then the number $= 10x + y$ and the number obtained on reversing the digits $= 10y + x$.

According to given conditions, we have
$$(10x + y) + (10y + x) = 132 \text{ i.e. } 11x + 11y = 132$$
$$\Rightarrow \quad x + y = 12 \qquad \qquad \qquad \text{...(i)}$$
and $x - y = 2$ \qquad \qquad ...(ii) \qquad or \qquad $y - x = 2$ \qquad \qquad ...(iii)

If $\quad x - y = 2$, then solving (i) and (ii), we get $x = 7$, $y = 5$.

In this case, the number is 75.

If $\quad y - x = 2$, then solving (i) and (iii), we get $y = 7$, $x = 5$.

In this case, the number is 57.

Hence, there are two numbers 75 and 57 satisfying the given conditions.

Example 7 A fraction becomes $\frac{9}{11}$, if 2 is added to both numerator and denominator. If 3 is added to both the numerator and denominator, it becomes $\frac{5}{6}$. Find the fraction.

Solution. Let the fraction be $\frac{x}{y}$. Then, according to given, we have

$$\frac{x+2}{y+2} = \frac{9}{11} \text{ and } \frac{x+3}{y+3} = \frac{5}{6}$$

$\Rightarrow \quad 11x + 22 = 9y + 18 \text{ and } 6x + 18 = 5y + 15$

$\Rightarrow \quad 11x - 9y + 4 = 0 \quad …(i) \quad \text{ and } \quad 6x - 5y + 3 = 0 \qquad …(ii)$

From (ii), $x = \dfrac{5y-3}{6}$ \qquad …(iii)

Substituting this value of x in (i), we get

$$11\left(\frac{5y-3}{6}\right) - 9y + 4 = 0$$

$\Rightarrow \quad 55y - 33 - 54y + 24 = 0$

$\Rightarrow \quad y = 9.$

From (iii), $x = \dfrac{5 \times 9 - 3}{6} = \dfrac{42}{6} = 7.$

Hence, the fraction is $\dfrac{7}{9}$.

Example 8 If the numerator and denominator of a fraction are increased by 2 and 1 respectively, it becomes $\frac{3}{4}$. If the numerator and denominator are decreased by 2 and 1 respectively, it becomes $\frac{1}{2}$. Find the fraction.

Solution. Let the fraction be $\frac{x}{y}$.

Since on increasing the numerator and denominator by 2 and 1 respectively it becomes $\frac{3}{4}$,

$\therefore \qquad \dfrac{x+2}{y+1} = \dfrac{3}{4}$

$\Rightarrow \qquad 4x + 8 = 3y + 3$

$\Rightarrow \qquad 4x - 3y + 5 = 0$ \qquad …(i)

On decreasing the numerator and denominator by 2 and 1 respectively, it becomes $\frac{1}{2}$,

$\therefore \qquad \dfrac{x-2}{y-1} = \dfrac{1}{2} \Rightarrow 2x - 4 = y - 1$

$\Rightarrow \qquad 2x - y - 3 = 0$ \qquad …(ii)

Multiplying both sides of (ii) by 2, we get

$\qquad 4x - 2y - 6 = 0$ \qquad …(iii)

Subtracting (i) from (iii), we get

$\qquad y - 11 = 0 \Rightarrow y = 11.$

On substituting this value of y in (ii), we get

$\qquad 2x - 11 - 3 = 0 \Rightarrow 2x = 14 \Rightarrow x = 7.$

Hence, the required fraction is $\dfrac{7}{11}$.

Example 9 The sum of the numerator and denominator of a fraction is 4 more than twice the numerator. If the numerator and denominator each are increased by 3, they are in the ratio 2 : 3. Determine the fraction.

Solution. Let the fraction be $\dfrac{x}{y}$. Then, according to given, we have

$$x + y = 2x + 4 \implies y = x + 4 \qquad \qquad \qquad \dots(i)$$

and $\dfrac{x+3}{y+3} = \dfrac{2}{3} \implies 3x + 9 = 2y + 6$

$$\implies \quad 3x + 3 = 2y \qquad \qquad \qquad \qquad \dots(ii)$$

Substituting the value of y from (i) in (ii), we get

$$3x + 3 = 2(x + 4) \implies 3x + 3 = 2x + 8$$

$$\implies \quad 3x - 2x = 8 - 3 \implies x = 5.$$

From (i), $y = 5 + 4 = 9$.

Hence, the fraction is $\dfrac{5}{9}$.

Example 10 Half the perimeter of a rectangular garden, whose length is 4 m more than its width, is 36 m. Find the dimensions of the garden.

Solution. Let the length and the breadth of the rectangular garden be x metres and y metres respectively.

Then, according to given, we have

$$x + y = 36 \qquad \dots(i) \qquad \text{and} \qquad x = y + 4 \qquad \dots(ii)$$

Substituting the value of x from (ii) in (i), we get

$$(y + 4) + y = 36 \implies 2y + 4 = 36$$

$$\implies \quad 2y = 32 \implies y = 16$$

From (ii), $x = y + 4 = 16 + 4 = 20$.

Hence, the length of garden = 20 m and its breadth = 16 m.

Example 11 Six years hence a man's age will be three times his son's age, and three years ago he was nine times as old as his son. Find their present ages.

Solution. Let the present age of the man be x years and the present age of his son be y years.

6 years hence, their ages will be $(x + 6)$ years and $(y + 6)$ years.

According to the problem,

$$x + 6 = 3(y + 6) \implies x + 6 = 3y + 18$$

$$\implies \qquad x - 3y = 12 \qquad \qquad \qquad \qquad \dots(i)$$

3 years ago, their ages were $(x - 3)$ years and $(y - 3)$ years.

According to the problem,

$$x - 3 = 9(y - 3) \implies x - 3 = 9y - 27$$

$$\implies \qquad x - 9y = -24 \qquad \qquad \qquad \qquad \dots(ii)$$

Subtracting (ii) from (i), we get

$$6y = 36 \implies y = 6.$$

Substituting this value of y in (i), we get

$$x - 3 \times 6 = 12 \implies x - 18 = 12 \implies x = 12 + 18 = 30.$$

Hence, the present age of the man is 30 years and that of his son is 6 years.

Example 12 The age of the father is twice the sum of ages of his two children. After 20 years, his age will be equal to the sum of the ages of his children. Find the age of the father.

Solution. Let the present age of the father be x years and the sum of the present ages of his two children be y years. Then

$$x = 2y \qquad \qquad \text{...(i)}$$

After 20 years

age of father $(x + 20)$ years,

sum of ages of his two children $= (y + 2 \times 20)$ years $= (y + 40)$ years.

According to given,

$$x + 20 = y + 40 \Rightarrow x = y + 20 \qquad \qquad \text{...(ii)}$$

Eliminating x from (i) and from (ii), we get

$$2y = y + 20 \Rightarrow y = 20$$

Substituting this value y in (i), we get

$$x = 2 \times 20 = 40$$

Hence, the present age of the father = 40 years.

Example 13 At a certain time in a deer park, the number of heads and the number of legs of deer and human visitors were counted and it was found that there were 41 heads and 136 legs. Find the number of deer and human visitors in the park.

Solution. Let there be x deer and y human visitors in the park at the given time.

As a deer and a human each has one head, we get

$$x + y = 41 \qquad \qquad \text{...(i)}$$

As a deer has 4 legs and a human has 2 legs, we get

$$4x + 2y = 136 \Rightarrow 2x + y = 68 \qquad \qquad \text{...(ii)}$$

Subtracting (i) from (ii), we get

$$x = 27.$$

Substituting $x = 27$ in (i), we get

$$27 + y = 41 \Rightarrow y = 14.$$

Hence, there were 27 deer and 14 human visitors in the park.

Example 14 Ten percent of the red balls were added to twenty percent of the blue balls and the total was 24. Yet three times the number of red balls exceeds the number of blue balls by 20. How many were red balls and how many were blue balls?

Solution. Let there be x red balls and y blue balls.

According to the problem,

$$10\% \text{ of } x + 20\% \text{ of } y = 24 \Rightarrow \frac{10}{100}x + \frac{20}{100}y = 24$$

$$\Rightarrow \qquad x + 2y = 240 \qquad \qquad \text{...(i)}$$

Also $\quad 3x = y + 20 \Rightarrow 3x - y = 20 \qquad \qquad \text{...(ii)}$

Multiplying (ii) by 2, we get

$$6x - 2y = 40 \qquad \qquad \text{...(iii)}$$

Adding (i) and (iii), we get

$$7x = 280 \Rightarrow x = 40.$$

Substituting $\quad x = 40$ in (i), we get

$$40 + 2y = 240 \Rightarrow 2y = 200 \Rightarrow y = 100.$$

Hence, there were 40 red balls and 100 blue balls.

Example 15 The taxi charges in a city consist of a fixed charge together with the charge for the distance covered. For a distance of 10 km, the charge paid is ₹105 and for a journey of 15 km, the charge paid is ₹155. What are the fixed charges and the charge per km? How much does a person have to pay for travelling a distance of 25 km?

Solution. Let the fixed charges be ₹ x and charges per km be ₹ y.

Then, according to given, we have

$$x + 10y = 105 \quad \text{...(1)} \qquad \text{and} \qquad x + 15y = 155 \quad \text{...(2)}$$

From (1), $x = 105 - 10y$ ...(3)

Substituting this value of x in (2), we get

$$(105 - 10y) + 15y = 155$$
$$\Rightarrow \quad -10y + 15y = 155 - 105$$
$$\Rightarrow \quad 5y = 50 \Rightarrow y = 10.$$

From (3), $x = 105 - 10 \times 10 = 105 - 100 = 5$.

Hence, the fixed charges are ₹ 5 and the charges per km are ₹ 10.

Taxi charges for a distance of 25 km

$$= \text{fixed charges} + \text{charges for travelling 25 km}$$
$$= ₹ 5 + ₹ (25 \times 10) = ₹ 5 + ₹ 250 = ₹ 255.$$

Example 16 The ratio of incomes of two persons is 9 : 7 and the ratio of their expenditures is 4 : 3. If each of them manages to save ₹ 2000 per months, find their monthly incomes.

Solution. Let the incomes per month of two persons be ₹ x and ₹ y respectively. As each person saves ₹ 2000 per month, so their expenditures are ₹ $(x - 2000)$ and ₹ $(y - 2000)$ respectively.

According to given, we have

$$\frac{x}{y} = \frac{9}{7} \ i.e. \ 7x - 9y = 0 \quad \text{...(i)}$$

and $\dfrac{x - 2000}{y - 2000} = \dfrac{4}{3} \ i.e. \ 3x - 4y + 2000 = 0$ ...(ii)

Multiplying equation (i) by 3 and equation (ii) by 7, we get

$$21x - 27y = 0 \quad \text{...(iii)} \qquad \text{and} \qquad 21x - 28y + 14000 = 0 \quad \text{...(iv)}$$

Subtracting equation (iv) from equation (iii), we get

$$y - 14000 = 0 \Rightarrow y = 14000$$

Substituting this value of y in (i), we get

$$7x - 9 \times 14000 = 0 \Rightarrow x = 18000$$

Hence, the monthly incomes of the two persons are ₹ 18000 and ₹ 14000 respectively.

Example 17 A railway half-ticket costs half the full fare but the reservation charges are the same of a half-ticket as on a full ticket. One reserved first class ticket from station A to station B costs ₹2530. Also, one reserved first class ticket and one reserved half first class ticket from station A to station B costs ₹3810. Find the full fare from station A to B and also the reservation charges for a ticket.

Solution. Let the reservation charges for one railway ticket be ₹ x and the fare for one first class ticket be ₹ y, then

Cost of one reserved first class ticket = ₹ $(x + y)$.

As the reservation charges for half-ticket are same as the full ticket, so the cost of reserved half-ticket = ₹ $\left(x + \dfrac{1}{2}y\right)$.

According to given, $x + y = 2530$ ...(1)

and $(x + y) + \left(x + \dfrac{1}{2}y\right) = 3810$

$\Rightarrow \quad 2x + \dfrac{3}{2}y = 3810$

$\Rightarrow \quad 4x + 3y = 7620$ ...(2)

Multiplying equation (1) by 3, we get

$\quad 3x + 3y = 7590$ ...(3)

Subtracting equation (3) from equation (2), we get

$\quad x = 30.$

Substituting this value of x in (1), we get

$\quad 30 + y = 2530 \Rightarrow y = 2500.$

Hence, the full fare for a ticket is ₹ 2500 and the reservation charges are ₹ 30.

Example 18 Vijay had some bananas, and he divided them into two lots A and B. He sold the first lot at the rate of ₹ 2 for 3 bananas and the second lot at the rate of ₹ 1 per banana, and got a total of ₹ 400. If he had sold the first lot at ₹ 1 per banana and the second lot at the rate of ₹ 4 for 5 bananas, his total collection would have been ₹ 460. Find the total number of bananas he had.

Solution. Let Vijay had x bananas in lot A and y bananas in lot B. Then, according to given, we have:

$\qquad \dfrac{2}{3}x + y = 400 \quad i.e. \quad 2x + 3y = 1200$ ...(i)

and $\quad x + \dfrac{4}{5}y = 460 \quad i.e. \quad 5x + 4y = 2300$ ...(ii)

Multiplying equation (i) by 5 and equation (ii) by 2, we get

$10x + 15y = 6000$ ...(iii) $\qquad\qquad 10x + 8y = 4600$ ...(iv)

Subtracting equation (iv) from equation (iii), we get

$\qquad 7y = 1400 \Rightarrow y = 200.$

Substituting this value of y in (i), we get

$\qquad 2x + 3 \times 200 = 1200 \Rightarrow 2x = 600 \Rightarrow x = 300.$

Hence, the total number of bananas that Vijay had

$\qquad = x + y = 300 + 200 = 500.$

Example 19 The area of a rectangle gets reduced by 9 sq. units, if its length is reduced by 5 units and the breadth is increased by 3 units. If we increase the length by 3 units and the breadth by 2 units, then the area is increased by 67 sq. units. Find the dimensions of the rectangle.

Solution. Let the length and the breadth of the rectangle be x units and y units respectively. Then the area of rectangle = xy sq. units

According to given conditions, we have

$\qquad (x - 5)(y + 3) = xy - 9 \text{ and } (x + 3)(y + 2) = xy + 67$

$\Rightarrow \quad xy + 3x - 5y - 15 = xy - 9$

and $\quad xy + 2x + 3y + 6 = xy + 67$

$\Rightarrow \quad 3x - 5y - 6 = 0$ ...(i)

and $\quad 2x + 3y - 61 = 0$ ...(ii)

Multiplying equation (*i*) by 2 and equation (*ii*) by 3, we get

$6x - 10y - 12 = 0$ ...(*iii*)   and $6x + 9y - 183 = 0$ ...(*iv*)

Subtracting equation (*iii*) from equation (*iv*), we get

$19y - 171 = 0 \Rightarrow y = 9$.

Substituting this value of y in equation (*ii*), we get

$2x + 3 \times 9 - 61 = 0 \Rightarrow 9x - 34 = 0 \Rightarrow x = 17$.

Hence, the length of rectangle = 17 units and breadth = 9 units.

Example 20 A chemist has one solution which is 50% acid and a second which is 25% acid. How much of each should be mixed to make 10 litres of a 40% acid solution?

Solution. Let x litres of 50% and y litres of 25% acid solutions be mixed. Then, according to given conditions, we have

$x + y = 10$ ...(*i*)

and   50% of x + 25% of y = 40% of 10

$\Rightarrow \quad \dfrac{50}{100}x + \dfrac{25}{100}y = \dfrac{40}{100} \times 10$

$\Rightarrow \quad \dfrac{1}{2}x + \dfrac{1}{4}y = 4$

$\Rightarrow \quad 2x + y = 16$ ...(*ii*)

Subtracting equation (*i*) from equation (*ii*), we get $x = 6$.

Substituting this value of x in equation (*i*), we get

$6 + y = 10 \Rightarrow y = 4$.

Hence, 6 litres of 50% and 4 litres of 25% acid solutions be mixed to get 10 litres of 40% acid solution.

Example 21 Susan invested certain amount of money in two schemes A and B, which offer interest at the rate of 8% per annum and 9% per annum respectively. She received ₹ 1860 as annual interest. However, had she interchanged the amount invested in the two schemes, she would have received ₹ 20 more as annual interest. How much did she invest in each scheme?

Solution. Let Susan invest ₹ x in scheme A and ₹ y in scheme B.

According to given conditions,

$\dfrac{x \times 8 \times 1}{100} + \dfrac{y \times 9 \times 1}{100} = 1860$

and $\dfrac{x \times 9 \times 1}{100} + \dfrac{y \times 8 \times 1}{100} = 1860 + 20$

$\Rightarrow \quad 8x + 9y = 186000$ ...(*i*)   and $9x + 8y = 188000$ ...(*ii*)

On adding equations (*i*) and (*ii*), we get

$17x + 17y = 374000$

$\Rightarrow \quad x + y = 22000$ ...(*iii*)

On subtracting equation (*i*) from equation (*ii*), we get

$x - y = 2000$ ...(*iv*)

On adding equations (*iii*) and (*iv*), we get

$2x = 24000 \Rightarrow x = 12000$

Substituting this value of x in (*iii*), we get

$12000 + y = 22000 \Rightarrow y = 10000$

Hence, the money invested in scheme A = ₹ 12000 and in scheme B = ₹ 10000.

Example 22 A shopkeeper sold a saree and a sweater together for ₹1050, thereby making a profit of 10% on the saree and 25% on the sweater. If he had taken a profit of 25% on the saree and 10% on the sweater, he would have got ₹15 more. Find the cost price of each.

Solution. Let the cost price of the saree be ₹x and the cost price of the sweater be ₹y.

Profit on saree = 10%,

∴ S.P. of saree = $\left(1 + \dfrac{10}{100}\right)$ of ₹x = ₹$\dfrac{11}{10}x$.

Profit on sweater = 25%,

∴ S.P. of sweater = $\left(1 + \dfrac{25}{100}\right)$ of ₹y = ₹$\dfrac{5}{4}y$.

As the selling price of both is ₹1050,

$$\frac{11}{10}x + \frac{5}{4}y = 1050 \Rightarrow 22x + 25y = 21000 \qquad \qquad ...(i)$$

Now, profit on saree = 25%,

∴ S.P. of saree = $\left(1 + \dfrac{25}{100}\right)$ of ₹x = ₹$\dfrac{5x}{4}$.

Profit on sweater = 10%,

∴ S.P. of sweater = $\left(1 + \dfrac{10}{100}\right)$ of ₹y = ₹$\dfrac{11}{10}y$.

New S.P. of saree and sweater together = ₹1050 + ₹15

= ₹1065,

∴ $\dfrac{5x}{4} + \dfrac{11}{10}y = 1065 \Rightarrow 25x + 22y = 21300$ ...(ii)

On adding (i) and (ii), we get

$$47x + 47y = 42300 \Rightarrow x + y = 900 \qquad \qquad ...(iii)$$

Subtracting (i) from (ii), we get

$$3x - 3y = 300 \Rightarrow x - y = 100 \qquad \qquad ...(iv)$$

Adding (iii) and (iv), we get

$$2x = 1000 \Rightarrow x = 500.$$

Substituting this value of x in (iii), we get

$$500 + y = 900 \Rightarrow y = 400.$$

Hence, the cost price of the saree is ₹500 and the cost price of the sweater is ₹400.

Example 23 Some amount is distributed equally among students. If there are 8 students less, every one will get ₹10 more. If there are 16 students more, every one will get ₹10 less. What is the number of students and how much does each get? What is the total amount distributed?

Solution. Let the number of students be x and let each student get ₹y.

Then the amount distributed = ₹xy.

In the first case, if there are 8 students less, every one will get ₹10 more

∴ $(x - 8) \times (y + 10) = xy$

⇒ $xy + 10x - 8y - 80 = xy \Rightarrow 10x - 8y = 80$

⇒ $5x - 4y = 40$ ...(i)

In the second case, if there are 16 students more, every one will get ₹10 less,

$\therefore \qquad (x + 16) \times (y - 10) = xy$

$\Rightarrow \qquad xy - 10x + 16y - 160 = xy \Rightarrow -10x + 16y = 160$

$\Rightarrow \qquad\qquad -5x + 8y = 80$ ...(ii)

On adding (i) and (ii), we get

$$4y = 120 \quad \Rightarrow y = 30.$$

Putting $\qquad\qquad\qquad y = 30$ in (i), we get

$$5x - 4 \times 30 = 40 \Rightarrow 5x = 40 + 120 \Rightarrow 5x = 160 \Rightarrow x = 32.$$

Hence, the number of students = 32 and each student gets ₹30.

$$\text{Amount distributed} = ₹(32 \times 30) = ₹960.$$

Example 24 In a triangle ABC, $\angle C = 3 \angle B = 2(\angle A + \angle B)$. Find all the angles in degrees.

Solution. Let $\angle A = x$ and $\angle B = y$

Given $\angle C = 3 \angle B = 2 (\angle A + \angle B)$

$\Rightarrow \quad \angle C = 3 \angle B$ and $3 \angle B = 2(\angle A + \angle B)$

$\Rightarrow \quad \angle C = 3y$ and $3y = 2(x + y)$

$\Rightarrow \quad \angle C = 3y$ and $2x - y = 0$ ...(i)

In $\triangle ABC$, $\angle A + \angle B + \angle C = 180°$

$\Rightarrow \quad x + y + 3y = 180° \Rightarrow x + 4y = 180°$ ...(ii)

Multiplying equation (i) by 4, we get

$8x - 4y = 0$ ...(iii)

On adding equations (ii) and (iii), we get

$9x = 180° \Rightarrow x = 20°$

Substituting this value of x in equation (i), we get

$(2 \times 20)° - y = 0 \Rightarrow y = 40°$

$\therefore \quad \angle C = 3y = (3 \times 40)° = 120°$

Hence, $\angle A = 20°$, $\angle B = 40°$ and $\angle C = 120°$.

Example 25 A train leaves New Delhi for Ludhiana, 324 km away, at 9 a.m. One hour later, another train leaves Ludhiana for New Delhi. They meet at noon. If the second train had started at 9 a.m. and the first train at 10.30 a.m., they would still have met at noon. Find the speed of each train.

Solution. Let the speed of the first train be x km/h and that of the second train be y km/h. The two trains meet at noon *i.e.* 12 noon.

Look at the following chart:

	Time	Rate	Distance
Train 1	3	x	$3x$
Train 2	2	y	$2y$
Train 1	1·5	x	$1·5x$
Train 2	3	y	$3y$

When the two trains meet, sum of distances covered by them is 324 km,

$\therefore \qquad\qquad 3x + 2y = 324$ ...(i)

and $\qquad\qquad 1·5x + 3y = 324$ ...(ii)

Multiplying (ii) by 2, we get

$$3x + 6y = 648 \qquad \qquad \ldots(iii)$$

Subtracting (i) from (ii), we get

$$4y = 324 \Rightarrow y = 81.$$

Substituting $\quad y = 81$ in (i), we get

$$3x + 2 \times 81 = 324 \Rightarrow 3x = 324 - 162$$

$$\Rightarrow \qquad \qquad 3x = 162 \Rightarrow x = 54.$$

Hence, the speed of the first train is 54 km/h and that of the second train is 81 km/h.

Example 26 Places A and B are 100 km apart on a highway. One car starts from A and another from B at the same time. If the cars travel in the same direction at different speeds, they meet in 5 hours. If they travel towards each other, they meet in one hour. What are the speeds of the two cars?

Solution. Name the cars at places A and B as P and Q respectively.

Let the speeds of the cars P and Q be x km/h and y km/h respectively, $x > y$.

When the cars move in the same direction:

Let the cars meet at place C after 5 hours (as shown in figure)

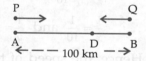

Distance covered by car P in 5 hours = AC = $5x$ km

and distance covered by car Q in 5 hours = BC = $5y$ km.

From figure, AC – BC = AB $\Rightarrow 5x - 5y = 100$

$$\Rightarrow \quad x - y = 20 \qquad \qquad \ldots(i)$$

When the cars move in opposite directions:

Let the cars meet at the place D after 1 hour (as shown in figure)

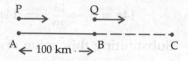

Distance covered by car P in 1 hour = AD = x km,

and distance covered by car Q in 1 hour = BD = y km.

From figure, AD + BD = AB

$$\Rightarrow \quad x + y = 100 \qquad \qquad \ldots(ii)$$

Adding equations (i) and (ii), we get

$$2x = 120 \Rightarrow x = 60.$$

Substituting this value of x in equation (ii), we get

$$60 + y = 100 \Rightarrow y = 40.$$

Hence, the speeds of the two cars are 60 km/h and 40 km/h.

Example 27 Ankita travels 14 km to her home partly by rickshaw and partly by bus. She takes half an hour if she travels 2 km by rickshaw and the remaining distance by bus. On the other hand, if she travels 4 km by rickshaw and the remaining distance by bus, she takes 9 minutes longer. Find the speed of rickshaw and of the bus.

Solution. Let the speeds of the rickshaw and the bus be x km/h and y km/h.

As Ankita has to travel a total distance of 14 km and she travels 2 km by the rickshaw, so the remaining distance of 12 km has to be travelled by the bus.

Time taken to cover 2 km by rickshaw = $\dfrac{2}{x}$ h and time taken to cover 12 km by bus = $\dfrac{12}{y}$ h.

Since the total time taken is half an hour *i.e.* $\frac{1}{2}$ hour,

$$\therefore \qquad \frac{2}{x} + \frac{12}{y} = \frac{1}{2} \qquad \qquad \dots(i)$$

On the other hand, if Ankita travels 4 km by rickshaw then the remaining distance of 10 km has to be covered by bus.

In this situation, the total time taken is 9 minutes more than the previous time, so the total time taken is 39 minutes *i.e.* $\frac{39}{60}$ hours *i.e.* $\frac{13}{20}$ h.

$$\therefore \qquad \frac{4}{x} + \frac{10}{y} = \frac{13}{20} \qquad \qquad \dots(ii)$$

Substituting $\frac{1}{x} = p$ and $\frac{1}{y} = q$ in equations (i) and (ii), we get

$$2p + 12q = \frac{1}{2} \qquad \dots(iii) \qquad \text{and} \qquad 4p + 10q = \frac{13}{20} \qquad \dots(iv)$$

Multiplying equation (iii) by 2, we get

$$4p + 24q = 1 \qquad \qquad \dots(v)$$

Subtracting equation (iv) from equation (v), we get

$$14q = 1 - \frac{13}{20} \quad \Rightarrow 14q = \frac{7}{20} \quad \Rightarrow q = \frac{1}{40}.$$

Substituting this value of q in equation (iii), we get

$$2p + 12 \times \frac{1}{40} = \frac{1}{2} \quad \Rightarrow 2p = \frac{1}{2} - \frac{3}{10}$$

$$\Rightarrow \quad 2p = \frac{2}{10} \quad \Rightarrow p = \frac{1}{10}.$$

$$\therefore \quad \frac{1}{x} = \frac{1}{10} \text{ and } \frac{1}{y} = \frac{1}{40} \quad \Rightarrow x = 10 \text{ and } y = 40.$$

Hence, the speed of the rickshaw is 10 km/h and that of the bus is 40 km/h.

Example 28 3 men and 4 boys can do a piece of work in 14 days, while 4 men and 6 boys can do it in 10 days. How long would it take 1 boy to finish the work?

Solution. Suppose 1 man can finish the work in x days and 1 boy can do it in y days, then

1 man's one day work $= \frac{1}{x}$ and 1 boy's one day work $= \frac{1}{y}$.

Given 3 men and 4 boys can do the work in 14 days,

$$\therefore \qquad 3 \text{ men's one day work} + 4 \text{ boy's one day work} = \frac{1}{14}$$

$$\Rightarrow \qquad 3.\frac{1}{x} + 4.\frac{1}{y} = \frac{1}{14} \qquad \qquad \dots(i)$$

Also 4 men and 6 boys can do the work in 10 days.

$$\therefore \qquad 4 \text{ men's one day work} + 6 \text{ boy's one day work} = \frac{1}{10}$$

$$\Rightarrow \qquad 4.\frac{1}{x} + 6.\frac{1}{y} = \frac{1}{10} \qquad \qquad \dots(ii)$$

Multiplying (i) by 4 and (ii) by 3, we get

$$\frac{12}{x} + \frac{16}{y} = \frac{2}{7} \qquad \qquad \dots(iii)$$

$$\frac{12}{x} + \frac{18}{y} = \frac{3}{10} \qquad \qquad \dots(iv)$$

Subtracting (*iii*) from (*iv*), we get

$$\frac{18-16}{y} = \frac{3}{10} - \frac{2}{7} \Rightarrow \frac{2}{y} = \frac{21-20}{70}$$

$$\Rightarrow \qquad \frac{2}{y} = \frac{1}{70} \Rightarrow y = 140.$$

Hence, one boy can finish the work in 140 days.

Example 29 It takes 12 hours to fill a swimming pool using two pipes. If the pipe of larger diameter is used for 4 hours and the pipe of smaller diameter for 9 hours, only half the pool can be filled. How long would it take for each pipe to fill the pool separately?

Solution. Let the pipes of larger diameter take x hours and the pipe of smaller diameter take y hours separately to fill the pool. Then,

the part of the pool filled by the larger pipe in one hour $= \dfrac{1}{x}$,

and the part of the pool filled by the smaller pipe in one hour $= \dfrac{1}{y}$.

Since it takes 12 hours to fill the swimming pool by using the two pipes together,

$$\therefore \qquad \frac{12}{x} + \frac{12}{y} = 1 \qquad\qquad\qquad \dots(i)$$

If the larger pipe is used for 4 hours and the smaller pipe for 9 hours, only half the pool is filled,

$$\therefore \qquad \frac{4}{x} + \frac{9}{y} = \frac{1}{2} \qquad\qquad\qquad \dots(ii)$$

Substituting $\dfrac{1}{x} = p$ and $\dfrac{1}{y} = q$ in these equations, we get

$$12p + 12q = 1 \qquad \dots(iii) \qquad \text{and} \qquad 4p + 9y = \frac{1}{2} \qquad \dots(iv)$$

Multiplying equation (*iv*) by 3, we get

$$12p + 27q = \frac{3}{2} \qquad\qquad\qquad \dots(v)$$

Subtracting equation (*iii*) from equation (*v*), we get

$$15q = \frac{3}{2} - 1 \Rightarrow 15q = \frac{1}{2} \Rightarrow q = \frac{1}{30}.$$

Substituting this value of q in equation (*iv*), we get

$$4p + 9 \times \frac{1}{30} = \frac{1}{2} \Rightarrow 4p = \frac{1}{2} - \frac{3}{10} = \frac{2}{10} \Rightarrow p = \frac{1}{20}.$$

$$\therefore \qquad \frac{1}{x} = \frac{1}{20} \text{ and } \frac{1}{y} = \frac{1}{30} \Rightarrow x = 20 \text{ and } y = 30.$$

Hence, the pipe of larger diameter alone can fill the pool in 20 hours and the pipe of smaller diameter alone can fill the pool in 30 hours.

Example 30 A boat goes 30 km upstream and 44 km downstream in 10 hours. In 13 hours it goes 40 km upstream and 55 km downstream. Determine the speed of the stream and that of the boat in still water.

Solution. Let the speed of the boat in the still water be x km/h and the speed of the stream be y km/h.

$\therefore$ In one hour, the boat goes $(x + y)$ km downstream and $(x - y)$ km upstream.

Since time taken by the boat in 30 km upstream and 44 km downstream is 10 hours,

$$\frac{30}{x-y} + \frac{44}{x+y} = 10 \qquad\qquad\qquad \dots(i)$$

Also time taken by the boat in 40 km upstream and 55 km downstream is 13 hours,

$$\frac{40}{x-y} + \frac{55}{x+y} = 13 \qquad \qquad \text{...(ii)}$$

Let $x - y = \frac{1}{a}$ and $x + y = \frac{1}{b}$, then the equations (i) and (ii) become

$$30a + 44b = 10 \qquad \qquad \text{...(iii)}$$
$$40a + 55b = 13 \qquad \qquad \text{...(iv)}$$

Multiplying (iii) by 4 and (iv) by 3, we get

$$120a + 176b = 40 \qquad \qquad \text{...(v)}$$
$$120a + 165b = 39 \qquad \qquad \text{...(vi)}$$

Subtracting (vi) from (v), we get $11b = 1 \Rightarrow b = \frac{1}{11}$.

Substituting $b = \frac{1}{11}$ in (iii), we get

$$30a + 44 \cdot \frac{1}{11} = 10 \Rightarrow 30a = 10 - 4 = 6 \Rightarrow a = \frac{6}{30} = \frac{1}{5}.$$

$\therefore \qquad \qquad x - y = 5 \qquad \qquad \text{...(vii)}$

and $\qquad \qquad x + y = 11 \qquad \qquad \text{...(viii)}$

On adding (vii) and (viii), we get $2x = 16 \Rightarrow x = 8$.

Substituting this value of x in (viii), we get

$$8 + y = 11 \Rightarrow y = 11 - 8 \Rightarrow y = 3.$$

$\therefore$ The speed of the boat in still water is 8 km/h and the speed of the stream is 3 km/h.

EXERCISE 6

1. The sum of two numbers is 50 and their difference is 16. Find the numbers.

2. The sum of two numbers is 2. If their difference is 20, find the numbers.

3. The sum of two numbers is 43. If the larger is doubled and the smaller is tripled, the difference is 36. Find the two numbers.

4. The cost of 5 kg of sugar and 7 kg of rice is ₹153, and the cost of 7 kg of sugar and 5 kg of rice is ₹147. Find the cost of 6 kg of sugar and 10 kg of rice.

5. The Class IX students of a certain public school wanted to give a farewell party to the outgoing students of Class X. They decided to purchase two kinds of sweets, one costing ₹70 per kg and the other costing ₹84 per kg. They estimated that 36 kg of sweets were needed. If the total money spent on sweets was ₹2800, find how much sweets of each kind they purchased.

6. If from twice the greater of two numbers 16 is subtracted, the result is half the other number. If from half the greater number 1 is subtracted, the result is still half the other number. What are the numbers?

7. There are 38 coins in a collection of 20 paise coins and 25 paise coins. If the total value of the collection is ₹8·50, how many of each are there?

8. A man has certain notes of denominations ₹20 and ₹5 which amount to ₹380. If the number of notes of each kind is interchanged, they amount to ₹60 less as before. Find the number of notes of each denomination.

9 The ratio of two numbers is $\frac{2}{3}$. If 2 is subtracted from the first and 8 from the second, the ratio becomes the reciprocal of the original ratio. Find the numbers.

10 If 1 is added to the numerator of a fraction, it becomes $\frac{1}{5}$; if 1 is taken from the denominator, it becomes $\frac{1}{7}$, find the fraction.

11 If the numerator of a certain fraction is increased by 2 and the denominator by 1, the fraction becomes equal to $\frac{5}{8}$ and if the numerator and denominator are each diminished by 1, the fraction becomes equal to $\frac{1}{2}$; find the fraction.

12 Find the fraction which becomes $\frac{1}{2}$ when the denominator is increased by 4 and is equal to $\frac{1}{8}$ when the numerator is diminished by 5.

13 In a two digit number the sum of the digits is 7. If the number with the order of the digits reversed is 28 greater than twice the unit's digit of the original number, find the number.

14 A number of two digits exceeds four times the sum of its digits by 6 and it is increased by 9 on reversing the digits. Find the number.

15 When a two digit number is divided by the sum of its digits the quotient is 8. If the ten's digit is diminished by three times the unit's digit, the remainder is 1. What is the number?

16 The result of dividing a number of two digits by the number with digits reversed is $1\frac{3}{4}$. If the sum of digits is 12, find the number.

17 The result of dividing a number of two digits by the number with the digits reversed is $\frac{5}{6}$. If the difference of digits is 1, find the number.

18 A number of three digits has the hundred digit 4 times the unit digit and the sum of three digits is 14. If the three digits are written in the reverse order, the value of the number is decreased by 594. Find the number.

19 Four years ago Marina was three times old as her daughter. Six years from now the mother will be twice as old as her daughter. Find their present ages.

20 On selling a tea set at 5% loss and a lemon set at 15% gain, a shopkeeper gains ₹70. If he sells the tea set at 5% gain and lemon set at 10% gain, he gains ₹130. Find the cost price of the lemon set.

21 A person invested some money at 12% simple interest and some other amount at 10% simple interest. He received yearly interest of ₹1300. If he had interchanged the amounts, he would have received ₹40 more as yearly interest. How much did he invest at different rates?

22 A shopkeeper sells a table at 8% profit and a chair at 10% discount, thereby getting ₹1008. If he had sold the table at 10% profit and chair at 8% discount, he would have got ₹20 more. Find the cost price of the table and the list price of the chair.

23 A and B have some money with them. A said to B, 'if you give me ₹100, my money will become 75% of the money left with you'. "B said to A" instead if you give me ₹100, your money will become 40% of my money. How much money did A and B have originally?

24 The students of a class are made to stand in (complete) rows. If one student is extra in a row, there would be 2 rows less, and if one student is less in a row, there would be 3 rows more. Find the number of students in the class.

25 A jeweller has bars of 18-carat gold and 12-carat gold. How much of each must be melted together to obtain a bar of 16-carat gold weighing 120 grams? (Pure gold is 24-carat).

26 A and B together can do a piece of work in 15 days. If A's one day work is $1\frac{1}{2}$ times the one day's work of B, find in how many days can each do the work.

Hint. Let A's one day work be x and B's one day work be y. Then

$$x = \frac{3}{2}y, \; x + y = \frac{1}{15}.$$

27 2 men and 5 women can do a piece of work in 4 days, while one man and one woman can finish it in 12 days. How long would it take for 1 man to do the work?

28 A train covered a certain distance at a uniform speed. If the train had been 30 km/h faster, it would have taken 2 hours less than the scheduled time. If the train were slower by 15 km/h, it would have taken 2 hours more than the scheduled time. Find the length of the journey.

Hint. Let the due speed of the train be x km/h and scheduled time by y hours, then length of journey $= xy$. Also $(x + 30)(y - 2) = xy$ and $(x - 15)(y + 2) = xy$.

29 A boat takes 2 hours to go 40 km down the stream and it returns in 4 hours. Find the speed of the boat in still water and the speed of the stream.

30 A boat sails a distance of 44 km in 4 hours with the current. It takes 4 hours 48 minutes longer to cover the same distance against the current. Find the speed of the boat in still water and the speed of the current.

31 An aeroplane flies 1680 km with a head wind in 3·5 hours. On the return trip with same wind blowing, the plane takes 3 hours. Find the plane's air speed and the wind speed.

32 A part of monthly hostel charges is fixed and the remaining depends on the number of days one has taken food in the mess. When Bhawana takes food for 20 days, she has to pay ₹2600 as hostel charges; whereas when Divya takes food for 26 days, she pays ₹3020 as hostel charges. Find the fixed charges and the cost of food per day.

Multiple Choice Questions
....

Choose the correct answer from the given four options (1 to 8):

1 Sum of digits of a two digit number is 8. If the number obtained by reversing the digits is 18 more than the original number, then the original number is
    (a) 35   (b) 53   (c) 26   (d) 62

2 The sum of two natural numbers is 25 and their difference is 7. The numbers are
    (a) 17 and 8   (b) 16 and 9   (c) 18 and 7   (d) 15 and 10

3 The sum of two natural numbers is 240 and their ratio is 3 : 5. Then the greater number is
    (a) 180   (b) 160   (c) 150   (d) 90

4 The sum of the digits of a two digit number is 9. If 27 is added to it, the digits of the number get reversed. The number is
    (a) 27   (b) 72   (c) 63   (d) 36

5 The sum of the digits of a two digit number is 12. If the number is decreased by 18, its digits get reversed. The number is
    (a) 48   (b) 84   (c) 57   (d) 75

6 Aruna has only ₹ 1 and ₹ 2 coins with her. If the total number of coins that she has is 50 and the amount of the money with her is ₹ 75, then the number of ₹ 1 and ₹ 2 coins are, respectively
    (a) 35 and 15   (b) 35 and 20   (c) 15 and 75   (d) 25 and 25

7 The age of a woman is four times the age of her daughter. Five years hence, the age of the woman will be three times the age of her daughter. The present age of the daughter is
    (a) 40 years   (b) 20 years   (c) 15 years   (d) 10 years

8 Father's age is six times his son's age. Four years hence, the age of the father will be four times his son's age. The present age in years of the son and the father are, respectively
    (a) 4 and 24   (b) 5 and 30   (c) 6 and 36   (d) 3 and 24

Summary

○ Problems stated in words are called **word problem**.

○ Solving word problems involves two steps. First translating the words of the problem into algebraic equations. Second, solving the resulting equations.

❑ **Solving word problems**

Due to the wide variety of word (or applied) problems, there is no single technique that works in all cases. However, the following general suggestions should prove helpful.

    (i) *Read and reread the statement of the problem carefully, and determine what quantities must be found.*

    (ii) *Represent the unknown quantities by letters.*

    (iii) *Determine which expressions are equal and write equations.*

    (iv) *Solve the resulting equations.*

1 A 700 g dry fruit pack costs ₹216. It contains some almonds and the rest cashew kernel. If almonds cost ₹288 per kg and cashew kernel cost ₹336 per kg, what are the quantities of the two dry fruits separately?

2 Drawing pencils cost 80 paise each and coloured pencils cost ₹1·10 each. If altogether two dozen pencils cost ₹21·60, how many coloured pencils are there?

3 Shikha works in a factory. In one week she earned ₹390 for working 47 hours, of which 7 hours were overtime. The next week she earned ₹416 for working 50 hours, of which 8 hours were overtime. What is Shikha's hourly earning rate?

Hint. Let Shikha's earning be ₹x per regular hour and ₹y per hour for overtime, then $40x + 7y = 390, 42x + 8y = 416$.

4 The sum of the digits of a two digit number is 7. If the digits are reversed, the new number increased by 3 equals 4 times the original number. Find the number.

5 Three years hence a man's age will be three times his son's age, and 7 years ago he was seven times as old as his son. How old are they now?

6 Rectangles are drawn on line segments of fixed lengths. When the breadths are 6 m and 5 m respectively the sum of the areas of the rectangles is 83 m². But if the breadths are 5 m and 4 m respectively the sum of the areas is 68 m². Find the sum of the areas of the squares drawn on the line segments.

7 If the length and the breadth of a room are increased by 1 metre each, the area is increased by 21 square metres. If the length is decreased by 1 metre and the breadth is increased by 2 metres, the area is increased by 14 square metres. Find the perimeter of the room.

8 The lengths (in metres) of the sides of a triangle are $2x + \dfrac{y}{2}, \dfrac{5x}{3} + y + \dfrac{1}{2}$ and $\dfrac{2}{3}x + 2y + \dfrac{5}{2}$. If the triangle is equilateral, find its perimeter.

9 On Diwali eve, two candles, one of which is 3 cm longer than the other, are lighted. The longer one is lighted at 5.30 p.m. and the shorter at 7 p.m. At 9.30 p.m. they both are of the same length. The longer one burns out at 11.30 p.m. and the shorter one at 11 p.m. How long was each candle originally?

Hint. Let the longer candle shorten at the rate of x cm/h when burning and the smaller candle shorten at the rate of y cm/h.

As the longer candle burns out completely in 6 hours and that the smaller candle in 4 hours, their lengths are $6x$ cm and $4y$ cm respectively.

According to given, $6x = 4y + 3$.

At 9.30 p.m., the length of longer candle $= (6x - 4x)$ cm $= 2x$ cm and the length of the smaller candle $= \left(4y - \dfrac{5}{2}y\right)$ cm $= \dfrac{3}{2}y$ cm. As both the candles have same length at 9.30 p.m., $2x = \dfrac{3}{2}y \Rightarrow 4x = 3y$.

7 Quadratic Equations

7.1 INTRODUCTION

In previous classes, you have learnt that an equation of the form $ax + b = 0$, where a, b are real numbers and $a \neq 0$ is called a linear equation in one variable. We also learnt that every linear equation in one variable has a unique solution.

In this chapter, we shall extend our knowledge to quadratic equations in one variable, and we shall also learn that a quadratic equation in one variable has atmost two solutions.

An equation of the form $ax^2 + bx + c = 0$, where a, b and c are real numbers and $a \neq 0$, is called a quadratic equation in the variable x.

For example :

$x^2 - 3x + 2 = 0$ and $6x^2 + x - 1 = 0$ are quadratic equations in the variable x.

A number α is a **root** (or **solution**) of the quadratic equation $ax^2 + bx + c = 0$ if it satisfies the equation *i.e.* if $a\alpha^2 + b\alpha + c = 0$.

For example :

When we substitute $x = 2$ in the quadratic equation $x^2 - 3x + 2 = 0$, we get $2^2 - 3 \times 2 + 2 = 0$ *i.e.* $4 - 6 + 2 = 0$ *i.e.* $0 = 0$, which is true. Therefore, 2 is a root of the quadratic equation $x^2 - 3x + 2 = 0$.

When we substitute $x = 3$ in the quadratic equation $x^2 - 3x + 2 = 0$, we get $3^2 - 3 \times 3 + 2 = 0$ *i.e.* $9 - 9 + 2 = 0$ *i.e.* $2 = 0$, which is wrong.

Therefore, 3 is not a root of the quadratic equation $x^2 - 3x + 2 = 0$.

7.2 SOLVING QUADRATIC EQUATIONS

Factorisation can be used to solve quadratic equations.

The equation $x^2 - 3x + 2 = 0$ can be written as $(x - 1)(x - 2) = 0$.

This equation can be solved by using a property of real numbers called *zero-product rule*.

7.2.1 Zero-product rule

If a and b are two numbers or expressions and if $ab = 0$, then either $a = 0$ or $b = 0$ or both $a = 0$ and $b = 0$.

Using this rule, the solutions of the equation $(x - 1)(x - 2) = 0$ can be obtained by putting each factor equal to zero and then solving for x. Thus, we get

$x - 1 = 0$ or $x - 2 = 0$

$\Rightarrow \quad x = 1$ or $x = 2$.

Hence, the solutions of the equation $x^2 - 3x + 2 = 0$ are 1 and 2.

7.2.2 Method to solve a quadratic equation by factorisation

Proceed as under :

* *Clear all fractions and write the equation in the form $ax^2 + bx + c = 0$.*

* *Factorise the left hand side into product of two linear factors.*

* *Put each linear factor equal to zero and solve the resulting linear equations.*

Remark

The solutions (roots) may be checked by substituting in the original equation.

Illustrative Examples

Example 1 Solve : $x^2 - 2x - 15 = 0$.

Solution. Given $x^2 - 2x - 15 = 0$

$\Rightarrow$ $x^2 - 5x + 3x - 15 = 0$

$\Rightarrow$ $x(x - 5) + 3(x - 5) = 0$

$\Rightarrow$ $(x - 5)(x + 3) = 0$

$\Rightarrow$ $x - 5 = 0$ or $x + 3 = 0$

$\Rightarrow$ $x = 5$ or $x = -3$.

Hence, the roots of the given equation are 5, –3.

Example 2 Solve : $6x^2 + x - 1 = 0$.

Solution. Given $6x^2 + x - 1 = 0$

$\Rightarrow$ $6x^2 + 3x - 2x - 1 = 0$

$\Rightarrow$ $3x(2x + 1) - 1(2x + 1) = 0$

$\Rightarrow$ $(2x + 1)(3x - 1) = 0$

$\Rightarrow$ $2x + 1 = 0$ or $3x - 1 = 0$

$\Rightarrow$ $x = -\dfrac{1}{2}$ or $x = \dfrac{1}{3}$.

Hence, the roots of the given equation are $-\dfrac{1}{2}, \dfrac{1}{3}$.

Example 3 Solve : $9x^2 + 6x + 1 = 0$.

Solution. Given $9x^2 + 6x + 1 = 0$

$\Rightarrow$ $9x^2 + 3x + 3x + 1 = 0$

$\Rightarrow$ $3x(3x + 1) + 1(3x + 1) = 0$

$\Rightarrow$ $(3x + 1)(3x + 1) = 0$

$\Rightarrow$ $3x + 1 = 0$ or $3x + 1 = 0$

$\Rightarrow$ $x = -\dfrac{1}{3}$ or $x = -\dfrac{1}{3}$.

Hence, the roots of the given equation are $-\dfrac{1}{3}, -\dfrac{1}{3}$.

Note that the given quadratic equation has equal roots.

Example 4 Solve : $2x - \dfrac{1}{x} = 1$.

Solution. To clear the fractions, multiply both sides of the given equation by x. We get

$2x^2 - 1 = x$

$\Rightarrow \quad 2x^2 - x - 1 = 0$

$\Rightarrow \quad 2x^2 - 2x + x - 1 = 0$

$\Rightarrow \quad 2x\,(x - 1) + 1\,(x - 1) = 0$

$\Rightarrow \quad (2x + 1)\,(x - 1) = 0$

$\Rightarrow \quad 2x + 1 = 0 \text{ or } x - 1 = 0$

$\Rightarrow \quad x = -\dfrac{1}{2} \text{ or } x = 1.$

Hence, the roots of the given equation are $-\dfrac{1}{2}$, 1.

Example 5 Solve : $\dfrac{x+3}{x-1} = \dfrac{2x+1}{3x-5}$.

Solution. Given $\dfrac{x+3}{x-1} = \dfrac{2x+1}{3x-5}$

$\Rightarrow \quad (x + 3)\,(3x - 5) = (x - 1)\,(2x + 1)$ 　　　　　　　　　　(by cross-multiplication)

$\Rightarrow \quad 3x^2 - 5x + 9x - 15 = 2x^2 + x - 2x - 1$

$\Rightarrow \quad 3x^2 + 4x - 15 = 2x^2 - x - 1$

$\Rightarrow \quad 3x^2 - 2x^2 + 4x + x - 15 + 1 = 0$

$\Rightarrow \quad x^2 + 5x - 14 = 0$

$\Rightarrow \quad x^2 + 7x - 2x - 14 = 0$

$\Rightarrow \quad x\,(x + 7) - 2\,(x + 7) = 0$

$\Rightarrow \quad (x + 7)\,(x - 2) = 0$

$\Rightarrow \quad x + 7 = 0 \text{ or } x - 2 = 0$

$\Rightarrow \quad x = -7 \text{ or } x = 2.$

Hence, the roots of the given equation are -7, 2.

Example 6 Solve : $\dfrac{x}{x-1} + \dfrac{x-1}{x} = 2\dfrac{1}{2}$.

Solution. Given $\dfrac{x}{x-1} + \dfrac{x-1}{x} = \dfrac{5}{2}$

To clear the fractions, multiply both sides of the given equation by L.C.M. of denominators *i.e.* by $2x\,(x - 1)$. We get

$2x \times x + 2\,(x - 1)\,(x - 1) = 5x\,(x - 1)$

$\Rightarrow \quad 2x^2 + 2x^2 - 4x + 2 = 5x^2 - 5x$

$\Rightarrow \quad 4x^2 - 4x + 2 = 5x^2 - 5x$

$\Rightarrow \quad 4x^2 - 5x^2 - 4x + 5x + 2 = 0$

$\Rightarrow \quad -x^2 + x + 2 = 0$

$\Rightarrow \quad x^2 - x - 2 = 0$

$\Rightarrow \quad x^2 - 2x + x - 2 = 0$

$\Rightarrow \quad x\,(x - 2) + 1\,(x - 2) = 0$

$\Rightarrow \quad (x + 1)\,(x - 2) = 0$

$\Rightarrow \quad x + 1 = 0$ or $x - 2 = 0$

$\Rightarrow \quad x = -1$ or $x = 2$.

Hence, the roots of the given equation are –1, 2.

EXERCISE 7

Solve the following (1 to 12) equations :

1   (i) $x^2 - 11x + 30 = 0$ (ii) $4x^2 - 25 = 0$.

2   (i) $2x^2 - 5x = 0$ (ii) $x^2 - 2x = 48$.

3   (i) $6 + x = x^2$ (ii) $2x^2 - 3x + 1 = 0$.

4   (i) $3x^2 = 2x + 8$ (ii) $4x^2 + 15 = 16x$.

5   (i) $x (2x + 5) = 25$ (ii) $(x + 3) (x - 3) = 40$.

6   (i) $(2x + 3) (x - 4) = 6$ (ii) $(3x + 1) (2x + 3) = 3$.

7   (i) $4x^2 + 4x + 1 = 0$ (ii) $(x - 4)^2 + 5^2 = 13^2$.

8   (i) $21x^2 = 4 (2x + 1)$ (ii) $\dfrac{2}{3}x^2 - \dfrac{1}{3}x - 1 = 0$.

9   (i) $6x + 29 = \dfrac{5}{x}$ (ii) $x + \dfrac{1}{x} = 2\dfrac{1}{2}$.

10   (i) $3x - \dfrac{8}{x} = 2$ (ii) $\dfrac{x}{3} + \dfrac{9}{x} = 4$.

11   (i) $\dfrac{x - 1}{x + 1} = \dfrac{2x - 5}{3x - 7}$ (ii) $\dfrac{1}{x + 2} + \dfrac{1}{x} = \dfrac{3}{4}$.

12   (i) $\dfrac{8}{x + 3} - \dfrac{3}{2 - x} = 2$ (ii) $\dfrac{x}{x + 1} + \dfrac{x + 1}{x} = 2\dfrac{1}{6}$.

Multiple Choice Questions

Choose the correct answer from the given four options (1 to 5):

1   Which of the following is not a quadratic equation :

     (a) $2x^2 = 3x - 5$ (b) $(2x - 1) (x - 1) = 2x^2 - 7x + 2$

     (c) $(2x - 1) (x + 2) = (x - 1) (x + 1)$ (d) $(x + 1)^3 = x^3 + 2x + 2$

2   If 2 is a root of the quadratic equation $2x^2 - kx + 1 = 0$, then the value of k is

     (a) 9   (b) -9 (c) $\dfrac{9}{2}$ (d) $-\dfrac{9}{2}$

3   If -3 is a root of the quadratic equation $kx^2 + 2x - 3 = 0$, then the value of k is

     (a) 1   (b) -1 (c) $\dfrac{1}{9}$ (d) $-\dfrac{1}{9}$

4   Which of the following quadratic equations has -1 as a root?

     (a) $x^2 + 5x + 6 = 0$ (b) $2x^2 - 3x + 1 = 0$

     (c) $2x^2 + x - 3 = 0$ (d) $2x^2 - x - 3 = 0$

5   The roots of the quadratic equation $x^2 - 3x - 4 = 0$ are

     (a) $-4, 1$ (b) $4, -1$ (c) $4, 1$ (d) $-4, -1$

Summary

○ An equation of the form $ax^2 + bx + c = 0$, where a, b and c are real numbers and $a \neq 0$, is called a quadratic equation in the variable x.

○ A number α is a root (or solution) of the equation $ax^2 + bx + c = 0$ if it satisfies it *i.e.* if $a\alpha^2 + b\alpha + c = 0$.

○ A quadratic equation can be solved by factorisation and then using zero-product rule.

○ To solve a quadratic equation, proceed as under :

    (*i*) Clear all fractions and write the equation in the form $ax^2 + bx + c = 0$.

    (*ii*) Factorise left hand side into product of two linear factors.

    (*iii*) Put each linear factor equal to zero and solve the resulting linear equations.

Chapter Test

Solve the following (1 to 3) equations :

1   (*i*) $x(2x + 5) = 3$ (*ii*) $3x^2 - 4x - 4 = 0$.

2   (*i*) $4x^2 - 2x + \dfrac{1}{4} = 0$ (*ii*) $2x^2 + 7x + 6 = 0$.

3   (*i*) $\dfrac{x-1}{x-2} + \dfrac{x-3}{x-4} = 3\dfrac{1}{3}$ (*ii*) $\dfrac{6}{x} - \dfrac{2}{x-1} = \dfrac{1}{x-2}$.

8 Indices

INTRODUCTION

In previous classes, we have read that if a is any real number and n is a natural number, then

$$a^n = a \times a \times a.... \, n \text{ times}$$

where a is called the **base**, n is called the **exponent** or **index** and a^n is the **exponential form**. We defined

$$a^0 = 1 \text{ and } a^{-n} = \left(\frac{1}{a}\right)^n = \frac{1}{a^n}, \, a \neq 0.$$

For example:

(i) $3^0 = 1, \quad 3^5 = 3.3.3.3.3 = 243, \quad 3^{-5} = \frac{1}{3^5} = \frac{1}{243}$.

(ii) $\left(\frac{2}{5}\right)^0 = 1, \left(\frac{2}{5}\right)^3 = \frac{2}{5} \cdot \frac{2}{5} \cdot \frac{2}{5} = \frac{8}{125}, \left(\frac{2}{5}\right)^{-3} = \frac{1}{\left(\frac{2}{5}\right)^3} = \frac{1}{\frac{8}{125}} = \frac{125}{8}$.

(iii) $(-2)^0 = 1, (-2)^3 = (-2)(-2)(-2) = -8, (-2)^{-3} = \frac{1}{(-2)^3} = \frac{1}{-8} = -\frac{1}{8}$.

Also, we have read the laws of exponents.

If a, b are rational numbers and m, n are integers, then the following results hold:

(i) $a^m \cdot a^n = a^{m+n}$

(ii) $(a^m)^n = a^{mn}$

(iii) $\dfrac{a^m}{a^n} = a^{m-n}, a \neq 0$

(iv) $a^m \cdot b^m = (ab)^m$

(v) $\left(\dfrac{a}{b}\right)^m = \dfrac{a^m}{b^m}, b \neq 0$

(vi) $a^0 = 1, a \neq 0$

(vii) $a^{-n} = \left(\dfrac{1}{a}\right)^n = \dfrac{1}{a^n}, a \neq 0$

(viii) $a^n = b^n, n \neq 0 \Rightarrow a = b$

(ix) $a^m = a^n, a \neq 1 \Rightarrow m = n$.

In this chapter, we shall extend these laws when the base is a positive real number and the exponents are rational numbers.

8.1 FRACTIONAL INDICES (OR SURDS)

We know that the square root of a positive real number a is that number which when multiplied by itself gives a as the product.

Thus, if b is the square root a, then $b \times b = a$ i.e. $b^2 = a$.

The square root of the number a is denoted by $\sqrt{a}$, so $b = \sqrt{a}$.

The concept of square root can be extended to cube root, fourth root, ..., nth root, where n is a natural number.

Let a be a positive real number and n be a natural number, then $\sqrt[n]{a} = b$ if and only if $b^n = a$, $b > 0$.

For example: $\sqrt[3]{8} = 2$ because $2^3 = 8$; $\sqrt[5]{243} = 3$ because $3^5 = 243$. Note that the symbol '$\sqrt{}$' used in $\sqrt{5}, \sqrt[3]{8}, \sqrt[5]{243}$ is called the **radical sign**.

In the language of exponents, we write $\sqrt[n]{a} = a^{\frac{1}{n}}$.

So, in particular, we write $\sqrt[3]{8} = 8^{\frac{1}{3}}, \sqrt[5]{243} = (243)^{\frac{1}{5}}$ etc.

Now let us try to understand what is $8^{\frac{2}{3}}$?

There are two ways:

$$8^{\frac{2}{3}} = \left(8^{\frac{1}{3}}\right)^2 = \left(\sqrt[3]{8}\right)^2 = 2^2 = 4; \qquad 8^{\frac{2}{3}} = (8^2)^{\frac{1}{3}} = (64)^{\frac{1}{3}} = \sqrt[3]{64} = 4.$$

This leads us to the following definition:

If $a > 0$ is a real number and m, n are integers, $n > 0$, m, n have no common factors except 1, then

$$a^{\frac{m}{n}} = \left(a^{\frac{1}{n}}\right)^m = \left(\sqrt[n]{a}\right)^m = \sqrt[n]{a^m}.$$

8.2 LAWS OF EXPONENTS FOR REAL NUMBERS

Laws of exponents for real numbers are:

If a, b are positive real numbers and m, n are rational numbers, then the following results hold:

(i) $a^m \cdot a^n = a^{m+n}$ (ii) $(a^m)^n = a^{mn}$ (iii) $\dfrac{a^m}{a^n} = a^{m-n}$

(iv) $a^m \cdot b^m = (ab)^m$ (v) $\left(\dfrac{a}{b}\right)^m = \dfrac{a^m}{b^m}$ (vi) $a^{-n} = \left(\dfrac{1}{a}\right)^n = \dfrac{1}{a^n}$

(vii) $a^n = b^n, n \neq 0 \Rightarrow a = b$ (viii) $a^m = a^n \Rightarrow m = n$ provided $a \neq 1$.

Note If p and q are different positive prime integers, then $p^m q^n = p^l q^k$ $\Rightarrow m = l$ and $n = k$.

Illustrative Examples

Example 1 Simplify the following:

(i) $(3x^4 y^3)(18x^3 y^5)$ (ii) $\dfrac{3x^4 y^3}{18x^3 y^5}$ (iii) $\left(-\dfrac{2x^2}{y^3}\right)^3$ (iv) $\sqrt[3]{27^{-2}}$.

Solution. (i) $(3x^4 y^3)(18x^3 y^5) = 3.18.x^4.x^3.y^3.y^5 = 54x^7 y^8$.

(ii) $\dfrac{3x^4 y^3}{18x^3 y^5} = \dfrac{3}{18} \cdot \dfrac{x^4}{x^3} \cdot \dfrac{y^3}{y^5} = \dfrac{1}{6}.x^{4-3} \cdot \dfrac{1}{y^{5-3}} = \dfrac{x}{6y^2}$.

(iii) $\left(-\dfrac{2x^2}{y^3}\right)^3 = (-2)^3 \cdot \dfrac{(x^2)^3}{(y^3)^3} = -8.\dfrac{x^6}{y^9}$.

(iv) $\sqrt[3]{27^{-2}} = (27^{-2})^{1/3} = (27)^{-2/3} = (3^3)^{-2/3} = 3^{3 \times (-2/3)} = 3^{-2} = \dfrac{1}{3^2} = \dfrac{1}{9}$.

Example 2 Simplify the following:

(i) $\left[\left((625)^{-\frac{1}{2}}\right)^{-\frac{1}{4}}\right]^2$

(ii) $\dfrac{9^{\frac{1}{3}} \times 27^{-\frac{1}{2}}}{36^{\frac{1}{6}} \times 3^{-\frac{2}{3}}}$

(ii) $(256)^{-\left(4^{-\frac{3}{2}}\right)}$

(iii) $\sqrt[4]{28} \div \sqrt[3]{7}$.

Solution. (i) $\left[\left((625)^{-\frac{1}{2}}\right)^{-\frac{1}{4}}\right]^2 = \left[(625)^{\left(-\frac{1}{2}\right)\times\left(-\frac{1}{4}\right)}\right]^2 = \left[(625)^{\frac{1}{8}}\right]^2$

$$= (625)^{\frac{1}{8}\times 2} = (625)^{\frac{1}{4}} = (5^4)^{\frac{1}{4}} = 5^{4\times\frac{1}{4}} = 5^1 = 5.$$

(ii) $\dfrac{9^{\frac{1}{3}} \times 27^{-\frac{1}{2}}}{36^{\frac{1}{6}} \times 3^{-\frac{2}{3}}} = \dfrac{(3^2)^{\frac{1}{3}} \times (3^3)^{-\frac{1}{2}}}{36^{\frac{1}{6}} \times 3^{-\frac{2}{3}}} = \dfrac{3^{\frac{2}{3}} \times 3^{-\frac{3}{2}}}{36^{\frac{1}{6}} \times 3^{-\frac{2}{3}}}$

$$= 3^{\frac{2}{3}+\left(-\frac{3}{2}\right)-\frac{1}{6}-\left(-\frac{2}{3}\right)} = 3^{\frac{2}{3}-\frac{3}{2}-\frac{1}{6}+\frac{2}{3}}$$

$$= 3^{\frac{4-9-1+4}{6}} = 3^{-\frac{2}{6}} = 3^{-\frac{1}{3}}.$$

(iii) Note that $4^{-\frac{3}{2}} = (2^2)^{-\frac{3}{2}} = 2^{2\times\left(-\frac{3}{2}\right)} = 2^{-3} = \dfrac{1}{2^3} = \dfrac{1}{8}$.

$$\therefore \quad (256)^{-\left(4^{-\frac{3}{2}}\right)} = (256)^{-\frac{1}{8}} = (2^8)^{-\frac{1}{8}} = 2^{8\times\left(-\frac{1}{8}\right)} = 2^{-1} = \dfrac{1}{2^1} = \dfrac{1}{2}.$$

(iv) $\sqrt[4]{28} \div \sqrt[3]{7} = (28)^{\frac{1}{4}} \div (7)^{\frac{1}{3}}$

L.C.M. of 4 and 3 = 12, so write each number with exponent $\dfrac{1}{12}$.

$(28)^{\frac{1}{4}} = ((28)^3)^{\frac{1}{12}}$ and $7^{\frac{1}{3}} = (7^4)^{\frac{1}{12}}$

$$\therefore \quad \sqrt[4]{28} \div \sqrt[3]{7} = \dfrac{((28)^3)^{\frac{1}{12}}}{(7^4)^{\frac{1}{12}}} = \left(\dfrac{(28)^3}{7^4}\right)^{\frac{1}{12}} = \left(\dfrac{28 \times 28 \times 28}{7 \times 7 \times 7 \times 7}\right)^{\frac{1}{12}}$$

$$= \left(\dfrac{4 \times 4 \times 4}{7}\right)^{\frac{1}{12}} = \left(\dfrac{64}{7}\right)^{\frac{1}{12}} = \sqrt[12]{\dfrac{64}{7}} .$$

Example 3 Simplify the following:

(i) $\left[5\left\{\left(\dfrac{1}{8}\right)^{-\frac{1}{3}} + \left(\dfrac{1}{27}\right)^{-\frac{1}{3}}\right\}\right]^{-\frac{1}{2}}$

(ii) $\sqrt[4]{81} - 8\sqrt[3]{216} + 15\sqrt[5]{32} + 2\sqrt{225}$

(iii) $3\sqrt[3]{40} - 4\sqrt[3]{320} - \sqrt[3]{5}$.

Solution. (i) $\left[5\left\{\left(\dfrac{1}{8}\right)^{-\frac{1}{3}} + \left(\dfrac{1}{27}\right)^{-\frac{1}{3}}\right\}\right]^{-\frac{1}{2}} = \left[5\left\{8^{\frac{1}{3}} + 27^{\frac{1}{3}}\right\}\right]^{-\frac{1}{2}}$

$$= \left[5\left\{(2^3)^{\frac{1}{3}} + (3^3)^{\frac{1}{3}}\right\}\right]^{-\frac{1}{2}} = \left[5(2^{3\times\frac{1}{3}} + 3^{3\times\frac{1}{3}})\right]^{-\frac{1}{2}}$$

$$= \left\{5(2+3)\right\}^{-\frac{1}{2}} = \left\{5 \times 5\right\}^{-\frac{1}{2}} = \left(5^2\right)^{-\frac{1}{2}}$$

$$= 5^{2\times\left(-\frac{1}{2}\right)} = 5^{-1} = \frac{1}{5}.$$

(ii) $\sqrt[4]{81} - 8\sqrt[3]{216} + 15\sqrt[5]{32} + 2\sqrt{225}$

$$= (3^4)^{\frac{1}{4}} - 8(6^3)^{\frac{1}{3}} + 15(2^5)^{\frac{1}{5}} + 2(15^2)^{\frac{1}{2}}$$

$$= 3^{4\times\frac{1}{4}} - 8\left(6^{3\times\frac{1}{3}}\right) + 15\left(2^{5\times\frac{1}{5}}\right) + 2\left(15^{2\times\frac{1}{2}}\right)$$

$$= 3^1 - 8 \times 6^1 + 15 \times 2^1 + 2 \times 15^1$$

$$= 3 - 8 \times 6 + 15 \times 2 + 2 \times 15$$

$$= 3 - 48 + 30 + 30 = 15.$$

(iii) $3\sqrt[3]{40} - 4\sqrt[3]{320} - \sqrt[3]{5} = 3(2^3 \times 5)^{\frac{1}{3}} - 4(2^6 \times 5)^{\frac{1}{3}} - 5^{\frac{1}{3}}$

$$= 3 \times (2^3)^{\frac{1}{3}}5^{\frac{1}{3}} - 4 \times (2^6)^{\frac{1}{3}}5^{\frac{1}{3}} - 5^{\frac{1}{3}}$$

$$= (3 \times 2^{3\times\frac{1}{3}} - 4 \times (2^6)^{\frac{1}{3}} - 1) \times 5^{\frac{1}{3}}$$

$$= (3 \times 2^1 - 4 \times 2^2 - 1) \times \sqrt[3]{5} = (6 - 16 - 1) \times \sqrt[3]{5}$$

$$= -11\sqrt[3]{5}.$$

Example 4 Simplify: $\left(\dfrac{81}{16}\right)^{-\frac{3}{4}} \times \left[\left(\dfrac{25}{9}\right)^{-\frac{3}{2}} \div \left(\dfrac{5}{2}\right)^{-3}\right]$.

Solution. $\left(\dfrac{81}{16}\right)^{-\frac{3}{4}} \times \left[\left(\dfrac{25}{9}\right)^{-\frac{3}{2}} \div \left(\dfrac{5}{2}\right)^{-3}\right]$

$$= \left(\left(\dfrac{3}{2}\right)^4\right)^{-\frac{3}{4}} \times \left[\left(\left(\dfrac{5}{3}\right)^2\right)^{-\frac{3}{2}} \div \left(\dfrac{5}{2}\right)^{-3}\right]$$

$$= \left(\dfrac{3}{2}\right)^{4\times\left(-\frac{3}{4}\right)} \times \left[\left(\dfrac{5}{3}\right)^{2\times\left(-\frac{3}{2}\right)} \div \left(\dfrac{5}{2}\right)^{-3}\right]$$

$$= \left(\dfrac{3}{2}\right)^{-3} \times \left[\left(\dfrac{5}{3}\right)^{-3} \div \left(\dfrac{5}{2}\right)^{-3}\right]$$

$$= \left(\frac{2}{3}\right)^3 \times \left[\left(\frac{3}{5}\right)^3 \div \left(\frac{2}{5}\right)^3\right] = \frac{2^3}{3^3} \times \left[\frac{3^3}{5^3} \div \frac{2^3}{5^3}\right] \qquad \left[\because a^{-n} = \left(\frac{1}{a}\right)^n\right]$$

$$= \frac{2^3}{3^3} \times \left(\frac{3^3}{5^3} \times \frac{5^3}{2^3}\right) = \frac{2^3}{3^3} \times \frac{3^3}{2^3} = 1.$$

Example 5 Find the value of $\dfrac{4}{(216)^{-\frac{2}{3}}} + \dfrac{1}{(256)^{-\frac{3}{4}}} + \dfrac{2}{(243)^{-\frac{1}{5}}}$.

Solution. $\dfrac{4}{(216)^{-\frac{2}{3}}} + \dfrac{1}{(256)^{-\frac{3}{4}}} + \dfrac{2}{(243)^{-\frac{1}{5}}}$

$$= 4(216)^{\frac{2}{3}} + (256)^{\frac{3}{4}} + 2(243)^{\frac{1}{5}}$$

$$= 4(6^3)^{\frac{2}{3}} + (4^4)^{\frac{3}{4}} + 2(3^5)^{\frac{1}{5}} = 4\left(6^{3\times\frac{2}{3}}\right) + 4^{4\times\frac{3}{4}} + 2\left(3^{5\times\frac{1}{5}}\right)$$

$$= 4(6^2) + 4^3 + 2(3^1) = 4 \times 36 + 64 + 6$$

$$= 144 + 64 + 6 = 214.$$

Example 6 Evaluate: $\sqrt{\dfrac{1}{4}} + (0{\cdot}01)^{-1/2} - (27)^{2/3}$. Leave your answer as a fraction.

Solution. $\sqrt{\dfrac{1}{4}} + (0{\cdot}01)^{-1/2} - (27)^{2/3} = \dfrac{1}{2} + \left(\dfrac{1}{100}\right)^{-1/2} - (3^3)^{2/3}$

$$= \frac{1}{2} + (100)^{1/2} - 3^2 \qquad \left[\because a^{-n} = \left(\frac{1}{a}\right)^n\right]$$

$$= \frac{1}{2} + ((10)^2)^{1/2} - 9$$

$$= \frac{1}{2} + 10 - 9 = \frac{1}{2} + 1 = 1\frac{1}{2}.$$

Example 7 Simplify: $\left(\dfrac{1}{4}\right)^{-2} - 3(8)^{2/3}(4)^0 + \left(\dfrac{9}{16}\right)^{-1/2}$.

Solution. $\left(\dfrac{1}{4}\right)^{-2} - 3(8)^{2/3}(4)^0 + \left(\dfrac{9}{16}\right)^{-1/2} = (4)^2 - 3.(2^3)^{2/3}.1 + \left(\dfrac{16}{9}\right)^{1/2}$

$$\left[\because a^{-n} = \left(\frac{1}{a}\right)^n \text{ and } a^0 = 1\right]$$

$$= 16 - 3 \times 2^2 \times 1 + \left(\left(\frac{4}{3}\right)^2\right)^{1/2}$$

$$= 16 - 3 \times 4 + \frac{4}{3} = 16 - 12 + \frac{4}{3}$$

$$= 4 + \frac{4}{3} = \frac{16}{3} = 5\frac{1}{3}.$$

Example 8 Simplify the following:

(i) $\dfrac{5^{n+2} - 6.5^{n+1}}{13.5^n - 2.5^{n+1}}$

(ii) $\left(\dfrac{x^m}{x^n}\right)^{m+n} \left(\dfrac{x^n}{x^l}\right)^{n+l} \left(\dfrac{x^l}{x^m}\right)^{l+m}$

(iii) $\left(x^{\frac{1}{3}} + x^{-\frac{1}{3}}\right)\left(x^{\frac{2}{3}} - 1 + x^{-\frac{2}{3}}\right)$.

Solution. (*i*) $\dfrac{5^{n+2} - 6.5^{n+1}}{13.5^n - 2.5^{n+1}} = \dfrac{5^n.5^2 - 6.5^n.5^1}{13.5^n - 2.5^1.5^n}$

$$= \dfrac{5^n(5^2 - 6.5)}{5^n(13 - 2.5)} = \dfrac{25 - 30}{13 - 10} = \dfrac{-5}{3} = -\dfrac{5}{3}.$$

(*ii*) $\left(\dfrac{x^m}{x^n}\right)^{m+n} \left(\dfrac{x^n}{x^l}\right)^{n+l} \left(\dfrac{x^l}{x^m}\right)^{l+m}$

$$= (x^{m-n})^{m+n}.(x^{n-l})^{n+l}.(x^{l-m})^{l+m}$$
$$= x^{m^2-n^2}.x^{n^2-l^2}.x^{l^2-m^2}$$
$$= x^{m^2-n^2+n^2-l^2+l^2-m^2} = x^0 = 1.$$

(*iii*) $\left(x^{\frac{1}{3}} + x^{-\frac{1}{3}}\right)\left(x^{\frac{2}{3}} - 1 + x^{-\frac{2}{3}}\right) = x^{\frac{1}{3}}.x^{\frac{2}{3}} - x^{\frac{1}{3}} + x^{\frac{1}{3}}.x^{-\frac{2}{3}} + x^{-\frac{1}{3}}.x^{\frac{2}{3}} - x^{-\frac{1}{3}} + x^{-\frac{1}{3}}.x^{-\frac{2}{3}}$

$$= x^1 - x^{\frac{1}{3}} + x^{-\frac{1}{3}} + x^{\frac{1}{3}} - x^{-\frac{1}{3}} + x^{-1}$$
$$= x + x^{-1} = x + \dfrac{1}{x}.$$

Example 9 If $a = b^{2x}$, $b = c^{2y}$ and $c = a^{2z}$, prove that $xyz = \dfrac{1}{8}$.

Solution. Given $\quad a = b^{2x} \quad$ ...(*i*) $\qquad b = c^{2y} \quad$ ...(*ii*) $\qquad c = a^{2z} \qquad$ ...(*iii*)

Substituting the value of b from (*ii*) in (*i*), we get

$$a = (c^{2y})^{2x} = c^{4xy} \qquad\qquad ...(iv)$$

Substituting the value of c from (*iii*) in (*iv*), we get

$$a = (a^{2z})^{4xy} = a^{8xyz}$$
$\Rightarrow \qquad\qquad a^1 = a^{8xyz} \Rightarrow 1 = 8xyz \qquad\qquad$ (Assume $a > 0$, $a \neq 1$)

$\Rightarrow \qquad\qquad xyz = \dfrac{1}{8}.$

Example 10 If $a^x = b^y = c^z$ and $b^2 = ac$, prove that $y = \dfrac{2xz}{z + x}$.

Solution. Let $a^x = b^y = c^z = k$ (say), then

$$a = k^{\frac{1}{x}}, b = k^{\frac{1}{y}} \text{ and } c = k^{\frac{1}{z}}.$$

Given $\qquad\qquad b^2 = ac \Rightarrow \left(k^{\frac{1}{y}}\right)^2 = k^{\frac{1}{x}}.k^{\frac{1}{z}}$

$\Rightarrow \qquad\qquad k^{\frac{2}{y}} = k^{\frac{1}{x}+\frac{1}{z}} \Rightarrow \dfrac{2}{y} = \dfrac{1}{x} + \dfrac{1}{z}$

$\Rightarrow \qquad\qquad \dfrac{2}{y} = \dfrac{z + x}{xz} \Rightarrow y = \dfrac{2xz}{z + x}.$

Example 11 Prove that $\dfrac{a^{-1}}{a^{-1} + b^{-1}} + \dfrac{a^{-1}}{a^{-1} - b^{-1}} = \dfrac{2b^2}{b^2 - a^2}$.

Solution. $\dfrac{a^{-1}}{a^{-1} + b^{-1}} + \dfrac{a^{-1}}{a^{-1} - b^{-1}} = \dfrac{\dfrac{1}{a}}{\dfrac{1}{a} + \dfrac{1}{b}} + \dfrac{\dfrac{1}{a}}{\dfrac{1}{a} - \dfrac{1}{b}}$

$$= \frac{\frac{1}{a}}{\frac{b+a}{ab}} + \frac{\frac{1}{a}}{\frac{b-a}{ab}} = \frac{1}{a} \times \frac{ab}{b+a} + \frac{1}{a} \times \frac{ab}{b-a}$$

$$= \frac{b}{b+a} + \frac{b}{b-a} = b\left(\frac{1}{b+a} + \frac{1}{b-a}\right)$$

$$= b\left(\frac{b-a+b+a}{b^2-a^2}\right) = \frac{2b^2}{b^2-a^2}.$$

Example 12 If $abc = 1$, show that

$$\frac{1}{1+a+b^{-1}} + \frac{1}{1+b+c^{-1}} + \frac{1}{1+c+a^{-1}} = 1.$$

Solution. $\dfrac{1}{1+a+b^{-1}} + \dfrac{1}{1+b+c^{-1}} + \dfrac{1}{1+c+a^{-1}}$

$$= \frac{1}{1+a+\frac{1}{b}} + \frac{1}{1+b+\frac{1}{c}} + \frac{1}{1+c+\frac{1}{a}}$$

$$= \frac{b}{b+ab+1} + \frac{1}{1+b+ab} + \frac{1}{1+\frac{1}{ab}+\frac{1}{a}} \qquad \left(\because abc = 1 \Rightarrow \frac{1}{c} = ab \text{ and } c = \frac{1}{ab}\right)$$

$$= \frac{b}{1+b+ab} + \frac{1}{1+b+ab} + \frac{ab}{ab+1+b} = \frac{b+1+ab}{1+b+ab} = 1.$$

Example 13 If $\dfrac{9^{n+1}(3^{-\frac{n}{2}})^{-2} - 27^n}{(2 \times 3^m)^3} = \dfrac{1}{729}$, then prove that $m - n = 2$.

Solution. Given $\dfrac{9^{n+1}(3^{-\frac{n}{2}})^{-2} - 27^n}{(2 \times 3^m)^3} = \dfrac{1}{729}$

$$\Rightarrow \quad \frac{(3^2)^{n+1}\left(3^{\left(-\frac{n}{2}\right)(-2)}\right) - (3^3)^n}{2^3 \times 3^{m \times 3}} = \frac{1}{729},$$

$$\Rightarrow \quad \frac{3^{2n+2} \times 3^n - 3^{3 \times n}}{2^3 \times 3^{3m}} = \frac{1}{3^6}$$

$$\Rightarrow \quad \frac{3^{3n}.3^2 - 3^{3n}}{2^3 \times 3^{3m}} = \frac{1}{3^6} \Rightarrow \frac{3^{3n}(3^2 - 1)}{8 \times 3^{3m}} = \frac{1}{3^6}$$

$$\Rightarrow \quad \frac{3^{3n} \times 8}{8 \times 3^{3m}} = \frac{1}{3^6} \Rightarrow 3^{3n-3m} = 3^{-6}$$

$$\Rightarrow \quad 3n - 3m = -6 \Rightarrow n - m = -2$$

$$\Rightarrow \quad m - n = 2.$$

Example 14 If $x = \sqrt[3]{28}$ and $y = \sqrt[3]{27}$, find the value of $x + y - \dfrac{1}{x^2 + xy + y^2}$.

Solution. $x + y - \dfrac{1}{x^2 + xy + y^2} = x + y - \dfrac{x-y}{(x-y)(x^2+xy+y^2)}$ (Note this step)

$$= x + y - \frac{x-y}{x^3 - y^3}$$

$$= x + y - \frac{x-y}{((28)^{1/3})^3 - ((27)^{1/3})^3}$$

$$= x + y - \frac{x-y}{28-27} = x + y - \frac{x-y}{1}$$

$$= x + y - (x - y) = 2y$$

$$= 2 \times \sqrt[3]{27} = 2 \times (27)^{1/3}$$

$$= 2 \times (3^3)^{\frac{1}{3}} = 2 \times 3^1 = 6.$$

Example 15 Given $1176 = 2^p . 3^q . 7^r$, find

    (i) the numerical values of p, q and r (ii) the value of $2^p.3^q.7^{-r}$ as a fraction.

Solution. (i) Given $1176 = 2^p.3^q.7^r$

$\Rightarrow$ $2 \times 2 \times 2 \times 3 \times 7 \times 7 = 2^p.3^q.7^r$

$\Rightarrow$ $2^3.3^1.7^2 = 2^p.3^q.7^r$

$\Rightarrow$ $p = 3$, $q = 1$ and $r = 2$.   (See note page 149)

(ii) $2^p.3^q.7^{-r} = 2^3.3^1.7^{-2} = \frac{8 \times 3}{7^2} = \frac{24}{49}$.

Example 16 If $\left(\frac{p^{-1}q^2}{p^3q^{-2}}\right)^{1/3} + \left(\frac{p^6q^{-3}}{p^{-2}q^3}\right)^{1/2} = p^a q^b$, prove that $a + b + 1 = 0$, where p and q are

different positive primes.

Solution. $\left(\frac{p^{-1}q^2}{p^3q^{-2}}\right)^{1/3} = (p^{-1-3}q^{2-(-2)})^{1/3} = (p^{-4}q^4)^{1/3} = p^{-\frac{4}{3}}q^{\frac{4}{3}},$

$$\left(\frac{p^6q^{-3}}{p^{-2}q^3}\right)^{1/2} = (p^{6-(-2)}q^{-3-3})^{1/2} = (p^8q^{-6})^{1/2} = p^4q^{-3}.$$

$\therefore$ $\left(\frac{p^{-1}q^2}{p^3q^{-2}}\right)^{1/3} \div \left(\frac{p^6q^{-3}}{p^{-2}q^3}\right)^{1/2} = p^a q^b$

$\Rightarrow$ $\frac{p^{-\frac{4}{3}}q^{\frac{4}{3}}}{p^4q^{-3}} \Rightarrow p^a q^b \Rightarrow p^{-\frac{4}{3}-4} q^{\frac{4}{3}-(-3)} = p^a q^b$

$\Rightarrow$ $p^{-\frac{16}{3}} q^{\frac{13}{3}} = p^a q^b$

$\Rightarrow$ $-\frac{16}{3} = a$ and $\frac{13}{3} = b$ ($\because$ p, q are different positive primes)

$\therefore$ $a + b + 1 = -\frac{16}{3} + \frac{13}{3} + 1 = \frac{-16 + 13 + 3}{3} = 0.$

Example 17 Solve the following equations for x:

  (i) $4^{2x} = \frac{1}{32}$ (ii) $\sqrt{\left(\frac{3}{5}\right)^{1-2x}} = 4\frac{17}{27}$.

Solution. (i) Given $4^{2x} = \frac{1}{32} \Rightarrow (2^2)^{2x} = \left(\frac{1}{2}\right)^5$

$\Rightarrow$ $2^{4x} = 2^{-5}$ $\left[\because \left(\frac{1}{a}\right)^n = a^{-n}\right]$

$\Rightarrow$ $4x = -5 \Rightarrow x = -\frac{5}{4}.$

(ii) Given $\sqrt{\left(\dfrac{3}{5}\right)^{1-2x}} = 4\dfrac{17}{27} \Rightarrow \left(\left(\dfrac{3}{5}\right)^{1-2x}\right)^{1/2} = \dfrac{125}{27}$

$\Rightarrow \left(\dfrac{3}{5}\right)^{\frac{1-2x}{2}} = \left(\dfrac{5}{3}\right)^3 \Rightarrow \left(\dfrac{3}{5}\right)^{\frac{1-2x}{2}} = \left(\dfrac{3}{5}\right)^{-3}$ $\left[\because \left(\dfrac{1}{a}\right)^n = a^{-n}\right]$

$\Rightarrow \dfrac{1-2x}{2} = -3 \Rightarrow 1 - 2x = -6$

$\Rightarrow -2x = -6 - 1 \Rightarrow -2x = -7 \Rightarrow x = \dfrac{7}{2}.$

Example 18 Solve the following equations for x:

(i) $\sqrt{\left(8^0 + \dfrac{2}{3}\right)} = (0 \cdot 6)^{2-3x}$ *(ii)* $2^3(5^0 + 3^{2x}) = 8\dfrac{8}{27}.$

Solution. *(i)* Given $\sqrt{\left(8^0 + \dfrac{2}{3}\right)} = (0 \cdot 6)^{2-3x}$

$\Rightarrow \sqrt{\left(1 + \dfrac{2}{3}\right)} = \left(\dfrac{3}{5}\right)^{2-3x} \Rightarrow \left(\dfrac{5}{3}\right)^{\frac{1}{2}} = \left(\dfrac{3}{5}\right)^{2-3x}$

$\Rightarrow \left(\dfrac{3}{5}\right)^{-\frac{1}{2}} = \left(\dfrac{3}{5}\right)^{2-3x}$ $\left[\because \left(\dfrac{1}{a}\right)^n = a^{-n}\right]$

$\Rightarrow -\dfrac{1}{2} = 2 - 3x$

$\Rightarrow 3x = 2 + \dfrac{1}{2} \Rightarrow 3x = \dfrac{5}{2} \Rightarrow x = \dfrac{5}{6}.$

(ii) Given $2^3(5^0 + 3^{2x}) = 8\dfrac{8}{27}$

$\Rightarrow 8(1 + 3^{2x}) = 8 + \dfrac{8}{27} \Rightarrow 8 + 8 \times 3^{2x} = 8 + \dfrac{8}{27}$

$\Rightarrow 8 \times 3^{2x} = \dfrac{8}{27} \Rightarrow 3^{2x} = \dfrac{1}{27}$

$\Rightarrow 3^{2x} = \dfrac{1}{3^3} \Rightarrow 3^{2x} = 3^{-3}$

$\Rightarrow 2x = -3 \Rightarrow x = -\dfrac{3}{2}.$

Example 19 If $a = \dfrac{2^{x-1}}{2^{x-2}}$, $b = \dfrac{2^{-x}}{2^{x+1}}$ and $a - b = 0$, then find the value of x.

Solution. $a - b = 0 \Rightarrow a = b \Rightarrow \dfrac{2^{x-1}}{2^{x-2}} = \dfrac{2^{-x}}{2^{x+1}}$

$\Rightarrow 2^{(x-1)-(x-2)} = 2^{-x-(x+1)}$

$\Rightarrow 2^1 = 2^{-2x-1} \Rightarrow 1 = -2x - 1$

$\Rightarrow 2x = -2 \Rightarrow x = -1.$

Example 20 If $5^{2x-1} = 25^{x-1} + 100$, find the value of 3^{1+x}.

Solution. Given $5^{2x-1} = 25^{x-1} + 100$

$\Rightarrow 5^{2x-1} = (5^2)^{x-1} + 100 \Rightarrow 5^{2x-1} - 5^{2x-2} = 100$

$\Rightarrow 5^{2x-2} \cdot 5^1 - 5^{2x-2} = 100 \Rightarrow 5^{2x-2}(5-1) = 100$

$\Rightarrow 5^{2x-2} \times 4 = 100 \Rightarrow 5^{2x-2} = 25$

$\Rightarrow 5^{2x-2} = 5^2 \Rightarrow 2x - 2 = 2$

$$\Rightarrow \quad 2x = 4 \Rightarrow x = 2.$$

$$\therefore \quad 3^{1+x} = 3^{1+2} = 3^3 = 27.$$

Example 21 Determine $(8x)^x$ if $9^{x+2} = 240 + 9^x$.

Solution. Given $9^{x+2} = 240 + 9^x$

$$\Rightarrow \quad 9^x . 9^2 - 9^x = 240 \Rightarrow (9^2 - 1)\, 9^x = 240$$

$$\Rightarrow \quad (81 - 1)\, 9^x = 240 \Rightarrow 80 \times (3^2)^x = 240$$

$$\Rightarrow \quad 3^{2x} = \frac{240}{80} = 3 = 3^1 \Rightarrow 2x = 1 \Rightarrow x = \frac{1}{2}.$$

$$\therefore \quad (8x)^x = \left(8 \times \frac{1}{2}\right)^{\frac{1}{2}} = 4^{\frac{1}{2}} = (2^2)^{\frac{1}{2}} = 2^{2 \times \frac{1}{2}} = 2^1 = 2.$$

Example 22 Solve for x and y:

$$(\sqrt{32})^x \div 2^{y+1} = 1, \quad 16^{4-\frac{x}{2}} - 8^y = 0.$$

Solution. Given $(\sqrt{32})^x \div 2^{y+1} = 1$

$$\Rightarrow \quad \left((2^5)^{\frac{1}{2}}\right)^x \div 2^{y+1} = 1$$

$$\Rightarrow \quad \frac{\left(2^{\frac{5}{2}}\right)^x}{2^{y+1}} = 1 \Rightarrow 2^{\frac{5x}{2}-y-1} = 2^0$$

$$\Rightarrow \quad \frac{5x}{2} - y - 1 = 0 \Rightarrow 5x - 2y - 2 = 0 \qquad \qquad \dots(i)$$

Also $\quad 16^{4-\frac{x}{2}} - 8^y = 0 \Rightarrow (2^4)^{4-\frac{x}{2}} = (2^3)^y$

$$\Rightarrow \quad 2^{16-2x} = 2^{3y} \Rightarrow 16 - 2x = 3y$$

$$\Rightarrow \quad 2x + 3y - 16 = 0 \qquad \qquad \dots(ii)$$

Multiplying (i) by 3 and (ii) by 2, we get

$$15x - 6y - 6 = 0 \qquad \qquad \dots(iii)$$

and $\quad 4x + 6y - 32 = 0 \qquad \qquad \dots(iv)$

Adding (iii) and (iv), we get

$$19x - 38 = 0 \Rightarrow x = 2.$$

Substituting $x = 2$ in (ii), we get

$$2.2 + 3y - 16 = 0 \Rightarrow 3y = 12 \Rightarrow y = 4.$$

Hence, the solution is $x = 2$, $y = 4$.

EXERCISE 8

Simplify the following (1 to 20):

1   (i) $\left(\dfrac{81}{16}\right)^{-\frac{3}{4}}$ (ii) $\left(1\dfrac{61}{64}\right)^{-\frac{2}{3}}$.

2   (i) $(2a^{-3}b^2)^3$ (ii) $\dfrac{a^{-1} + b^{-1}}{(ab)^{-1}}$.

3   (i) $\dfrac{x^{-1}y^{-1}}{x^{-1}+y^{-1}}$ (ii) $\dfrac{(4\times 10^7)(6\times 10^{-5})}{8\times 10^{10}}$.

4   (i) $\dfrac{3a}{b^{-1}}+\dfrac{2b}{a^{-1}}$ (ii) $5^0\times 4^{-1}+8^{1/3}$.

5   (i) $\left(\dfrac{8}{125}\right)^{-\frac{1}{3}}$ (ii) $(0{\cdot}027)^{-\frac{1}{3}}$.

6   (i) $\left(-\dfrac{1}{27}\right)^{-\frac{2}{3}}$ (ii) $(64)^{-\frac{2}{3}}\div 9^{-\frac{3}{2}}$.

7   (i) $\dfrac{(27)^{\frac{2n}{3}}\times(8)^{-\frac{n}{6}}}{(18)^{-\frac{n}{2}}}$ (ii) $\dfrac{5.(25)^{n+1}-25.(5)^{2n}}{5.(5)^{2n+3}-(25)^{n+1}}$.

8   (i) $\left[8^{-\frac{4}{3}}\div 2^{-2}\right]^{1/2}$ (ii) $\left(\dfrac{27}{8}\right)^{2/3}-\left(\dfrac{1}{4}\right)^{-2}+5^0$.

9   (i) $(3x^2)^{-3}\times(x^9)^{2/3}$ (ii) $(8x^4)^{1/3}\div x^{1/3}$.

10   (i) $(3^2)^0+3^{-4}\times 3^6+\left(\dfrac{1}{3}\right)^{-2}$ (ii) $9^{5/2}-3.(5)^0-\left(\dfrac{1}{81}\right)^{-1/2}$.

11   (i) $16^{3/4}+2\left(\dfrac{1}{2}\right)^{-1}(3)^0$ (ii) $(81)^{3/4}-\left(\dfrac{1}{32}\right)^{-2/5}+(8)^{1/3}\left(\dfrac{1}{2}\right)^{-1}(2)^0$.

12   (i) $\left(\dfrac{64}{125}\right)^{-\frac{2}{3}}\div\dfrac{1}{\left(\dfrac{256}{625}\right)^{\frac{1}{4}}}+\left(\dfrac{\sqrt{25}}{\sqrt[3]{64}}\right)^0$ (ii) $\dfrac{5^{n+3}-6\times 5^{n+1}}{9\times 5^n-2^2\times 5^n}$.

13   (i) $\left[(64)^{\frac{2}{3}}2^{-2}\div 8^0\right]^{-1/2}$ (ii) $3^n\times 9^{n+1}\div(3^{n-1}\times 9^{n-1})$.

14   (i) $\dfrac{\sqrt{2^2}\times\sqrt[4]{256}}{\sqrt[3]{64}}-\left(\dfrac{1}{2}\right)^{-2}$ (ii) $\dfrac{3^{-\frac{6}{7}}\times 4^{-\frac{3}{7}}\times 9^{\frac{3}{7}}\times 2^{\frac{6}{7}}}{2^2+2^0+2^{-2}}$.

15   (i) $\dfrac{(32)^{\frac{2}{5}}\times(4)^{-\frac{1}{2}}\times(8)^{\frac{1}{3}}}{2^{-2}\div(64)^{-1/3}}$ (ii) $\dfrac{5^{2(x+6)}\times(25)^{-7+2x}}{(125)^{2x}}$.

16   (i) $\dfrac{7^{2n+3}-(49)^{n+2}}{((343)^{n+1})^{2/3}}$ (ii) $(27)^{4/3}+(32)^{0.8}+(0{\cdot}8)^{-1}$.

17   (i) $(\sqrt{32}-\sqrt{5})^{\frac{1}{3}}(\sqrt{32}+\sqrt{5})^{\frac{1}{3}}$ (ii) $\left(x^{\frac{1}{3}}-x^{-\frac{1}{3}}\right)\left(x^{\frac{2}{3}}+1+x^{-\frac{2}{3}}\right)$.

18   (i) $\left(\dfrac{x^m}{x^n}\right)^l\cdot\left(\dfrac{x^n}{x^l}\right)^m\cdot\left(\dfrac{x^l}{x^m}\right)^n$ (ii) $\left(\dfrac{x^{a+b}}{x^c}\right)^{a-b}\cdot\left(\dfrac{x^{b+c}}{x^a}\right)^{b-c}\cdot\left(\dfrac{x^{c+a}}{x^b}\right)^{c-a}$.

19 (i) $\sqrt[lm]{\dfrac{x^l}{x^m}} \cdot \sqrt[mn]{\dfrac{x^m}{x^n}} \cdot \sqrt[nl]{\dfrac{x^n}{x^l}}$

(ii) $\left(\dfrac{x^a}{x^b}\right)^{a^2+ab+b^2} \cdot \left(\dfrac{x^b}{x^c}\right)^{b^2+bc+c^2} \cdot \left(\dfrac{x^c}{x^a}\right)^{c^2+ac+a^2}$

(iii) $\left(\dfrac{x^a}{x^{-b}}\right)^{a^2-ab+b^2} \cdot \left(\dfrac{x^b}{x^{-c}}\right)^{b^2-bc+c^2} \cdot \left(\dfrac{x^c}{x^{-a}}\right)^{c^2-ca+a^2}$.

20 (i) $(a^{-1} + b^{-1}) \div (a^{-2} - b^{-2})$

(ii) $\dfrac{1}{1+a^{m-n}} + \dfrac{1}{1+a^{n-m}}$.

21 Prove the following:

(i) $(a + b)^{-1} \, (a^{-1} + b^{-1}) = \dfrac{1}{ab}$

(ii) $\dfrac{x+y+z}{x^{-1}y^{-1} + y^{-1}z^{-1} + z^{-1}x^{-1}} = xyz$.

22 If $a = c^z$, $b = a^x$ and $c = b^y$, prove that $xyz = 1$.

23 If $a = xy^{p-1}$, $b = xy^{q-1}$ and $c = xy^{r-1}$, prove that

$a^{q-r} \cdot b^{r-p} \cdot c^{p-q} = 1$.

24 If $2^x = 3^y = 6^{-z}$, prove that $\dfrac{1}{x} + \dfrac{1}{y} + \dfrac{1}{z} = 0$.

25 If $2^x = 3^y = 12^z$, prove that $x = \dfrac{2yz}{y-z}$.

Hint. Let $2^x = 3^y = 12^z = k$, then $2 = k^{\frac{1}{x}}$, $3 = k^{\frac{1}{y}}$ and $12 = k^{\frac{1}{z}}$.

Now $12 = 2^2 \times 3 \Rightarrow k^{\frac{1}{z}} = \left(k^{\frac{1}{x}}\right)^2 \times k^{\frac{1}{y}}$

$\Rightarrow \dfrac{1}{z} = \dfrac{2}{x} + \dfrac{1}{y} \Rightarrow \dfrac{1}{z} - \dfrac{1}{y} = \dfrac{2}{x}$.

26 Simplify and express with positive exponents:

$(3x^2)^0$, $(xy)^{-2}$, $(-27a^9)^{2/3}$.

27 If $a = 3$ and $b = -2$, find the values of:

(i) $a^a + b^b$

(ii) $a^b + b^a$.

28 If $x = 10^3 \times 0.0099$, $y = 10^{-2} \times 110$, find the value of $\sqrt{\dfrac{x}{y}}$.

29 Evaluate $x^{1/2} \cdot y^{-1} \cdot z^{2/3}$ when $x = 9$, $y = 2$ and $z = 8$.

30 If $x^4y^2z^3 = 49392$, find the values of x, y and z, where x, y and z are different positive primes.

31 If $\sqrt[3]{a^6b^{-4}} = a^x \cdot b^{2y}$, find x and y, where a, b are different positive primes.

32 If $(p + q)^{-1} \, (p^{-1} + q^{-1}) = p^aq^b$, prove that $a + b + 2 = 0$, where p and q are different positive primes.

33 If $\left(\dfrac{p^{-1}q^2}{p^2q^{-4}}\right)^7 \div \left(\dfrac{p^3q^{-5}}{p^{-2}q^3}\right)^{-5} = p^xq^y$, find $x + y$, where p and q are different positive primes.

34 Solve the following equations for x:

    (i) $5^{2x+3} = 1$ (ii) $(13)^{\sqrt{x}} = 4^4 - 3^4 - 6$

    (iii) $\left(\sqrt{\dfrac{3}{5}}\right)^{x+1} = \dfrac{125}{27}$ (iv) $(\sqrt[3]{4})^{2x+\frac{1}{2}} = \dfrac{1}{32}$.

35 Solve the following equations for x:

    (i) $\sqrt{\dfrac{p}{q}} = \left(\dfrac{q}{p}\right)^{1-2x}$ (ii) $4^{x-1} \times (0.5)^{3-2x} = \left(\dfrac{1}{8}\right)^x$.

36 If $5^{3x} = 125$ and $(10)^y = 0.001$, find x and y.

37 If $\dfrac{9^n.3^2.3^n - (27)^n}{3^{3m}.2^3} = \dfrac{1}{27}$, prove that $m = 1 + n$.

38 If $3^{4x} = (81)^{-1}$ and $(10)^{1/y} = 0.0001$, find the value of $2^{-x} \cdot (16)^y$.

39 If $3^{x+1} = 9^{x-2}$, find the value of 2^{1+x}.

40 Solve the following equations:

    (i) $3(2^x +1) - 2^{x+2} + 5 = 0$ (ii) $3^x = 9.3^y$, $8.2^y = 4^x$.

Multiple Choice Questions

Choose the correct answer from the given four options (1 to 6):

1 The value of $\left(5\dfrac{1}{16}\right)^{-\frac{3}{4}}$ is

    (a) $\dfrac{4}{9}$ (b) $\dfrac{9}{4}$ (c) $\dfrac{27}{8}$ (d) $\dfrac{8}{27}$

2 $\sqrt[4]{\sqrt[3]{2^2}}$ is equal to

    (a) $2^{-\frac{1}{6}}$ (b) 2^{-6} (c) $2^{\frac{1}{6}}$ (d) 2^6

3 The product $\sqrt[3]{2}.\sqrt[4]{2}.\sqrt[12]{32}$ equals

    (a) $\sqrt{2}$ (b) 2 (c) $\sqrt[12]{2}$ (d) $\sqrt[12]{32}$

4 The value of $\sqrt[4]{(81)^{-2}}$ is

    (a) $\dfrac{1}{9}$ (b) $\dfrac{1}{3}$ (c) 9 (d) $\dfrac{1}{81}$

5 Value of $(256)^{0.16} \times (256)^{0.09}$ is

    (a) 4 (b) 16 (c) 64 (d) 256.25

6 Which of the following is equal to x?

    (a) $x^{\frac{12}{7}} - x^{\frac{5}{7}}$ (b) $\sqrt[12]{(x^4)^{\frac{1}{3}}}$ (c) $(\sqrt{x^3})^{\frac{2}{3}}$ (d) $x^{\frac{12}{7}} \times x^{\frac{7}{12}}$

Summary

○ If $a > 0$ is a real number and n is a positive integer, then $\sqrt[n]{a} = b$ if and only if $b^n = a$, $b > 0$. $\sqrt[n]{a}$ is also written as $a^{1/n}$.

○ If $a > 0$ is a real number and m, n are integers, $n > 0$, m, n have no common factors except 1, then

$$a^{\frac{m}{n}} = \left(a^{\frac{1}{n}}\right)^m = (\sqrt[n]{a})^m = \sqrt[n]{a^m} .$$

❏ **Laws of exponents for real numbers are:**

○ If a, b are positive real numbers and m, n are rational numbers, then the following results hold:

(i) $a^m . a^n = a^{m+n}$ (ii) $(a^m)^n = a^{mn}$ (iii) $\dfrac{a^m}{a^n} = a^{m-n}$

(iv) $a^m . b^m = (ab)^m$ (v) $\left(\dfrac{a}{b}\right)^m = \dfrac{a^m}{b^m}$ (vi) $a^{-n} = \left(\dfrac{1}{a}\right)^n = \dfrac{1}{a^n}$

(vii) $a^n = b^n, n \neq 0 \Rightarrow a = b$ (viii) $a^m = a^n \Rightarrow m = n$ provided $a \neq 1$.

1. If $2^x.3^y.5^z = 2160$, find the values of x, y and z. Hence, compute the value of $3^x.2^{-y}.5^{-z}$.

2. If $x = 2$ and $y = -3$, find the values of (i) $x^x + y^y$ (ii) $x^y + y^x$.

3. If $p = x^{m+n}.y^l$, $q = x^{n+l}.y^m$ and $r = x^{l+m}.y^n$, prove that
$$p^{m-n}.q^{n-l}.r^{l-m} = 1.$$

4. If $x = a^{m+n}$, $y = a^{n+l}$ and $z = a^{l+m}$, prove that $x^m y^n z^l = x^n y^l z^m$.

5. Show that $\dfrac{\left(p+\dfrac{1}{q}\right)^m \times \left(p-\dfrac{1}{q}\right)^n}{\left(q+\dfrac{1}{p}\right)^m \times \left(q-\dfrac{1}{p}\right)^n} = \left(\dfrac{p}{q}\right)^{m+n}$.

6. If x is a positive real number and exponents are rational numbers, then simplify the following:

   (i) $\dfrac{(x^{(a+b)})^2 (x^{(b+c)})^2 (x^{(c+a)})^2}{(x^a x^b x^c)^4}$

   (ii) $\left(\dfrac{x^{a^2}}{x^{b^2}}\right)^{\frac{1}{a+b}} \left(\dfrac{x^{b^2}}{x^{c^2}}\right)^{\frac{1}{b+c}} \left(\dfrac{x^{c^2}}{x^{a^2}}\right)^{\frac{1}{c+a}}$

   (iii) $\left(\dfrac{x^b}{x^c}\right)^{b+c-a} \left(\dfrac{x^c}{x^a}\right)^{c+a-b} \left(\dfrac{x^a}{x^b}\right)^{a+b-c}$.

7. Show that $\dfrac{1}{1+a^{y-x}+a^{z-x}} + \dfrac{1}{1+a^{z-y}+a^{x-y}} + \dfrac{1}{1+a^{x-z}+a^{y-z}} = 1$.

   Hint. $\dfrac{1}{1+a^{y-x}+a^{z-x}} = \dfrac{1}{1+\dfrac{a^y}{a^x}+\dfrac{a^z}{a^x}} = \dfrac{a^x}{a^x+a^y+a^z}$ etc.

8. If $3^x = 5^y = (75)^z$, show that $z = \dfrac{xy}{2x+y}$.

9. Solve the following equations:

   (i) $3^{x+1} = 27.3^4$

   (ii) $4^{2x} = (\sqrt[3]{16})^{-\frac{6}{y}} = (\sqrt{8})^2$

   (iii) $3^{x-1} \times 5^{2y-3} = 225$

   (iv) $8^{x+1} = 16^{y+2}$, $\left(\dfrac{1}{2}\right)^{3+x} = \left(\dfrac{1}{4}\right)^{3y}$.

9 Logarithms

INTRODUCTION

Logarithms were developed for making complicated calculations simple. However, with the advent of computers and hand calculators, doing calculations with the use of logarithms is no longer necessary. But still, logarithmic and exponential equations and functions are very common in mathematics.

9.1 LOGARITHMS

To learn the concept of *logarithm*, consider the equality $2^3 = 8$, another way of writing this is $\log_2 8 = 3$.

It is read as "*logarithm* (abbreviated 'log') of 8 to the *base* 2 is equal to 3". Thus, $2^3 = 8$ is equivalent to $\log_2 8 = 3$. In general, we have:

Definition. *If a is any positive real number (except 1), n is any rational number and $a^n = b$, then n is called **logarithm** of b to the base a. It is written as $\log_a b$ (read as log of b to the base a).* *Thus,*

$a^n = b$ *if and only if* $\log_a b = n$.

$a^n = b$ is called the *exponential form* and $\log_a b = n$ is called the *logarithmic form*.

For example:

(i)	$3^2 = 9,$		$\therefore$	$\log_3 9 = 2.$
(ii)	$5^4 = 625,$		$\therefore$	$\log_5 625 = 4.$
(iii)	$7^0 = 1,$		$\therefore$	$\log_7 1 = 0.$
(iv)	$2^{-3} = \dfrac{1}{2^3} = \dfrac{1}{8},$		$\therefore$	$\log_2 \dfrac{1}{8} = -3.$
(v)	$(10)^{-2} = \dfrac{1}{100} = \cdot 01,$		$\therefore$	$\log_{10}(\cdot 01) = -2.$

Remarks

❏ Since a is any positive real number (except 1), a^n is always a positive real number for every rational number n i.e. b is always a positive real number, therefore, logarithm of only positive real numbers are defined.

❏ Since $a^0 = 1$, $\log_a 1 = 0$ and $a^1 = a$, $\log_a a = 1$.

Thus, remember that

(i) $\log_a 1 = 0$ (ii) $\log_a a = 1$

where a is any positive real number (except 1).

❏ If $\log_a x = \log_a y = n$ (say), then $x = a^n$ and $y = a^n$, so $x = y$.

Thus, remember that

$\log_a x = \log_a y \Rightarrow x = y.$

❑ Logarithms to the base 10 are called **common logarithms**.

❑ If no base is given, the base is always taken as 10.

For example, $\log 2 = \log_{10} 2$.

Illustrative Examples

Example 1 Convert the following to logarithmic form:

(i) $(10)^4 = 10000$ (ii) $3^{-5} = x$ (iii) $(0.3)^3 = 0.027$.

Solution. (i) $(10)^4 = 10000 \Rightarrow \log_{10} 10000 = 4$.

(ii) $3^{-5} = x \Rightarrow \log_3 x = -5$.

(iii) $(0.3)^3 = 0.027 \Rightarrow \log_{0.3}(0.027) = 3$.

Example 2 Convert the following to exponential form:

(i) $\log_3 81 = 4$ (ii) $\log_8 32 = \dfrac{5}{3}$ (iii) $\log_{10}(0.1) = -1$.

Solution. (i) $\log_3 81 = 4 \Rightarrow 3^4 = 81$.

(ii) $\log_8 32 = \dfrac{5}{3} \Rightarrow (8)^{5/3} = 32$.

(iii) $\log_{10}(0.1) = -1 \Rightarrow (10)^{-1} = 0.1$.

Example 3 Find the value of the following (by converting to exponential form):

(i) $\log_2 16$ (ii) $\log_{16} 2$ (iii) $\log_3 \dfrac{1}{3}$ (iv) $\log_{\sqrt{2}} 8$ (v) $\log_5 (0.008)$.

Solution. (i) Let $\log_2 16 = x \Rightarrow 2^x = 16 \Rightarrow 2^x = (2)^4 \Rightarrow x = 4$,

∴ $\log_2 16 = 4$.

(ii) Let $\log_{16} 2 = x \Rightarrow 16^x = 2 \Rightarrow (2^4)^x = 2$

$\Rightarrow \quad 2^{4x} = 2^1 \Rightarrow 4x = 1 \Rightarrow x = \dfrac{1}{4}$,

∴ $\log_{16} 2 = \dfrac{1}{4}$.

(iii) Let $\log_3 \dfrac{1}{3} = x \Rightarrow 3^x = \dfrac{1}{3}$

$\Rightarrow \quad 3^x = (3)^{-1} \Rightarrow x = -1$,

∴ $\log_3 \dfrac{1}{3} = -1$.

(iv) Let $\log_{\sqrt{2}} 8 = x \Rightarrow (\sqrt{2})^x = 8 \Rightarrow (2^{1/2})^x = 2^3$

$\Rightarrow \quad 2^{x/2} = 2^3 \Rightarrow \dfrac{x}{2} = 3 \Rightarrow x = 6$,

∴ $\log_{\sqrt{2}} 8 = 6$.

(v) Let $\log_5 (0.008) = x \Rightarrow 5^x = 0.008$

$\Rightarrow \quad 5^x = \dfrac{8}{1000} \Rightarrow 5^x = \dfrac{1}{125}$

$\Rightarrow \quad 5^x = (5)^{-3} \Rightarrow x = -3$,

∴ $\log_5 (0.008) = -3$.

Example 4 Find the value of $\log_{2\sqrt{3}} 1728$.

Solution. Let $\log_{2\sqrt{3}} 1728 = x \Rightarrow (2\sqrt{3})^x = 1728$

$\Rightarrow \quad (2\sqrt{3})^x = (12)^3 \Rightarrow (2\sqrt{3})^x = ((2\sqrt{3})^2)^3$

$\Rightarrow \quad (2\sqrt{3})^x = (2\sqrt{3})^6 \Rightarrow x = 6.$

$\therefore \quad \log_{2\sqrt{3}} 1728 = 6.$

Example 5 Find the value of x in each of the following:

(i) $\log_2 x = 5$ (ii) $\log_4 x = 2 \cdot 5$ (iii) $\log_{64} x = \dfrac{2}{3}$ (iv) $\log_{\sqrt{3}} x = 4.$

Solution. (i) $\log_2 x = 5 \Rightarrow x = 2^5 \Rightarrow x = 32.$

(ii) $\log_4 x = 2 \cdot 5 \Rightarrow x = 4^{2 \cdot 5} \Rightarrow x = (2^2)^{5/2}$

$\Rightarrow \quad x = 2^{2 \times \frac{5}{2}} \Rightarrow x = 2^5 \Rightarrow x = 32.$

(iii) $\log_{64} x = \dfrac{2}{3} \Rightarrow x = (64)^{2/3} \Rightarrow x = (4^3)^{2/3}$

$\Rightarrow \quad x = 4^{3 \times \frac{2}{3}} \Rightarrow x = 4^2 \Rightarrow x = 16.$

(iv) $\log_{\sqrt{3}} x = 4 \Rightarrow x = (\sqrt{3})^4 \Rightarrow x = (3^{1/2})^4$

$\Rightarrow \quad x = 3^2 \Rightarrow x = 9.$

Example 6 Solve for x:

(i) $\log_x 243 = -5$ (ii) $\log_x 16 = 2$ (iii) $\log_9 27 = 2x + 3$

(iv) $\log (3x - 2) = 2$ (v) $\log_x 64 = \dfrac{3}{2}$ (vi) $\log_2 (x^2 - 4) = 5.$

Solution. (i) Given $\log_x 243 = -5 \Rightarrow x^{-5} = 243$

$\Rightarrow \quad x^{-5} = 3^5 \Rightarrow \left(\dfrac{1}{x}\right)^5 = 3^5$ $\left[\because a^{-n} = \left(\dfrac{1}{a}\right)^n\right]$

$\Rightarrow \quad \dfrac{1}{x} = 3 \Rightarrow x = \dfrac{1}{3}.$

(ii) Given $\log_x 16 = 2 \Rightarrow x^2 = 16 \Rightarrow x = \pm 4.$

But the base of a logarithm cannot be negative, so $x = -4$ is rejected.

$\therefore$ The solution of the given equation is $x = 4.$

(iii) Given $\log_9 27 = 2x + 3 \Rightarrow 9^{2x+3} = 27 \Rightarrow (3^2)^{2x+3} = 3^3$

$\Rightarrow \quad 3^{2(2x + 3)} = 3^3 \Rightarrow 2(2x + 3) = 3 \Rightarrow 4x + 6 = 3$

$\Rightarrow \quad 4x = -3 \Rightarrow x = -\dfrac{3}{4}.$

(iv) Given $\log (3x - 2) = 2 \Rightarrow \log_{10}(3x - 2) = 2$ [If no base is given, we take it as 10.]

$\Rightarrow \quad 3x - 2 = 10^2 \Rightarrow 3x - 2 = 100$

$\Rightarrow \quad 3x = 102 \Rightarrow x = 34.$

(v) Given $\log_x 64 = \dfrac{3}{2} \Rightarrow x^{3/2} = 64$

$\Rightarrow \quad x = (64)^{2/3} = (2^6)^{2/3} = 2^{6 \times 2/3} = 2^4$

$\Rightarrow \quad x = 16.$

(vi) Given $\log_2 (x^2 - 4) = 5 \Rightarrow x^2 - 4 = 2^5$

$\Rightarrow x^2 - 4 = 32 \Rightarrow x^2 = 36 \Rightarrow x = \pm 6$.

Example 7 Given $\log_{10} x = a$, $\log_{10} y = b$,

(i) write down 10^{a-1} in terms of x. (ii) write down 10^{2b} in terms of y.

(iii) if $\log_{10} P = 2a - b$, express P in terms of x and y.

Solution. Given $\log_{10} x = a \Rightarrow 10^a = x$, and $\log_{10} y = b \Rightarrow 10^b = y$.

(i) $10^{a-1} = 10^a \cdot 10^{-1} = 10^a \cdot \dfrac{1}{10} = \dfrac{x}{10}$.

(ii) $10^{2b} = (10^b)^2 = y^2$.

(iii) $\log_{10} P = 2a - b \Rightarrow 10^{2a-b} = P$,

$\therefore \quad P = 10^{2a} \cdot 10^{-b} = (10^a)^2 \cdot \dfrac{1}{10^b} = \dfrac{x^2}{y}$.

Example 8 If $\log_3 x = a$, find 81^{a-1} in terms of x.

Solution. Given $\log_3 x = a \Rightarrow 3^a = x$ ...(i)

$\therefore \quad 81^{a-1} = (3^4)^{a-1} = 3^{4a-4} = 3^{4a} \times 3^{-4}$

$= \dfrac{(3^a)^4}{3^4} = \dfrac{x^4}{81}$ (using (i))

Example 9 If $\log_2 x = a$ and $\log_3 y = a$, find 12^{2a-1} in terms of x and y.

Solution. Given $\log_2 x = a$ and $\log_3 y = a$

$\Rightarrow \quad 2^a = x$ and $3^a = y$ ...(i)

$\therefore \quad 12^{2a-1} = (2^2 \times 3)^{2a-1} = 2^{2(2a-1)} \times 3^{2a-1}$

$= 2^{4a-2} \times 3^{2a-1} = 2^{4a} \times 2^{-2} \times 3^{2a} \times 3^{-1}$

$= \dfrac{(2^a)^4 \times (3^a)^2}{2^2 \times 3^1} = \dfrac{x^4 y^2}{12}$ (using (i))

EXERCISE 9.1

1 Convert the following to logarithmic form:

(i) $5^2 = 25$ (ii) $a^5 = 64$ (iii) $7^x = 100$ (iv) $9^0 = 1$

(v) $6^1 = 6$ (vi) $3^{-2} = \dfrac{1}{9}$ (vii) $10^{-2} = 0.01$ (viii) $(81)^{3/4} = 27$.

2 Convert the following into exponential form:

(i) $\log_2 32 = 5$ (ii) $\log_3 81 = 4$ (iii) $\log_3 \dfrac{1}{3} = -1$

(iv) $\log_8 4 = \dfrac{2}{3}$ (v) $\log_8 32 = \dfrac{5}{3}$ (vi) $\log_{10} (0.001) = -3$

(vii) $\log_2 0.25 = -2$ (viii) $\log_a \left(\dfrac{1}{a}\right) = -1$.

3 By converting to exponential form, find the values of:

(i) $\log_2 16$ (ii) $\log_5 125$ (iii) $\log_4 8$ (iv) $\log_9 27$

(v) $\log_{10} (0.01)$ (vi) $\log_7 \dfrac{1}{7}$ (vii) $\log_{0.5} 256$ (viii) $\log_2 0.25$.

4 Solve the following equations for x:

(i) $\log_3 x = 2$ (ii) $\log_x 25 = 2$ (iii) $\log_{10} x = -2$

(iv) $\log_4 x = \dfrac{1}{2}$ (v) $\log_x 11 = 1$ (vi) $\log_x \dfrac{1}{4} = -1$

(vii) $\log_{81} x = \dfrac{3}{2}$ (viii) $\log_9 x = 2 \cdot 5$ (ix) $\log_4 x = -1 \cdot 5$

(x) $\log_{\sqrt{5}} x = 2$ (xi) $\log_x 0 \cdot 001 = -3$ (xii) $\log_{\sqrt{3}} (x + 1) = 2$

(xiii) $\log_4 (2x + 3) = \dfrac{3}{2}$ (xiv) $\log_{\sqrt[3]{2}} x = 3$ (xv) $\log_2 (x^2 - 1) = 3$

(xvi) $\log x = -1$ (xvii) $\log (2x - 3) = 1$ (xviii) $\log x = -2, 0, \dfrac{1}{3}$.

5   Given $\log_{10} a = b$, express 10^{2b-3} in terms of a.

6   Given $\log_{10} x = a$, $\log_{10} y = b$ and $\log_{10} z = c$,

    (i) write down 10^{2a-3} in terms of x.

    (ii) write down 10^{3b-1} in terms of y.

    (iii) if $\log_{10} P = 2a + \dfrac{b}{2} - 3c$, express P in terms of x, y and z.

7   If $\log_{10} x = a$ and $\log_{10} y = b$, find the value of xy.

8   Given $\log_{10} a = m$ and $\log_{10} b = n$, express $\dfrac{a^3}{b^2}$ in terms of m and n.

9   Given $\log_{10} x = 2a$ and $\log_{10} y = \dfrac{b}{2}$,

    (i) write 10^a in terms of x.

    (ii) write 10^{2b+1} in terms of y.

    (iii) if $\log_{10} P = 3a - 2b$, express P in terms of x and y.

10   If $\log_2 y = x$ and $\log_3 z = x$, find 72^x in terms of y and z.

11   If $\log_2 x = a$ and $\log_5 y = a$, write 100^{2a-1} in terms of x and y.

9.2 THREE STANDARD LAWS OF LOGARITHMS

❏ $\log_a mn = \log_a m + \log_a n$.   (Product Law)

    The above result is capable of extension *i.e.*

    $\log_a (mnp...) = \log_a m + \log_a n + \log_a p + ...$

❏ $\log_a \dfrac{m}{n} = \log_a m - \log_a n$.   (Quotient Law)

❏ $\log_a m^n = n \log_a m$.   (Power Law)

Deductions

    1. $\log_a a^x = x$ 2. $a^{\log_a x} = x$.

9.2.1 Base changing formula

$\log_a m = \dfrac{\log_b m}{\log_b a}$, $m > 0$, $a, b > 0$, $a \neq 1$, $b \neq 1$.

Deductions

    1. $\log_b m = \log_a m \times \log_b a$.

    2. $\log_b a \times \log_a b = 1$.   (Put $m = b$ in 1)

    3. $\log_b a = \dfrac{1}{\log_a b}$.   (Reciprocal formula)

Illustrative Examples

Example 1 Express $\log_{10} \dfrac{a^2c}{\sqrt{b}}$ in terms of $\log_{10}a$, $\log_{10}b$, $\log_{10}c$.

Solution. $\log_{10} \dfrac{a^2c}{\sqrt{b}} = \log_{10} a^2c - \log_{10} \sqrt{b}$ (Quotient Law)

$$= \log_{10} a^2 + \log_{10} c - \log_{10} (b)^{\frac{1}{2}} \qquad \text{(Product Law)}$$

$$= 2 \log_{10} a + \log_{10} c - \frac{1}{2} \log_{10} b. \qquad \text{(Power Law)}$$

Example 2 Evaluate the following :

    (i) $3 + \log_{10} (10^{-2})$ (ii) $5 + \log_{10} (0.001)$.

Solution. (i) $3 + \log_{10}(10^{-2}) = 3 + (-2) \log_{10} 10$ (Power Law)

$$= 3 + (-2).1 \qquad (\because \log_{10} 10 = 1)$$

$$= 3 - 2 = 1.$$

    (ii) $5 + \log_{10} (0.001) = 5 + \log_{10} \left(\dfrac{1}{1000} \right)$

$$= 5 + \log_{10} (10^{-3})$$

$$= 5 + (-3) \log_{10}10$$

$$= 5 + (-3) \times 1$$

$$= 5 - 3 = 2.$$

Example 3 Evaluate the following:

    (i) $\dfrac{\log 125}{\log \sqrt{5}}$ (ii) $\log_6 72 - \log_6 2$ (iii) $\log_4 8 - \log_8 32$.

Solution. (i) $\dfrac{\log 125}{\log \sqrt{5}} = \dfrac{\log 5^3}{\log 5^{1/2}} = \dfrac{3 \log 5}{\frac{1}{2} \log 5} = 6.$

    (ii) $\log_6 72 - \log_6 2 = \log_6 \dfrac{72}{2} = \log_6 36 = \log_6 6^2$

$$= 2 \log_6 6 = 2 \times 1 \qquad (\because \log_a a = 1)$$

$$= 2.$$

    (iii) $\log_4 8 - \log_8 32 = \log_4 2^3 - \log_8 2^5 = \log_4 (2^2)^{3/2} - \log_8 (2^3)^{5/3}$

$$= \log_4 4^{3/2} - \log_8 8^{5/3} = \frac{3}{2} \log_4 4 - \frac{5}{3} \log_8 8$$

$$= \frac{3}{2} \times 1 - \frac{5}{3} \times 1 \qquad (\because \log_a a = 1)$$

$$= \frac{3}{2} - \frac{5}{3} = \frac{9 - 10}{6} = -\frac{1}{6}.$$

Example 4 Express as a single logarithm: $2 + \dfrac{1}{2} \log_{10}9 - 2 \log_{10}5$.

Solution. $2 + \dfrac{1}{2} \log_{10}9 - 2 \log_{10}5 = 2.1 + \dfrac{1}{2} \log_{10}9 - 2 \log_{10}5$

$$= 2 \log_{10}10 + \log_{10} (9)^{1/2} - \log_{10}(5)^2 \qquad (\because \log_{10}10 = 1)$$

$$= \log_{10}(10)^2 + \log_{10}3 - \log_{10}25$$

$$= \log_{10} \frac{(10)^2 \times 3}{25} = \log_{10} \frac{100 \times 3}{25}$$

$$= \log_{10} 12.$$

Example 5 Prove that $16^{\log 3} = 9^{\log 4}$.

Solution. $16^{\log 3} = 9^{\log 4}$ is true

if $\quad \log 16^{\log 3} = \log 9^{\log 4}$ is true $\hfill$ (Taking logs of both sides)

i.e. if $\quad \log 3 \times \log 16 = \log 4 \times \log 9$ is true

i.e. if $\quad \log 3 \times \log 2^4 = \log 2^2 \times \log 3^2$ is true

i.e. if $\quad \log 3 \times 4 \log 2 = 2 \log 2 \times 2 \log 3$ is true

i.e. if $\quad 4 \log 3 \times \log 2 = 4 \log 2 \times \log 3$ is true, which is true.

Hence, $\quad 16^{\log 3} = 9^{\log 4}$.

Example 6 Prove that :

(i) $7 \log \dfrac{16}{15} + 5 \log \dfrac{25}{24} + 3 \log \dfrac{81}{80} = \log 2$.

(ii) $\dfrac{1}{2} \log 9 + 2 \log 6 + \dfrac{1}{4} \log 81 - \log 12 = 3 \log 3$.

Solution. (i) $7 \log \dfrac{16}{15} + 5 \log \dfrac{25}{24} + 3 \log \dfrac{81}{80}$

$$= \log \left(\dfrac{16}{15}\right)^7 + \log \left(\dfrac{25}{24}\right)^5 + \log \left(\dfrac{81}{80}\right)^3$$

$$= \log \left(\left(\dfrac{16}{15}\right)^7 \times \left(\dfrac{25}{24}\right)^5 \times \left(\dfrac{81}{80}\right)^3\right)$$

$$= \log \left(\left(\dfrac{2^4}{3 \times 5}\right)^7 \times \left(\dfrac{5^2}{2^3 \times 3}\right)^5 \times \left(\dfrac{3^4}{2^4 \times 5}\right)^3\right)$$

$$= \log \left(\dfrac{2^{28}}{3^7 \times 5^7} \times \dfrac{5^{10}}{2^{15} \times 3^5} \times \dfrac{3^{12}}{2^{12} \times 5^3}\right)$$

$$= \log(2^{28 - 15 - 12} \times 5^{10 - 7 - 3} \times 3^{12 - 7 - 5})$$

$$= \log(2^1 \times 5^0 \times 3^0) = \log(2 \times 1 \times 1) = \log 2.$$

(ii) $\dfrac{1}{2} \log 9 + 2 \log 6 + \dfrac{1}{4} \log 81 - \log 12$

$$= \dfrac{1}{2} \log 3^2 + 2 \log 6 + \dfrac{1}{4} \log 3^4 - \log 12$$

$$= \log (3^2)^{\frac{1}{2}} + \log 6^2 + \log (3^4)^{\frac{1}{4}} - \log 12$$

$$= \log 3 + \log 36 + \log 3 - \log 12$$

$$= \log \dfrac{3 \times 36 \times 3}{12} = \log 27 = \log 3^3 = 3 \log 3.$$

Example 7 If $\log 7 - \log 2 + \log 16 - 2 \log 3 - \log \dfrac{7}{45} = 1 + \log n$, find n.

Solution. Given $\log 7 - \log 2 + \log 16 - 2 \log 3 - \log \dfrac{7}{45} = 1 + \log n$

$\Rightarrow \quad \log 7 - \log 2 + \log 16 - \log (3)^2 - \log \dfrac{7}{45} = \log 10 + \log n \hfill (\because \log 10 = 1)$

$\Rightarrow \quad \log \dfrac{7 \times 16}{2 \times 3^2 \times \dfrac{7}{45}} = \log (10 \times n) \Rightarrow \log \dfrac{7 \times 16 \times 45}{2 \times 9 \times 7} = \log 10n$

$\Rightarrow \quad \log 40 = \log 10n \Rightarrow 40 = 10n \Rightarrow n = 4.$

Example 8 If $3 \log \sqrt{m} + 2 \log \sqrt[3]{n} - 1 = 0$, find the value of $m^9 n^4$.

Solution. Given $3 \log \sqrt{m} + 2 \log \sqrt[3]{n} - 1 = 0$

$\Rightarrow \quad \log (\sqrt{m})^3 + \log (\sqrt[3]{n})^2 = 1$

$\Rightarrow \quad \log (m^{3/2} \times n^{2/3}) = \log 10$ $\qquad (\because \log 10 = 1)$

$\Rightarrow \quad m^{3/2} . n^{2/3} = 10$, raising both sides to the power 6, we get

$\qquad (m^{3/2} . n^{2/3})^6 = 10^6$

$\Rightarrow \quad (m^{3/2})^6 . (n^{2/3})^6 = 10^6 \Rightarrow m^9 n^4 = 10^6.$

Example 9 Given $2 \log_{10} x + \frac{1}{2} \log_{10} y = 1$, express y in terms of x.

Solution. Given $2 \log_{10} x + \frac{1}{2} \log_{10} y = 1 \Rightarrow \log_{10} x^2 + \log_{10} y^{\frac{1}{2}} = 1$

$\Rightarrow \quad \log_{10} x^2 y^{\frac{1}{2}} = 1 \Rightarrow x^2 y^{\frac{1}{2}} = 10^1$ $\qquad$ (squaring)

$\Rightarrow \quad x^4 y = 10^2 \Rightarrow y = \frac{100}{x^4}.$

Example 10 Simplify the following:

(i) $\dfrac{\log_3 8}{\log_9 16 \, \log_4 10}$ $\qquad$ (ii) $(\sqrt{x})^{4 \log_x a}$ $\qquad$ (iii) $\log (\log x^2) - \log (\log x)$

(iv) $\log_b a . \log_c b . \log_a c$ $\quad$ (v) $\log_2 (\log_2 (\log_2 16))$ $\quad$ (vi) $3^{-\frac{1}{2} \log_3 9}.$

Solution. (i) $\dfrac{\log_3 8}{\log_9 16 \, \log_4 10} = \dfrac{\log_{10} 8}{\log_{10} 3} . \dfrac{\log_{10} 9 \, \log_{10} 4}{\log_{10} 16 \, \log_{10} 10}$ $\qquad$ (Changing all logs to base 10)

$\qquad = \dfrac{\log_{10} 2^3 . \log_{10} 3^2 . \log_{10} 2^2}{\log_{10} 3 . \log_{10} 2^4 . 1} = \dfrac{(3 \log_{10} 2)(2 \log_{10} 3)(2 \log_{10} 2)}{(\log_{10} 3)(4 \log_{10} 2)}$

$\qquad = 3 \log_{10} 2.$

(ii) $(\sqrt{x})^{4 \log_x a} = x^{\frac{1}{2} \times 4 \log_x a} = x^{2 \log_x a} = x^{\log_x a^2} = a^2.$ $\qquad (\because a^{\log_a x} = x)$

(iii) $\log (\log x^2) - \log (\log x) = \log (2 \log x) - \log (\log x) = \log \left(\dfrac{2 \log x}{\log x} \right) = \log 2.$

(iv) $\log_b a . \log_c b . \log_a c = (\log_b a . \log_c b) . \log_a c = \log_c a . \log_a c = 1.$

(v) $\log_2 (\log_2 (\log_2 16)) = \log_2 (\log_2 (\log_2 2^4)) = \log_2 (\log_2 (4))$

$\qquad\qquad\qquad\qquad = \log_2 (\log_2 2^2) = \log_2 (2) = 1.$

(vi) $3^{-\frac{1}{2} \log_3 9} = 3^{\log_3 9^{-1/2}} = 9^{-1/2} = \dfrac{1}{9^{1/2}} = \dfrac{1}{3}.$

Example 11 (i) If $\dfrac{\log a}{b - c} = \dfrac{\log b}{c - a} = \dfrac{\log c}{a - b}$, prove that $a^a . b^b . c^c = 1$.

(ii) If $\dfrac{1}{\log_a n} + \dfrac{1}{\log_c n} = \dfrac{2}{\log_b n}$, prove that $b^2 = ac$.

(iii) Show that $\dfrac{\log_a n}{\log_{ab} n} = 1 + \log_a b$.

Solution. (i) Let $\dfrac{\log a}{b - c} = \dfrac{\log b}{c - a} = \dfrac{\log c}{a - b} = k$

$\Rightarrow \quad \log a = k (b - c); \log b = k (c - a); \log c = k (a - b)$

$\Rightarrow \quad a \log a + b \log b + c \log c = ka\,(b - c) + kb\,(c - a) + kc\,(a - b) = 0$

$\Rightarrow \quad \log a^a . b^b . c^c = 0 = \log 1 \Rightarrow a^a . b^b . c^c = 1.$

(ii) Given $\dfrac{1}{\log_a n} + \dfrac{1}{\log_c n} = \dfrac{2}{\log_b n}$

$\Rightarrow \quad \log_n a + \log_n c = 2\log_n b$ (using reciprocal formula)

$\Rightarrow \quad \log_n ac = \log_n b^2$

$\Rightarrow \quad ac = b^2$, as required.

(iii) $\dfrac{\log_a n}{\log_{ab} n} = \dfrac{1 / \log_n a}{1 / \log_n ab} = \dfrac{\log_n ab}{\log_n a} = \log_a ab = \log_a a + \log_a b = 1 + \log_a b.$

Example 12 If $a = \log_x yz$, $b = \log_y zx$ and $c = \log_z xy$, then prove that $\dfrac{1}{1 + a} + \dfrac{1}{1 + b} + \dfrac{1}{1 + c} = 1.$

Solution. $\dfrac{1}{1 + a} = \dfrac{1}{1 + \log_x yz} = \dfrac{1}{\log_x x + \log_x yz} = \dfrac{1}{\log_x xyz} = \log_{xyz} x.$

Similarly, $\dfrac{1}{1 + b} = \log_{xyz} y$ and $\dfrac{1}{1 + c} = \log_{xyz} z.$

$\therefore \quad \dfrac{1}{1 + a} + \dfrac{1}{1 + b} + \dfrac{1}{1 + c} = \log_{xyz} x + \log_{xyz} y + \log_{xyz} z$

$= \log_{xyz} xyz = 1.$

Example 13 Solve for x:

(i) $\log x = \dfrac{\log 125}{\log \frac{1}{5}}$ (ii) $\log_2 (\log_3 x) = 4$

(iii) $\log_x 15\sqrt{5} = 2 - \log_x 3\sqrt{5}$ (iv) $\log (5x - 4) - \log (x + 1) = \log 4$

(v) $\log (x + 5) + \log (x - 5) = 2 \log 3 + 4 \log 2.$

Solution. (i) $\log x = \dfrac{\log 125}{\log \frac{1}{5}} = \dfrac{\log (5)^3}{\log 5^{-1}} = \dfrac{3 \log 5}{(-1) \log 5} = -3$

$\Rightarrow \quad x = 10^{-3} \Rightarrow x = \dfrac{1}{(10)^3} = \dfrac{1}{1000} = 0{\cdot}001$

(ii) $\log_2 (\log_3 x) = 4 \Rightarrow \log_3 x = 2^4 = 16 \Rightarrow x = 3^{16}.$

(iii) Given $\log_x 15\sqrt{5} = 2 - \log_x 3\sqrt{5} \Rightarrow \log_x 15\sqrt{5} + \log_x 3\sqrt{5} = 2$

$\Rightarrow \quad \log_x (15\sqrt{5} \times 3\sqrt{5}) = 2 \Rightarrow \log_x 225 = 2$

$\Rightarrow \quad \log_x (15)^2 = 2 \Rightarrow 2\log_x 15 = 2$

$\Rightarrow \quad \log_x 15 = 1 \Rightarrow x^1 = 15$

$\Rightarrow \quad x = 15.$

(iv) Given $\log (5x - 4) - \log (x + 1) = \log 4$

$\Rightarrow \quad \log \dfrac{5x - 4}{x + 1} = \log 4$

$\Rightarrow \quad \dfrac{5x - 4}{x + 1} = 4 \Rightarrow 5x - 4 = 4x + 4 \Rightarrow x = 8.$

(v) Given $\log (x + 5) + \log (x - 5) = 2 \log 3 + 4 \log 2$

$\Rightarrow \quad \log (x + 5)(x - 5) = \log 3^2 + \log 2^4$

$\Rightarrow \quad \log (x^2 - 25) = \log (3^2 \times 2^4)$

$$\Rightarrow \quad x^2 - 25 = 3^2 \times 2^4 \Rightarrow x^2 - 25 = 144$$

$$\Rightarrow \quad x^2 = 169 \Rightarrow x = \pm\, 13.$$

When $x = -13$, then $x + 5$ and $x - 5$ are both negative and the logarithm of a negative number is not defined, so $x = -13$ is rejected.

$\therefore$ The solution of the given equation is $x = 13$.

Example 14 Find the value of x if $\log_{10} x - \log_{10} (2x - 1) = 1$.

Solution. Given $\log_{10} x - \log_{10} (2x - 1) = 1$

$$\Rightarrow \quad \log_{10} \frac{x}{2x-1} = 1 \Rightarrow \frac{x}{2x-1} = 10^1$$

$$\Rightarrow \quad \frac{x}{2x-1} = 10 \Rightarrow 20x - 10 = x$$

$$\Rightarrow \quad 19x = 10 \Rightarrow x = \frac{10}{19}.$$

Example 15 Solve the following equations for x:

(i) $\log_x 25 - \log_x 5 + \log_x \dfrac{1}{125} = 2$

(ii) $\log_x (8x - 3) - \log_x 4 = 2$

(iii) $3^{\log x} - 2^{\log x} = 2^{\log x + 1} - 3^{\log x - 1}$.

Solution. (i) Given $\log_x 25 - \log_x 5 + \log_x \dfrac{1}{125} = 2$

$$\Rightarrow \quad \log_x \frac{25 \times \dfrac{1}{125}}{5} = 2 \Rightarrow \log_x \frac{1}{25} = 2$$

$$\Rightarrow \quad \log_x \left(\frac{1}{5}\right)^2 = 2 \Rightarrow 2\, \log_x \frac{1}{5} = 2$$

$$\Rightarrow \quad \log_x \frac{1}{5} = 1 \Rightarrow x^1 = \frac{1}{5}$$

$$\Rightarrow \quad x = \frac{1}{5}.$$

(ii) Given $\log_x (8x - 3) - \log_x 4 = 2$

$$\Rightarrow \quad \log_x \frac{8x-3}{4} = 2 \Rightarrow x^2 = \frac{8x-3}{4} \Rightarrow 4x^2 = 8x - 3$$

$$\Rightarrow \quad 4x^2 - 8x + 3 = 0 \Rightarrow 4x^2 - 6x - 2x + 3 = 0$$

$$\Rightarrow \quad 2x(2x - 3) - 1(2x - 3) = 0 \Rightarrow (2x - 3)(2x - 1) = 0$$

$$\Rightarrow \quad 2x - 3 = 0,\ 2x - 1 = 0$$

$$\Rightarrow \quad x = \frac{3}{2}, \frac{1}{2}.$$

(iii) Given $3^{\log x} - 2^{\log x} = 2^{\log x + 1} - 3^{\log x - 1}$

$$\Rightarrow \quad 3^{\log x} + 3^{\log x - 1} = 2^{\log x + 1} + 2^{\log x}$$

$$\Rightarrow \quad 3^{\log x} + 3^{\log x} \times 3^{-1} = 2^{\log x} \times 2^1 + 2^{\log x}$$

$$\Rightarrow \quad \left(1 + \frac{1}{3}\right) 3^{\log x} = (2 + 1)\, 2^{\log x}$$

$$\Rightarrow \quad \frac{4}{3} \times 3^{\log x} = 3 \times 2^{\log x}$$

$$\Rightarrow \quad \frac{3^{\log x}}{2^{\log x}} = \frac{9}{4} \Rightarrow \left(\frac{3}{2}\right)^{\log x} = \left(\frac{3}{2}\right)^2$$

$\Rightarrow \quad \log x = 2 \Rightarrow x = 10^2$

$\Rightarrow \quad x = 100.$

Example 16 Solve for x: $\log_2 x + \log_4 x + \log_{16} x = \dfrac{21}{4}$.

Solution. Given $\log_2 x + \log_4 x + \log_{16} x = \dfrac{21}{4}$

$\Rightarrow \quad \dfrac{1}{\log_x 2} + \dfrac{1}{\log_x 4} + \dfrac{1}{\log_x 16} = \dfrac{21}{4}$

$\Rightarrow \quad \dfrac{1}{\log_x 2} + \dfrac{1}{\log_x 2^2} + \dfrac{1}{\log_x 2^4} = \dfrac{21}{4} \Rightarrow \dfrac{1}{\log_x 2} + \dfrac{1}{2\log_x 2} + \dfrac{1}{4\log_x 2} = \dfrac{21}{4}$

$\Rightarrow \quad \dfrac{1}{\log_x 2}\left(1 + \dfrac{1}{2} + \dfrac{1}{4}\right) = \dfrac{21}{4} \Rightarrow \dfrac{7}{4}\cdot\dfrac{1}{\log_x 2} = \dfrac{21}{4}$

$\Rightarrow \quad \log_x 2 = \dfrac{7}{4}\cdot\dfrac{4}{21} = \dfrac{1}{3}$

$\Rightarrow \quad x^{1/3} = 2 \Rightarrow x = 2^3 = 8.$

Example 17 Solve the following equations for x :

(i) $\log_x 2 \times \log_{x/16} 2 = \log_{x/64} 2$

(ii) $\log_5(5^{1/x} + 125) = \log_5 6 + 1 + \dfrac{1}{2x}$.

Solution. (i) Given $\log_x 2 \times \log_{x/16} 2 = \log_{x/64} 2$

$\Rightarrow \quad \dfrac{1}{\log_2 x} \times \dfrac{1}{\log_2\left(\dfrac{x}{16}\right)} = \dfrac{1}{\log_2\left(\dfrac{x}{64}\right)}$

$\Rightarrow \quad \log_2(x/64) = \log_2 x \times \log_2(x/16)$

$\Rightarrow \quad \log_2 x - \log_2 64 = \log_2 x(\log_2 x - \log_2 16)$

$\Rightarrow \quad \log_2 x - \log_2 2^6 = \log_2 x(\log_2 x - \log_2 2^4)$

$\Rightarrow \quad \log_2 x - 6\log_2 2 = \log_2 x(\log_2 x - 4\log_2 2)$

$\Rightarrow \quad \log_2 x - 6 \times 1 = \log_2 x(\log_2 x - 4 \times 1)$

$\Rightarrow \quad (\log_2 x)^2 - 5\log_2 x + 6 = 0$

$\Rightarrow \quad y^2 - 5y + 6 = 0$ where $y = \log_2 x$

$\Rightarrow \quad (y - 3)(y - 2) = 0 \Rightarrow y = 3$ or $y = 2$

$\Rightarrow \quad \log_2 x = 3$ or $\log_2 x = 2$

$\Rightarrow \quad x = 2^3$ or $x = 2^2 \Rightarrow x = 8$ or $x = 4.$

Hence, the solutions of the given equation are 8, 4.

(ii) Given $\log_5(5^{1/x} + 125) = \log_5 6 + 1 + \dfrac{1}{2x}$

$\Rightarrow \quad \log_5(5^{1/x} + 125) = \log_5 6 + \log_5 5 + \dfrac{1}{2x}$ $\qquad (\because \log_5 5 = 1)$

$\Rightarrow \quad \log_5(5^{1/x} + 125) - \log_5 6 - \log_5 5 = \dfrac{1}{2x}$

$\Rightarrow \quad \log_5\left(\dfrac{5^{1/x} + 125}{6 \times 5}\right) = \dfrac{1}{2x} \Rightarrow \dfrac{5^{1/x} + 125}{30} = 5^{1/2x}$

$\Rightarrow \quad 5^{\frac{1}{x}} + 125 = 30 \times 5^{\frac{1}{2x}}$

$\Rightarrow \quad (5^{\frac{1}{2x}})^2 - 30 \times 5^{\frac{1}{2x}} + 125 = 0$

$$\Rightarrow \quad y^2 - 30y + 125 = 0 \text{ where } y = 5^{\frac{1}{2x}}$$

$$\Rightarrow \quad (y - 25)(y - 5) = 0 \Rightarrow y = 25 \text{ or } y = 5$$

$$\Rightarrow \quad 5^{\frac{1}{2x}} = 25 \text{ or } 5^{\frac{1}{2x}} = 5$$

$$\Rightarrow \quad 5^{\frac{1}{2x}} = 5^2 \text{ or } 5^{\frac{1}{2x}} = 5^1$$

$$\Rightarrow \quad \frac{1}{2x} = 2 \text{ or } \frac{1}{2x} = 1 \Rightarrow x = \frac{1}{4} \text{ or } x = \frac{1}{2}$$

Hence, the solutions of the given equation are $\frac{1}{4}, \frac{1}{2}$.

Example 18 If $a = 1 + \log_{10} 2 - \log_{10} 5$, $b = 2 \log_{10} 3$ and $c = \log_{10} m - \log_{10} 5$, find the value of m given that $a + b = 2c$.

Solution. Given $a + b = 2c$

$$\Rightarrow \quad 1 + \log_{10} 2 - \log_{10} 5 + 2 \log_{10} 3 = 2(\log_{10} m - \log_{10} 5)$$
$$\Rightarrow \quad \log_{10} 10 + \log_{10} 2 - \log_{10} 5 + 2 \log_{10} 3 + 2 \log_{10} 5 = 2 \log_{10} m \qquad (\because \log_{10} 10 = 1)$$
$$\Rightarrow \quad \log_{10} 10 + \log_{10} 2 + \log_{10} 5 + \log_{10} 3^2 = 2 \log_{10} m$$
$$\Rightarrow \quad \log_{10} (10 \times 2 \times 5 \times 3^2) = 2 \log_{10} m$$
$$\Rightarrow \quad \log_{10} 900 = 2 \log_{10} m \Rightarrow \log_{10} (30)^2 = 2 \log_{10} m$$
$$\Rightarrow \quad 2 \log_{10} 30 = 2 \log_{10} m \Rightarrow \log_{10} 30 = \log_{10} m$$
$$\Rightarrow \quad 30 = m \quad i.e. \quad m = 30.$$

Example 19 If $a^2 + b^2 = 7ab$, prove that $2 \log (a + b) = \log 9 + \log a + \log b$.

Solution. Given $a^2 + b^2 = 7ab$.

Adding $2ab$ to both sides, we get

$$a^2 + 2ab + b^2 = 9ab$$

$$\Rightarrow \quad (a + b)^2 = 9ab, \text{ taking logs of both sides, we get}$$

$$\log (a + b)^2 = \log 9ab$$

$$\Rightarrow \quad 2 \log (a + b) = \log 9 + \log a + \log b.$$

Example 20 If $\dfrac{\log(x + y)}{\log 2} = \dfrac{\log(x - y)}{\log 3} = \dfrac{\log 64}{\log 0\text{·}125}$, find the values of x and y.

Solution. $\dfrac{\log 64}{\log 0\text{·}125} = \dfrac{\log 64}{\log \frac{1}{8}} = \dfrac{\log 8^2}{\log 8^{-1}} = \dfrac{2 \log 8}{(-1) \log 8} = -2.$

$$\therefore \qquad \frac{\log(x + y)}{\log 2} = -2 \Rightarrow \log (x + y) = -2 \log 2 = \log 2^{-2} = \log \frac{1}{4}$$

$$\Rightarrow \qquad x + y = \frac{1}{4} \qquad \qquad \qquad \qquad \qquad \qquad \qquad \qquad \qquad \dots(i)$$

Also, $\qquad \dfrac{\log(x - y)}{\log 3} = -2 \Rightarrow \log (x - y) = -2 \log 3 = \log 3^{-2} = \log \frac{1}{9}$

$$\Rightarrow \qquad x - y = \frac{1}{9} \qquad \qquad \qquad \qquad \qquad \qquad \qquad \qquad \qquad \dots(ii)$$

On adding (i) and (ii), we get

$$2x = \frac{1}{4} + \frac{1}{9} = \frac{9 + 4}{36} = \frac{13}{36} \Rightarrow x = \frac{13}{72}.$$

Subtracting (*ii*) from (*i*), we get

$$2y = \frac{1}{4} - \frac{1}{9} = \frac{9-4}{36} = \frac{5}{36} \Rightarrow y = \frac{5}{72}.$$

Hence, $x = \dfrac{13}{72}$ and $y = \dfrac{5}{72}$.

Example 21 Solve the following equations for x and y:

$$\log_{10}(xy) = 2, \quad \log_{10}\left(\frac{x}{y}\right) + 2\log_{10}2 = 2.$$

Solution. $\log_{10}(xy) = 2 \Rightarrow xy = 10^2 \Rightarrow xy = 100$ ...(*i*)

$$\log_{10}\left(\frac{x}{y}\right) + 2\log_{10}2 = 2$$

$$\Rightarrow \quad \log_{10}\left(\frac{x}{y}\right) = 2 - 2\log_{10}2 = 2(1 - \log_{10}2)$$

$$= 2(\log_{10}10 - \log_{10}2) = 2\log_{10}\frac{10}{2} = 2\log_{10}5$$

$$= \log_{10}5^2 = \log_{10}25$$

$$\Rightarrow \quad \frac{x}{y} = 25 \qquad\qquad\qquad\qquad ...(ii)$$

Multiplying (*i*) and (*ii*), we get

$$(xy) \times \left(\frac{x}{y}\right) = 100 \times 25 \Rightarrow x^2 = 2500 \Rightarrow x = \pm\, 50.$$

When $x = 50$, from (*i*), $y = \dfrac{100}{x} = \dfrac{100}{50} = 2;$

when $x = -50$, from (*i*), $y = \dfrac{100}{x} = \dfrac{100}{-50} = -2.$

Hence, the solutions are $x = 50,\, y = 2;\, x = -50,\, y = -2.$
Note that both these solutions satisfy the given equations.

EXERCISE 9.2

1 Simplify the following:

    (*i*) $\log a^3 - \log a^2$ (*ii*) $\log a^3 \div \log a^2$ (*iii*) $\dfrac{\log 4}{\log 2}$

    (*iv*) $\dfrac{\log 8\, \log 9}{\log 27}$ (*v*) $\dfrac{\log 27}{\log \sqrt{3}}$ (*vi*) $\dfrac{\log 9 - \log 3}{\log 27}$.

2 Evaluate the following:

    (*i*) $\log(10 \div \sqrt[3]{10})$ (*ii*) $2 + \dfrac{1}{2}\log(10^{-3})$

    (*iii*) $2\log 5 + \log 8 - \dfrac{1}{2}\log 4$

    (*iv*) $2\log 10^3 + 3\log 10^{-2} - \dfrac{1}{3}\log 5^{-3} + \dfrac{1}{2}\log 4$

    (*v*) $2\log 2 + \log 5 - \dfrac{1}{2}\log 36 - \log \dfrac{1}{30}$

    (*vi*) $2\log 5 + \log 3 + 3\log 2 - \dfrac{1}{2}\log 36 - 2\log 10$

(vii) $\log 2 + 16 \log \dfrac{16}{15} + 12 \log \dfrac{25}{24} + 7 \log \dfrac{81}{80}$

(viii) $2 \log_{10} 5 + \log_{10} 8 - \dfrac{1}{2} \log_{10} 4$.

3 Express each of the following as a single logarithm:

(i) $2 \log 3 - \dfrac{1}{2} \log 16 + \log 12$

(ii) $2 \log_{10} 5 - \log_{10} 2 + 3 \log_{10} 4 + 1$

(iii) $\dfrac{1}{2} \log 36 + 2 \log 8 - \log 1 \cdot 5$

(iv) $\dfrac{1}{2} \log 25 - 2 \log 3 + 1$

(v) $\dfrac{1}{2} \log 9 + 2 \log 3 - \log 6 + \log 2 - 2$.

4 Prove the following:

(i) $\log_{10} 4 \div \log_{10} 2 = \log_3 9$

(ii) $\log_{10} 25 + \log_{10} 4 = \log_5 25$.

5 If $x = (100)^a$, $y = (10000)^b$ and $z = (10)^c$, express $\log \dfrac{10\sqrt{y}}{x^2 z^3}$ in terms of a, b, c.

6 If $a = \log_{10} x$, find the following in terms of a:

(i) x 　　(ii) $\log_{10} \sqrt[5]{x^2}$.

7 If $a = \log \dfrac{2}{3}$, $b = \log \dfrac{3}{5}$ and $c = 2 \log \sqrt{\dfrac{5}{2}}$, find the value of

(i) $a + b + c$ 　　(ii) 5^{a+b+c}.

8 If $x = \log \dfrac{3}{5}$, $y = \log \dfrac{5}{4}$ and $z = 2 \log \dfrac{\sqrt{3}}{2}$, find the values of

(i) $x + y - z$ 　　(ii) 3^{x+y-z}.

9 If $x = \log_{10} 12$, $y = \log_4 2 \times \log_{10} 9$ and $z = \log_{10} 0 \cdot 4$, find the values of

(i) $x - y - z$ 　　(ii) 7^{x-y-z}.

Hint. (i) $x - y - z = \log_{10} 12 - \log_4 2 \times \log_{10} 9 - \log_{10} 0 \cdot 4$

$$= \log_{10} (4 \times 3) - \log_4 4^{1/2} \times \log_{10} 3^2 - \log_{10} \dfrac{4}{10}$$

$$= \log_{10} 4 + \log_{10} 3 - \dfrac{1}{2} \log_4 4 \times 2 \log_{10} 3 - (\log_{10} 4 - \log_{10} 10)$$

$$= \log_{10} 4 + \log_{10} 3 - \dfrac{1}{2} \times 1 \times 2 \log_{10} 3 - \log_{10} 4 + 1 = 1.$$

10 If $\log V + \log 3 = \log \pi + \log 4 + 3 \log r$, find V in terms of other quantities.

11 Given $3 (\log 5 - \log 3) - (\log 5 - 2 \log 6) = 2 - \log n$, find n.

12 Given that $\log_{10} y + 2 \log_{10} x = 2$, express y in terms of x.

13 Express $\log_{10} 2 + 1$ in the form $\log_{10} x$.

14 If $a^2 = \log_{10} x$, $b^3 = \log_{10} y$ and $\dfrac{a^2}{2} - \dfrac{b^3}{3} = \log_{10} z$, express z in terms of x and y.

15 Given that $\log m = x + y$ and $\log n = x - y$, express the value of $\log m^2 n$ in terms of x and y.

16 Given that $\log x = m + n$ and $\log y = m - n$, express the value of $\log \left(\dfrac{10x}{y^2} \right)$ in terms of m and n.

17 If $\dfrac{\log x}{2} = \dfrac{\log y}{3}$, find the value of $\dfrac{y^4}{x^6}$.

18 Solve for x:

    (i) $\log x + \log 5 = 2 \log 3$ (ii) $\log_3 x - \log_3 2 = 1$

    (iii) $x = \dfrac{\log 125}{\log 25}$ (iv) $\dfrac{\log 8}{\log 2} \times \dfrac{\log 3}{\log \sqrt{3}} = 2 \log x.$

19 Given $2 \log_{10} x + 1 = \log_{10} 250$, find (i) x (ii) $\log_{10} 2x.$

20 If $\dfrac{\log x}{\log 5} = \dfrac{\log y^2}{\log 2} = \dfrac{\log 9}{\log \dfrac{1}{3}}$, find x and y.

21 Prove the following:

    (i) $3^{\log 4} = 4^{\log 3}$ (ii) $27^{\log 2} = 8^{\log 3}.$

22 Solve the following equations:

    (i) $\log (2x + 3) = \log 7$

    (ii) $\log (x + 1) + \log (x - 1) = \log 24$

    (iii) $\log (10x + 5) - \log (x - 4) = 2$

    (iv) $\log_{10} 5 + \log_{10} (5x + 1) = \log_{10}(x + 5) + 1$

    (v) $\log (4y - 3) = \log (2y + 1) - \log 3$

    (vi) $\log_{10}(x + 2) + \log_{10}(x - 2) = \log_{10} 3 + 3 \log_{10} 4$

    (vii) $\log(3x + 2) + \log(3x - 2) = 5 \log 2.$

23 Solve for x: $\log_3 (x + 1) - 1 = 3 + \log_3 (x - 1).$

24 Solve for x: $5^{\log x} + 3^{\log x} = 3^{\log x + 1} - 5^{\log x - 1}.$

25 If $\log \dfrac{x - y}{2} = \dfrac{1}{2} (\log x + \log y)$, prove that $x^2 + y^2 = 6xy.$

26 If $x^2 + y^2 = 23xy$, prove that $\log \dfrac{x + y}{5} = \dfrac{1}{2} (\log x + \log y).$

27 If $p = \log_{10} 20$ and $q = \log_{10} 25$, find the value of x if

    $2 \log_{10}(x + 1) = 2p - q.$

28 Show that:

    (i) $\dfrac{1}{\log_2 42} + \dfrac{1}{\log_3 42} + \dfrac{1}{\log_7 42} = 1$ (ii) $\dfrac{1}{\log_8 36} + \dfrac{1}{\log_9 36} + \dfrac{1}{\log_{18} 36} = 2.$

29 Prove the following identities:

    (i) $\dfrac{1}{\log_a abc} + \dfrac{1}{\log_b abc} + \dfrac{1}{\log_c abc} = 1$ (ii) $\log_b a \cdot \log_c b \cdot \log_d c = \log_d a.$

30 Given that $\log_a x = \dfrac{1}{\alpha}$, $\log_b x = \dfrac{1}{\beta}$, $\log_c x = \dfrac{1}{\gamma}$, find $\log_{abc} x.$

    Hint. $\dfrac{1}{\alpha} = \log_a x = \dfrac{\log x}{\log a} \Rightarrow \log a = \alpha \log x$ etc. and

    $\log_{abc} x = \dfrac{\log x}{\log abc} = \dfrac{\log x}{\log a + \log b + \log c}.$

31 Solve for x:

    (i) $\log_3 x + \log_9 x + \log_{81} x = \dfrac{7}{4}$ (ii) $\log_2 x + \log_8 x + \log_{32} x = \dfrac{23}{15}.$

Multiple Choice Questions

Choose the correct answer from the given four options (1 to 7):

1 If $\log_{\sqrt{3}} 27 = x$, then the value of x is

    (a) 3   (b) 4   (c) 6   (d) 9

2 If $\log_5 (0.04) = x$, then the value of x is

    (a) 2   (b) 4   (c) -4 (d) -2

3 If $\log_{0.5} 64 = x$, then the value of x is

    (a) -4 (b) -6 (c) 4   (d) 6

4 If $\log_{\sqrt[3]{5}} x = -3$, then the value of x is

    (a) $\dfrac{1}{5}$ (b) $-\dfrac{1}{5}$ (c) -1 (d) 5

5 If $\log (3x + 1) = 2$, then the value of x is

    (a) $\dfrac{1}{3}$ (b) 99   (c) 33   (d) $\dfrac{19}{3}$

6 The value of $2 + \log_{10} (0.01)$ is

    (a) 4   (b) 3   (c) 1   (d) 0

7 The value of $\dfrac{\log 8 - \log 2}{\log 32}$ is

    (a) $\dfrac{2}{5}$ (b) $\dfrac{1}{4}$ (c) $-\dfrac{2}{5}$ (d) $\dfrac{1}{3}$

Summary

- $a^n = b \Leftrightarrow \log_a b = n$, $a > 0$ and $a \neq 1$.

- $\log_a 1 = 0$, $\log_a a = 1$.

- $\log_a mn = \log_a m + \log_a n$.

- $\log_a \dfrac{m}{n} = \log_a m - \log_a n$.

- $\log_a m^n = n \log_a m$.

- $\log_a m = \dfrac{\log_b m}{\log_b a}$, $m > 0$, $a, b > 0$, $a \neq 1$, $b \neq 1$.

- $\log_b m = \log_a m \times \log_b a$.

- $\log_b a \times \log_a b = 1$.

- $\log_b a = \dfrac{1}{\log_a b}$.

- $a^{\log_a x} = x$.

1 Expand $\log_a \sqrt[3]{x^7 y^8 \div \sqrt[4]{z}}$.

2 Find the value of $\log_{\sqrt{3}} 3\sqrt{3} - \log_5 (0.04)$.

3 Prove the following:

(i) $(\log x)^2 - (\log y)^2 = \log \dfrac{x}{y} \cdot \log xy$

(ii) $2 \log \dfrac{11}{13} + \log \dfrac{130}{77} - \log \dfrac{55}{91} = \log 2$.

4 If $\log (m + n) = \log m + \log n$, show that $n = \dfrac{m}{m - 1}$.

5 If $\log \dfrac{x + y}{2} = \dfrac{1}{2} (\log x + \log y)$, prove that $x = y$.

6 If a, b are positive real numbers, $a > b$ and $a^2 + b^2 = 27ab$, prove that

$$\log \left(\dfrac{a - b}{5} \right) = \dfrac{1}{2} (\log a + \log b).$$

7 Solve the following equations for x:

(i) $\log_x \dfrac{1}{49} = -2$

(ii) $\log_x \dfrac{1}{4\sqrt{2}} = -5$

(iii) $\log_x \dfrac{1}{243} = 10$

(iv) $\log_4 32 = x - 4$

(v) $\log_7 (2x^2 - 1) = 2$

(vi) $\log (x^2 - 21) = 2$

(vii) $\log_6 (x - 2) (x + 3) = 1$

(viii) $\log_6 (x - 2) + \log_6 (x + 3) = 1$

(ix) $\log (x + 1) + \log (x - 1) = \log 11 + 2 \log 3$.

8 Solve for x and y:

$\dfrac{\log x}{3} = \dfrac{\log y}{2}$ and $\log (xy) = 5$.

Hint. $\dfrac{\log x}{3} = \dfrac{\log y}{2} \Rightarrow 2 \log x - 3 \log y = 0$ ...(i)

$\log (xy) = 5 \Rightarrow \log x + \log y = 5$ ...(ii)

Multiplying (ii) by 3 and adding to (i), we get

$5 \log x = 15 \Rightarrow \log x = 3 \Rightarrow x = 10^3 = 1000$.

9 If $a = 1 + \log_x yz$, $b = 1 + \log_y zx$ and $c = 1 + \log_z xy$, then show that

$ab + bc + ca = abc$.

Hint. $a = 1 + \log_x yz = \log_x x + \log_x yz = \log_x xyz \Rightarrow \dfrac{1}{a} = \log_{xyz} x$ etc.

$\Rightarrow \dfrac{1}{a} + \dfrac{1}{b} + \dfrac{1}{c} = \log_{xyz} x + \log_{xyz} y + \log_{xyz} z = 1$.

10 Triangles

INTRODUCTION

In previous classes, we have studied about triangles and various types of triangles on the basis of sides and on the basis of angles. We have also studied the following:

    (*i*) angles sum property of a triangle and exterior angle property

    (*ii*) congruence of triangles

    (*iii*) inequalities in a triangle.

In this chapter, we shall review these and shall study about congruence of triangles in detail, rules of congruency, some more properties of triangles and inequalities in a triangle.

10.1 TRIANGLE

A triangle is a closed curve formed by three line segments. 'Tri' means 'three'. A triangle has three sides, three angles and three vertices.

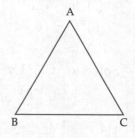

The adjoining figure shows a triangle ABC. The line segments AB, BC and CA are called its **sides**. The angles ∠A, ∠B and ∠C are called its **interior angles** or simply **angles**. The points A, B and C are called its **vertices**. Three sides and the three angles are called its six **elements**.

In the above figure, look at the vertex A. It is the point of intersection of the sides AB and AC, BC is the remaining side. We say that vertex A and side BC are opposite to each other. Also ∠A and side BC are opposite to each other.

Similarly, vertex B and side CA are opposite to each other; ∠B and side CA are opposite to each other. Same can be said about vertex C, ∠C and side AB.

10.1.1 Types of triangles

Types of triangles on the basis of sides.

    (*i*) **Scalene triangle.** *If all the sides of a triangle are unequal, it is called a **scalene triangle**.*

       In the adjoining diagram, AB ≠ BC ≠ CA, so ΔABC is a scalene triangle.

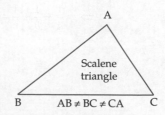

(ii) **Isosceles triangle.** *If any two sides of a triangle are equal, it is called an **isosceles triangle**.*

In the adjoining diagram, AB = AC, so △ABC is an isosceles triangle. Usually, equal sides are indicated by putting marks on each of them.

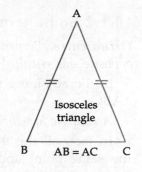

(iii) **Equilateral triangle.** *If all the three sides of a triangle are equal, it is called an **equilateral triangle**.*

In the adjoining diagram, AB = BC = AC, so △ABC is an equilateral triangle.

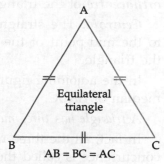

Types of triangles on the basis of angles.

(i) **Acute angled triangle.** *If all the three angles of a triangle are acute (less than 90°), it is called an **acute-angled triangle**.*

In the adjoining diagram, each angle is less than 90°, so △ABC is an acute angled triangle.

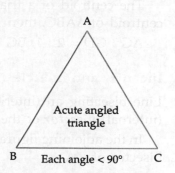

(ii) **Right-angled triangle.** *If one angle of a triangle is a right angle (= 90°), it is called a **right-angled triangle**.*

In a right angled triangle, the side opposite to right angle is called **hypotenuse**.

In the adjoining diagram, ∠B = 90°, so △ABC is a right angled triangle and side AC is the hypotenuse.

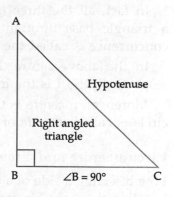

(iii) **Obtuse angled triangle.** *If one angle of a triangle is obtuse (greater than 90°), it is called an **obtuse-angled triangle**.*

In the adjoining diagram, ∠B is obtuse (greater than 90°), so △ABC is an obtuse angled triangle.

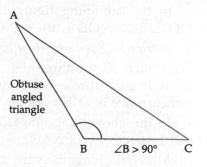

10.1.2 Some terms connected with a triangle

Orthocentre. *Perpendicular from a vertex of a triangle to the opposite side is called an* **altitude** *of the triangle.*

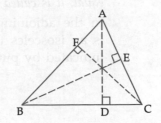

In the adjoining figure, AD ⊥ BC, so AD is an altitude of △ABC.

A triangle has three altitudes.

In fact, all the three altitudes of a triangle pass through the same point and the point of concurrence is called the ***orthocentre*** of the triangle.

Centroid. The straight line joining a vertex of a triangle to the mid-point of the opposite side is called a *median* of the triangle.

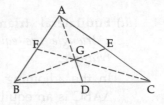

In the adjoining figure, D is mid-point of BC, so AD is a median of △ABC.

A triangle has three medians.

In fact, all the three medians of a triangle pass through the same point and the point of concurrence is called the ***centroid*** of the triangle.

The centroid of a triangle divides every median in the ratio of 2 : 1. Thus, if G is the centroid of △ABC, then

AG : GD = 2 : 1, BG : GE = 2 : 1 and CG : GF = 2 : 1.

Incentre and incircle

Line bisecting an (interior) angle of a triangle is called the (internal) *bisector* of the angle of the triangle.

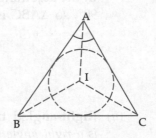

In the adjoining figure, ∠BAI = ∠IAC, so AI is the (internal) bisector of ∠A.

A triangle has three internal bisectors of its angles.

In fact, all the three (internal) bisectors of the angles of a triangle pass through the same point and the point of concurrence is called the ***incentre*** of the triangle.

In the above figure, IA, IB and IC are the (internal) bisectors of ∠A, ∠B and ∠C respectively. So I is the incentre of △ABC.

Moreover, incentre is the centre of a circle which touches all the sides of △ABC and this circle is called ***incircle*** of △ABC.

Circumcentre and circumcircle

Line bisecting a side of a triangle and perpendicular to it is called the ***right bisector*** of the side of the triangle.

In the adjoining figure, D is mid-point of BC and OD ⊥ BC, so OD is the right bisector of the side BC.

A triangle has three right bisectors of its sides.

In fact, all the three right bisectors of the sides of a triangle pass through the same point and the point of concurrence is called the ***circumcentre*** of the triangle.

In the above diagram, OD, OE and OF are the right bisectors of the sides BC, CA and AB respectively of △ABC. So O is the circumcentre of △ABC.

Moreover, circumcentre is the centre of a circle which passes through the vertices of △ABC and this circle is called ***circumcircle*** of △ABC.

10.1.3 Angles sum property of a triangle

The sum of angles of a triangle is 180°.

In the adjoining figure, ABC is a triangle.

$$\angle A + \angle B + \angle C = 180°.$$

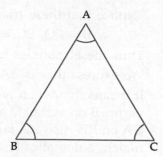

Activity

To verify that sum of angles of a triangle is 180° by cutting and pasting.

Steps

1. Take a sheet of paper and draw any triangle ABC on it and cut off the three angles *i.e.* $\angle A$, $\angle B$ and $\angle C$ along the dotted lines (as shown in the adjoining figure).

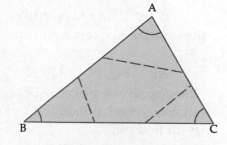

2. Draw any line PQ on the sheet of paper and mark a point O on it. Paste the cut outs of $\angle A$, $\angle B$ and $\angle C$ on the line PQ such that their vertices A, B and C all fall at the point O (as shown in the adjoining figure).

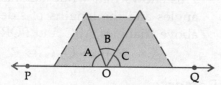

Note that the outer arms of $\angle A$ and $\angle C$ coincide with the line PQ. The three angles now constitute one angle *i.e.* $\angle POQ$.

But POQ is a straight angle,

$\therefore \quad \angle A + \angle B + \angle C = 180°.$

10.1.4 An exterior angle property of a triangle

Let ABC be a triangle and its side BC be produced to D, then $\angle ACD$ is called an *exterior angle* at C. The two interior angles of the triangle that are opposite to the exterior $\angle ACD$ are called its *interior opposite angles* or *remote interior angles*. Thus, $\angle ABC$ and $\angle BAC$ of $\triangle ABC$ are interior opposite angles of the exterior $\angle ACD$.

An exterior angle of a triangle is equal to sum of its interior opposite angles.

In the above figure, $\angle ACD = \angle A + \angle B$.

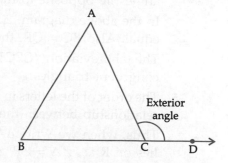

Exterior angle

10.2 CONGRUENCE OF TRIANGLES

Two triangles are called **congruent** *if and only if they have exactly the same shape and the same size.*

In the adjoining figure, two triangles ABC and PQR are congruent. It means that the sketch of one triangle can be slided onto the sketch of the other so that they fit each other exactly *i.e.* when one triangle is superimposed on the other, they cover each other exactly.

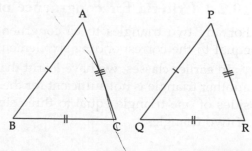

Notice that these triangles are such that

$$AB = PQ, BC = QR, AC = PR, \angle A = \angle P, \angle B = \angle Q \text{ and } \angle C = \angle R.$$

Thus these triangles have the same shape and same size, so they are congruent.

We express this as $\triangle ABC \cong \triangle PQR$.

It means that when we place a trace-copy of $\triangle ABC$ on $\triangle PQR$, vertex A falls on vertex P, vertex B on vertex Q and vertex C on vertex R. Then side AB falls on PQ, BC on QR and CA on RP. Also $\angle A$ falls on $\angle P$, $\angle B$ on $\angle Q$ and $\angle C$. Thus, the order in which the vertices match, automatically determines a correspondence between the sides and the angles of the two triangles. It follows that if the vertices of $\triangle ABC$ match the vertices of $\triangle PQR$ in the order:

$$A \leftrightarrow P, B \leftrightarrow Q, C \leftrightarrow R$$

then all the six corresponding parts (3 sides and 3 angles) of two triangles are equal *i.e.*

$$AB = PQ, BC = QR, CA = RP, \angle A = \angle P, \angle B = \angle Q \text{ and } \angle C = \angle R.$$

However, if we place $\triangle ABC$ on $\triangle PQR$ such that A falls on Q, then other vertices may not correspond suitably. Take a trace-copy of $\triangle ABC$ and place vertex A on vertex Q and try to find out!

This shows that while talking about congruence of triangles, not only the measures of angles and the lengths of sides matter, but also the matching of vertices matter. In the above triangles ABC and PQR, the correspondence is

$$A \leftrightarrow P, B \leftrightarrow Q, C \leftrightarrow R.$$

Remarks

1. Congruent triangles are 'equal in all respects' *i.e.* they are the exact *duplicate* of each other.

2. If two triangles are congruent, then any one can be *superposed* on the other to cover it exactly.

3. In congruent triangles, the sides and the angles which coincide by superposition are called *corresponding sides* and *corresponding angles*.

4. The corresponding sides lie opposite to the equal angles and the corresponding angles lie opposite to the equal sides.

   In the above diagram, $\angle A = \angle P$, therefore, the corresponding sides BC and QR are equal. Also BC = QR, therefore, the corresponding angles A and P are equal.

   The abbreviation 'CPCT' or 'c.p.c.t.' will be used for corresponding parts of congruent triangles.

5. The order of the letters in the names of congruent triangles displays the corresponding relationship between the two triangles.

   Thus, when we write $\triangle ABC \cong \triangle PQR$, it means that A lies on P, B lies on Q and C lies on R *i.e.* $\angle A = \angle P$, $\angle B = \angle Q$, $\angle C = \angle R$ and BC = QR, CA = RP, AB = PQ.

   Writing any other correspondence *i.e.* $\triangle ABC \cong \triangle PRQ$, $\triangle ABC \cong \triangle RPQ$ etc. will be incorrect.

10.2.1 Criteria for congruence of triangles

For any two triangles to be congruent, the *six elements* of one triangle *need not be proved* equal to the corresponding six elements of the other triangle.

In earlier classes, we have learnt that three angles of one triangle equal to three angles of another triangle is not sufficient for the congruence of two triangles. Let us see whether three sides of one triangle equal to three sides of another triangle is enough for the congruence of two triangles.

Draw two triangles ABC and PQR such that AB = PQ = 3·7 cm, BC = QR = 4 cm and CA = RP = 3·2 cm.

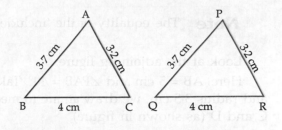

Make a trace-copy of ΔABC and place it over ΔPQR. We observe that the two triangles cover each other exactly and so they are congruent.

Repeat this activity with more pairs of triangles satisfying these conditions. We observe that the equality of three sides of two triangles is sufficient for the congruence of two triangles. We record it as:

❑ **SSS congruence rule**

Two triangles are congruent if the three sides of one triangle are equal to the three sides of the other triangle.

In the adjoining figure,

$$AB = PQ, BC = QR$$

and $$AC = PR$$

∴ $$ΔABC \cong ΔPQR.$$

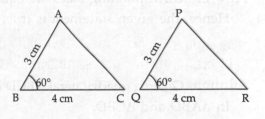

Note that SSS stands for **Side-Side-Side**.

Now, let us see whether two sides and the included angle of one triangle are equal to two sides and the included angle of another triangle is enough for the congruence of two triangles.

Draw two triangles ABC and PQR such that BC = QR = 4 cm, ∠B = ∠Q = 60° and AB = PQ = 3 cm.

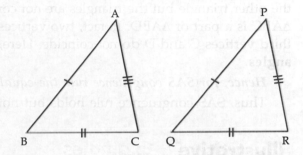

Make a trace-copy of ΔABC and place it over ΔPQR. We observe that the two triangles cover each other exactly and so they are congruent.

Repeat this activity with more pairs of triangles satisfying these conditions. We observe that equality of two sides and the included angle is enough for the congruence of two triangles. We record it as:

❑ **SAS congruence rule**

Two triangles are congruent if two sides and the included angle of one triangle are equal to two sides and the included angle of the other triangle.

In the adjoining figure,

$$AB = PQ, BC = QR \text{ and}$$

$$∠B = ∠Q$$

∴ $$ΔABC \cong ΔPQR$$

This is known as **Side-Angle-Side** criterion (or rule) of congruency.

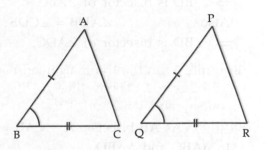

Look at the adjoining figure:

Here, AB = 5 cm and ∠PAB = 40°. Taking B as centre and radius 3·5 cm, we draw an arc to meet AP at points C and D (as shown in figure).

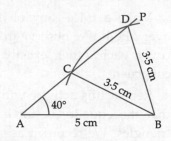

We consider two triangles ABC and ABD. In these triangles, we have

$$AB = AB, BC = BD \text{ and}$$
$$∠CAB = ∠DAB \qquad (\text{each} = 40°)$$

Thus, two sides and one angle of one triangle are equal to two sides and one angle of the other triangle but the triangles are not congruent which is clear from the figure because ΔABC is a part of ΔABD. In fact, two vertices A and B are same for both triangles but their third vertices C and D do not coincide. Here, note that ∠CAB and ∠DAB are not **included angles.**

Hence, for SAS congruence rule the equality of the included angle is essential.

Thus, SAS congruence rule holds but not ASS or SSA rule.

Illustrative Examples

Example 1 If ΔPQR ≅ ΔEDF, then is it true to say that PR = EF? Give reason for your answer.

Solution. Given ΔPQR ≅ ΔEDF. It means that P ↔ E, Q ↔ D and R ↔ F, therefore, PR = EF (corresponding sides are equal).

Hence, the given statement is true.

Example 2 ABCD is a quadrilateral in which AB = BC and AD = CD. Show that BD bisects both the angles ABC and ADC.

Solution. Given a quadrilateral ABCD in which AB = BC and AD = CD. Join B and D.

In ΔABD and ΔCBD,

AB = BC	(given)	
AD = CD	(given)	
BD = BD	(common)	
∴ ΔABD ≅ ΔCBD	(by SSS congruence rule)	
∴ ∠ABD = ∠CBD	(c.p.c.t.)	

⇒   BD is bisector of ∠ABC.

Also   ∠ADB = ∠CDB   (c.p.c.t.)

⇒   BD is bisector of ∠ADC.

Example 3 In the adjoining quadrilateral, AC = AD and AB bisects ∠A. Show that ΔABC ≅ ΔABD. What can you say about BC and BD?

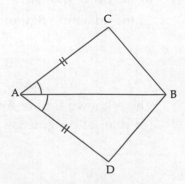

Solution. As AB bisects ∠A, ∠CAB = ∠DAB.

In ΔABC and ΔABD,

AC = AD	(given)
AB = AB	(common)
∠CAB = ∠DAB	(∵ AB bisects ∠A)

$$\therefore \qquad \triangle ABC \cong \triangle ABD \qquad \text{(by SAS rule of congruency)}$$
$$\therefore \qquad BC = BD \qquad \text{(c.p.c.t.)}$$

Example 4 In the adjoining figure, OA = OB and OD = OC.
Show that

  (i) $\triangle AOD \cong \triangle BOC$

  (ii) AD ∥ CB.

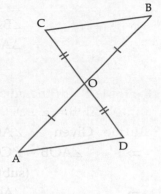

Solution. (i) In $\triangle AOD$ and $\triangle BOC$,

$$OA = OB \qquad \text{(given)}$$
$$OD = OC \qquad \text{(given)}$$
$$\angle AOD = \angle BOC \qquad \text{(vert. opp. } \angle\text{s)}$$
$$\therefore \qquad \triangle AOD \cong \triangle BOC$$
$$\text{(by SAS rule of congruency)}$$
$$(ii) \qquad \angle OAD = \angle OBC \qquad \text{(c.p.c.t.)}$$

But these form a pair of alternate angles for line segments AD and BC.
Therefore, AD ∥ CB.

Example 5 In the adjoining figure, E and F are respectively
the mid-points of equal sides AB and AC of $\triangle ABC$. Show
that BF = CE.

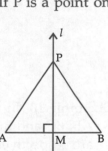

Solution. In $\triangle ABF$ and $\triangle ACE$,

$$AB = AC \qquad \text{(given)}$$
$$AF = AE$$
$$\text{(halves of equal sides AC and AB)}$$
$$\angle A = \angle A \qquad \text{(common)}$$
$$\therefore \qquad \triangle ABF \cong \triangle ACE$$
$$\text{(by SAS rule of congruency)}$$
$$\therefore \qquad BF = CE \qquad \text{(c.p.c.t.)}$$

Example 6 AB is a line segment and line l is its perpendicular bisector. If P is a point on
l, show that P is equidistant from A and B.

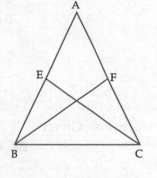

Solution. Given line l is perpendicular bisector of AB and P is a point
on l, so M is mid-point of AB and MP ⊥ AB.

In $\triangle AMP$ and $\triangle BMP$,

$$AM = MB \qquad (\because \text{ M is mid-point of AB})$$
$$MP = MP \qquad \text{(common)}$$
$$\angle AMP = \angle BMP \qquad \text{(each} = 90°)$$
$$\therefore \qquad \triangle AMP \cong \triangle BMP \qquad \text{(by SAS rule of congruency)}$$
$$\therefore \qquad AP = BP \qquad \text{(c.p.c.t.)}$$
$$\Rightarrow \quad \text{P is equidistant from A and B.}$$

Example 7 In the adjoining figure, AC = AE, AB = AD and
∠BAD = ∠EAC. Show that BC = DE.

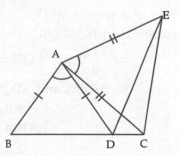

Solution. Given $\qquad \angle BAD = \angle EAC$

$$\Rightarrow \qquad \angle BAD + \angle DAC = \angle EAC + \angle DAC$$
$$\text{(adding } \angle DAC \text{ to both sides)}$$
$$\Rightarrow \qquad \angle BAC = \angle DAE.$$

In ΔABC and ΔADE,

	AB = AD	(given)
	AC = AE	(given)
	∠BAC = ∠DAE	(proved above)
∴	ΔABC ≅ ΔADE	(by SAS rule of congruency)
∴	BC = DE	(c.p.c.t.)

Example 8 In the adjoining figure, OA = OB, OC = OD and ∠AOB = ∠COD. Prove that AC = BD.

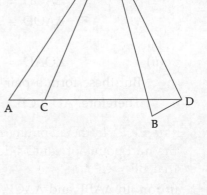

Solution. Given   ∠AOB = ∠COD

⇒   ∠AOB − ∠COB = ∠COD − ∠COB.

          (subtracting ∠COB from both sides)

⇒   ∠AOC = ∠BOD.

In ΔAOC and ΔBOD,

	OA = OB	(given)
	OC = OD	(given)
	∠AOC = ∠BOD	(proved above)
∴	ΔAOC ≅ ΔBOD	
	(by SAS rule of congruency)	
⇒	AC = BD	(c.p.c.t.)

Example 9 In the adjoining figure, AB = PQ, BR = CQ, AB ⊥ BC and PQ ⊥ RQ. Prove that AC = PR.

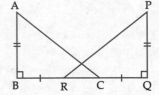

Solution. Given   BR = CQ

⇒   BR + RC = CQ + RC

           (adding RC to both sides)

⇒   BC = QR

In ΔABC and ΔPQR,

	AB = PQ	(given)
	BC = QR	(proved above)
	∠ABC = ∠PQR	(each = 90°, ∵ AB ⊥ BC and PQ ⊥ RQ)
∴	ΔABC ≅ ΔPQR	(by SAS rule of congruency)
∴	AC = PR	(c.p.c.t.)

Example 10 In the adjoining figure, two sides AB, BC and median AM of one triangle ABC are respectively equal to two sides PQ, QR and median PN of triangle PQR. Show that

  (i) ΔABM ≅ ΔPQN

  (ii) ΔABC ≅ ΔPQR.

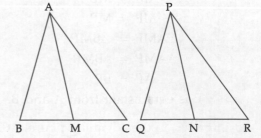

Solution. (i) BC = QR   (given)

⇒ $\frac{1}{2}$ BC = $\frac{1}{2}$ QR ⇒ BM = QN

In ΔABM and ΔPQN,

      AB = PQ, BM = QN, AM = PN

∴	ΔABM ≅ ΔPQN	(by SSS rule of congruency)
∴	∠B = ∠Q	(c.p.c.t.)

(ii) In △ABC and △PQR,

$$AB = PQ, BC = QR \text{ and } \angle B = \angle Q$$

∴   △ABC ≅ △PQR   (by SAS rule of congruency)

Example 11 In the adjoining figure, AB = AC and AD is bisector of ∠A. Prove that

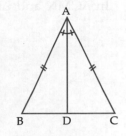

 (*i*) D is mid-point of BC

 (*ii*) AD ⊥ BC.

Given. △ABC, AB = AC and ∠BAD = ∠CAD.

To prove. (*i*) BD = DC

 (*ii*) ∠ADB = 90°.

Proof.

Statements	Reasons
1. AB = AC	1. Given.
2. ∠BAD = ∠CAD	2. AD is bisector of ∠A.
3. AD = AD	3. Common.
4. △ABD ≅ △ACD	4. SAS rule of congruency
5. (*i*) BD = DC	5. 'c.p.c.t.'
6. ∠ADB = ∠ADC	6. 'c.p.c.t.'
7. ∠ADB + ∠ADC = 180°	7. BDC is a straight line.
8. (*ii*) 2 ∠ADB = 180° ⇒ ∠ADB = 90°. Hence, (*i*) BD = DC and (*ii*) ∠ADB = 90°. **Q.E.D.**	8. From 6 and 7.

Example 12 In the adjoining figure, AB is a line segment. P and Q are points on opposite sides of AB such that each of them is equidistant from the points A and B. Show that the line PQ is the perpendicular bisector of AB.

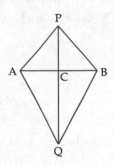

Solution. Given AP = BP and AQ = BQ.

We need to show that PQ ⊥ AB and PQ bisects AB.

In △APQ and △BPQ,

$$AP = BP, AQ = BQ \text{ and } PQ = PQ \quad \text{(common)}$$

∴   △APQ ≅ △BPQ   (by SSS rule of congruency)

∴   ∠APC = ∠BPC   (c.p.c.t.)

In △APC and △BPC,

$$AP = BP, \angle APC = \angle BPC \text{ and } CP = CP \quad \text{(common)}$$

∴   △APC ≅ △BPC   (by SAS rule of congruency)

∴   AC = CB ⇒ C is mid-point of AB

⇒   PQ bisects AB.

Also   ∠ACP = ∠BCP   (c.p.c.t.)

But   ∠ACP + ∠BCP = 180°   (linear pair)

⇒   ∠ACP + ∠ACP = 180° ⇒ ∠ACP = 90°

⇒   PQ ⊥ AB.

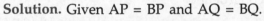

Example 13 Line segment joining the mid-points M and N of parallel sides AB and DC respectively of a trapezium ABCD is perpendicular to both the sides AB and DC. Prove that AD = BC.

Solution. Join CM and DM.

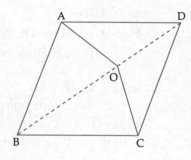

In △CMN and △DMN,

$$MN = MN \qquad \text{(common)}$$
$$CN = DN \quad (\because \text{ N is mid-point of DC)}$$
$$\angle CNM = \angle DNM$$
$$\text{(each} = 90°, \because \text{ MN} \perp \text{DC)}$$
$$\therefore \quad △CMN \cong △DMN$$
$$\text{(by SAS rule of congruency)}$$
$$\therefore \qquad CM = DM \qquad \text{(c.p.c.t.)}$$
and $\qquad \angle CMN = \angle DMN \qquad \text{(c.p.c.t.)}$

As MN ⊥ AB, $\quad \angle AMN = \angle BMN \qquad \text{(each} = 90°)$

$\Rightarrow \quad \angle AMN - \angle DMN = \angle BMN - \angle CMN \quad (\because \angle DMN = \angle CMN, \text{ proved above)}$

$\Rightarrow \qquad \angle AMD = \angle BMC$

In △AMD and △BMC,

$$AM = BM \qquad (\because \text{ M is mid-point of AB)}$$
$$DM = CM \qquad \text{(proved above)}$$
$$\angle AMD = \angle BMC \qquad \text{(proved above)}$$
$$\therefore \qquad △AMD \cong △BMC \qquad \text{(by SAS rule of congruency)}$$
$$\therefore \qquad AD = BC \qquad \text{(c.p.c.t.)}$$

Example 14 In a rhombus ABCD, O is any interior point such that OA = OC. Prove that points B, O and D are collinear.

Solution. Join OB and OD.

In △OBA and △OBC,

$$OA = OC \qquad \text{(given)}$$
$$AB = BC \qquad \text{(sides of a rhombus)}$$
$$OB = OB \qquad \text{(common)}$$
$$\therefore \qquad △OBA \cong △OBC \quad \text{(SSS rule of congruency)}$$
$$\therefore \qquad \angle AOB = \angle BOC \qquad \qquad \text{...(i) (c.p.c.t.)}$$

Similarly, $\quad △OAD \cong △OCD$

$$\therefore \qquad \angle AOD = \angle COD \qquad \qquad \text{...(ii) (c.p.c.t.)}$$

As the sum of angles at a point is 360°,

$$\angle AOB + \angle BOC + \angle COD + \angle AOD = 360°$$
$$\Rightarrow \quad \angle BOC + \angle BOC + \angle COD + \angle COD = 360° \qquad \text{(using (i) and (ii))}$$
$$\Rightarrow \quad 2(\angle BOC + \angle COD) = 360° \Rightarrow \angle BOC + \angle COD = 180°.$$

Thus, the sum of two adjacent angles is 180°, so BOD is a straight line.

Hence, the points B, O and D are collinear.

EXERCISE 10.1

1 It is given that △ABC ≅ △RPQ. Is it true to say that BC = QR? Why?

2 "If two sides and an angle of one triangle are equal to two sides and an angle of another triangle, then the two triangles must be congruent." Is the statement true? Why?

3 In the adjoining figure, AB = AC and AP = AQ. Prove that
    (i) △APC ≅ △AQB
    (ii) CP = BQ
    (iii) ∠APC = ∠AQB.

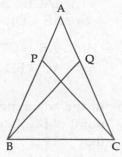

4 In the adjoining figure, AB = AC, P and Q are points on BA and CA respectively such that AP = AQ. Prove that
    (i) △APC ≅ △AQB
    (ii) CP = BQ
    (iii) ∠ACP = ∠ABQ.

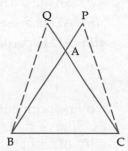

5 In the adjoining figure, AD = BC and BD = AC. Prove that:
    ∠ADB = ∠BCA
  and ∠DAB = ∠CBA.

    Hint. △ABD ≅ △BAC (SSS)

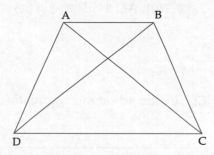

6 In the adjoining figure, ABCD is a quadrilateral in which AD = BC and ∠DAB = ∠CBA. Prove that
    (i) △ABD ≅ △BAC
    (ii) BD = AC
    (iii) ∠ABD = ∠BAC.

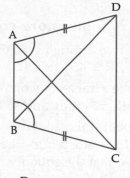

7 In the adjoining figure, AB = DC and AB ∥ DC. Prove that AD = BC.

    Hint. As AB ∥ DC, ∠ABD = ∠CDB (alt. ∠s).
    Show that △ABD ≅ △CDB.

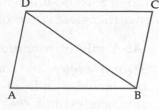

8 In the adjoining figure, AC = AE, AB = AD and ∠BAD = ∠CAE. Show that BC = DE.

    Hint. Join DE.
    Show that △ABC ≅ △ADE.

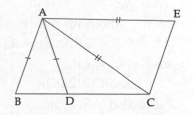

9 In the adjoining figure, AB = CD, CE = BF and ∠ACE = ∠DBF. Prove that

    (*i*) ΔACE ≅ ΔDBF

    (*ii*) AE = DF.

    Hint. AB = CD ⟹ AB + BC = CD + BC

    ⟹   AC = BD.

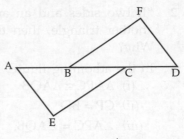

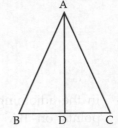

10 In the adjoining figure, AB = AC and D is mid-point of BC. Use SSS rule of congruency to show that

    (*i*) ΔABD ≅ ΔACD

    (*ii*) AD is bisector of ∠A

    (*iii*) AD is perpendicular to BC.

11 Two line segments AB and CD bisect each other at O. Prove that

    (*i*) AC = BD   (*ii*) ∠CAB = ∠ABD

    (*iii*) AD ∥ CB   (*iv*) AD = CB.

12 In the adjoining figure, find the values of *x* and *y*.

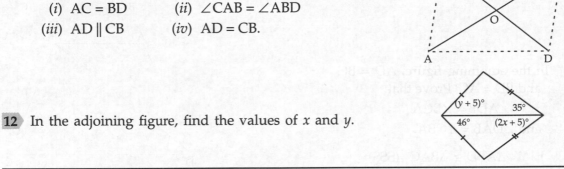

10.2.2 Some more criteria for congruence of triangles

Draw two triangles ABC and PQR such that BC = QR = 3.5 cm, ∠B = ∠Q = 60° and ∠C = ∠R = 45°.

Make a trace-copy of ΔABC and place it over ΔPQR. We observe that the two triangles cover each other exactly and so they are congruent.

Repeat this activity with more pairs of triangles satisfying these conditions. We observe that the equality of two angles and the included side is sufficient for the congruence of two triangles. We record it as:

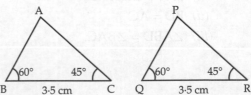

❑ **ASA rule of congruency**

Two triangles are congruent if two angles and the included side of one triangle are equal to two angles and the included side of the other triangle.

In the adjoining figure,

    BC = QR, ∠B = ∠Q

and ∠C = ∠R.

∴   ΔABC ≅ ΔPQR.

Note that ASA stands for **Angle-Side-Angle**.

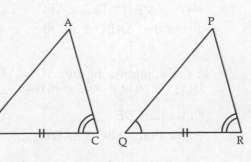

❏ **AAS congruency rule**

Two triangles are congruent if any two pairs of angles and a pair of corresponding sides are equal.

In the adjoining figure,

∠A = ∠P, ∠B = ∠Q and

BC = QR

∴   ΔABC ≅ ΔPQR

(The result follows immediately from ASA congruence rule because if two angles of a triangle are equal to two angles of another triangle, then the third angles of both triangles are also equal.)

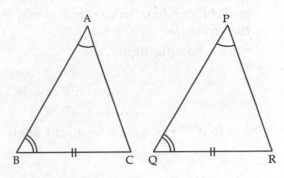

Note   The equality of 'corresponding sides' is essential.

Look at the adjoining figure:

Here, AB = 4 cm and ∠PAB = 60°.

Draw ∠ABQ = 50° to meet AP at C.

Also draw ∠ABR = 70° to meet AP at D.

Thus, we get two triangles ABC and ABD.

In ΔABC, ∠CAB = 60° and ∠ABC = 50° so that

∠ACB = 180° – 60° – 50° = 70°

$\qquad$ (∵ sum of angles in a triangle = 180°)

In ΔABD, ∠DAB = 60° and ∠ABD = 70° so that

∠ADB = 180° – 60° – 70° = 50°   (as shown in the figure).

We consider two triangles ABC and ABD. In these triangles, we have

$\qquad$ ∠CAB = ∠DAB $\hfill$ (each = 60°)

$\qquad$ ∠ABC = ∠ADB $\hfill$ (each = 50°)

and $\qquad$ AB = AB.

Thus, two angles and one side of one triangle is equal to two angles and one side of another triangle but the triangles are not congruent which is clear from the figure because ΔABC is a part of ΔABD. In fact, two vertices A and B are same for both triangles but their third vertices C and D do not coincide. Here, note that the side AB is not corresponding side (because in ΔABC, side AB is opposite to angle of 70° and in ΔABD, side AB is opposite to angle of 50°).

In SAS congruence rule, we know that the pair of equal angles must be the included angle between the pairs of corresponding pair of equal sides and if this is not so, the two triangles may not be congruent.

Now perform the following activity:

Draw two right angled triangles ABC and PQR such that hypotenuse BC = QR = 4·5 cm and one side = AB = PQ = 2·5 cm.

Make a trace-copy of ΔABC and place it over ΔPQR. We observe that the two triangles cover each other exactly and so they are congruent. Repeat this activity with more pairs of triangles satisfying these conditions. We observe that two right angled triangles are congruent if one pair of sides and the hypotenuse are equal. Thus, we get another rule of congruency. We record it as:

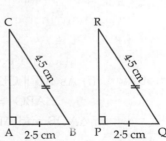

□ **RHS congruence rule**

Two right triangles are congruent if the hypotenuse and one side of one triangle are equal to the hypotenuse and one side of the other triangle.

In the adjoining figure,

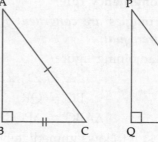 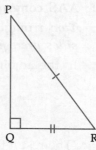

$$\angle B = \text{a right angle} = \angle Q,$$
$$AC = PR \text{ and } BC = QR$$
$$\therefore \qquad \triangle ABC \cong \triangle PQR.$$

Note that RHS stands for **Right angle-Hypotenuse-Side.**

Remark

In the above congruence rule, right angle is **not** included angle between hypotenuse and side.

Illustrative Examples

Example 1 In the adjoining figure, PQ = PR and $\angle Q = \angle R$. Prove that

(i) $\triangle PQS \cong \triangle PRT$

(ii) QS = RT.

Solution. (i) In $\triangle PQS$ and $\triangle PRT$,

$$\angle Q = \angle R \qquad \text{(given)}$$
$$\angle P = \angle P \qquad \text{(common)}$$
$$PQ = PR \qquad \text{(given)}$$
$$\therefore \qquad \triangle PQS \cong \triangle PRT$$
$$\text{(by ASA congruence rule)}$$

(ii) $$QS = RT \qquad \text{(c.p.c.t.)}$$

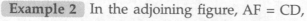

Example 2 In the adjoining figure, AF = CD,

If $\angle AFE = \angle CDE$, prove that EF = ED.

Solution. In $\triangle AFE$ and $\triangle CDE$,

$$AF = CD \qquad \text{(given)}$$
$$\angle AFE = \angle CDE \qquad \text{(given)}$$
$$\angle E = \angle E \qquad \text{(common)}$$
$$\therefore \qquad \triangle AFE \cong \triangle CDE$$
$$\text{(by AAS rule of congruency)}$$
$$\therefore \qquad EF = ED \qquad \text{(c.p.c.t.)}$$

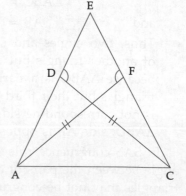

Example 3 In the adjoining figure, line segment AB is parallel to another line segment CD. O is mid-point of AD. Show that

(i) $\triangle AOB \cong \triangle DOC$

(ii) O is also mid-point of BC.

Solution. (i) As AB ∥ CD and BC is a transversal,

$$\angle ABO = \angle DCO \qquad \text{(alt. } \angle\text{s)}$$

In $\triangle AOB$ and $\triangle DOC$,

$$OA = OD \qquad \text{(O is mid-point of AD)}$$

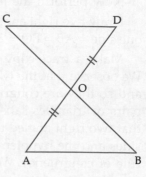

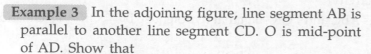

$$\angle ABO = \angle DCO, \qquad \text{(proved above)}$$

and $\angle AOB = \angle DOC$ (vert. opp. ∠s)

∴ $\triangle AOB \cong \triangle DOC$ (by AAS rule of congruency)

(ii) OB = OC (c.p.c.t.)

⇒ O is mid-point of BC.

Example 4 ABCD is a quadrilateral such that diagonal AC bisects the angles A and C. Prove that AB = AD and CB = CD.

Solution. As AC is bisector of ∠A and of ∠C,

∴ ∠BAC = ∠DAC and ∠BCA = ∠DCA.

In △ABC and △ADC,

∠BAC = ∠DAC (from given)

∠BCA = ∠DCA (from given)

AC = AC (common)

∴ △ABC ≅ △ADC (ASA rule)

∴ AB = AD and CB = CD (c.p.c.t.)

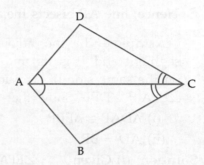

Example 5 In the adjoining figure, AD and BC are equal perpendiculars to a line segment AB. Show that CD bisects AB.

Solution. In △OBC and △OAD,

BC = AD (given)

∠OBC = ∠OAD (each = 90°)

∠BOC = ∠AOD (vert. opp. ∠s)

∴ △OBC ≅ △OAD (AAS rule of congruency)

∴ OB = OA (c.p.c.t.)

⇒ CD bisects AB.

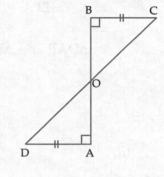

Example 6 In the adjoining figure, line *l* is the bisector of an angle A and B is any point on *l*. BP and BQ are perpendiculars from B to the arms of ∠A. Show that

(i) △APB ≅ △AQB

(ii) B is equidistant from the arms of ∠A.

Solution. (i) In △APB and △AQB,

∠BAP = ∠BAQ (∵ line *l* is bisector of ∠A)

∠APB = ∠AQB (each = 90°)

and AB = AB (common)

∴ △APB ≅ △AQB (by AAS rule of congruency)

(ii) BP = BQ (c.p.c.t.)

⇒ B is equidistant from the arms of ∠A.

Example 7 P is a point equidistant from two lines l and m intersecting at point A. Show that the line AP bisects the angle between them.

Solution. Given lines *l* and *m* intersect each other at the point A.

Let PB ⊥ *l* and PC ⊥ *m*,

then PB = PC (given)

We need to show that
$$\angle PAB = \angle PAC.$$
In $\triangle APB$ and $\triangle APC$,

$\angle ABP = \angle ACP$		(each $= 90°$)
$AP = AP$		(common)
$PB = PC$		(given)

$\therefore \qquad \triangle APB \cong \triangle APC$

$\qquad\qquad$ (by RHS rule of congruency)

$\therefore \qquad \angle PAB = \angle PAC.$

Hence, line AP bisects the angle between the given lines.

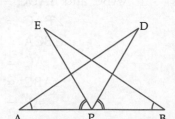

Example 8 In the adjoining figure, AB is a line segment and P is its mid-point. D and E are points on the same side of AB such that $\angle BAD = \angle ABE$ and $\angle EPA = \angle DPB$. Show that

(i) $\triangle DAP \cong \triangle EBP$

(ii) $AD = BE$.

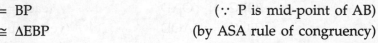

Solution. (i) Given $\qquad \angle EPA = \angle DPB$

$\Rightarrow \qquad \angle EPA + \angle EPD = \angle EPD + \angle DPB \qquad$ (adding $\angle EPD$ to both sides)

$\Rightarrow \qquad\qquad \angle APD = \angle EPB.$

In $\triangle DAP$ and $\triangle EBP$,

$\angle PAD = \angle PBE$		($\because \angle BAD = \angle ABE$ given)
$\angle APD = \angle EPB$		(proved above)
$AP = BP$		($\because$ P is mid-point of AB)

$\therefore \qquad \triangle DAP \cong \triangle EBP \qquad$ (by ASA rule of congruency)

(ii) $\qquad\qquad AD = BE \qquad$ (c.p.c.t.)

Example 9 In the figure alongside, $AD \perp BC$, $AD \perp EF$ and $\angle 1 = \angle 4$. Prove that $\triangle ABD \cong \triangle ACD$.

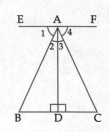

Solution. Since $AD \perp EF$, $\angle EAD = 90° = \angle DAF$.

$\therefore \quad \angle 1 + \angle 2 = 90°$ and $\angle 3 + \angle 4 = 90°$

but $\quad \angle 1 = \angle 4 \qquad$ (given)

$\Rightarrow \quad \angle 2 = \angle 3.$

In $\triangle ABD$ and $\triangle ACD$, we have

$\angle 2 = \angle 3$		(proved above)
$\angle ADB = \angle ADC$		[each angle $= 90°$, $\because AD \perp BC$]
AD is common.		

$\therefore \quad \triangle ABD \cong \triangle ACD \qquad$ (by ASA rule of congruency)

Example 10 In the adjoining figure, $PQ = RQ$ and $\angle x = \angle y$. Prove that $BP = AR$.

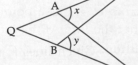

Solution. For $\triangle AQR$, $\angle x = \angle Q + \angle ARQ$

$\qquad\qquad$ (ext. $\angle$ = sum of two int. opp. $\angle$s)

For $\triangle BPQ$, $\angle y = \angle Q + \angle BPQ$

$\qquad\qquad$ (ext. $\angle$ = sum of two int. opp. $\angle$s)

But $\qquad\qquad \angle x = \angle y \qquad$ (given)

$$\Rightarrow \qquad \angle Q + \angle ARQ = \angle Q + \angle BPQ \Rightarrow \angle ARQ = \angle BPQ.$$

In $\triangle BPQ$ and $\triangle ARQ$,

$\angle BPQ = \angle ARQ$		(proved above)
$\angle Q = \angle Q$		(common)
$PQ = RQ$		(given)
$\therefore \qquad \triangle BPQ \cong \triangle ARQ$		(by ASA rule of congruency)
$\therefore \qquad BP = AR$		(c.p.c.t.)

Example 11 In the adjoining figure, ABCD is a square and M is the mid-point of AB. PQ is any line segment through M which meets AD at P and CB produced as Q. Prove that M is also mid-point of PQ.

Solution. We know that each angle of a square is 90°, so $\angle A = 90° = \angle B$. As M is mid-point of AB, AM = BM.

In $\triangle APM$ and $\triangle BOM$,

$AM = BM$		
$\angle PAM = \angle QBM$	$(\because$ each $\angle = 90°)$	
$\angle AMP = \angle BMQ$	(vert. opp. $\angle$s)	
$\therefore \qquad \triangle APM \cong \triangle BQM$		(by ASA rule of congruency)
$\therefore \qquad MP = MQ$		(c.p.c.t)
$\Rightarrow$ M is mid-point of PQ.		

Example 12 In the adjoining figure, $\angle B = \angle E$, BD = CE and $\angle 1 = \angle 2$. Prove that $\triangle ABC \cong \triangle AED$.

Solution. Given

$BD = CE$		
$\Rightarrow \qquad BD + DC = CE + DC$		
(adding DC to both sides)		
$\Rightarrow \qquad BC = ED.$		
Also $\qquad \angle 1 = \angle 2$	(given)	
$\Rightarrow \qquad \angle 1 + \angle DAC = \angle 2 + \angle DAC$		
(adding $\angle DAC$ to both sides)		
$\Rightarrow \qquad \angle BAC = \angle EAD.$		

In $\triangle ABC$ and $\triangle AED$,

$\angle B = \angle E$		(given)
$\angle BAC = \angle EAD$		(proved above)
$BC = ED$		(proved above)
$\therefore \qquad \triangle ABC \cong \triangle AED$		(by AAS rule of congruency)

Example 13 AD is an altitude of an isosceles triangle ABC in which AB = AC. Show that

(i) AD bisects BC (ii) AD bisects $\angle A$.

Solution. Given ABC is an isosceles triangle with AB = AC and AD $\perp$ BC.

In $\triangle ABD$ and $\triangle ACD$,

$\angle ADB = \angle ADC$		(each $= 90°$ as AD $\perp$ BC)
$AB = AC$		(given)
$AD = AD$		(common)

$$\therefore \qquad \Delta ABD \cong \Delta ACD$$
(by RHS rule of congruency)
$$\therefore \qquad BD = CD \qquad\qquad\qquad \text{(c.p.c.t.)}$$
$\Rightarrow$ AD bisects BC.

Also $\qquad\qquad \angle BAD = \angle CAD \qquad\qquad\quad \text{(c.p.c.t.)}$

$\Rightarrow$ AD bisects $\angle A$.

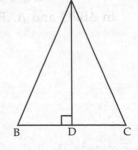

Example 14 In the adjoining figure, AB = CD and
$\angle ABC = \angle BCD$. Prove that

(*i*) AC = BD   (*ii*) BE = CE.

Solution. In ΔABC and ΔDCB,

$$AB = CD \qquad\qquad\qquad \text{(given)}$$
$$\angle ABC = \angle BCD \qquad\qquad \text{(given)}$$
$$BC = BC \qquad\qquad\qquad \text{(common)}$$
$$\therefore \qquad \Delta ABC \cong \Delta DCB \qquad\qquad \text{(by SAS rule of congruency)}$$
$$(i) \qquad\qquad AC = BD \qquad\qquad\qquad\qquad \text{(c.p.c.t.)}$$

Also $\qquad\qquad \angle BAC = \angle BDC \qquad\qquad\qquad\qquad \text{(c.p.c.t.)}$

(*ii*) In ΔAEB and ΔDEC,

$$\angle BAE = \angle EDC \qquad (\because \angle BAC = \angle BDC, \text{proved above})$$
$$\angle AEB = \angle CED \qquad\qquad\qquad\qquad\qquad \text{(vert. opp. } \angle s)$$
$$AB = CD \qquad\qquad\qquad\qquad\qquad\qquad \text{(given)}$$
$$\therefore \qquad \Delta AEB \cong \Delta DEC \qquad\qquad\qquad \text{(AAS rule of congruency)}$$
$$\Rightarrow \qquad BE = CE \qquad\qquad\qquad\qquad\qquad\qquad \text{(c.p.c.t.)}$$

Example 15 In the adjoining figure, AB = AD, $\angle BAP = \angle QAD$
and $\angle PAC = \angle CAQ$. Prove that AP = AQ.

Solution. Given $\qquad \angle BAP = \angle QAD$

and $\qquad\qquad\qquad \angle PAC = \angle CAQ$

$\Rightarrow \qquad \angle BAP + \angle PAC = \angle QAD + \angle CAQ$

$\Rightarrow \qquad\qquad\qquad \angle BAC = \angle CAD$

In ΔABC and ΔADC,

$$AB = AD \qquad\qquad\qquad\qquad\qquad\qquad \text{(given)}$$
$$AC = AC \qquad\qquad\qquad\qquad\qquad\quad \text{(common)}$$
$$\angle BAC = \angle CAD \qquad\qquad\qquad \text{(proved above)}$$
$$\therefore \qquad \Delta ABC \cong \Delta ADC \qquad \text{(by SAS rule of congruency)}$$
$$\Rightarrow \qquad \angle ABC = \angle ADC \qquad\qquad\qquad\qquad \text{(c.p.c.t.)}$$
$$\Rightarrow \qquad \angle ABP = \angle ADQ.$$

In ΔABP and ΔADQ,

$$AB = AD \qquad\qquad\qquad\qquad\qquad\qquad \text{(given)}$$
$$\angle BAP = \angle QAD \qquad\qquad\qquad\qquad\quad \text{(given)}$$
$$\angle ABP = \angle ADQ \qquad\qquad\qquad \text{(proved above)}$$
$$\therefore \qquad \Delta ABP \cong \Delta ADQ \qquad\qquad \text{(by ASA congruence rule)}$$
$$\Rightarrow \qquad AP = AQ.$$

Example 16 In a triangle ABC, the internal bisectors of ∠B and ∠C meet at O. Prove that OA is also internal bisector of ∠A.

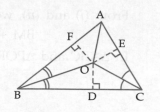

Given. A triangle ABC, OB and OC are bisectors of ∠B and ∠C respectively.

To prove. OA bisects ∠A.

Construction. Draw OD ⊥ BC, OE ⊥ CA and OF ⊥ AB.

Proof.

Statements	Reasons
In △ODC and △OEC	
1. ∠ODC = ∠OEC	1. Each being a right angle (by construction).
2. ∠OCD = ∠OCE	2. OC bisects ∠C.
3. OC = OC	3. Common.
4. △ODC ≅ △OEC	4. AAS rule of congruency.
5. OD = OE	5. 'c.p.c.t.'
6. OD = OF	6. △OBD ≅ △OBF (similarly).
In △OAE and △OAF	
1'. OE = OF	1'. From 5 and 6.
2'. ∠OEA = ∠OFA	2'. Each being a rt. angle.
3'. OA = OA	3'. Common.
4'. △OAE ≅ △OAF	4'. RHS rule of congruency.
5'. ∠OAE = ∠OAF	5'. 'c.p.c.t.'
⇒ OA bisects ∠A.	**Q.E.D.**

Example 17 In the adjoining figure, two sides AB, AC and altitude AM of △ABC are respectively equal to two sides PQ, PR and altitude PN of △PQR. Prove that

$$\triangle ABC \cong \triangle PQR.$$

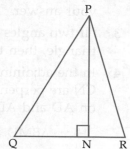

Solution. In △ABM and △PQN,

But

	∠AMB = ∠PNQ (each = 90°)
	AB = PQ (given)
	AM = PN (given)
∴	△ABM ≅ △PQN (RHS rule of congruency)
∴	BM = QN ...(i) (c.p.c.t.)

In △AMC and △PNR,

	∠AMC = ∠PNR (each = 90°)
	AC = PR (given)
	AM = PN (given)
∴	△AMC ≅ △PNR (RHS rule of congruency)
∴	MC = NR ...(ii) (c.p.c.t.)

From (*i*) and (*ii*), we get

BM + MC = QN + NR $\Rightarrow$ BC = QR   (from fig.)

In $\triangle$ABC and $\triangle$PQR,

AB = PQ   (given)

AC = PR   (given)

BC = QR   (proved above)

∴ $\triangle$ABC $\cong$ $\triangle$PQR   (SSS rule of congruency)

Example 18 In the $\triangle$ABC given below, BD bisects $\angle$B and is perpendicular to AC. If the lengths of the sides of the triangle are expressed in terms of x and y as shown, find the values of x and y.

Solution. In $\triangle$ABD and $\triangle$CBD,

$\angle$ABD = $\angle$CBD   [∵ BD bisects $\angle$B]

$\angle$ADB = $\angle$CDB [each being = 90°, ∵   BD $\perp$ AC]

Side BD is common

∴ $\triangle$ABD $\cong$ $\triangle$CBD   [ASA rule of congruency]

∴   AD = DC $\Rightarrow$ x = 2y ...(*i*)

and   AB = CB $\Rightarrow$ 2x = 3y + 8   ...(*ii*)

Substituting the value of x from (*i*) in (*ii*), we get

4y = 3y + 8 $\Rightarrow$ y = 8, ∴ x = 16   [from (*i*)]

Hence, x = 16, y = 8.

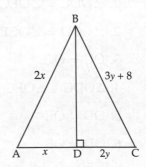

EXERCISE 10.2

1 In triangles ABC and PQR, $\angle$A = $\angle$Q and $\angle$B = $\angle$R. Which side of $\triangle$PQR should be equal to side AB of $\triangle$ABC so that the two triangles are congruent? Give reason for your answer.

2 In triangles ABC and PQR, $\angle$A = $\angle$Q and $\angle$B = $\angle$R. Which side of $\triangle$PQR should be equal to side BC of $\triangle$ABC so that the two triangles are congruent? Give reason for your answer.

3 "If two angles and a side of one triangle are equal to two angles and a side of another triangle, then the two triangles must be congruent". Is the statement true? Why?

4 In the adjoining figure, AD is median of $\triangle$ABC, BM and CN are perpendiculars drawn from B and C respectively on AD and AD produced. Prove that BM = CN.

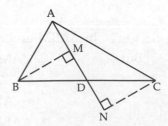

Hint. $\triangle$BMD $\cong$ $\triangle$CND by AAS.

4 In the adjoining figure, BM and DN are perpendiculars to the line segment AC. If BM = DN, prove that AC bisects BD.

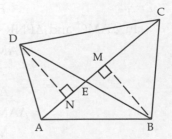

Hint. $\triangle$BEM $\cong$ $\triangle$DEN by AAS.

6 In the adjoining figure, *l* and *m* are two parallel lines intersected by another pair of parallel lines *p* and *q*. Show that △ABC ≅ △CDA.

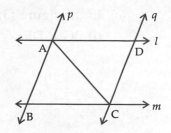

7 In the adjoining figure, two lines AB and CD intersect each other at the point O such that BC ∥ DA and BC = DA. Show that O is the mid-point of both the line segments AB and CD.

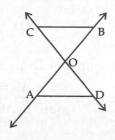

8 In the adjoining figure, ∠BCD = ∠ADC and ∠BCA = ∠ADB. Show that
   (*i*) △ACD ≅ △BDC
   (*ii*) BC = AD
   (*iii*) ∠A = ∠B.

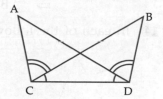

9 In the adjoining figure, ∠ABC = ∠ACB, D and E are points on the sides AC and AB respectively such that BE = CD. Prove that
   (*i*) △EBC ≅ △DCB
   (*ii*) △OEB ≅ △ODC
   (*iii*) OB = OC.

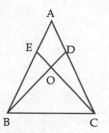

10 ABC is an isosceles triangle with AB = AC. Draw AP ⊥ BC to show that ∠B = ∠C.

11 In the adjoining figure, BA ⊥ AC, DE ⊥ DF such that BA = DE and BF = EC. Show that △ABC ≅ △DEF.

   Hint. BF = EC ⇒ BF + FC = EC + FC
   ⇒   BC = FE.
   △ABC ≅ △DEF (RHS).

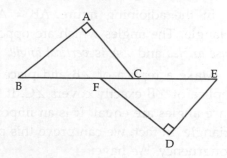

12 ABCD is a rectangle. X and Y are points on sides AD and BC respectively such that AY = BX. Prove that BY = AX and ∠BAY = ∠ABX.

   Hint. △ABX ≅ △BAY (RHS).

13   (*a*) In the figure (1) given below, QX, RX are bisectors of angles PQR and PRQ respectively of △PQR. If XS ⊥ QR and XT ⊥ PQ, prove that
      (*i*) △XTQ ≅ △XSQ   (*ii*) PX bisects the angle P.
   (*b*) In the figure (2) given below, AB ∥ DC and ∠C = ∠D. Prove that
      (*i*) AD = BC   (*ii*) AC = BD.

(c) In the figure (3) given below, BA ∥ DF and CA ∥ EG and BD = EC. Prove that

(i) BG = DF   (ii) EG = CF.

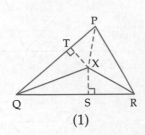 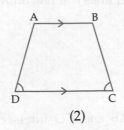 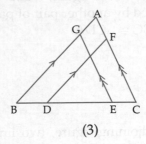

(1)   (2)   (3)

Hint. (b) Draw AE ⊥ CD, BF ⊥ CD.

AE = BF (distance between parallel lines).

(c) In ΔBEG and ΔDCF, ∠B = ∠D (∵ BA ∥ DF, corres. ∠s are equal),

∠E = ∠C and BE = BC – EC = BC – BD = DC

⇒ ΔBEG ≅ ΔDCF.

14 In each of the following figures, find the values of x and y.

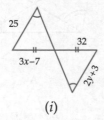   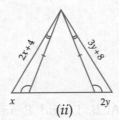

(i)   (ii)

10.3 ISOSCELES TRIANGLE

A triangle in which lengths of two sides are equal is called an isosceles triangle.

In the adjoining figure, AB = AC, so ΔABC is an isosceles triangle. The angles which are opposite to equal sides are called *base angles* and ∠A is *vertical angle*.

Make a replica of ∠B and place it over ∠C. We observe that replica of ∠B exactly covers ∠C. It follows that ∠B = ∠C *i.e.* the base angles are equal. It is an important property of an isosceles triangle. In fact, we can prove this property by using SAS rule of congruency. We have:

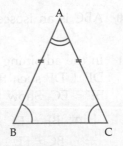

Theorem 10.1. *The angles opposite to equal sides of an isosceles triangle are equal.*

Given. An isosceles triangle ABC in which

AB = AC.

To prove. ∠B = ∠C.

Construction. Draw AD bisector of ∠A to meet BC at D.

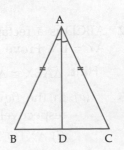

Proof.

Statements	Reasons
In △ABD and △ACD	
1. AB = AC	1. Given
2. AD = AD	2. Common
3. ∠BAD = ∠CAD	3. AD is bisector of ∠A by construction.
4. △ABD ≅ △ACD	4. SAS rule of congruency
5. ∠B = ∠C	5. c.p.c.t.

The converse of the above theorem is also true *i.e.* the sides opposite to equal angles of a triangle are equal. We can prove this property of a triangle by using AAS congruence rule. We have:

Theorem 10.2. *The sides opposite to equal angles of a triangle are equal.*

Given. A triangle ABC in which ∠B = ∠C.

To prove. AB = AC.

Construction. Draw AD bisector of ∠A to meet BC at D.

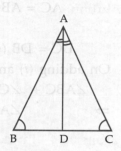

Proof.

Statements	Reasons
In △ABD and △ACD	
1. ∠B = ∠C	1. Given
2. AD = AD	2. Common
3. ∠BAD = ∠CAD	3. AD is bisector of ∠A by construction.
4. △ABD ≅ △ACD	4. AAS rule of congruency
5. AB = AC	5. c.p.c.t.

Illustrative Examples

Example 1 In △ABC, AD is the perpendicular bisector of BC. Show that △ABC is isosceles in which AB = AC.

Solution. In △ABD and △ACD,

$$BD = CD$$

(∵ AD is bisector of BC *i.e.* D is mid-point of BC)

$$∠ADB = ∠ADC \quad \text{(each = 90° as AD ⊥ BC)}$$

$$AD = AD \quad \text{(common)}$$

∴ $$△ABD ≅ △ACD$$

(by SAS rule of congruency)

∴ $$AB = AC ⇒ △ABC \text{ is isosceles.}$$

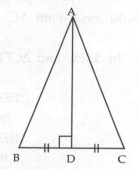

Example 2 In △ABC, the bisector AD of ∠A is perpendicular to the side BC. Show that AB = AC and △ABC is isosceles.

Solution. In △ABD and △ACD,

$$∠BAD = ∠CAD \qquad \qquad (∵ AD \text{ is bisector of } ∠A)$$

$$\angle ADB = \angle ADC \quad \text{(each = 90° as AD} \perp \text{BC)}$$
$$AD = AD \qquad \text{(common)}$$
∴ $\qquad \triangle ABD \cong \triangle ACD$
$$\text{(by ASA rule of congruency)}$$
∴ $\qquad AB = AC \Rightarrow \triangle ABC \text{ is isosceles.}$

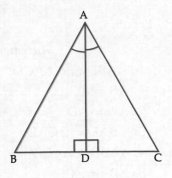

Example 3 In the adjoining figure, ABC and DBC are two isosceles triangles on the same base BC.

Show that $\angle ABD = \angle ACD$.

Solution. $AC = AB \text{ (given)} \Rightarrow \angle ABC = \angle ACB \qquad ...(i)$
$$\text{(} \because \angle \text{s opp. equal sides are equal)}$$
$$DC = DB \text{ (given)} \Rightarrow \angle CBD = \angle BCD \qquad ...(ii)$$
On adding (i) and (ii), we get
$$\angle ABC + \angle CBD = \angle ACB + \angle BCD$$
$\Rightarrow \qquad \angle ABD = \angle ACD.$

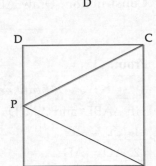

Example 4 In the adjoining figure, ABCD is a square and P is mid-point of AB. BP and CP are joined. Prove that $\angle PBC = \angle PCB$.

Solution. As P is mid-point of AD, $AP = DP$.

In $\triangle ABP$ and $\triangle DCP$,
$$AP = DP$$
$$AB = DC \quad \text{(sides of a square are equal)}$$
$$\angle BAP = \angle CDP \text{ (each } \angle \text{ of a square is 90°)}$$
∴ $\qquad \triangle ABP \cong \triangle DCP \qquad \text{(SAS axiom of congruency)}$
∴ $\qquad BP = CP \qquad \text{(c.p.c.t.)}$
$\Rightarrow \qquad \angle PBC = \angle PCB \qquad \text{(}\angle\text{s opp. equal sides are equal)}$

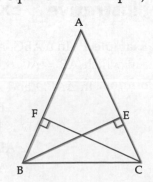

Example 5 ABC is an isosceles triangle in which altitudes BE and CF are drawn to equal sides AC and AB respectively. Show that these altitudes are equal.

Solution. Given $AC = AB \Rightarrow \angle B = \angle C$
$$\text{(}\because \angle\text{s opp. equal sides are equal)}$$

In $\triangle BEC$ and $\triangle CFB$,
$$\angle C = \angle B \qquad \text{(from above)}$$
$$\angle BEC = \angle CFB \qquad \text{(each = 90°)}$$
$$BC = CB \qquad \text{(common)}$$
∴ $\qquad \triangle BEC \cong \triangle CFB \quad \text{(by AAS rule of congruency)}$
∴ $\qquad BE = CF \qquad \text{(c.p.c.t.)}$

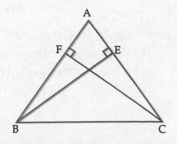

Example 6 ABC is a triangle in which altitudes BE and CF to sides AC and AB respectively are equal. Show that

(i) $\triangle ABE \cong \triangle ACF$

(ii) $AB = AC$ and $\triangle ABC$ is isosceles.

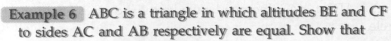

Solution. (*i*) In ΔABE and ΔACF,

	BE = CF	(given)
	∠AEB = ∠AFC	(each = 90°)
	∠A = ∠A	(common)
∴	ΔABE ≅ ΔACF	(by AAS rule of congruency)
(*ii*)	AB = AC	(c.p.c.t.)

⇒ ΔABC is isosceles.

Example 7 BE and CF are two equal altitudes of a triangle ABC. Using RHS congruence rule, prove that the triangle ABC is isosceles.

Solution. Given BE ⊥ CA, CF ⊥ AB and

BE = CF.

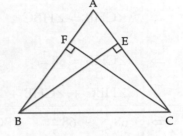

In ΔBEC and ΔCFB,

	∠BEC = ∠CFB	(each = 90°)
	BC = CB	(common)
and	BE = CF	(given)
∴	ΔBEC ≅ ΔCFB	
	(by RHS rule of congruency)	
∴	∠BCE = ∠CBF	(c.p.c.t.)
⇒	∠BCA = ∠CBA	
⇒	AB = AC	(∵ sides opp. equal angles are equal)

⇒ ΔABC is isosceles.

Example 8 In the adjoining figure, MN is parallel to PR, ∠LBN = 70° and AB = BC. Find the value of ∠ABC.

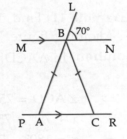

Solution. ∠BAC = ∠LBN = 70°   ...(*i*)

[∵ MN ∥ PR, corres. ∠s are equal]

∴ ∠ACB = ∠BAC = 70°   ...(*ii*)

[∵ AB = BC, angles opp. to equal sides are equal]

In ΔABC, ∠ABC + ∠BAC + ∠ACB = 180°

⇒ ∠ABC + 70° + 70° = 180°   [using (*i*) and (*ii*)]

⇒ ∠ABC = 180° − 140° = 40°.

Example 9 In the adjoining figure, ABC is an isosceles triangle with AB = AC and LM is parallel to BC. If ∠A = 50°, find ∠LMC.

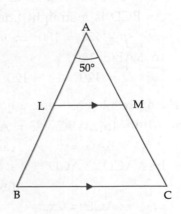

Solution. In ΔABC, AB = AC

⇒ ∠C = ∠B   (∠s opp. equal sides are equal)

In ΔABC, ∠A + ∠B + ∠C = 180° (sum of ∠s of a Δ)

⇒ 50° + ∠C + ∠C = 180° ⇒ 2∠C = 130°

⇒ ∠C = 65°.

Given LM ∥ BC and AC is a transversal

∠LMC + ∠C = 180°

(sum of interior ∠s on the same side of transversal)

⇒ ∠LMC + 65° = 180° ⇒ ∠LMC = 115°.

Example 10 In the adjoining figure, AB = AC, CH = CB and HK ∥ BC. If ∠CAD = 137°, find ∠CHK.

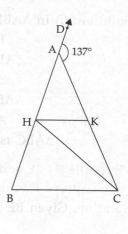

Solution. In △ABC, AB = AC

∠ACB = ∠ABC   (∠s opp. equal sides are equal)

∠CAD = ∠ACB + ∠ABC

          (ext. ∠ = sum of two int. opp. ∠s)

⇒ $137° = ∠ACB + ∠ACB ⇒ ∠ACB = \left(\dfrac{137}{2}\right)° = 68\dfrac{1}{2}°$

⇒ $∠ABC = 68\dfrac{1}{2}°$ i.e. $∠HBC = 68\dfrac{1}{2}°$.

In △HBC, CH = CB   (given)

∴   ∠CHB = ∠HBC   (∠s opp. equal sides are equal)

⇒ $∠CHB = 68\dfrac{1}{2}°$

∠HBC + ∠CHB + ∠BCH = 180°   (sum of ∠s of a △)

⇒ $68\dfrac{1}{2}° + 68\dfrac{1}{2}° + ∠BCH = 180°$

⇒   ∠BCH = 43°.

Now HK ∥ BC (given) and CH is a transversal,

∠CHK = ∠BCH   (alt. ∠s)

⇒   ∠CHK = 43°   (∵ ∠BCH = 43°)

$\left(∵ ∠HBC = 68\dfrac{1}{2}°\right)$

Example 11 Find the measure of each lettered angle in the adjoining figure.

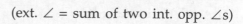

Solution. In △ACD, ∠ACD = ∠ADC

          (angles opp. equal sides are equal)

⇒   ∠ACD = 75°   (∵ ∠ADC = 75° given)

∴   x + 75° + 75° = 180°   (angles of △ACD)

⇒   x = 180° − 75° − 75° = 30°.

In △ADE, 75° = y + 52°   (ext. ∠ = sum of two int. opp. ∠s)

⇒   y = 75° − 52° = 23°.

As BCD is a straight line, p + ∠ACD = 180°

⇒   p + 75° = 180° ⇒ p = 105°.

In △ABC, 120° = z + p   (ext. ∠ = sum of two int. opp. ∠s)

⇒   z = 120° − p = 120° − 105° = 15°.

Example 12 From the adjoining figure, find the value of x.

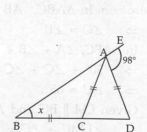

Solution. In △ABC, BC = AC   (given)

∴   ∠BAC = x   (angles opp. equal sides are equal)

In △ACD, ∠ACD = x + x

          (ext. ∠ = sum of two int. opp. ∠s)

⇒   ∠ACD = 2x.

In △ACD, AC = AD   (given)

∴   ∠ADC = 2x   (angles opp. equal sides are equal)

In △ABD, ∠EAD = ∠ABD + ∠ADB   (ext. ∠ = sum of two int. opp. ∠s)

⇒   98° = x + 2x ⇒ 3x = 98°

⇒ $x = \left(\dfrac{98}{3}\right)° = 32°40'$.

Example 13 In △ABC, AB = AC and D is a point on AB such that AD = DC = BC. Show that ∠BAC = 36°.

Solution. Let ∠BAC = x°.

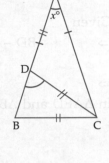

In △ADC, AD = DC, ∴ ∠ACD = x°.

∴   ∠BDC = x° + x°   (sum of two int. opp. ∠s)

                = 2x°.

In △BDC, DC = BC, ∴ ∠DBC = 2x°.

In △ABC, AB = AC, ∴ ∠ACB = 2x°.

Also ∠BAC + ∠ABC + ∠ACB = 180°

                                        (angles of a triangle)

⇒   x° + 2x° + 2x° = 180° ⇒ 5x = 180 ⇒ x = 36.

∴   ∠BAC = 36°, as required.

Example 14 ABCD is a square and ABE is an equilateral triangle outside the square, prove that $\angle ACE = \dfrac{1}{2}\angle ABE$.

Solution. Draw the figure and mark the angles as shown.

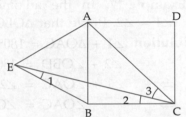

We know that each angle of an equilateral triangle is 60° and each angle of a square is 90°.

As AC is a diagonal of the square ABCD, ∠ACB = 45°.

In △EBC,

                ∠EBC = ∠EBA + ∠ABC

                        = 60° + 90° = 150°.

                EB = BC   (∵ EB = AB and AB = BC)

⇒   ∠2 = ∠1   (∵ ∠s opp. equal sides are equal)

        ∠1 + ∠2 + ∠EBC = 180°   (sum of angles of a △)

⇒   ∠2 + ∠2 + 150° = 180°

⇒   2 ∠2 = 30° ⇒ ∠2 = 15°.

        ∠ACE = ∠ACB − ∠2 = 45° − 15° = 30°.

⇒ $\angle ACE = \dfrac{1}{2} \times 60° = \dfrac{1}{2} \angle ABE$.

Hence, $\angle ACE = \dfrac{1}{2} \angle ABE$.

Example 15 In the adjoining figure, ABC is an isosceles triangle in which AB = AC. If D and E are points on BC such that BE = DC, show that AD = AE.

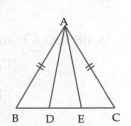

Solution. Given AB = AC ⇒ ∠B = ∠C

                                (∵ ∠s opp. equal sides are equal)

Also   BE = DC ⇒ BE − DE = DC − DE

⇒   BD = EC.

In △ABD and △ACE,

                AB = AC, ∠B = ∠C and BD = EC

$\therefore$ $\triangle ABD \cong \triangle ACE$ (by SAS rule of congruency)

$\therefore$ AD = AE   (c.p.c.t.)

Example 16 In the adjoining figure, $\angle EAB = \angle EBA$ and AC = BD. Prove that AD = BC.

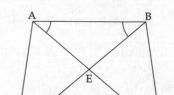

Solution. In $\triangle EAB$,

               $\angle EAB = \angle EBA$ (given)

$\therefore$ EB = EA

             (sides opp. equal $\angle$s are equal)

Given   BD = AC

$\Rightarrow$ BD – EB = AC – EA

             ($\because$ EB = EA, prove above)

$\Rightarrow$ ED = EC.

In $\triangle AED$ and $\triangle BEC$,

              AE = BE   (given)

              ED = EC   (proved above)

           $\angle AED = \angle BEC$ (vert. opp. $\angle$s)

$\therefore$ $\triangle AED \cong \triangle BEC$ (SAS axiom of congruency)

$\therefore$ AD = BC   (c.p.c.t.)

Example 17 In the adjoining figure, OA = OD and $\angle 1 = \angle 2$. Prove that $\triangle OBC$ is an isosceles triangle.

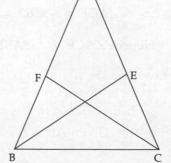

Solution. $\angle 1 + \triangle OAC = 180°$ (linear pair)

       $\angle 2 + \angle OBD = 180°$ (linear pair)

$\Rightarrow$ $\angle 1 + \angle OAC = \angle 2 + \angle OBD$ but $\angle 1 = \angle 2$ (given)

$\Rightarrow$ $\angle OAC = \angle ODB$

In $\triangle OAC$ and $\triangle ODB$,

          $\angle OAC = \angle ODB$ (proved above)

          $\angle AOC = \angle DOB$ (vert. opp. $\angle$s)

             OA = OB   (given)

$\therefore$ $\triangle OAC \cong \triangle ODB$ (by ASA rule of congruency)

$\therefore$ OC = OB   (c.p.c.t.)

$\Rightarrow$ $\triangle OBC$ is an isosceles triangle.

Example 18 In the adjoining figure, AB = AC and BE, CF are bisectors of $\angle B$, $\angle C$ respectively. Prove that

     (i) $\triangle EBC \cong \triangle FCB$ (ii) BE = CF.

Solution. Given AB = AC

$\Rightarrow$ $\angle C = \angle B$

            ($\angle$s opp. equal sides are equal)

As BE and CF are bisectors of $\angle B$ and $\angle C$ respectively,

       $\angle EBC = \dfrac{1}{2} \angle B$ and $\angle FCB = \dfrac{1}{2} \angle C$

$\Rightarrow$ $\angle EBC = \angle FCB$

            ($\because \angle B = \angle C$, proved above)

  (i) In $\triangle EBC$ and $\triangle FCB$,

          $\angle ECB = \angle FBC$ ($\because \angle ECB = \angle C$ and $\angle FBC = \angle B$)

         $\angle EBC = \angle FCB$ (proved above)

	BC = BC	(common)
∴	ΔEBC ≅ ΔFCB	(ASA rule of congruency)
(ii)	ΔEBC ≅ ΔFCB	(proved in part (i))
⇒	BE = CF	(c.p.c.t)

Example 19 In an isosceles triangle ABC, with AB = AC, the bisectors of ∠B and ∠C intersect each other at O. Show that

(i) OB = OC   (ii) OA bisects ∠A

Solution. (i) Given AB = AC ⇒ ∠B = ∠C

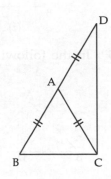

(∵ ∠s opp. equal sides are equal)

⇒ $\frac{1}{2}∠B = \frac{1}{2}∠C$

⇒   ∠OBC = ∠OCB

(∵ OB and OC are bisectors of ∠B and ∠C)

⇒   OB = OC

(sides opp. equal angles are equal)

(ii) Also $\frac{1}{2}∠B = \frac{1}{2}∠C ⇒ ∠ABO = ∠ACO$

(∵ OB and OC are bisectors of ∠B and ∠C respectively)

In ΔOAB and ΔOAC,

	∠ABO = ∠ACO	(proved above)
	OB = OC	(proved above)
	AB = AC	(given)
∴	ΔOAB ≅ ΔOAC	(by SAS rule of congruency)
∴	∠OAB = ∠OAC	(c.p.c.t.)

⇒ OA bisects ∠A.

Example 20 In the adjoining figure, ABC is an isosceles triangle in which AB = AC. If side BA is produced to D such that AD = AB, then show that ∠BCD is a right angle.

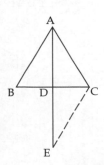

Solution. In ΔABC, AB = AC ⇒ ∠ABC = ∠ACB   ...(i)

AD = AB (given) but AB = AC ⇒ AD = AC

In ΔACD, AD = AC ⇒ ∠ADC = ∠ACD   ...(ii)

Adding (i) and (ii), we get

∠ABC + ∠ADC = ∠ACB + ∠ACD = ∠BCD   ...(iii)

In ΔBCD, ∠DBC + ∠BDC + ∠BCD = 180°   (∠s of ΔBCD)

⇒   ∠ABC + ∠ADC + ∠BCD = 180°

⇒   ∠BCD + ∠BCD = 180°   [using (iii)]

⇒   2∠BCD = 180° ⇒ ∠BCD = 90°.

Hence, ∠BCD is a right angle.

Example 21 If the bisector of an angle of a triangle also bisects the opposite side, prove that the triangle is isosceles.

Solution. Let the bisector AD of ∠A meet side BC of ΔABC at point D.

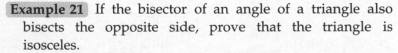

As the bisector AD bisects opposite side BC, so D is mid-point of BC.

Produce AD to a point E such that DE = AD. Join C and E.

In ΔABD and ΔECD,

BD = CD		(∵ D is mid-point of BC)
AD = DE		(by construction)
∠ADB = ∠EDC		(vert. opp. ∠s)
∴ ΔABD ≅ ΔECD		(by SAS rule of congruency)
∴ AB = EC and ∠BAD = ∠CED		(c.p.c.t.)

As AD is bisector of ∠A, ∠BAD = ∠CAD

⇒ ∠CED = ∠CAD ⇒ ∠CEA = ∠CAE

Thus, in ΔACE, ∠CEA = ∠CAE

⇒ AC = EC   (sides opp. equal ∠s are equal)

∴ AB = EC = AC ⇒ AB = AC

⇒ ΔABC is an isosceles triangle.

EXERCISE 10.3

1. ABC is a right angled triangle in which ∠A = 90° and AB = AC. Find ∠B and ∠C.

2. Show that the angles of an equilateral triangle are 60° each.

3. Show that every equiangular triangle is equilateral.

4. In the following figures, find the value of x:

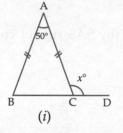
(i)

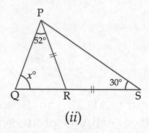
(ii)

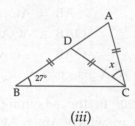
(iii)

5. In the following figures, find the value of x:

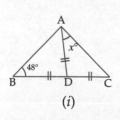
(i)

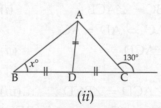
(ii)

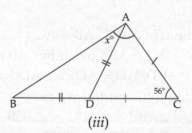
(iii)

6. (a) In the figure (1) given below, AB = AD, BC = DC. Find ∠ABC.

   (b) In the figure (2) given below, BC = CD. Find ∠ACB.

   (c) In the figure (3) given below, AB ∥ CD and CA = CE. If ∠ACE =74° and ∠BAE = 15°, find the values of x and y.

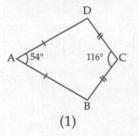
(1)

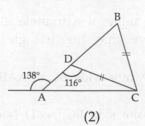
(2)

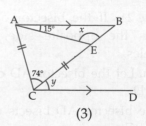
(3)

Hint.

(a) Join BD.

(b) ∠ACD = 22° (why?), ∠BCD + (90° − $\frac{1}{2}$ ∠BCD) = 116° (why?)

7 In △ABC, AB = AC, ∠A = (5x + 20)° and each of the base angle is $\frac{2}{5}$ th of ∠A. Find the measure of ∠A.

8 (a) In the figure (1) given below, ABC is an equilateral triangle. Base BC is produced to E, such that BC = CE. Calculate ∠ACE and ∠AEC.

(b) In the figure (2) given below, prove that ∠BAD : ∠ADB = 3 : 1.

(c) In the figure (3) given below, AB ∥ CD. Find the values of x, y and z.

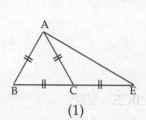
(1)

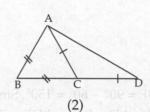
(2)

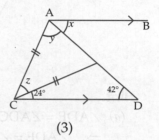
(3)

9 In the adjoining figure, D is mid-point of BC, DE and DF are perpendiculars to AB and AC respectively such that DE = DF. Prove that ABC is an isosceles triangle.

Hint. △BED ≅ △CFD (RHS).

⇒ ∠B = ∠C ⇒ AC = AB.

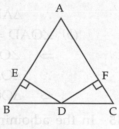

10 In the adjoining figure, AD, BE and CF are altitudes of △ABC. If AD = BE = CF, prove that ABC is an equilateral triangle.

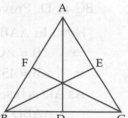

11 In a triangle ABC, AB = AC, D and E are points on the sides AB and AC respectively such that BD = CE. Show that:

(i) △DBC ≅ △ECB
(ii) ∠DCB = ∠EBC

(iii) OB = OC, where O is the point of intersection of BE and CD.

12 ABC is an isosceles triangle in which AB = AC. P is any point in the interior of △ABC such that ∠ABP = ∠ACP. Prove that
(a) BP = CP
(b) AP bisects ∠BAC.

13 In the adjoining figure, D and E are points on the side BC of △ABC such that BD = EC and AD = AE. Show that △ABD ≅ △ACE.

Hint. AD = AE ⇒ ∠ADE = ∠AED

⇒ 180° − ∠ADE = 180° − ∠AED

⇒ ∠ADB = ∠AEC.

△ABD ≅ △ACE (SAS).

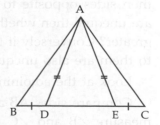

14. (a) In the figure (i) given below, CDE is an equilateral triangle formed on a side CD of a square ABCD. Show that ΔADE ≅ ΔBCE and hence, AEB is an isosceles triangle.

(b) In the figure (ii) given below, O is a point in the interior of a square ABCD such that OAB is an equilateral triangle. Show that OCD is an isosceles triangle.

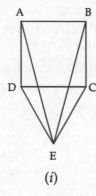

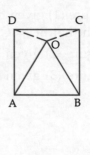

(i)   (ii)

Hint.

(a) ∠ADE = ∠ADC + ∠CDE = 90° + 60° = 150°. Similarly, ∠BCE = 150°.

⇒   ∠ADE = ∠BCE. Also AD = BC and DE = EC.

∴   ΔADE ≅ ΔBCE (SAS) ⇒ AE = BE   (c.p.c.t.)

(b) ∠OAD = ∠DAB − ∠OAB = 90° − 60° = 30°. Similarly, ∠OBC = 30°.

⇒   ∠OAD = ∠OBC. Also AD = BC and OA = OB.

∴   ΔOAD ≅ ΔOBC (SAS) ⇒ OD = OC   (c.p.c.t.)

⇒   ΔOCD is an isosceles triangle.

15. In the adjoining figure, ABC is a right triangle with AB = AC. Bisector of ∠A meets BC at D. Prove that BC = 2AD.

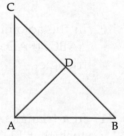

Hint. In ΔABC, ∠A = 90° and AB = AC

⇒   ∠B = ∠C but ∠A + ∠B + ∠C = 180°

⇒   ∠B = 45°.

As AD is bisector of ∠A, ∠BAD = ∠CAD = 45°.

ΔABD ≅ ΔACD (SAS) ⇒ BD = CD   (c.p.c.t.)

In ΔABD, ∠BAD = ∠ABD (each = 45°) ⇒ AD = BD.

∴   BC = BD + CD = BD + BD = 2BD = 2AD.

10.4 INEQUALITIES IN A TRIANGLE

In section 10.3 of this chapter, we have learnt that if two sides of triangle are equal then angles opposite to them are also equal and conversely if two angles of a triangle are equal then sides opposite to them are also equal. The question arises if two sides of a triangle are unequal then whether the angles opposite to them are also unequal, and which angle is greater? Conversely if two angles of a triangle are unequal then whether the sides opposite to them are also unequal, and which side is longer?

Look at the adjoining figure:

Compare sides AB and AC. We note that AC > AB. Now measure ∠B and ∠C, we find that ∠B > ∠C. Repeat this activity with more triangles having unequal sides.

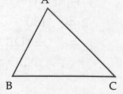

We observe that longer side has greater angle opposite to it.

Conversely, compare ∠B and ∠C. We note that ∠B > ∠C.

Now measure sides AB and AC, we find that AC > AB.

Repeat this activity with more triangles having unequal angles. We observe that greater angle has longer side opposite to it. In fact, these results are true in general. We have:

Theorem 10.3. *If two sides of a triangle are unequal, then the longer side has greater angle opposite to it.*

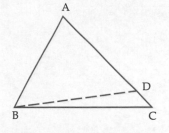

Given. A triangle ABC, AC > AB.

To prove. ∠ABC > ∠BCA.

Construction. Take a point D on AC such that AD = AB. Join B and D.

Proof.

Statements	Reasons
1. AD = AB	1. By construction.
2. ∠ABD = ∠BDA	2. Angles opp. to equal sides.
3. ∠BDA > ∠BCD	3. ∠BDA is an ext. ∠ of △BCD, and ext. ∠ is greater than each of int. opp. ∠.
4. ∠ABD > ∠BCD	4. From 2 and 3.
5. ∠ABC > ∠ABD	5. Since ∠ABD is a part of ∠ABC.
6. ∠ABC > ∠BCD Hence, ∠ABC > ∠BCA.	6. From 4 and 5.

Theorem 10.4. *(Converse of theorem 10.3)*

If two angles of a triangle are unequal, the greater angle has longer side opposite to it.

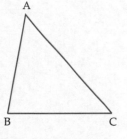

Given. A triangle ABC, ∠B > ∠C.

To prove. AC > AB.

Proof.

Statements	Reasons
If AC is not greater than AB, then either (*i*) AC = AB or (*ii*) AC < AB.	Order property of real numbers.
Case I. If AC = AB, then ∠B = ∠C which is contrary to what is given.	Angles opp. to equal sides.
Case II. If AC < AB, then ∠B < ∠C which is contrary to what is given. Hence, AC > AB.	Greater side has greater angle opposite to it.

Remarks

From theorems 10.3 and 10.4, it follows that in a triangle:

* The longest side has the greatest angle opposite to it and conversely.

* The shortest side has the smallest angle opposite to it and conversely.

Example 4 In the adjoining figure, AB = AC and D is any point on BC. Prove that AB > AD.

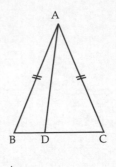

Solution. Given AB = AC ⇒ ∠B = ∠C.

In ∆ADC, ∠ADB > ∠C

⟶⟶⟶⟶(ext. ∠ is greater than each int. opp. ∠)

⇒   ∠ADB > ∠B   (∵ ∠C = ∠B)

⇒   AB > AD   (side opposite to greater angle is longer)

Example 5 In the adjoining figure, AD is bisector of ∠BAC. Prove that AB > BD.

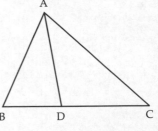

Solution. As AD is bisector of ∠BAC, ∠BAD = ∠CAD.

For ∆ADC, ∠ADB is an exterior angle

∴   ∠ADB > ∠CAD

⟶⟶⟶⟶(ext. ∠ is greater than each int. opp. ∠)

⇒   ∠ADB > ∠BAD   (∵ ∠BAD = ∠CAD)

⇒   AB > BD   (side opposite to greater angle is longer)

Example 6 In the adjoining figure, D is a point on the side BC of ∆ABC such that AD = AC. Show that AB > AD.

Solution. Given AD = AC

⇒   ∠ACD = ∠ADC   (angles opp. equal sides are equal)

For ∆ABD, ∠ADC is an exterior angle,

∴   ∠ADC > ∠ABD   (ext. ∠ is greater than each int. opp. ∠)

⇒   ∠ACD > ∠ABD   (∵ ∠ACD = ∠ADC)

⇒   AB > AC but AC = AD

∴   AB > AD.

Example 7 In the adjoining figure, AD bisects ∠A. Arrange AB, BD and DC in ascending order.

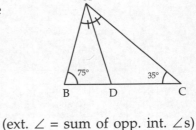

Solution. ∠A = 180° − 75° − 35° = 70°.

Since AD bisects ∠A,

∠BAD = ∠DAC = $\frac{1}{2}$. 70° = 35°.

∴   ∠ADB = ∠DAC + ∠C   (ext. ∠ = sum of opp. int. ∠s)

         = 35° + 35° = 70°.

∴   In ∆ABD, ∠BAD < ∠ADB < ∠ABD

⇒   BD < AB < AD   [side opp. to smaller angle is smaller]   ...(i)

Also in ∆ADC, ∠DAC = 35° = ∠C ⇒ AD = DC   ...(ii)

∴   BD < AB < DC   (from (i) and (ii))

Example 8 D is any point on the side AC of a ∆ABC with AB = AC. Show that CD < BD.

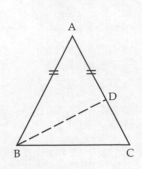

Solution. Given, in ∆ABC, AB = AC

⇒   ∠B = ∠C   (∠s opp. equal sides are equal)

⇒   ∠CBD < ∠B   (∵ ∠CBD is a part of ∠B)

⇒   ∠CBD < ∠C   (∵ ∠B = ∠C)

⇒   CD < BD.   (Theorem 10.4)

Example 9 In the adjoining figure, sides AB and AC are extended to points P and Q respectively. If ∠PBC < ∠BCQ, show that AC > AB.

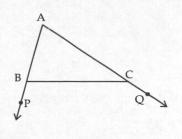

Solution. ∠PBC = ∠A + ∠ACB

(ext. ∠ = sum of int. opp. ∠s)

∠QCB = ∠A + ∠ABC

Given ∠PBC < ∠QCB

⇒   ∠A + ∠ACB < ∠A + ∠ABC ⇒ ∠ACB < ∠ABC

⇒   AB < AC ⇒ AC > AB.

Example 10 In the adjoining figure, AB = AC. Prove that AF > AE.

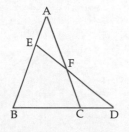

Proof.

Statements	Reasons
1. ∠B = ∠C	1. AB = AC (given)
2. ∠AEF > ∠B	2. ∠AEF is ext. ∠ of △EBD, and ext. ∠ is > each int. opp. ∠.
3. ∠C > ∠CFD	3. ∠C is ext. ∠ of △CFD, and ext. ∠ is > each int. opp. ∠.
4. ∠B > ∠CFD	4. ∠B = ∠C.
5. ∠AEF > ∠CFD	5. From 2 and 4.
6. ∠EFA = ∠CFD	6. Vert. opp. ∠s.
7. ∠AEF > ∠EFA	7. From 5 and 6.
8. AF > AE Q.E.D.	8. Greater angle has greater opp. side.

Example 11 In the adjoining figure, AB and CD are respectively the smallest and longest sides of a quadrilateral ABCD. Show that ∠A > ∠C and ∠B > ∠D.

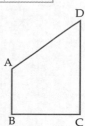

Solution. Join AC and mark the angles as shown in the figure.

As AB is the smallest side,

BC > AB ⇒ ∠1 > ∠2   ...(i)

As CD is the longest side,

CD > AD ⇒ ∠3 > ∠4   ...(ii)

From (i) and (ii), we get

(∠1 + ∠3) > (∠2 + ∠4)

⇒   ∠A > ∠C.

Similarly, ∠B > ∠D.   (join BD and proceed as above)

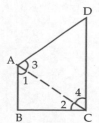

I

We know that sum of two sides of a triangle
is greater than the third.

In ∆POS, PO + OS > ...

In ∆POR, OP + RP > ...

On adding A and

⇒   PR + OS

⇒   OS + ... < ...

Given, S .... interior of ∆PQR

Produce ... to intersect ...

      ...Q + ... > ...

      (∵ sum of two sides of a triangle > third side)

      PQ + ...

⇒   X... + ... > ...

            (∵ sum of two sides of a triangle > third ...)

On adding ...... and ... we get

      ...QS + ... + (...)(...) + ... > ... + ...

⇒   PQ + ...   (∵ ... is common in both ...)

⇒   ...Q + SR >

⇒   SQ + ... > ...

Let ∆BC be the ...... triangle and BCD the ...... drawn from A so ...(∵)... We need to
show that ....

Produce AD to E such that AD = DE.

Join ...

In ∆AFD and ∆FCD ....

      FD = ...D   (∵ D is mid-point of BC)

6 In figure given alongside, ∠B = 30°, ∠C = 40° and the bisector of ∠A meets BC at D. Show that
  (*i*) BD > AD   (*ii*) DC > AD
  (*iii*) AC > DC   (*iv*) AB > BD.

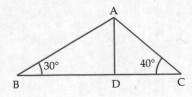

7 In the adjoining figure, AD bisects ∠A. Arrange AB, BD and DC in the descending order of their lengths.

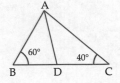

8 (*a*) In the figure (1) given below, prove that (*i*) CF > AF (*ii*) DC > DF.
  (*b*) In the figure (2) given below, AB = AC. Prove that AB > CD.
  (*c*) In the figure (3) given below, AC = CD. Prove that BC < CD.

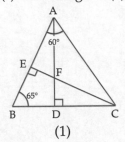 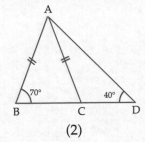 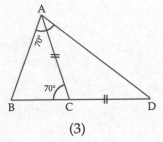

  (1)   (2)   (3)

Hint. (*b*) In △ ACD, ∠CAD = 30°, AC > CD but AB = AC.

9 (*a*) In the figure (*i*) given below, ∠B < ∠A and ∠C < ∠D. Show that AD < BC.
  (*b*) In the figure (*ii*) given below, D is any point on the side BC of △ABC. If AB > AC, show that AB > AD.

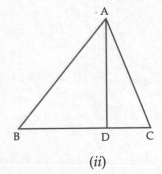

  (*i*)   (*ii*)

10 (*i*) Is it possible to construct a triangle with lengths of its sides as 4 cm, 3 cm and 7 cm? Give reason for your answer.
  (*ii*) Is it possible to construct a triangle with lengths of its sides as 9 cm, 7 cm and 17 cm? Give reason for your answer.
  (*iii*) Is it possible to construct a triangle with lengths of its sides as 8 cm, 7 cm and 4 cm? Give reason for your answer.

Multiple Choice Questions

Choose the correct answer from the given four options (1 to 18):

1 Which of the following is not a criterion for congruency of triangles?
  (*a*) SAS   (*b*) ASA   (*c*) SSA   (*d*) SSS

2 In the adjoining figure, AB = FC, EF = BD and ∠AFE = ∠CBD. Then the rule by which ΔAFE ≅ ΔCBD is

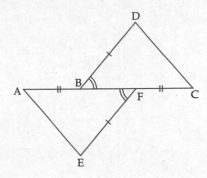

    (a) SAS

    (b) ASA

    (c) SSS

    (d) AAS

3 In the adjoining figure, AB ⊥ BE and FE ⊥ BE. If AB = FE and BC = DE, then

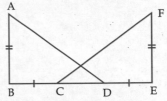

    (a) ΔABD ≅ ΔEFC

    (b) ΔABD ≅ ΔFEC

    (c) ΔABD ≅ ΔECF

    (d) ΔABD ≅ ΔCEF

4 In the adjoining figure, AB = AC and AD is median of ΔABC, then ∠ADC is equal to

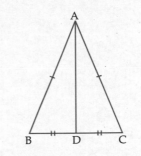

    (a) 60°

    (b) 120°

    (c) 90°

    (d) 75°

5 In the adjoining figure, O is mid-point of AB. If ∠ACO = ∠BDO, then ∠OAC is equal to

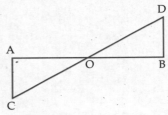

    (a) ∠OCA

    (b) ∠ODB

    (c) ∠OBD

    (d) ∠BOD

6 In the adjoining figure, AC = BD. If ∠CAB = ∠DBA, then ∠ACB is equal to

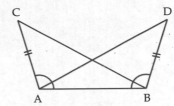

    (a) ∠BAD

    (b) ∠ABC

    (c) ∠ABD

    (d) ∠BDA

7 In the adjoining figure, ABCD is a quadrilateral in which BN and DM are drawn perpendiculars to AC such that BN = DM. If OB = 4 cm, then BD is

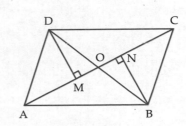

    (a) 6 cm

    (b) 8 cm

    (c) 10 cm

    (d) 12 cm

8 In ΔABC, AB = AC and ∠B = 50°. Then ∠C is equal to

    (a) 40°   (b) 50°   (c) 80°   (d) 130°

9 In ΔABC, BC = AB and ∠B = 80°. Then ∠A is equal to

    (a) 80°   (b) 40°   (c) 50°   (d) 100°

1. In triangles ABC and DEF, ∠A = ∠D, ∠B = ∠E and AB = EF. Will the two triangles be congruent? Give reasons for your answer.

2. In the adjoining figure, ABCD is a square. P, Q and R are points on the sides AB, BC and CD respectively such that AP = BQ = CR and ∠PQR = 90°. Prove that
    (a) ΔPBQ ≅ ΔQCR
    (b) PQ = QR
    (c) ∠PRQ = 45°.

3. In the adjoining figure, OA ⊥ OD, OC ⊥ OB, OD = OA and OB = OC. Prove that AB = CD.

    Hint. ΔAOB ≅ ΔDOC   (SAS)

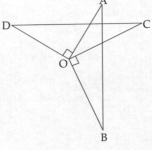

4. In the adjoining figure, PQ ∥ BA and RS ∥ CA. If BP = RC, prove that:
    (i) ΔBSR ≅ ΔPQC
    (ii) BS = PQ
    (iii) RS = CQ.

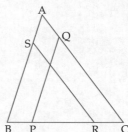

5. In the adjoining figure, AB = AC, D is a point in the interior of ΔABC such that ∠DBC = ∠DCB. Prove that AD bisects ∠BAC of ΔABC.

    Hint. ∠DBC = ∠DCB ⇒ CD = BD.
    ΔABD ≅ ΔACD by SSS rule of congruency.

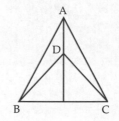

6. In the adjoining figure, AB ∥ DC. CE and DE bisects ∠BCD and ∠ADC respectively. Prove that
        AB = AD + BC.

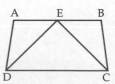

7. In ΔABC, D is a point on BC such that AD is the bisector of ∠BAC. CE is drawn parallel to DA to meet BA produced at E. Prove that ΔCAE is isosceles.

8. In the adjoining figure, ABC is a right angled triangle at B. ADEC and BCFG are squares.
    Prove that AF = BE.

    Hint. ∠BCE = ∠BCA + 90°,
        ∠ACF = ∠BCA + 90°
    ⇒   ∠BCE = ∠ACF.
        ΔBCE ≅ ΔFCA (SAS)

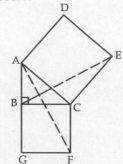

9 In the adjoining figure, BD = AD = AC. If ∠ABD = 36°, find the value of *x*.

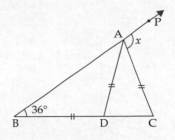

10 In the adjoining figure, TR = TS, ∠1 = 2 ∠2 and ∠4 = 2 ∠3. Prove that RB = SA.

Hint. ∠1 = ∠4 (vert. opp. ∠s)

⇒   2 ∠2 = 2 ∠3 ⇒ ∠2 = ∠3.

  TS = TR ⇒ ∠TRS = ∠TSR

⇒   ∠TRS − ∠2 = ∠TSR − ∠3

⇒   ∠ARB = ∠BSA.

  ΔRBT ≅ ΔSAT (ASA)

11   (*a*) In the figure (1) given below, find the value of *x*.

   (*b*) In the figure (2) given below, AB = AC and DE ∥ BC. Calculate
   (*i*) *x*   (*ii*) *y*   (*iii*) ∠BAC.

   (*c*) In the figure (3) given below, calculate the size of each lettered angle.

 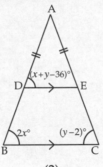

(1)   (2)   (3)

12   (*a*) In the figure (1) given below, AD = BD = DC and ∠ACD = 35°. Show that
   (*i*) AC > DC   (*ii*) AB > AD.

   (*b*) In the figure (2) given below, prove that
   (*i*) *x* + *y* = 90°   (*ii*) *z* = 90°   (*iii*) AB = BC.

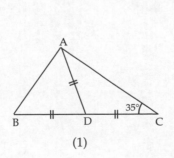  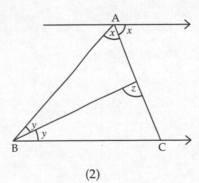

(1)   (2)

7. BE = CD	7. From 5 and 6
8. EBCD is a parallelogram.	8. BA ∥ CD (const.) and BE = CD (from 7)
9. EF ∥ BC and ED = BC	9. Since EBCD is a parallelogram.
10. EF = $\frac{1}{2}$ ED	10. Since EF = FD, from 5
11. EF = $\frac{1}{2}$ BC	11. Since ED = BC, from 9

Hence, EF ∥ BC and EF = $\frac{1}{2}$ BC.

The converse of the above theorem is also true. In fact, we have

❑ **Converse of mid-point theorem**

The line drawn through the mid-point of one side of a triangle parallel to another side bisects the third side.

Given. A triangle ABC, E is mid-point of AB. Line *l* drawn through E and parallel to BC meeting AC at F.

To prove. AF = FC.

Construction. Through C, draw a line *m* parallel BA to meet line *l* at D.

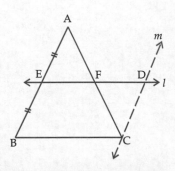

Proof.

Statements	Reasons
1. EBCD is a parallelogram	1. EF ∥ BC (given), BA ∥ CD (const.).
2. BE = CD	2. Opp. sides of a parallelogram are equal.
3. EA = BE	3. E is mid-point of AB (given).
4. EA = CD	4. From 2 and 3.
In ∆AEF and ∆CDF	
5. ∠EAF = ∠DCF	5. Alt. ∠s, CD ∥ BA and AC is a transversal.
6. ∠EFA = ∠DFC	6. Vert. opp. ∠s
7. EA = CD	7. From 4
8. ∆AEF ≅ ∆CDF	8. AAS rule of congruency
9. AF = FC	9. c.p.c.t.
Hence, F is mid-point of AC.	

❑ **Intercepts**

If a line *n* intersects two lines *l* and *m* (drawn in a plane) at points A and B respectively, then the line segment AB is called the *intercept* made on line *n* by the lines *l* and *m*.

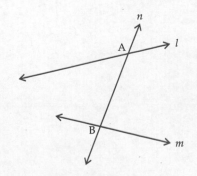

❑ Theorem on intercepts

If a transversal makes equal intercepts on three (or more) parallel lines, then any other line cutting them also makes equal intercepts.

Given. Three parallel lines *l*, *m* and *n*. A transversal *p* cutting them at points A, B and C respectively such that AB = BC. Any other line *q* cuts them at points D, E and F respectively.

To prove. DE = EF.

Construction. Through E, draw a line *r* parallel to line *p* to meet line *l* at G and line *n* at H.

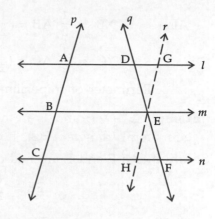

Proof.

Statements	Reasons
1. ABEG is a parallelogram.	1. AG ∥ BE (given), AB ∥ GE (const.).
2. AB = GE	2. Opp. sides of a parallelogram are equal.
3. BCHE is a parallelogram.	3. BE ∥ CH (given), BC ∥ EH (const.).
4. BC = EH	4. Opp. sides of a parallelogram are equal.
5. GE = EH	5. From 2 and 4; also AB = BC (given)
In ΔDEG and ΔFEH	
6. ∠EGD = ∠FHE	6. Alt. ∠s, AG ∥ CH (given) and GH is a transversal.
7. ∠DEG = ∠FEH	7. Vert. opp. ∠s are equal.
8. GE = EH	8. From 5 (proved above)
9. ΔDEG ≅ ΔFEH	9. ASA rule of congruency.
10. DE = EF	10. c.p.c.t.

Illustrative Examples

Example 1 In the adjoining figure, X and Y are mid-points of sides AB and AC respectively of ΔABC. If BC = 6 cm, AB = 7·4 cm and AC = 6·4 cm, then find the perimeter of trapezium XBCY.

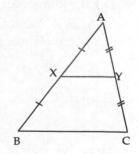

Solution. Since X is mid-point of AB and Y is mid-point of AC, therefore, XY is parallel to BC and XY = $\frac{1}{2}$ BC = ($\frac{1}{2}$ × 6) cm

$$= 3 \text{ cm.}$$

Also $XB = \frac{1}{2} AB = (\frac{1}{2} \times 7.4)$ cm = 3.7 cm and

$YC = \frac{1}{2} AC = (\frac{1}{2} \times 6.4)$ cm = 3.2 cm

∴   Perimeter of trapezium XBCY = (3.7 + 6 + 3.2 + 3) cm = 15.9 cm.

Example 2 D, E and F are mid-points of the sides BC, CA and AB respectively of an equilateral triangle ABC. Show that ΔDEF is also an equilateral triangle.

Solution. As F and E are mid-points of AB and CA respectively of ΔABC.

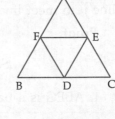

$$FE = \frac{1}{2} BC \qquad \text{(by Mid-point theorem)}$$

Similarly, $FD = \frac{1}{2} AC$ and $DE = \frac{1}{2} AB$

Given, ΔABC is equilateral triangle.

∴   AB = BC = CA

⇒ $\frac{1}{2} AB = \frac{1}{2} BC = \frac{1}{2} CA$

⇒   DE = FE = FD.

Hence, ΔDEF is also an equilateral triangle.

Example 3 Show that the line segments joining the mid-points of the opposite sides of a quadrilateral bisect each other.

Solution. Let ABCD be a quadrilateral and P, Q, R, S be mid-points of sides AB, BC, CD, AD respectively. We need to show that the line segments PR and SQ bisect each other.

In ΔABC, P and Q are mid-points of sides AB and BC respectively, therefore,

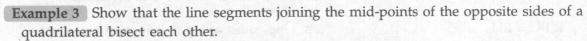

$$PQ \parallel AC \text{ and } PQ = \frac{1}{2} AC.$$

Similarly, $SR \parallel AC$ and $SR = \frac{1}{2} AC$

⇒ $PQ \parallel SR$ and $PQ = SR$ ⇒ PQRS is a parallelogram.

As the diagonals of a parallelogram bisect other, therefore, the line segments PR and SQ bisect each other.

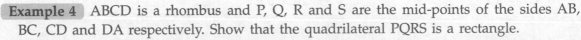

Example 4 ABCD is a rhombus and P, Q, R and S are the mid-points of the sides AB, BC, CD and DA respectively. Show that the quadrilateral PQRS is a rectangle.

Solution. Given ABCD is a rhombus and P, Q, R and S are mid-points of the sides AB, BC, CD and DA respectively. We need to show that PQRS is a rectangle.

Let the diagonals AC and BD of the rhombus ABCD intersect at O.

In ΔABC, P and Q are the mid-points of the sides AB and BC respectively, therefore, by mid-point theorem,

$$PQ \parallel AC \text{ and } PQ = \frac{1}{2} AC.$$

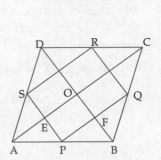

Similarly, $SR \parallel AC$ and $SR = \frac{1}{2} AC$

⇒ $PQ \parallel SR$ and $PQ = SR$

Thus, in quadrilateral PQRS, PQ ∥ SR and PQ = SR, therefore, PQRS is a parallelogram.

In △ABD, P and S are mid-points of AB and AD respectively, therefore,

$$PS \parallel BD$$

Thus, EP ∥ OF and PF ∥ EO, therefore, OEPF is a parallelogram

But ∠EOF = 90° (∵ diagonals of a rhombus intersect at right angles)

Also, in a parallelogram opposite angles are equal

∴ ∠EPF = ∠EOF = 90°.

Thus, PQRS is a parallelogram in which one angle *i.e.* ∠P = 90°, therefore, PQRS is a rectangle.

Example 5 ABCD is a rectangle and P, Q, R and S are the mid-points of the sides AB, BC, CD and DA respectively. Show that the quadrilateral PQRS is a rhombus.

Solution. Given ABCD is a rectangle and P, Q, R and S are mid-points of the sides AB, BC, CD and DA respectively. We need to prove that PQRS is a rhombus.

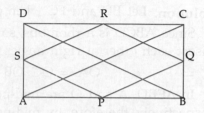

In △ABC, P and Q are mid-points of the sides AB and BC respectively, therefore, by mid-point theorem

$$PQ \parallel AC \text{ and } PQ = \frac{1}{2}AC.$$

Similarly, $$SR \parallel AC \text{ and } SR = \frac{1}{2}AC$$

⇒ PQ ∥ SR and PQ = SR

Thus, in quadrilateral PQRS, PQ ∥ SR and PQ = SR, therefore, PQRS is a parallelogram.

In △ABD, P and S are mid-points of the sides AB and AD respectively, therefore,

$$PS \parallel BD \text{ and } PS = \frac{1}{2}BD.$$

But AC = BD (∵ diagonals of a rectangle are equal)

∴ PQ = PS.

Thus, PQRS is a parallelogram in which two adjacent sides are equal, therefore, PQRS is a rhombus.

Example 6 ABC is an isosceles triangle with AB = AC and D, E, F are the mid-points of the sides BC, CA, AB respectively. Show that AD and FE bisect each other at right angles.

Solution. Join DE and DF.

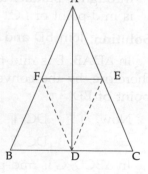

In △ABC, D and E are mid-points of the sides BC and CA respectively, therefore, by mid-point theorem.

$$ED \parallel AB \text{ and } ED = \frac{1}{2}AB \qquad ...(i)$$

Again in △ABC, D and F are mid-points of the sides BC and AB respectively, therefore, by mid-point theorem,

$$FD \parallel AC \text{ and } FD = \frac{1}{2}AC \qquad ...(ii)$$

From (*i*) and (*ii*), we have

ED ∥ AB *i.e.* ED ∥ AF and FD ∥ AC *i.e.* FD ∥ AE,

therefore, DEAF is a parallelogram.

Given $\quad$ AB = AC $\Rightarrow \frac{1}{2}$ AB = $\frac{1}{2}$ AC

$\Rightarrow \quad$ ED = FD $\hfill$ (using (i) and (ii))

Thus, DEAF is a parallelogram with ED = FD,

therefore, DEAF is a rhombus.

We know that the diagonals of a rhombus bisect each other at right angles. Here, AD and FE are diagonals of the rhombus DEFA. Therefore, AD and FE bisect each other at right angles.

Example 7 ABCD is a rhombus, EABF is a straight line such that EA = AB = BF. Prove that ED and FC when produced meet at right angles.

Solution. Let ED and FC when produced meet at G.

Since ABCD is a rhombus, so its diagonals *i.e.* AC and BD bisect each other at right angles

$\Rightarrow \quad$ OA = OC, OB = OD and $\angle$COD = 90°.

In $\triangle$EBD, A and O are mid-points of the sides EB and BD respectively, therefore, by mid-point theorem, AO *i.e.* ED

$\Rightarrow \quad$ OC || DG.

In $\triangle$AFC, B and O are mid-points of the sides AF and AC respectively, therefore, by mid-point theorem, BO || FC

$\Rightarrow \quad$ OD || CG.

Thus, in quadrilateral OCGD, OC || DG and OD || CG, therefore, OCGD is a parallelogram.

As the opposite angles in a parallelogram are equal,

$\angle$CGD = $\angle$COD but $\angle$COD = 90°,

$\therefore \quad \angle$CGD = 90° *i.e.* $\angle$ECF = 90°.

Hence, ED and FC when produced meet at right angles.

Example 8 In the adjoining figure, ABCD is a trapezium in which AB || DC and E is mid-point of AD. A line is drawn through E parallel to AB intersecting BC at F. Show that F is mid-point of BC.

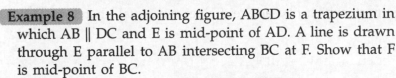

Solution. Join BD and let BD intersect EF at G.

In $\triangle$DAB, E is mid-point of AD and EF || AB *i.e.* EG || AB, therefore, by the converse of mid-point theorem, G is mid-point of BD.

Now, $\quad$ DC || AB (given) and EF || AB

$\Rightarrow \quad$ DC || EF $\Rightarrow$ DC || GF.

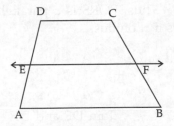

In $\triangle$BCD, G is mid-point of BD and GF || DC, therefore, by the converse of mid-point theorem, F is mid-point of BC.

Example 9 ABC is a triangle right angled at C. A line through the mid-point M of hypotenuse AB and parallel to BC intersects AC at D. Show that

(i) D is mid-point of AC $\quad\quad$ (ii) MD ⊥ AC $\quad\quad$ (iii) CM = MA = $\frac{1}{2}$ AB.

Solution. (*i*) In $\triangle ABC$, M is mid-point of AB and MD is drawn parallel to BC, therefore, by the converse of mid-point theorem, D is mid-point of AC.

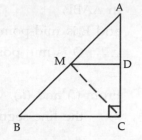

(*ii*) As MD $\parallel$ BC and AC is a transversal,

$$\angle BCD + \angle CDM = 180° \qquad \text{(sum of co-int. } \angle s)$$
$$\Rightarrow \quad 90° + \angle CDM = 180° \qquad (\because \angle BCA = 90°, \text{ given})$$
$$\Rightarrow \quad \angle CDM = 90° \Rightarrow MD \perp AC.$$

(*iii*) In $\triangle AMD$ and $\triangle CMD$,

$$AD = DC \qquad (\because \text{D is mid-point of AC from part (}i\text{)})$$
$$\angle ADM = \angle CDM \qquad (\text{each} = 90°, MD \perp AC)$$
$$MD = MD \qquad (\text{common})$$
$$\therefore \quad \triangle ADM \cong \triangle CMD \qquad (\text{by SAS rule of congruency})$$
$$\therefore \quad AM = CM \qquad (\text{c.p.c.t.})$$

Also, as M is mid-point of AB, $AM = \frac{1}{2}AB$.

$$\therefore \quad CM = AM = \frac{1}{2}AB.$$

Example 10 In the adjoining figure, D, E and F are the mid-points of the sides AB, BC and CA respectively of a triangle ABC. Show that $\triangle ABC$ is divided into four congruent triangles by joining the points D, E and F.

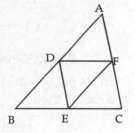

Solution. In $\triangle ABC$, D and E are mid-points of the sides AB and BC respectively, therefore, by mid-point theorem, DE $\parallel$ AC.

Similarly, FE $\parallel$ AB and DF $\parallel$ BC

$\Rightarrow$ ADEF, BEFD and CFDE are all parallelograms.

Now, as DE is a diagonal of the parallelogram BEFD, so DE divides the parallelogram BEFD into two congruent triangles

i.e. $\qquad \triangle BDE \cong \triangle FED.$

Similarly, $\qquad \triangle DAF \cong \triangle FED$

and $\qquad \triangle EFC \cong \triangle FED.$

Therefore, all the four triangles are congruent.

Example 11 In the adjoining figure, ABCD is a parallelogram and E, F are the mid-points of the sides AB, CD respectively. Show that the line segments AF and EC trisect the diagonal BD.

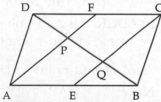

Solution. As ABCD is a parallelogram, AB $\parallel$ DC

$$\Rightarrow \qquad AE \parallel FC.$$
$$\text{Also} \qquad AB = DC \qquad (\text{opp. sides of a} \parallel \text{gm are equal})$$
$$\Rightarrow \qquad \frac{1}{2}AB = \frac{1}{2}DC$$
$$\Rightarrow \qquad AE = FC \qquad (\because \text{E is mid-point of AB and F is mid-point of CD})$$

Thus, in the quadrilateral AECF, AE = FC and AE $\parallel$ FC

$\Rightarrow$ AECF is a parallelogram $\Rightarrow$ AF $\parallel$ EC.

In $\triangle DQC$, $\qquad PF \parallel QC \qquad (\because AF \parallel EC \text{ proved above})$

and F is mid-point of CD.

$$\therefore \quad \text{P is mid-point of DQ} \qquad (\text{using converse of mid-point theorem})$$
$$\Rightarrow \qquad DP = PQ \qquad \qquad \dots(i)$$

In $\triangle ABP$,   EQ ‖ AP   ($\because$ EC ‖ AF, from above)

and E is mid-point of AB

$\therefore$ Q is mid-point of BP   (using converse of mid-point theorem)

$\Rightarrow$ BQ = PQ   ...(ii)

From (i) and (ii), we get DP = PQ = BQ

$\Rightarrow$ the line segments AF and EC trisect the diagonal BD.

Example 12 In the adjoining figure, ABCD is a parallelogram. E is mid-point of DC and F is a point on AC such that $CF = \dfrac{1}{4} AC$. If EF produced meets BC at G, prove that:

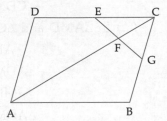

   (i) G is mid-point of BC

   (ii) 2EG = DB.

Solution. (i) Join BD. Let the diagonals AC and BD of ‖ gm ABCD intersect at O.

As the diagonals of a ‖ gm bisect each other,

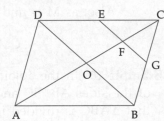

          OC = OA

i.e.   AC = 2OC.

Given, $CF = \dfrac{1}{4} AC = \dfrac{1}{4} \times 2OC = \dfrac{1}{2} OC$

$\Rightarrow$ F is mid-point of OC.

In $\triangle OCD$, E and F are mid-points of the sides DC and OC respectively, therefore, by mid-point theorem, EF ‖ DO

$\Rightarrow$ FG ‖ OB.

In $\triangle OBC$, F is mid-point of OC and FG ‖ OB, therefore, by converse of mid-point theorem, G is mid-point of BC.

(ii) In $\triangle DBC$, E and G are mid-points of sides DC and CB respectively, therefore, by mid-point theorem, EG ‖ DB and $EG = \dfrac{1}{2} DB$

$\Rightarrow$ 2EG = DB

Example 13 P is the mid-point of the side CD of a parallelogram. A line through C parallel to PA intersects AB at Q and DA produced at R. Prove that DA = AR and CQ = QR.

Solution. Draw the figure according to given conditions.

In $\triangle DCR$, P is mid-point of side CD and PA ‖ CR, therefore, by converse of mid-point theorem, A is mid-point of DR.

As A is mid-point of DR, so DA = AR.

Now   AB ‖ DC   ($\because$ ABCD is a ‖ gm)

$\Rightarrow$ AQ ‖ DC.

In $\triangle RCD$, A is mid-point of DR and AQ ‖ DC, therefore, by converse of mid-point theorem, Q is mid-point of CR

$\Rightarrow$ CQ = QR.

Example 14 E is mid-point of the median AD of $\triangle ABC$ and BE is produced to meet AC at F. Show that $AF = \dfrac{1}{3} AC$.

Solution. Through D, draw a line parallel to BF to meet AC at G.

In $\triangle ADG$, E is mid-point of side AD and DG ‖ BF i.e. DG ‖ EF, therefore, by converse of mid-point theorem, F is mid-point of AG i.e. AF = FG   ...(i)

In $\triangle BCF$, D is mid-point of side BC and DG $\parallel$ BF, therefore, by converse of mid-point theorem, G is mid-point of CF *i.e.*

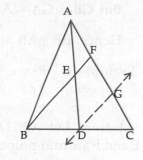

$$FG = GC \qquad \qquad ...(ii)$$

From (*i*) and (*ii*), we get

$$AF = FG = GC \qquad \qquad ...(iii)$$

Now $\qquad AC = AF + FG + GC = AF + AF + AF \quad$ (using (*iii*))

$\Rightarrow \qquad AC = 3AF \Rightarrow AF = \dfrac{1}{3} AC.$

Example 15 In $\triangle ABC$, the medians BE and CF are produced to points P and Q respectively such that EP = BE and FQ = CF. Prove that :

   (*i*) Q, A and P are collinear   (*ii*) A is mid-point of QP.

Solution. Join AP, AQ and FE.

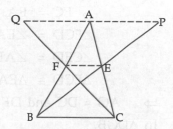

  Given. EP = BE and FQ = CF, therefore, E and F are mid-points of BP and CQ respectively.

  In $\triangle ABP$, F is mid-point of AB and E is mid-point of BP, therefore, FE $\parallel$ AP and FE $= \dfrac{1}{2}$ AP.

  In $\triangle ACQ$, E is mid-point of AC and F is mid-point of CQ, therefore, FE $\parallel$ QA and FE $= \dfrac{1}{2}$ QA.

   (*i*) Thus FE $\parallel$ AP and FE $\parallel$ QA, therefore, QA and AP lie along the same straight line (because both QA and AP pass through the same point A and are parallel to the straight line EF).

     It follows that Q, A and P are collinear.

  (*ii*) As FE $= \dfrac{1}{2}$ AP and FE $= \dfrac{1}{2}$ QA

$\Rightarrow \qquad \dfrac{1}{2}$ AP $= \dfrac{1}{2}$ QA $\Rightarrow$ AP $=$ QA

$\Rightarrow \qquad$ A is mid-point of QP.

Example 16 E and F are respectively the mid-points of non-parallel sides AD and BC of a trapezium ABCD. Prove that EF $\parallel$ AB and EF $= \dfrac{1}{2}$ (AB + CD).

Solution. ABCD is a trapezium in which AB $\parallel$ DC and E, F are mid-points of AD, BC respectively.

  Join CE and produce it to meet BA produced at G.

  In $\triangle EDC$ and $\triangle EAG$,

$$\begin{aligned}
ED &= EA && (\because \text{E is mid-point of AD}) \\
\angle CED &= \angle GEA && (\text{Vert. opp. } \angle s) \\
\angle ECD &= \angle EGA && (\text{Alt. } \angle s, \text{ DC} \parallel \text{AB } i.e. \text{ DC} \parallel \text{GB and CG is transversal})
\end{aligned}$$

$\therefore \qquad \triangle EDC \cong \triangle EAG$

$\Rightarrow \qquad$ CD $=$ GA and EC $=$ EG $\qquad \qquad \qquad$ (c.p.c.t.)

In $\triangle CGB$,

E is mid-point of CG $\qquad \qquad \qquad \qquad (\because$ EC $=$ EG proved above)

F is mid-point of BC $\qquad \qquad \qquad \qquad \qquad \qquad \qquad$ (given)

Therefore, by mid-point theorem, EF $\parallel$ AB and EF $= \dfrac{1}{2}$ GB.

But GB = GA + AB = CD + AB.   (∵ GA = CD proved above)

Hence, EF ∥ AB and EF = $\frac{1}{2}$ (AB + CD).

Example 17 Prove that the line segment joining the mid-points of the diagonals of a trapezium is parallel to the parallel sides of trapezium and is equal to half the difference of these sides.

Solution. Let ABCD be a trapezium in which AB ∥ CD.
E and F are mid-points of its diagonals AC and BD respectively.

We want to prove that EF ∥ AB and EF = $\frac{1}{2}$ (AB – DC).

Join DE and produce it to meet AB at G.

In ΔECD and ΔEAG,

$\qquad$ EC = EA $\qquad\qquad$ (∵ E is mid-point of AC)

$\qquad$ ∠ECD = ∠EAG $\qquad$ (Alt. ∠s, AB ∥ DC *i.e.* AG ∥ DC and AC is transversal)

$\qquad$ ∠CED = ∠AEG $\qquad\qquad\qquad\qquad\qquad\qquad\qquad$ (Vert. opp. ∠s)

∴ $\qquad$ ΔECD ≅ ΔEAG $\qquad\qquad\qquad\qquad\qquad$ (by ASA rule of congruency)

⇒ $\quad$ AG = DC and DE = EG.

In ΔDGB,

E is mid-point of DG $\qquad\qquad\qquad\qquad\qquad$ (∵ DE = EG, proved above)

F is mid-point of BD $\qquad\qquad\qquad\qquad\qquad\qquad\qquad\qquad$ (given)

Therefore, by mid-point theorem,

$\qquad$ EF ∥ GB *i.e.* EF ∥ AB and EF = $\frac{1}{2}$ GB.

But $\quad$ GB = AB – AG = AB – DC $\qquad\qquad\qquad$ (∵ AG = DC, proved above)

Hence, EF ∥ AB and EF = $\frac{1}{2}$ (AB – DC).

Example 18 P, Q and R are the mid-points of the sides BC, CA and AB respectively of a triangle ABC. PR and BQ meet at X, CR and PQ meet at Y. Prove that XY = $\frac{1}{4}$ BC.

Solution. ABC is a triangle and P, Q, R are mid-points of the sides BC, CA, AB respectively. PR and BQ meet at X, CR and PQ meet at Y.

Join RQ and XY.

Since R and Q are mid-points of sides AB and AC respectively, therefore, by mid-point theorem,

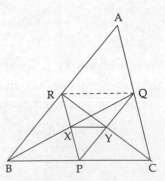

$\qquad$ RQ ∥ BC and RQ = $\frac{1}{2}$ BC

⇒ $\qquad$ RQ ∥ BP and RQ = BP

$\qquad\qquad$ (as P is mid-point of BC, BP = $\frac{1}{2}$ BC)

⇒ $\quad$ BPQR is a parallelogram.

As the diagonals of a parallelogram bisect each other, X is mid-point of PR.

Also $\qquad$ RQ ∥ BC and RQ = $\frac{1}{2}$ BC

⇒ $\qquad$ RQ ∥ PC and RQ = PC $\qquad$ (as P is mid-point of BC, PC = $\frac{1}{2}$ BC)

⇒ $\quad$ PCQR is a parallelogram

⇒ $\qquad$ Y is mid-point of PQ $\qquad\qquad$ (∵ diagonals of a ∥ gm bisect each other)

Thus, in $\triangle PQR$, X and Y are the mid-points of the sides PR and PQ respectively, therefore, by mid-point theorem,

$$XY \parallel RQ \text{ and } XY = \frac{1}{2}RQ.$$

$$\therefore \qquad XY = \frac{1}{2}RQ = \frac{1}{2}\left(\frac{1}{2}BC\right) = \frac{1}{4}BC.$$

Example 19 In the adjoining figure, ABCD is a parallelogram. E and F are mid-points of sides AB and CD respectively. PQ is any line that meets AD, EF and BC in points P, O and Q respectively. Prove that PO = OQ.

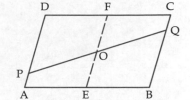

Solution. $AE = \frac{1}{2}AB$ ($\because$ E is mid-point of AB)

and $DF = \frac{1}{2}DC$ ($\because$ F is mid-point of CD)

$\Rightarrow$ $AE = DF$ ($\because$ AB $\parallel$ DC, opp. sides of $\parallel$ gm)

Also $AE \parallel DF$ (AB $\parallel$ DC, ABCD is a $\parallel$ gm)

$\Rightarrow$ AEFD is a $\parallel$ gm ($\because$ opp. sides of quad. AEFD are equal and parallel)

$\Rightarrow$ AD $\parallel$ EF

Also AD $\parallel$ BC ($\because$ ABCD is a $\parallel$ gm)

$\Rightarrow$ AD, EF and BC are parallel lines.

Now, as the transversal AB makes equal intercepts AE = EB on the three parallel lines AD, EF and BC, therefore, the transversal PQ also makes equal intercepts on these parallel lines (theorem on intercepts)

$\Rightarrow$ PO = OQ, as required.

Example 20 Points A and B are on the same side of a line *l*. AM and BN are perpendiculars to the line *l*. If C is the mid-points of AB, prove that CM = CN.

Solution. From C, draw CD perpendicular to the line *l*.

Since AM, CD and BN are perpendiculars to the same line *l*, AM, CD and BN are parallel lines. Now, as the transversal AB makes equal intercepts AC = CB (given C is mid-point of AB) on the three parallel lines AM, CD and BN, therefore, the transversal *l* also makes equal intercepts on these parallel lines

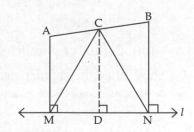

$\Rightarrow$ MD = DN.

In $\triangle CMD$ and $\triangle CND$,

MD = DN (proved above)

$\angle CDM = \angle CDN$ (each angle = 90°, CD is perpendicular to *l*)

and CD is common.

$\because$ $\triangle CMD \cong \triangle CND$ (by SAS rule of congruency)

$\Rightarrow$ CM = CN (c.p.c.t.)

EXERCISE 11

1 (*a*) In the figure (1) given below, D, E and F are mid-points of the sides BC, CA and AB respectively of $\triangle ABC$. If AB = 6 cm, BC = 4·8 cm and CA = 5·6 cm, find the perimeter of

  (*i*) the trapezium FBCE (*ii*) the triangle DEF.

(b) In the figure (2) given below, D and E are mid-points of the sides AB and AC respectively. If BC = 5·6 cm and ∠B = 72°, compute

(i) DE   (ii) ∠ADE.

(c) In the figure (3) given below, D and E are mid-points of AB, BC respectively and DF ∥ BC. Prove that DBEF is a parallelogram. Calculate AC if AF = 2·6 cm.

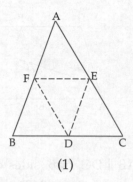
(1)

(2)

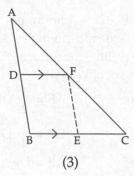
(3)

2 Prove that the four triangles formed by joining in pairs the mid-points of the sides of a triangle are congruent to each other.

3 If D, E and F are mid-points of the sides AB, BC and CA respectively of an isosceles triangle ABC, prove that ∆DEF is also isosceles.

4 The diagonals AC and BD of a parallelogram ABCD intersect at O. If P is the mid-point of AD, prove that

(i) PO ∥ AB   (ii) PO = $\frac{1}{2}$ CD.

5 In the adjoining figure, ABCD is a quadrilateral in which P, Q, R and S are mid-points of AB, BC, CD and DA respectively. AC is its diagonal. Show that

(i) SR ∥ AC and SR = $\frac{1}{2}$ AC

(ii) PQ = SR

(iii) PQRS is a parallelogram.

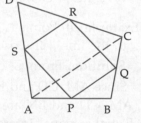

6 Show that the quadrilateral formed by joining the mid-points of the adjacent sides of a square, is also a square.

7 In the adjoining figure, AD and BE are medians of ∆ABC. If DF ∥ BE, prove that CF = $\frac{1}{4}$ AC.

Hint. In ∆BCE, D is mid-point of BC and DF ∥ BE, therefore, F is mid-point of CE (converse of mid-point theorem)

⇒   CF = $\frac{1}{2}$ CE = $\frac{1}{2}$ ($\frac{1}{2}$ AC).

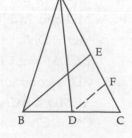

8 In the adjoining figure, ABCD is a parallelogram. E and F are mid-points of the sides AB and CD respectively. The straight lines AF and BF meet the straight lines ED and EC in points G and H respectively. Prove that

(i) ∆HEB ≅ ∆HCF

(ii) GEHF is a parallelogram.

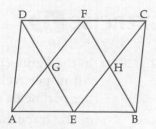

9 ABC is an isosceles triangle with AB = AC. D, E and F are mid-points of the sides BC, AB and AC respectively. Prove that the line segment AD is perpendicular to EF and is bisected by it.

    Hint. ΔABD ≅ ΔACD.

10   (*a*) In the quadrilateral (1) given below, AB ∥ DC, E and F are mid-points of AD and BD respectively. Prove that

      (*i*) G is mid-point of BC   (*ii*) EG = $\frac{1}{2}$ (AB + DC).

  (*b*) In the quadrilateral (2) given below, AB ∥ DC ∥ EG. If E is mid-point of AD, prove that

      (*i*) G is mid-point of BC   (*ii*) 2EG = AB + CD.

  (*c*) In the quadrilateral (3) given below, AB ∥ DC. E and F are mid-points of non-parallel sides AD and BC respectively. Calculate:

      (*i*) EF if AB = 6 cm and DC = 4 cm   (*ii*) AB if DC = 8 cm and EF = 9 cm.

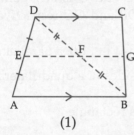 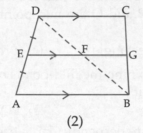 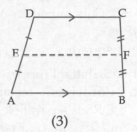

        (1)   (2)   (3)

11   (*a*) In the quadrilateral (1) given below, AD = BC. P, Q, R and S are mid-points of AB, BD, CD and AC respectively. Prove that PQRS is a rhombus.

  (*b*) In the figure (2) given below, ABCD is a kite in which BC = CD, AB = AD. E, F, G are mid-points of CD, BC and AB respectively. Prove that

    (*i*) ∠EFG = 90°.

    (*ii*) the line drawn through G and parallel to FE bisects DA.

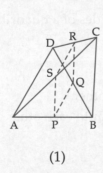 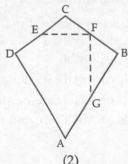

        (1)   (2)

  Hint.   (*a*) PQ ∥ AD and PQ = $\frac{1}{2}$ AD, SR ∥ AD and SR = $\frac{1}{2}$ AD.

      (*b*) Diagonals of a kite intersect at right angles.

12 In the adjoining figure, the lines *l*, *m* and *n* are parallel to each other, and G is mid-point of CD. Calculate:

    (*i*) BG if AD = 6 cm

    (*ii*) CF if GE = 2·3 cm

    (*iii*) AB if BC = 2·4 cm

    (*iv*) ED if FD = 4·4 cm.

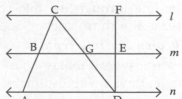

Multiple Choice Questions

Choose the correct answer from the given four options (1 to 6):

1 In a ΔABC, AB = 3 cm, BC = 4 cm and CA = 5 cm. If D and E are mid-points of AB and BC respectively, then the length of DE is

    (*a*) 1·5 cm   (*b*) 2 cm   (*c*) 2·5 cm   (*d*) 3·5 cm

2 In the adjoining figure, ABCD is a rectangle in which AB = 6 cm and AD = 8 cm. If P and Q are mid-points of the sides BC and CD respectively, then the length of PQ is

    (*a*) 7 cm   (*b*) 5 cm

    (*c*) 4 cm   (*d*) 3 cm

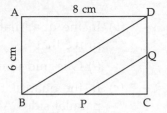

3 D and E are mid-points of the sides AB and AC of ΔABC and O is any point on the side BC. O is joined to A. If P and Q are mid-points of OB and OC respectively, then DEQP is

    (*a*) a square   (*b*) a rectangle   (*c*) a rhombus   (*d*) a parallelogram

4 The quadrilateral formed by joining the mid-points of the sides of a quadrilateral PQRS, taken in order, is a rectangle if

    (*a*) PQRS is a parallelogram   (*b*) PQRS is a rectangle

    (*c*) the diagonals of PQRS are perpendicular to each other

    (*d*) the diagonals of PQRS are equal.

5 The quadrilateral formed by joining the mid-points of the sides of a quadrilateral ABCD, taken in order, is a rhombus if

    (*a*) ABCD is a parallelogram   (*b*) ABCD is a rhombus

    (*c*) the diagonals of ABCD are equal

    (*d*) the diagonals of ABCD are perpendicular to each other.

6 The figure formed by joining the mid-points of the sides of a quadrilateral ABCD, taken in order, is a square only if

    (*a*) ABCD is a rhombus

    (*b*) diagonals of ABCD are equal

    (*c*) diagonals of ABCD are perpendicular to each other

    (*d*) diagonals of ABCD are equal and perpendicular to each other.

Summary

❏ *Mid-point theorem*

The line segment joining the mid-points of any two sides of a triangle is parallel to the third side and is equal to half of it.

❏ *Converse of mid-point theorem*

The line through the mid-point of one side of a triangle and parallel to another side bisects the third side.

❏ *Theorem on intercepts*

If a transversal makes equal intercepts on three (or more) parallel lines, then any other line cutting them also makes equal intercepts.

1. ABCD is a rhombus with P, Q and R as mid-points of AB, BC and CD respectively. Prove that PQ ⊥ QR.

2. The diagonals of a quadrilateral ABCD are perpendicular. Show that the quadrilateral formed by joining the mid-points of its adjacent sides is a rectangle.

3. If D, E, F are mid-points of the sides BC, CA and AB respectively of a ∆ABC, prove that AD and FE bisect each other.

4. In ∆ABC, D and E are mid-points of the sides AB and AC respectively. Through E, a straight line is drawn parallel to AB to meet BC at F. Prove that BDEF is a parallelogram. If AB = 8 cm and BC = 9 cm, find the perimeter of the parallelogram BDEF.

[**Ans.** 17 cm.]

5. In the adjoining figure, ABCD is a parallelogram and E is mid-point of AD. DL ∥ EB meets AB produced at F. Prove that B is mid-point of AF and EB = LF.

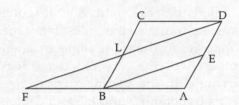

6. In the adjoining figure, ABCD is a parallelogram. If P and Q are mid-points of sides CD and BC respectively. Show that $CR = \frac{1}{4} AC$.

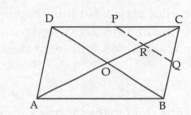

12 Pythagoras Theorem

INTRODUCTION

Pythagoras, a Greek philospher of sixth century B.C. discovered a very important and useful property of right angled triangles, named Pythagoras property. In a right angled triangle, the sides have special names. The side opposite to the right angle is called **hypotenuse** and the other two sides are called the **legs** of the right angled triangle. In the adjoining triangle ABC, $\angle C = 90°$. So, AB is its hypotenuse and BC and CA are the two legs. You are already familiar with the Pythagoras theorem from your earlier classes. In this chapter, we shall prove this theorem by using similarity of triangles. We shall also prove its converse and will learn their applications.

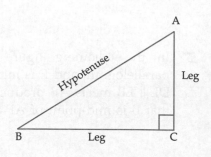

12.1 PYTHAGORAS THEOREM

In a right triangle, the square of the hypotenuse is equal to the sum of the squares of the other two sides.

Given. ABC is a right angled triangle at A *i.e.* $\angle A = 90°$, so that BC is its hypotenuse.

To prove. $BC^2 = CA^2 + AB^2$ *i.e.* $a^2 = b^2 + c^2$, where BC = a, CA = b and AB = c.

Construction. Extend the side AB to a point D such that BD = CA = b. At D, draw DE $\perp$ AD and cut off DE = AB = c. Join CE.

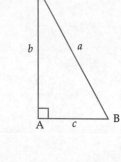

Proof. In $\triangle ABC$ and $\triangle DEB$,

CA = BD	(by construction)	
AB = DE	(by construction)	
$\angle A = \angle D$	(each = 90°)	

$\therefore \quad \triangle ABC \cong \triangle DEB$ (SAS rule of congruency)

$\Rightarrow \quad$ BC = BE (c.p.c.t)

$\Rightarrow \quad$ BE = a ($\because$ BC = a)

and $\quad \angle ACB = \angle DBE \quad$ ...(i) (c.p.c.t)

In $\triangle ABC$, $\angle A + \angle ABC + \angle ACB = 180°$

$\Rightarrow \quad 90° + \angle ABC + \angle ACB = 180°$

$\Rightarrow \quad \angle ABC + \angle ACB = 90°$

$\Rightarrow \quad \angle ABC + \angle DEB = 90° \qquad\qquad ...(ii)$ (using (i))

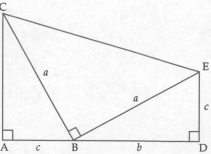

Since sum of angles at a point on one side of a straight line is 180°,

∴   ∠ABC + ∠CBE + ∠DBE = 180°

⇒   (∠ABC + ∠DBE) + ∠CBE = 180°

⇒   90° + ∠CBE = 180°   (using (ii))

⇒   ∠CBE = 90°

⇒   CBE is a right angled triangle at B.

Now, ∠A + ∠D = 90° + 90° = 180°

⇒   AC ∥ DE   (∵ sum of co-int. ∠s = 180°)

⇒   CADE is a trapezium.

From figure,

area of trapezium CADE = area of ΔCAB + area of ΔBDE + area of ΔCBE

⇒ $\frac{1}{2}$(CA + ED) × AD = $\frac{1}{2}$CA × AB + $\frac{1}{2}$BD × DE + $\frac{1}{2}$CB × EB

       (∵ area of a trapezium = $\frac{1}{2}$(sum of ∥ sides × height and

                 area of a triangle = $\frac{1}{2}$ base × height)

⇒   (b + c)(c + b) = bc + bc + a × a   (∵ AD = AB + BD = c + b)

⇒   (b + c)² = 2bc + a²

⇒   b² + c² + 2bc = 2bc + a²

⇒   b² + c² = a²

⇒   CA² + AB² = BC²

Hence, BC² = CA² + AB²

The above result is known as **Pythagoras Theorem**.

The above theorem was earlier given by an ancient mathematician **Baudhayan** (about 800 B.C.) in the following form:

The diagonal of a rectangle produces by itself the same area as produced by its both sides (i.e. length and breadth).

Therefore, the above theorem is sometimes also referred to as the *Baudhayan Theorem*.

The converse of the Pythagoras theorem is also true. We record it as:

❐ **Converse of Pythagoras Theorem**

In a triangle, if square of one side is equal to the sum of the squares of the other two sides, then the angle opposite to the first side is a right angle.

Given. In a triangle ABC, BC² = AB² + AC².

To prove. ∠A = 90°.

Construction. Construct a ΔPQR such that

      ∠P = 90°, PQ = AB and PR = AC.

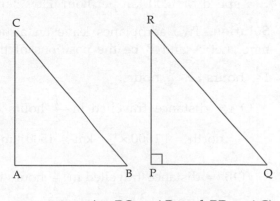

Proof. In ΔPQR, ∠P = 90°.

By Pythagoras theorem, we have

      QR² = PQ² + PR²

⇒   QR² = AB² + AC²   (∵ PQ = AB and PR = AC)

But   BC² = AB² + AC²   (given)

∴   QR² = BC² ⇒ QR = BC.

In $\triangle ABC$ and $\triangle PQR$,

	AB = PQ	(by construction)
	AC = PR	(by construction)
and	BC = QR	(proved above)
$\therefore$	$\triangle ABC \cong \triangle PQR$	(SSS rule of congruency)
$\Rightarrow$	$\angle A = \angle P$	(c.p.c.t.)
$\Rightarrow$	$\angle A = 90°$	($\because \angle P = 90°$, by construction)

Illustrative Examples

Example 1 Lengths of sides of triangles are given below. Determine which of them are right triangles. In case of a right triangle, write the length of its hypotenuse:

(i) 7 cm, 24 cm, 25 cm   (ii) 50 cm, 80 cm, 100 cm

Solution. Choose the greatest length. Check whether the square of greatest length is equal to the sum of squares of other two lengths.

(i) Here, greatest length is 25 cm and other lengths are 7 cm, 24 cm.

Note that $25^2 = 625$ and $7^2 + 24^2 = 49 + 576 = 625$.

Thus, $25^2 = 7^2 + 24^2$.

Therefore, the triangle with given lengths of sides is a right triangle and the length of its hypotenuse is 25 cm.

(ii) Here, greatest length is 100 cm and other lengths are 50 cm, 80 cm.

Note that $50^2 + 80^2 = 2500 + 6400 = 8900 \neq 100^2$.

Therefore, the triangle with given lengths of sides is not a right triangle.

Example 2 ABC is an isosceles triangle with AC = BC. If $AB^2 = 2AC^2$, prove that ABC is a right triangle.

Solution. Given $AB^2 = 2AC^2 \Rightarrow AB^2 = AC^2 + AC^2$

$\Rightarrow$	$AB^2 = AC^2 + BC^2$	($\because$ AC = BC, given)
$\Rightarrow$	$\angle C = 90°$	(converse of Pythagoras theorem)

Hence, $\triangle ABC$ is a right triangle.

Example 3 An aeroplane leaves an airport and flies due north at a speed of 1000 km per hour. At the same time, another aeroplane leaves the same airport and flies due west at a speed of 1200 km per hour. How far apart will be the two planes after $1\frac{1}{2}$ hours?

Solution. Two aeroplanes leave an airport O at the same time. Let A and B be the positions of the aeroplanes after $1\frac{1}{2}$ hours *i.e.* $\frac{3}{2}$ hours.

OA = distance travelled in $\frac{3}{2}$ hours by the aeroplane due

north $= \left(1000 \times \frac{3}{2}\right)$ km = 1500 km,

OB = distance travelled in $\frac{3}{2}$ hours by the aeroplane due west

$= \left(1200 \times \frac{3}{2}\right)$ km = 1800 km

In $\triangle AOB$, $\angle O = 90°$. By Pythagoras theorem, we get

$AB^2 = OA^2 + OB^2 = 1500^2 + 1800^2 = (300)^2 (5^2 + 6^2)$

$\Rightarrow$ AB = $300\sqrt{61}$ km

Hence, the distance between two aeroplanes = $300\sqrt{61}$ km.

Example 4 For going to a city B from city A, there is route via city C such that AC $\perp$ CB, AC = $2x$ km and CB = $2(x + 7)$ km. It is proposed to construct a 26 km highway which directly connects the two cities A and B. Find how much distance will be saved in reaching city B from city A after the construction of highway.

Solution. The cities A, B and C are marked in the figure.

In $\triangle$ABC, $\angle$C = 90° $\qquad\qquad\qquad\qquad\qquad$ ($\because$ AC $\perp$ CB)

By Pythagoras theorem, we get

$\qquad$ AC^2 + BC^2 = AB^2

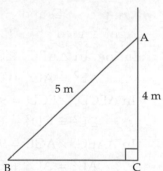

$\Rightarrow$ $(2x)^2 + (2(x + 7))^2 = 26^2$

$\Rightarrow$ $4(x^2 + x^2 + 14x + 49) = 676$

$\Rightarrow$ $2x^2 + 14x + 49 = 169 \Rightarrow 2x^2 + 14x - 120 = 0$

$\Rightarrow$ $x^2 + 7x - 12 = 0 \Rightarrow x^2 + 12x - 5x - 60 = 0$

$\Rightarrow$ $x(x + 12) - 5(x + 12) = 0 \Rightarrow (x + 12)(x - 5) = 0$

$\Rightarrow$ $x = -12$ or $x = 5$ but x cannot be negative

$\Rightarrow$ $x = 5$.

$\therefore$ AC = $2x$ km = (2×5) km = 10 km

and   BC = $2(x + 7)$ km = $2(5 + 7)$ km = 24 km.

Thus, the original distance between two cities A and B = 10 km + 24 km = 34 km.

New distance between cities A and B = 26 km.

$\therefore$ The distance saved = 34 km – 26 km = 8 km.

Example 5 A 5 m long ladder is placed leaning towards a vertical wall such that it reaches the wall at a point 4 m high. If the foot of the ladder is moved 1·6 m towards the wall, then find the distance by which the top of the ladder would slide upwards on the wall.

Solution. The point C is the base of wall.

Originally, let the top of ladder reach the wall at the point A.

In $\triangle$ABC, $\angle$C = 90°. By Pythagoras theorem, we get

$\therefore$ BC^2 + AC^2 = AB^2

$\Rightarrow$ BC^2 + 4^2 = 5^2

$\Rightarrow$ BC^2 = 25 – 16 = 9

$\Rightarrow$ BC = 3 m.

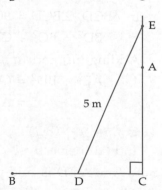

Now, the foot of ladder is moved 1·6 m towards the wall. Let D be new position of foot of ladder and E be the new position of its top.

DC = BC – BD = 3 m – 1·6 m = 1·4 m

In $\triangle$ECD, $\angle$C = 90°. By Pythagoras theorem, we get

$\therefore$ EC^2 + DC^2 = DE^2

$\Rightarrow$ EC^2 + $(1·4)^2$ = 5^2

$\Rightarrow$ EC^2 = 25 – 1·96 = 23·04

$\Rightarrow$ EC = 4·8 m.

$\therefore$ AE = EC – AC = 4·8 m – 4 m = 0·8 m

Hence, the distance by which the top of ladder would slide upwards = 0·8 m

Example 6 In a triangle ABC, AD is perpendicular to BC. Prove that :

$$AB^2 + CD^2 = AC^2 + BD^2.$$

Solution. In $\triangle ABD$, $\angle ADB = 90°$

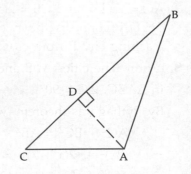

$\therefore$ $AB^2 = AD^2 + BD^2$ ...(i) (Pythagoras theorem)

In $\triangle ACD$, $\angle ADC = 90°$

$\therefore$ $AC^2 = AD^2 + CD^2$ ...(ii) (Pythagoras theorem)

Subtracting (ii) from (i), we get

$AB^2 - AC^2 = BD^2 - CD^2$

$\Rightarrow$ $AB^2 + CD^2 = AC^2 + BD^2.$

Example 7 In $\triangle ABC$, $\angle B = 90°$ and D is mid-point of BC. Prove that :

$$AC^2 = AD^2 + 3CD^2.$$

Solution. As D is mid-point of BC,

BD = CD and BC = 2CD.

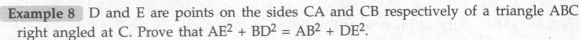

In $\triangle ABD$, $\angle ABD = 90°$,

$\therefore$ $AD^2 = AB^2 + BD^2$ (Pythagoras theorem)

$\Rightarrow$ $AB^2 = AD^2 - BD^2$ ...(i)

In $\triangle ABC$, $\angle B = 90°$,

$\therefore$ $AC^2 = AB^2 + BC^2$

$\Rightarrow$ $AC^2 = (AD^2 - BD^2) + BC^2$ (using (i))

$\Rightarrow$ $AC^2 = AD^2 - CD^2 + (2CD)^2$ ($\because$ BD = CD, BC = 2CD)

$\Rightarrow$ $AC^2 = AD^2 - CD^2 + 4CD^2$

$\Rightarrow$ $AC^2 = AD^2 + 3CD^2.$

Example 8 D and E are points on the sides CA and CB respectively of a triangle ABC right angled at C. Prove that $AE^2 + BD^2 = AB^2 + DE^2$.

Solution. In $\triangle ABC$, $\angle C = 90°$

$\therefore$ $AB^2 = AC^2 + BC^2$ ...(i)

In $\triangle ECD$, $\angle ECD = 90°$

$\therefore$ $DE^2 = CD^2 + EC^2$ ...(ii)

In $\triangle AEC$, $\angle ACE = 90°$

$\therefore$ $AE^2 = AC^2 + EC^2$ ...(iii)

In $\triangle BCD$, $\angle BCD = 90°$

$\therefore$ $BD^2 = BC^2 + CD^2$ ...(iv)

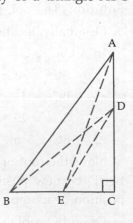

Adding (iii) and (iv), we get

$AE^2 + BD^2 = (AC^2 + BC^2) + (CD^2 + EC^2)$

$= AB^2 + DE^2$ (using (i) and (ii))

Example 9 ABC is a right angled triangle at B. If D and E are mid-points of sides BC and AB respectively, prove that $AD^2 + CE^2 = 5 DE^2$.

Solution. As D is mid-point of BC, BC = 2BD.

Also, as E is mid-point of AB, AB = 2BE.

In $\triangle ABD$, $\angle B = 90°$, by Pythagoras theorem,

$$AD^2 = AB^2 + BD^2$$
$$= (2BE)^2 + BD^2 \qquad (\because AB = 2BE)$$
$$\Rightarrow \qquad AD^2 = 4BE^2 + BD^2 \qquad ...(i)$$

In $\triangle EBC$, $\angle B = 90°$, by Pythagoras theorem,

$$CE^2 = BE^2 + BC^2$$
$$= BE^2 + (2BD)^2 \qquad (\because BC = 2BD)$$
$$\Rightarrow \qquad CE^2 = BE^2 + 4BD^2 \qquad ...(ii)$$

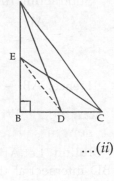

Adding (i) and (ii), we get

$$AD^2 + CE^2 = 5(BE^2 + BD^2) \qquad ...(iii)$$

In $\triangle EBD$, $\angle B = 90°$, by Pythagoras theorem,

$$DE^2 = BE^2 + BD^2 \qquad ...(iv)$$

From (iii) and (iv), we get

$$AD^2 + CE^2 = 5DE^2, \text{ as required.}$$

Example 10 ABC is an equilateral triangle of side 2a. Find each of its altitude.

Solution. Given ABC is an equilateral triangle of side 2a.

Draw $AD \perp BC$

In $\triangle ABD$ and $\triangle ACD$,

$$\begin{aligned} AB &= AC & \text{(given)} \\ \angle ADB &= \angle ADC & \text{(each = 90°, } AD \perp BC) \\ AD &= AD & \text{(common)} \\ \therefore \quad \triangle ABD &\cong \triangle ACD & \text{(RHS rule of congruency)} \\ \Rightarrow \quad BD &= DC & \text{(c.p.c.t.)} \\ \Rightarrow \quad BD &= \frac{1}{2} BC = \frac{1}{2} . 2a = a. \end{aligned}$$

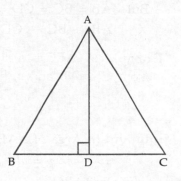

In $\triangle ABD$, $\angle ADB = 90°$,

$$\therefore \quad AB^2 = AD^2 + BD^2 \qquad \text{(Pythagoras theorem)}$$

$$\Rightarrow \quad (2a)^2 = AD^2 + a^2 \Rightarrow AD^2 = 3a^2 \Rightarrow AD = \sqrt{3}\,a.$$

In an equilateral triangle, all altitudes are equal.

Hence, the length of each altitude = $\sqrt{3}\,a$.

Example 11 ABC is a triangle in which AB = AC and D is a point on BC. Prove that

$$AB^2 - AD^2 = BD \times DC.$$

Solution. Draw $AN \perp BC$.

In $\triangle ABN$ and $\triangle ANC$,

$$\begin{aligned} AB &= AC & \text{(given)} \\ \angle ANB &= 90° = \angle ANC \end{aligned}$$

and AN is common,

$$\begin{aligned} \therefore \quad \triangle ABN &\cong \triangle ANC \text{ (RHS rule of congruency)} \\ \Rightarrow \quad BN &= NC. \end{aligned}$$

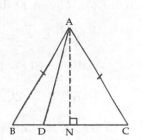

In $\triangle ABN$, $\angle N = 90°$,

$$\therefore \qquad AB^2 = AN^2 + BN^2 \qquad ...(i)$$

In $\triangle ADN$, $\angle N = 90°$,

$$\therefore \qquad AD^2 = AN^2 + DN^2 \qquad ...(ii)$$

Subtracting (ii) from (i), we get

$$AB^2 - AD^2 = BN^2 - DN^2$$
$$= (BN + DN)(BN - DN) \qquad (\because \ BN = NC)$$
$$= (NC + DN) \times BD = DC \times BD$$

Hence, $AB^2 - AD^2 = BD \times DC$.

Example 12 Prove that the sum of the squares on the sides of a rhombus is equal to the sum of squares on its diagonals.

Solution. Let ABCD be a rhombus whose diagonals AC and BD intersect at the point O.

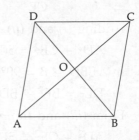

As the diagonals of a rhombus bisect each other at right angles, $\angle AOB = 90°$ and $OA = \frac{1}{2}AC$, $OB = \frac{1}{2}BD$.

In $\triangle OAB$, $\angle AOB = 90°$,

$$\therefore \quad AB^2 = OA^2 + OB^2 \qquad \text{(Pythagoras theorem)}$$

$$\Rightarrow \quad AB^2 = \left(\frac{1}{2}AC\right)^2 + \left(\frac{1}{2}BD\right)^2 \Rightarrow 4AB^2 = AC^2 + BD^2$$

But $AB = BC = CD = DA$ $\qquad$ ($\because$ in a rhombus, sides are equal)

$$\therefore \quad AB^2 + BC^2 + CD^2 + DA^2 = AC^2 + BD^2.$$

Example 13 ABC is a right triangle, right angled at C. If p is the length of perpendicular from C to AB and a, b, c have usual meanings, then prove that

(i) $pc = ab$ $\qquad\qquad$ (ii) $\dfrac{1}{p^2} = \dfrac{1}{a^2} + \dfrac{1}{b^2}$.

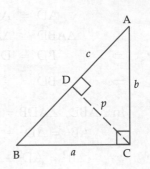

Solution. (i) Area of $\triangle ABC = \frac{1}{2}AB \times CD = \frac{1}{2}BC \times AC$

$$\Rightarrow \quad c \times p = ab.$$

(ii) In $\triangle ABC$, $\angle C = 90°$, so $c^2 = a^2 + b^2$

$$\Rightarrow \quad \left(\frac{ab}{p}\right)^2 = a^2 + b^2 \qquad \text{(using part (i))}$$

$$\Rightarrow \quad \frac{1}{p^2} = \frac{a^2 + b^2}{a^2 b^2} = \frac{1}{b^2} + \frac{1}{a^2}.$$

Example 14 In the adjoining figure, AD ⊥ BC. If D divides BC in the ratio 1 : 3, prove that $2AC^2 = 2AB^2 + BC^2$.

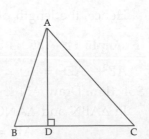

Solution. Given D divides BC in the ratio 1 : 3,

$$\therefore \quad \frac{BD}{DC} = \frac{1}{3} \Rightarrow DC = 3BD$$

$$\therefore \quad BC = BD + DC = BD + 3BD = 4BD$$

$$\Rightarrow \quad BD = \frac{1}{4}BC.$$

In $\triangle ADC$, $\angle D = 90°$,

$$\therefore \quad AC^2 = AD^2 + DC^2$$
$$= AD^2 + (3BD)^2 = AD^2 + 9BD^2 \qquad\qquad \dots(i)$$

In $\triangle ABD$, $\angle D = 90°$,

$$\therefore \quad AB^2 = AD^2 + BD^2 \Rightarrow AD^2 = AB^2 - BD^2 \qquad\qquad \dots(ii)$$

From (*i*) and (*ii*), we get

$$AC^2 = (AB^2 - BD^2) + 9BD^2$$

$$= AB^2 + 8BD^2 = AB^2 + 8 \cdot \left(\frac{1}{4}BC\right)^2$$

$$= AB^2 + \frac{1}{2}BC^2$$

$$\Rightarrow \quad 2AC^2 = 2AB^2 + BC^2.$$

Example 15 In an equilateral triangle ABC, a point D is taken on base BC such that BD : DC = 2 : 1. Prove that $9AD^2 = 7AB^2$.

Solution. As $\triangle ABC$ is equilateral, BC = AB.

Given BD : DC = 2 : 1 $\Rightarrow$ BD = $\frac{2}{3}$BC = $\frac{2}{3}$AB.

Draw AE $\perp$ BC, then E is mid-point of BC,

so BE = $\frac{1}{2}$BC = $\frac{1}{2}$AB.

From fig., ED = BD – BE = $\frac{2}{3}$AB – $\frac{1}{2}$AB = $\frac{1}{6}$AB.

In $\triangle ABE$, $\angle AEB = 90°$,

$\therefore \quad AB^2 = AF^2 + BE^2$ ...(*i*)

In $\triangle AED$, $\angle AED = 90°$,

$\therefore \quad AD^2 = AE^2 + ED^2$ ...(*ii*)

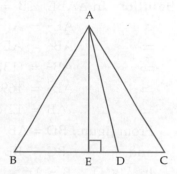

Subtracting (*ii*) from (*i*), we get

$$AB^2 - AD^2 = BE^2 - ED^2 = \left(\frac{1}{2}AB\right)^2 - \left(\frac{1}{6}AB\right)^2 = \left(\frac{1}{4} - \frac{1}{36}\right)AB^2 = \frac{2}{9}AB^2$$

$$\Rightarrow \quad AD^2 = AB^2 - \frac{2}{9}AB^2 = \frac{7}{9}AB^2$$

$$\Rightarrow \quad 9AD^2 = 7AB^2.$$

Example 16 From a point O in the interior of a $\triangle ABC$, perpendiculars OD, OE and OF are drawn to the sides BC, CA and AB respectively. Prove that:

(*i*) $AF^2 + BD^2 + CE^2 = OA^2 + OB^2 + OC^2 - OD^2 - OE^2 - OF^2$

(*ii*) $AF^2 + BD^2 + CE^2 = AE^2 + CD^2 + BF^2$.

Solution. (*i*) From right angled triangles

OAF, OBD and OCE, we have

$$OA^2 = AF^2 + OF^2 \quad ...(1)$$

$$OB^2 = BD^2 + OD^2 \quad ...(2)$$

$$OC^2 = CE^2 + OE^2 \quad ...(3)$$

On adding (1), (2) and (3), we get

$$OA^2 + OB^2 + OC^2$$

$$= AF^2 + BD^2 + CE^2 + OF^2 + OD^2 + OE^2$$

$$\Rightarrow \quad AF^2 + BD^2 + CE^2 = OA^2 + OB^2 + OC^2 - OD^2 - OE^2 - OF^2.$$

(*ii*) From right triangle OBD and OCD, we have

$$OB^2 = OD^2 + BD^2 \qquad ...(4)$$

and $OC^2 = OD^2 + CD^2 \qquad ...(5)$

Subtracting (5) from (4), we get

$$OB^2 - OC^2 = BD^2 - CD^2 \qquad ...(6)$$

Similarly, $OC^2 - OA^2 = CE^2 - AE^2$ ...(7)

and $OA^2 - OB^2 = AF^2 - BF^2$ ...(8)

On adding (6), (7) and (8), we get

$$0 = (AF^2 + BD^2 + CE^2) - (AE^2 + BF^2 + CD^2)$$

$$\Rightarrow \quad AF^2 + BD^2 + CE^2 = AE^2 + BF^2 + CD^2.$$

Example 17 In the adjoining figure, AE = DC = 13 cm, BE = 5 cm, $\angle ABC = 90°$ and AD = EC = x cm. Calculate the length of AB and the value of x.

Solution. In $\triangle ABE$, $\angle B = 90°$,

$\therefore \qquad AE^2 = AB^2 + BE^2$

$\Rightarrow \qquad AB^2 = AE^2 - BE^2$

$\Rightarrow \qquad AB^2 = (13)^2 - (5)^2 \quad (\because AE = 13 \text{ cm}, BE = 5 \text{ cm})$

$\Rightarrow \qquad AB^2 = 169 - 25 = 144$

$\Rightarrow \qquad AB = 12 \text{ cm}.$

From figure, $BD = AB - AD = (12 - x)$ cm $\qquad (\because AB = 12 \text{ cm}, AD = x \text{ cm})$

and $\qquad BC = BE + EC = (5 + x)$ cm.

In $\triangle BCD$, $\angle B = 90°$,

$\therefore \qquad CD^2 = BD^2 + BC^2$

$\Rightarrow \qquad (13)^2 = (12 - x)^2 + (5 + x)^2$

$\Rightarrow \qquad 169 = 144 + x^2 - 24x + 25 + x^2 + 10x$

$\Rightarrow \qquad 169 = 169 + 2x^2 - 14x$

$\Rightarrow \qquad 2x^2 - 14x = 0 \Rightarrow 2x (x - 7) = 0$

$\Rightarrow \qquad x = 7 \text{ cm}. \qquad\qquad (\because x \neq 0)$

Example 18 In $\triangle ABC$, AD $\perp$ BC such that $AD^2 = BD \times DC$. Using Pythagoras theorem and its converse, prove that $\triangle ABC$ is right angled at A.

Solution. In $\triangle ABD$, $\angle ADB = 90°$,

$\therefore \quad AB^2 = AD^2 + BD^2 \qquad ...(i)$ (Pythagoras theorem)

In $\triangle ACD$, $\angle ADC = 90°$,

$\therefore \quad AC^2 = AD^2 + DC^2 \qquad ...(ii)$ (Pythagoras theorem)

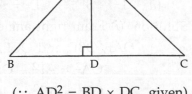

On adding (i) and (ii), we get

$AB^2 + AC^2 = 2AD^2 + BD^2 + CD^2$

$\qquad\qquad = 2 BD \times DC + DB^2 + DC^2 \qquad (\because AD^2 = BD \times DC, \text{ given})$

$\qquad\qquad = (BD + DC)^2 = BC^2$

$\therefore$ By converse of Pythagoras theorem, $\triangle ABC$ is right angled at A.

Example 19 In the adjoining figure, AB = BC and AD $\perp$ CB (produced). Prove that

$$AC^2 = 2BC \times CD.$$

Solution. In $\triangle ADC$, $\angle ADC = 90°$, so $AC^2 = AD^2 + DC^2 \quad ...(i)$

In $\triangle ADB$, $\angle ADB = 90°$, so $AB^2 = AD^2 + DB^2 \qquad ...(ii)$

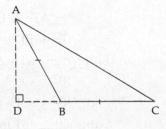

Subtracting (ii) from (i), we get

$$AC^2 - AB^2 = DC^2 - DB^2$$

$$\Rightarrow \quad AC^2 - BC^2 = (DB + BC)^2 - DB^2 \qquad\qquad (\because AB = BC)$$

$$\Rightarrow \quad AC^2 = BC^2 + BC^2 + 2DB \times BC = 2BC^2 + 2DB \times BC$$
$$= 2BC(BC + DB) = 2BC \times DC.$$

Example 20 In the adjoining figure, $\angle B$ of $\triangle ABC$ is an acute angle and $AD \perp BC$. Prove that

$$AC^2 = AB^2 + BC^2 - 2BC \times BD.$$

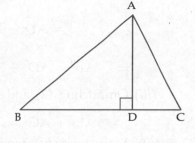

Solution. In $\triangle ABD$, $\angle ADB = 90°$,

$\therefore \quad AB^2 = AD^2 + BD^2$ ...(i)

In $\triangle ADC$, $\angle ADC = 90°$,

$\therefore \quad AC^2 = AD^2 + DC^2$

$\Rightarrow \quad AC^2 = AD^2 + (BC - BD)^2 = AD^2 + BC^2 + BD^2 - 2BC \times BD$

$\qquad = (AD^2 + BD^2) + BC^2 - 2BC \times BD$

$\qquad = AB^2 + BC^2 - 2BC \times BD$ (using (i))

Example 21 In the adjoining figure, $\angle B$ of $\triangle ABC$ is obtuse and $AD \perp BC$ (produced). Prove that

$$AC^2 = AB^2 + BC^2 + 2BC \times BD.$$

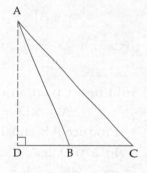

Solution. In $\triangle ADB$, $\angle ADB = 90°$,

$\therefore \quad AB^2 = AD^2 + DB^2$ ...(i)

In $\triangle ADC$, $\angle ADC = 90°$,

$\therefore \quad AC^2 = AD^2 + DC^2$

$\Rightarrow \quad AC^2 = AD^2 + (DB + BC)^2 = AD^2 + DB^2 + BC^2 + 2BC \times BD$

$\Rightarrow \quad AC^2 = AB^2 + BC^2 + 2BC \times BD$ (using (i))

Example 22 In the adjoining figure, AD is median of $\triangle ABC$ and $AM \perp BC$. Prove that

(i) $AC^2 = AD^2 + BC \times DM + \dfrac{1}{4}BC^2$

(ii) $AB^2 = AD^2 - BC \times DM + \dfrac{1}{4}BC^2$

(iii) $AB^2 + AC^2 = 2AD^2 + \dfrac{1}{2}BC^2$

(iv) $AB^2 + AC^2 = 2(AD^2 + BD^2).$

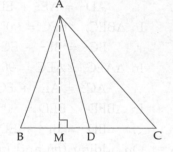

Solution. Note that in the given figure, $AC > AB$.

As AD is median, $BD = DC$.

$\Rightarrow \quad BD = DC = \dfrac{1}{2}BC.$

In $\triangle AMD$, $\angle AMD = 90°$,

$\therefore \quad AD^2 = AM^2 + MD^2 \Rightarrow AM^2 = AD^2 - MD^2$ ...(1)

(i) In $\triangle AMC$, $\angle AMC = 90°$,

$\therefore \quad AC^2 = AM^2 + MC^2$

$\qquad = (AD^2 - MD^2) + (MD + DC)^2$ (using (1))

$\qquad = AD^2 - MD^2 + \left(MD + \dfrac{1}{2}BC\right)^2$ $\left(\because DC = \dfrac{1}{2}BC\right)$

$\Rightarrow \quad AC^2 = AD^2 + MD \times BC + \dfrac{1}{4}BC^2$ ...(2)

(ii) In $\triangle ABM$, $\angle AMB = 90°$,

$$\therefore \quad AB^2 = AM^2 + BM^2$$
$$= (AD^2 - MD^2) + (BD - MD)^2 \qquad \text{(using (1))}$$
$$= AD^2 - MD^2 + \left(\frac{1}{2}BC - MD\right)^2 \qquad \left(\because BD = \frac{1}{2}BC\right)$$
$$\Rightarrow \quad AB^2 = AD^2 - MD \times BC + \frac{1}{4}BC^2 \qquad \ldots(3)$$

(iii) On adding (2) and (3), we get

$$AB^2 + AC^2 = 2AD^2 + \frac{1}{2}BC^2$$

(iv) From part (iii), we have

$$AB^2 + AC^2 = 2AD^2 + \frac{1}{2}(2BD)^2 \qquad \left(\because BD = \frac{1}{2}BC\right)$$
$$\Rightarrow \quad AB^2 + AC^2 = 2AD^2 + \frac{1}{2}.4\,BD^2$$
$$\Rightarrow \quad AB^2 + AC^2 = 2(AD^2 + BD^2).$$

Example 23 In a quadrilateral ABCD, $\angle A + \angle D = 90°$. Prove that

$$AC^2 + BD^2 = AD^2 + BC^2.$$

Solution. Given, in quadrilateral ABCD,

$$\angle A + \angle D = 90° \qquad \ldots(i)$$

Produce AB and DC to meet at the point E.

In $\triangle AED$, $\angle A + \angle D + \angle E = 180°$

$$\Rightarrow \quad 90° + \angle E = 180° \qquad \text{(using (i))}$$
$$\Rightarrow \quad \angle E = 90°.$$

In $\triangle AED$, $\angle AED = 90°$

$$\therefore \quad AD^2 = AE^2 + ED^2 \qquad \ldots(ii)$$

In $\triangle BEC$, $\angle BEC = 90°$

$$\therefore \quad BC^2 = BE^2 + EC^2 \qquad \ldots(iii)$$

In $\triangle AEC$, $\angle AEC = 90°$

$$\therefore \quad AC^2 = AE^2 + EC^2 \qquad \ldots(iv)$$

In $\triangle BED$, $\angle BED = 90°$

$$\therefore \quad BD^2 = BE^2 + ED^2 \qquad \ldots(v)$$

On adding (iv) and (v), we get

$$AC^2 + BD^2 = (AE^2 + ED^2) + (BE^2 + EC^2)$$
$$\Rightarrow \quad AC^2 + BD^2 = AD^2 + BC^2 \qquad \text{(using (ii) and (iii))}$$

Example 24 If O is any point in the interior of a rectangle ABCD. Prove that

$$OA^2 + OC^2 = OB^2 + OD^2.$$

Hence, find the length of OD, if the lengths of OA, OB and OC are 3 cm, 4 cm and 5 cm respectively.

Solution. Through O, draw EF ∥ AB.

As ABCD is a rectangle, AD ⊥ AB.

Since EF ∥ AB and AD ⊥ AB, therefore, EF ⊥ AD.

Similarly, EF ⊥ BC.

In $\triangle OEA$, $\angle OEA = 90°$,

$$OA^2 = AE^2 + OE^2 \qquad \ldots(i)$$

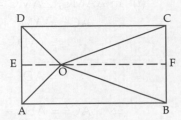

In $\triangle OFC$, $\angle OFC = 90°$,

$$OC^2 = FC^2 + OF^2 \qquad \text{...(ii)}$$

Adding (i) and (ii), we get

$$OA^2 + OC^2 = OE^2 + OF^2 + AE^2 + FC^2 \qquad \text{...(iii)}$$

In $\triangle OBF$, $\angle OFB = 90°$, $OB^2 = OF^2 + BF^2 \qquad \text{...(iv)}$

In $\triangle EOD$, $\angle DEO = 90°$, $OD^2 = OE^2 + ED^2 \qquad \text{...(v)}$

Adding (iv) and (v), we get

$$OB^2 + OD^2 = OF^2 + OE^2 + BF^2 + ED^2 \qquad \text{...(vi)}$$

But $AE = BF$ and $FC = ED$.

$\therefore$ From (iii) and (vi), we get

$$OA^2 + OC^2 = OB^2 + OD^2.$$

Further, $OA = 3$ cm, $OB = 4$ cm and $OC = 5$ cm

$\therefore$ $3^2 + 5^2 = 4^2 + OD^2 \Rightarrow OD^2 = 18 \Rightarrow OD = 3\sqrt{2}$ cm.

Example 25 Prove that the sum of the squares of the diagonals of a parallelogram is equal to the sum of squares of its sides.

Solution. Let ABCD be a parallelogram, then AC and BD are its diagonals.

So, we are required to prove that

$$AC^2 + BD^2 = AB^2 + BC^2 + CD^2 + AD^2.$$

Draw $DM \perp AB$ and $AN \perp DC$ (produced), AMDN is a rectangle

$\Rightarrow$ $AM = ND \qquad \text{...(i)}$

In $\triangle AND$, $\angle AND = 90°$, so $AD^2 = AN^2 + ND^2 \qquad \text{...(ii)}$

In $\triangle ANC$, $\angle ANC = 90°$,

$\therefore$ $AC^2 = AN^2 + NC^2 = AN^2 + (ND + CD)^2$

$\qquad = AN^2 + ND^2 + CD^2 + 2ND \times CD$

$\Rightarrow$ $AC^2 = AD^2 + CD^2 + 2\,ND \times CD \qquad \text{...(iii) (using (ii))}$

In $\triangle AMD$, $\angle AMD = 90°$, so $AD^2 = AM^2 + MD^2 \qquad \text{...(iv)}$

In $\triangle DMB$, $\angle DMB = 90°$,

$\therefore$ $BD^2 = MD^2 + MB^2 = MD^2 + (AB - AM)^2$

$\qquad = MD^2 + AM^2 + AB^2 - 2AM \times AB$

$\qquad = AD^2 + AB^2 - 2AM \times AB \qquad \text{(using (iv))}$

$\qquad = AD^2 + AB^2 - 2ND \times CD \qquad \text{...(v) ($\because$ AM = ND and AB = CD)}$

On adding (iii) and (v), we get

$$AC^2 + BD^2 = 2AD^2 + CD^2 + AB^2 = AD^2 + BC^2 + AB^2 + CD^2 \qquad (\because AD = BC)$$

EXERCISE 12

1 Lengths of sides of triangles are given below. Determine which of them are right triangles. In case of a right triangle, write the length of its hypotenuse:

    (i) 3 cm, 8 cm, 6 cm   (ii) 13 cm, 12 cm, 5 cm

    (iii) 1·4 cm, 4·8 cm, 5 cm

2 Foot of a 10 m long ladder leaning against a vertical well is 6 m away from the base of the wall. Find the height of the point on the wall where the top of the ladder reaches.

3 A guy attached a wire 24 m long to a vertical pole of height 18 m and has a stake attached to the other end. How far from the base of the pole should the stake be driven so that the wire will be taught?

4 Two poles of heights 6 m and 11 m stand on a plane ground. If the distance between their feet is 12 m, find the distance between their tops.

5 In a right-angled triangle, if hypotenuse is 20 cm and the ratio of the other two sides is 4 : 3, find the sides.

6 If the sides of a triangle are in the ratio 3 : 4 : 5, prove that it is right-angled triangle.

7 For going to a city B from city A, there is route via city C such that AC ⊥ CB, AC = $2x$ km and CB = $2(x + 7)$ km. It is proposed to construct a 26 km highway which directly connects the two cities A and B. Find how much distance will be saved in reaching city B from city A after the construction of highway.

8 The hypotenuse of a right triangle is 6 m more than twice the shortest side. If the third side is 2 m less than the hypotenuse, find the sides of the triangle.

9 ABC is an isosceles triangle right angled at C. Prove that $AB^2 = 2AC^2$.

10 In a triangle ABC, AD is perpendicular to BC. Prove that $AB^2 + CD^2 = AC^2 + BD^2$.

11 In ΔPQR, PD ⊥ QR, such that D lies on QR. If PQ = a, PR = b, QD = c and DR = d, prove that $(a + b)(a - b) = (c + d)(c - d)$.

12 ABC is an isosceles triangle with AB = AC = 12 cm and BC = 8 cm. Find the altitude on BC and hence calculate its area.

13 Find the area and the perimeter of a square whose diagonal is 10 cm long.

14 (*a*) In figure (*i*) given below, ABCD is a quadrilateral in which AD = 13 cm, DC = 12 cm, BC = 3 cm, ∠ABD = ∠BCD = 90°. Calculate the length of AB.

   (*b*) In figure (*ii*) given below, ABCD is a quadrilateral in which AB = AD, ∠A = 90° = ∠C, BC = 8 cm and CD = 6 cm. Find AB and calculate the area of ΔABD.

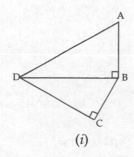
(*i*)

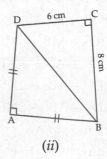
(*ii*)

15 (*a*) In figure (*i*) given below, AB = 12 cm, AC = 13 cm, CE = 10 cm and DE = 6 cm. Calculate the length of BD.

   (*b*) In figure (*ii*) given below, ∠PSR = 90°, PQ = 10 cm, QS = 6 cm and RQ = 9 cm. Calculate the length of PR.

   (*c*) In figure (*iii*) given below, ∠D = 90°, AB = 16 cm, BC = 12 cm and CA = 6 cm. Find CD.

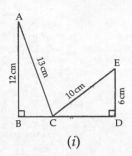

(i)

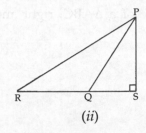

(ii)

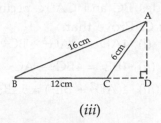

(iii)

16 (*a*) In figure (*i*) given below, BC = 5 cm, ∠B = 90°, AB = 5AE, CD = 2AE and AC = ED. Calculate the lengths of EA, CD, AB and AC.

(*b*) In figure (*ii*) given below, ABC is a right triangle right angled at C. If D is mid-point of BC, prove that $AB^2 = 4AD^2 - 3AC^2$.

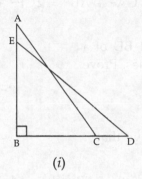

(i)

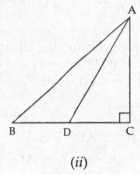

(ii)

17 In △ABC, AB = AC = x, BC = 10 cm and the area of △ABC is 60 cm². Find x.

18 In a rhombus, if diagonals are 30 cm and 40 cm, find its perimeter.

19 (*a*) In figure (*i*) given below, AB ∥ DC, BC = AD = 13 cm, AB = 22 cm and DC = 12 cm. Calculate the height of the trapezium ABCD.

(*b*) In figure (*ii*) given below, AB ∥ DC, ∠A = 90°, DC = 7 cm, AB = 17 cm and AC = 25 cm. Calculate BC.

(*c*) In figure (*iii*) given below, ABCD is a square of side 7 cm. If

AE = FC = CG = HA = 3 cm,

(*i*) prove that EFGH is a rectangle.

(*ii*) find the area and perimeter of EFGH.

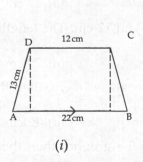

(i)

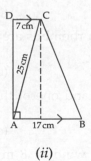

(ii)

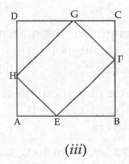

(iii)

Hint. (*c*) (*i*) ∠AEH = 45°, ∠BEF = 45°.

20 AD is perpendicular to the side BC of an equilateral △ABC. Prove that $4AD^2 = 3AB^2$.

21 In the adjoining figure, D and E are mid-points of the sides BC and CA respectively of a $\triangle ABC$, right angled at C. Prove that:

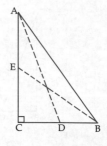

(i) $4AD^2 = 4AC^2 + BC^2$

(ii) $4BE^2 = 4BC^2 + AC^2$

(iii) $4(AD^2 + BE^2) = 5AB^2$.

22 If AD, BE and CF are medians of $\triangle ABC$, prove that
$$3(AB^2 + BC^2 + CA^2) = 4(AD^2 + BE^2 + CF^2).$$

Hint. From part (iii) of example 22, $AB^2 + AC^2 = 2AD^2 + \frac{1}{2}BC^2$.

Similarly, $BC^2 + CA^2 = 2BE^2 + \frac{1}{2}CA^2$, $CA^2 + AB^2 = 2CF^2 + \frac{1}{2}AB^2$. Add all these.

23 In the adjoining figure, the diagonals AC and BD of a quadrilateral ABCD intersect at O, at right angles. Prove that $AB^2 + CD^2 = AD^2 + BC^2$.

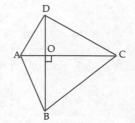

24 In a quadrilateral ABCD, $\angle B = 90° = \angle D$. Prove that
$$2AC^2 - BC^2 = AB^2 + AD^2 + DC^2.$$

25 In a $\triangle ABC$, $\angle A = 90°$, CA = AB and D is a point on AB produced. Prove that
$$DC^2 - BD^2 = 2AB \times AD.$$

26 In an isosceles triangle ABC, AB = AC and D is a point on BC produced. Prove that
$$AD^2 = AC^2 + BD \times CD.$$

Multiple Choice Questions

Choose the correct answer from the given four options (1 to 7):

1 In a $\triangle ABC$, if $AB = 6\sqrt{3}$ cm, BC = 6 cm and AC = 12 cm, then $\angle B$ is
(a) 120° (b) 90° (c) 60° (d) 45°

2 If the sides of a rectangular plot are 15 m and 8 m, then the length of its diagonal is
(a) 17 m (b) 23 m (c) 21 m (d) 17 cm

3 The lengths of the diagonals of a rhombus are 16 cm and 12 cm. The length of the side of the rhombus is
(a) 9 cm (b) 10 cm (c) 8 cm (d) 20 cm

4 If a side of a rhombus is 10 cm and one of the diagonals is 16 cm, then the length of the other diagonal is
(a) 6 cm (b) 12 cm (c) 20 cm (d) 12 cm

5 If a ladder 10 m long reaches a window 8 m above the ground, then the distance of the foot of the ladder from the base of the wall is
(a) 18 m (b) 8 m (c) 6 m (d) 4 m

6 A girl walks 200 towards East and then she walks 150 m towards North. The distance of the girl from the starting point is
(a) 350 m (b) 250 m (c) 300 m (d) 225 m

7 A ladder reaches a window 12 m above the ground on one side of the street. Keeping its foot at the same point, the ladder is turned to the other side of the street to reach a window 9 m high. If the length of the ladder is 15 m, then the width of the street is

    (*a*) 30 m   (*b*) 24 m   (*c*) 21 m   (*d*) 18 m

Summary

□ In a right triangle, the side opposite the right angle is called hypotenuse and the other two sides are called legs of the triangle.

□ **Pythagoras Theorem**

In a right triangle, the square of the hypotenuse is equal to the sum of the squares of the other two sides.

□ **Converse of Pythagoras Theorem**

In a triangle, if the square of one side is equal to the sum of the squares of the other two sides then the angle opposite to the first side is a right angle.

1 (a) In figure (i) given below, AD ⊥ BC, AB = 25 cm, AC = 17 cm and AD = 15 cm. Find the length of BC.

(b) In figure (ii) given below, ∠BAC = 90°, ∠ADC = 90°, AD = 6 cm, CD = 8 cm and BC = 26 cm. Find

    (i) AC   (ii) AB   (iii) area of the shaded region.

(c) In figure (iii) given below, triangle ABC is right angled at B. Given that AB = 9 cm, AC = 15 cm and D, E are mid-points of the sides AB and AC respectively, calculate (i) the length of BC (ii) the area of △ADE.

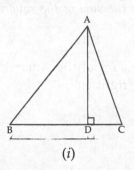
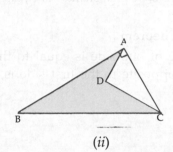
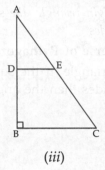

      (i)   (ii)   (iii)

2 If in △ABC, AB > AC and AD ⊥ BC, prove that $AB^2 - AC^2 = BD^2 - CD^2$.

3 In a right angled triangle ABC, right angled at C, P and Q are the points on the sides CA and CB respectively which divide these sides in the ratio 2 : 1. Prove that

    (i) $9AQ^2 = 9AC^2 + 4BC^2$ (ii) $9BP^2 = 9BC^2 + 4AC^2$

    (iii) $9(AQ^2 + BP^2) = 13AB^2$.

4 In the adjoining figure, △PQR is right angled at Q and points S and T trisect side QR. Prove that

        $8\,PT^2 = 3PR^2 + 5PS^2$.

Hint. RT = TS = SQ = x (say).

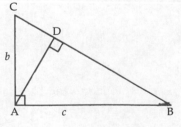

5 In a quadrilateral ABCD, ∠B = 90°. If $AD^2 = AB^2 + BC^2 + CD^2$, prove that ∠ACD = 90°.

6 In the adjoining figure, find the length of AD in terms of b and c.

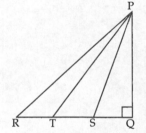

7 ABCD is a square, F is mid-point of AB and BE is one-third of BC. If area of △FBE is 108 cm², find the length of AC.

8 In a triangle ABC, AB = AC and D is a point on side AC such that BC² = AC × CD. Prove that BD = BC.

13 Rectilinear Figures

INTRODUCTION

If we put the sharp tip of a pencil on a sheet of paper and move from one point to the other, without lifting the pencil, then the shapes so formed are called **plane curves**.

Some plane curves are shown below:

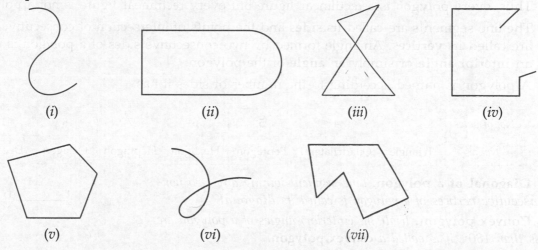

| (i) | (ii) | (iii) | (iv) |

| (v) | (vi) | (vii) |

The (plane) curves which have different beginning and end points are called **open curves** and the curves which have same beginning and end points are called **closed curves.** In the above figure, (i), (iv) and (vi) are open curves where as (ii), (iii), (v) and (vii) are closed curves.

A curve which does not cross itself at any point is called a **simple curve**. In the above figure, (i), (ii), (iv), (v) and (vii) are all simple curves. Note that (ii), (v) and (vii) are **simple closed curves**. A simple closed plane curve made up entirely of line segments is called a **polygon**. In the above figure, (v) and (vii) are polygons.

In this chapter, we shall study about different kinds of polygons (parallelograms, rectangles, rhombuses, squares, kites) and their various properties. We shall also construct some quadrilaterals and regular hexagons by using ruler and compass.

13.1 RECTILINEAR FIGURES

A plane figure made up entirely of line segments is called a rectilinear figure.

Look at the following plane figures:

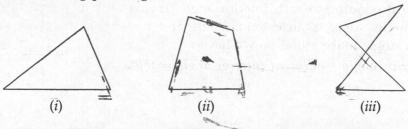

| (i) | (ii) | (iii) |

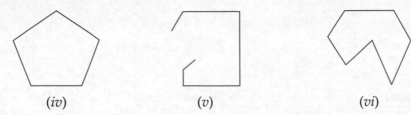

| | (iv) | (v) | (vi) |

All the six figures are made up entirely of line segments, so these are all rectilinear figures.

❑ Polygon

*A **polygon** is a simple closed rectilinear figure i.e. a **polygon** is a simple closed plane figure made up entirely of line segments.*

The figures (shown above) (*i*), (*ii*), (*iv*) and (*vi*) are polygons where as figures (*iii*) and (*v*) are not polygons since figure (*iii*) is not simple and figure (*v*) is not closed.

Thus, every polygon is a rectilinear figure but every rectilinear figure is not a polygon.

The line segments are called its **sides** and the points of intersection of consecutive sides are called its **vertices**. An angle formed by two consecutive sides of a polygon is called an **interior angle** or simply an **angle** of the polygon.

A polygon is named according to the number of sides it has.

No. of sides	3	4	5	6	7	8	10
Name	Triangle	Quadrilateral	Pentagon	Hexagon	Heptagon	Octagon	Decagon

Diagonal of a polygon. *Line segment joining any two non-consecutive vertices of a polygon is called its **diagonal**.*

Convex polygon. *If all the (interior) angles of a polygon are less than 180°, it is called a **convex polygon**.*

In the adjoining figure, ABCDEF is a convex polygon. In fact, it is a convex hexagon.

Concave polygon. *If one or more of the (interior) angles of a polygon is greater than 180° i.e. reflex, it is called **concave** (or **re-entrant**) polygon.*

In the adjoining figure, ABCDEFG is a concave polygon. In fact, it is a concave pentagon.

However, we shall be dealing with convex polygons only.

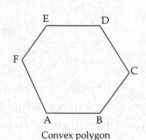

Convex polygon

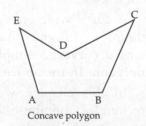

Concave polygon

❑ Exterior angle of convex polygon

If we produce a side of a polygon, the angle it makes with the next side is called an **exterior angle**.

In the adjoining figure, ABCDE is a pentagon. Its side AB has been produced to P, then ∠CBP is an exterior angle.

Note that corresponding to each interior angle, there is an exterior angle. Also, as an exterior angle and its adjacent interior angle make a line, so we have :

an exterior angle + adjacent interior angle = 180°.

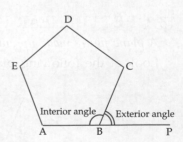

Regular polygon. *A polygon is called* **regular polygon** *if all its sides have equal length and all its angles have equal size.*

Thus, in a regular polygon:

(*i*) *all sides are equal in length*

(*ii*) *all interior angles are equal in size*

(*iii*) *all exterior angles are equal in size.*

All regular polygons are convex. All equilateral triangles and all squares are regular polygons.

13.2 QUADRILATERALS

A simple closed plane figure bounded by four line segments is called a **quadrilateral**.

In the adjoining figure, ABCD is a quadrilateral.

It has

four sides — AB, BC, CD and DA

four (interior) angles — $\angle A$, $\angle B$, $\angle C$ and $\angle D$

four vertices — A, B, C and D

two diagonals — AC and BD.

In quadrilateral ABCD, sides AB, BC; BC, CD; CD, DA; DA, AB are pairs of **adjacent sides**.

Sides AB, CD; BC, DA are pairs of **opposite sides**.

Angles $\angle A$, $\angle B$; $\angle B$, $\angle C$; $\angle C$, $\angle D$; $\angle D$, $\angle A$ are pairs of **adjacent angles**.

Angles $\angle A$, $\angle C$; $\angle B$, $\angle D$ are pairs of **opposite angles**.

❑ **Angle sum property of a quadrilateral**

Sum of (interior) angles of a quadrilateral is 360°.

In an adjoining figure, ABCD is *any* quadrilateral. Diagonal AC divides it inot two triangles. We know that the sum of angles of a triangle is 180°,

in $\triangle ABC$, $\angle 1 + \angle B + \angle 2 = 180°$ ...(*i*)

in $\triangle ACD$, $\angle 4 + \angle D + \angle 3 = 180°$ ...(*ii*)

On adding (*i*) and (*ii*), we get

$\angle 1 + \angle 4 + \angle B + \angle D + \angle 2 + \angle 3 = 360°$

$\angle A + \angle B + \angle D + \angle C = 360°$ (from figure)

Hence, the sum of (interior) angles of a quadrilateral is 360°.

❑ **Types of quadrilaterals**

1. Trapezium

A quadrilateral in which one pair of opposite sides is parallel is called a **trapezium** *(abbreviated trap.)*

The parallel sides are called **bases** of the trapezium. The line segment joining mid-points of non-parallel sides is called its **median.**

In the adjoining quadrilateral, AB ∥ DC whereas AD and BC are non-parallel, so ABCD is a trapezium, AB and CD are its *bases*, and EF is its *median* where E, F are mid-points of the sides AD, BC respectively.

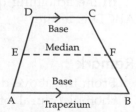

Isosceles trapezium

*If non-parallel sides of a trapezium are equal, then it is called an **isosceles trapezium**.*

Here AB ∥ DC, AD and BC are non-parallel and AD = BC, so ABCD is an isosceles trapezium.

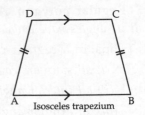

Isosceles trapezium

2. Parallelogram

*A quadrilateral in which both pairs of opposite sides are parallel is called a **parallelogram**. It is usually written as '∥gm'.*

In the adjoining quadrilateral, AB ∥ DC and AD ∥ BC, so ABCD is a parallelogram.

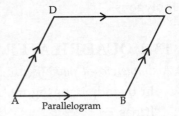

Parallelogram

3. Rectangle

*If one of the angles of a parallelogram is a right angle, then it is called a **rectangle**.*

In the adjoining parallelogram, ∠A = 90°, so ABCD is a rectangle. Of course, the remaining angles will also be right angles.

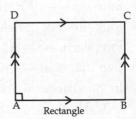

Rectangle

4. Rhombus

*If all the sides of a quadrilateral are equal, then it is called a **rhombus**.*

In the adjoining quadrilateral, AB = BC = CD = DA, so ABCD is a rhombus.

[Every rhombus is a parallelogram, see corollary to theorem 13.3]

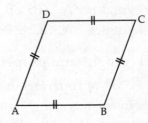

5. Square

*If two adjacent sides of a rectangle are equal, then it is called a **square**. Alternatively, if one angle of a rhombus is a right angle, it is called a **square**.*

In the adjoining rectangle, AB = AD, so ABCD is a square.

Of course, the remaining sides are also equal.

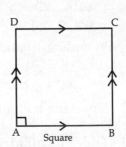

Square

6. Kite

*A quadrilateral in which two pairs of adjacent sides are equal is called a **kite** (or **diamond**).*

In the adjoining quadrilateral, AD = AB and DC = BC, so ABCD is a kite.

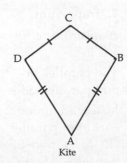

Kite

Remark

From the above definitions it follows that parallelograms include rectangles, squares and rhombi (plural of rhombus), therefore, any result which is true for a parallelogram is certainly true for all these figures.

13.2.1 Properties of parallelograms

Theorem 13.1

A diagonal of a parallelogram divides it into two congruent triangles.

Given. A parallelogram ABCD and diagonal AC divides it into two triangles △ABC and △CDA.

To prove. △ABC ≅ △CDA.

Proof.

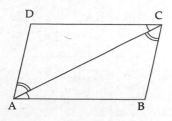

Statements	Reasons
In △ABC and △CDA	
1. ∠BAC = ∠ACD	1. Alt. ∠s, AB ∥ DC and AC is transversal.
2. ∠BCA = ∠CAD	2. Alt. ∠s, BC ∥ AD and AC is transversal.
3. AC = CA	3. Common
4. △ABC ≅ △CDA	4. ASA rule of congruency.

Theorem 13.2

In a parallelogram, opposite sides are equal.

Given. A parallelogram ABCD.

To prove. AB = DC and BC = AD.

Construction. Join AC.

Proof.

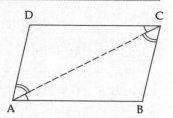

Statements	Reasons
In △ABC and △CDA	
1. ∠BAC = ∠ACD	1. Alt. ∠s, AB ∥ DC and AC is transversal.
2. ∠BCA = ∠CAD	2. Alt. ∠s, BC ∥ AD and AC is transversal.
3. AC = CA	3. Common
4. △ABC ≅ △CDA	4. ASA rule of congruency.
5. AB = DC and BC = AD	5. c.p.c.t.

The converse of the above theorem is also true. In fact we have:

Theorem 13.3

If each pair of opposite sides of a quadrilateral is equal, then it is a parallelogram.

Given. A quadrilateral ABCD in which AB = DC and BC = AD.

To prove. ABCD is a parallelogram.

Construction. Join AC.

Proof.

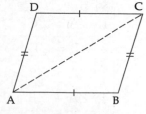

Statements	Reasons
In △ABC and △CDA	
1. AB = DC	1. Given.
2. BC = AD	2. Given.
3. AC = AC	3. Common.

4. △ABC ≅ △CDA	4. SSS rule of congruency
5. ∠BAC = ∠ACD ⇒ AB ∥ DC	5. c.p.c.t. alt. ∠s are equal formed by lines AB, DC and transversal AC.
6. ∠ACB = ∠CAD ⇒ BC ∥ AD	6. c.p.c.t. alt. ∠s are equal formed by lines AD, BC and transversal AC.

Hence, ABCD is a parallelogram.

Corollary. *Every rhombus is a parallelogram.*

[In a rhombus, all sides are equal, so opposite sides are equal. Therefore, every rhombus is a parallelogram.]

Theorem 13.4

In a parallelogram, opposite angles are equal.

Given. A parallelogram ABCD.

To prove. ∠A = ∠C and ∠B = ∠D.

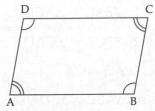

Proof.

Statements	Reasons
1. ∠A + ∠B = 180°	1. AD ∥ BC and AB is a transversal, sum of co-interior angles = 180°
2. ∠B + ∠C = 180°	2. AB ∥ DC and BC is a transversal, sum of co-interior angles = 180°
3. ∠A + ∠B = ∠B + ∠C ⇒ ∠A = ∠C Similarly, ∠B = ∠D.	3. From 1 and 2

The converse of the above theorem is also true. In fact, we have:

Theorem 13.5

If each pair of opposite angles of a quadrilateral is equal, then it is a parallelogram.

Given. A quadrilateral ABCD in which ∠A = ∠C and ∠B = ∠D.

To prove. ABCD is a parallelogram.

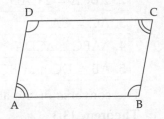

Proof.

Statements	Reasons
1. ∠A = ∠C	1. Given
2. ∠B = ∠D	2. Given
3. ∠A + ∠B = ∠C + ∠D	3. Adding 1 and 2
4. ∠A + ∠B + ∠C + ∠D = 360°	4. Sum of angles of a quadrilateral.
5. 2(∠A + ∠B) = 360° ⇒ ∠A + ∠B = 180° ⇒ BC ∥ AD	5. Using 3 Sum of co-interior angles = 180°, formed by lines BC, AD and transversal AB.
Similarly, AB ∥ DC Hence, ABCD is a parallelogram.	

Theorem 13.6

If a pair of opposite sides of a quadrilateral is equal and parallel, then it is a parallelogram.

Given. A quadrilateral ABCD in which AB ∥ DC and AB = DC.

To prove. ABCD is a parallelogram.

Construction. Join AC.

Proof.

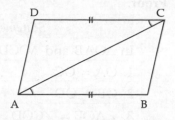

Statements	Reasons
In △ABC and △CDA	
1. ∠BAC = ∠ACD	1. Alt. ∠s, AB ∥ DC and AC is a transversal.
2. AB = DC	2. Given
3. AC = CA	3. Common
4. △ABC ≅ △CDA	4. SAS rule of congruency.
5. ∠ACB = ∠CAD ⇒ AD ∥ BC Hence, ABCD is a parallelogram.	5. c.p.c.t. Alt. ∠s are equal formed by lines AD, BC and transversal AC.

Theorem 13.7

The diagonals of a parallelogram bisect each other.

Given. A parallelogram ABCD whose diagonals AC and BD intersect at O.

To prove. OA = OC and OB = OD.

Proof.

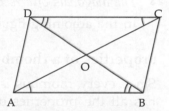

Statements	Reasons
In △OAB and △OCD	
1. ∠BAC = ∠ACD	1. Alt. ∠s, AB ∥ DC and AC is a transversal.
2. ∠ABD = ∠CDB	2. Alt. ∠s, AB ∥ DC and BD is a transversal.
3. AB = CD	3. Opp. sides of a parallelogram are equal.
4. △OAB ≅ △OCD ∴ OA = OC and OB = OD	4. ASA rule of congruency c.p.c.t.

The converse of the above theorem is also true. In fact, we have:

Theorem 13.8

If the diagonals of a quadrilateral bisect each other, then it is a parallelogram.

Given. A quadrilateral ABCD whose diagonals AC and BD intersect at O such that OA = OC and OB = OD.

To prove. ABCD is a parallelogram.

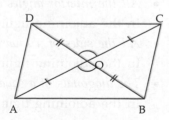

Proof.

Statements	Reasons
In △OAB and △OCD	
1. OA = OC	1. Given
2. OB = OD	2. Given
3. ∠AOB = ∠COD	3. Vert. opp. ∠s
4. △OAB ≅ △OCD	4. SAS rule of congruency
5. ∠OAB = ∠OCD ⇒ ∠CAB = ∠ACD ⇒ AB ∥ DC	5. c.p.c.t. Alt. ∠s are equal formed by lines AB, DC and transversal AC.
6. AB = CD	6. c.p.c.t.
7. ABCD is a parallelogram.	7. In quadrilateral ABCD, AB ∥ DC and AB = DC (Theorem 13.6)

❑ **Properties of a rectangle**

Since every rectangle is a parallelogram, therefore, it has all the properties of a parallelogram. Additional properties of a rectangle are:

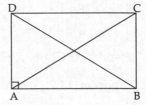

- *All the (interior) angles of a rectangle are right angles.*

  In the adjoining figure, ∠A = ∠B = ∠C = ∠D = 90°.

- *The diagonals of a rectangle are equal.*

  In the adjoining figure, AC = BD.

❑ **Properties of a rhombus**

Since every rhombus is a parallelogram, therefore, it has all the properties of a parallelogram. Additional properties of a rhombus are:

- *All the sides of a rhombus are equal.*

  In the adjoining figure, AB = BC = CD = DA.

- *The diagonals of a rhombus intersect at right angles.*

  In the adjoining figure, AC ⊥ BD.

- *The diagonals bisect the angles of a rhombus.*

  In the adjoining figure, diagonal AC bisects ∠A as well as ∠C and diagonal BD bisects ∠B as well as ∠D.

❑ **Properties of a square**

Since every square is a parallelogram, therefore, it has all the properties of a parallelogram. Additional properties of a square are:

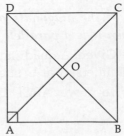

- *All the interior angles of a square are right angles.*

  In the adjoining figure, ∠A = ∠B = ∠C = ∠D = 90°.

- *All the sides of a square are equal.*

  In the adjoining figure, AB = BC = CD = DA.

- *The diagonals of a square are equal.*

  In the adjoining figure, AC = BD.

- *The diagonals of a square intersect at right angles.*
  In the adjoining figure, AC ⊥ BD.
- *The diagonals bisect the angles of a square.*
  In the adjoining figure, diagonal AC bisects ∠A as well as ∠C and diagonal BD bisects ∠B as well as ∠D.

In fact, a square is a rectangle as well as a rhombus, so it has all the properties of a rectangle as well as that of a rhombus.

Illustrative Examples

Example 1 The angles of a quadrilateral are $(4x)°$, $(7x)°$, $(15x)°$ and $(10x)°$. Find the smallest and the largest angles of the quadrilateral.

Solution. As the sum of angles of a quadrilateral is 360°,

∴ $(4x)° + (7x)° + (15x)° + (10x)° = 360°$

⇒ $(36x)° = 360° ⇒ 36x = 360 ⇒ x = 10.$

∴   The smallest angle $= (4 × 10)° = 40°$ and the largest angle $= (15 × 10)° = 150°$.

Example 2 If angles A, B, C and D of a quadrilateral ABCD, taken in order, are in the ratio 3 : 7 : 6 : 4 then ABCD is a trapezium. Is this statement true? Give reason for your answer.

Solution. As the angles are in the ratio 3 : 7 : 6 : 4,

let these angles be $3x$, $7x$, $6x$ and $4x$.

Since sum of angles of a quadrilateral is 360°,

$3x + 7x + 6x + 4x = 360°$

⇒ $20x = 360° ⇒ x = 18°.$

∴ The angles are: $∠A = 3 × 18° = 54°$,

$∠B = 7 × 18° = 126°$, $∠C = 6 × 18° = 108°$ and

$∠D = 4 × 18° = 72°$.

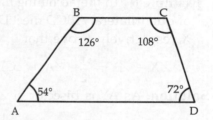

We note that $∠A + ∠B = 54° + 126° = 180°$.

Thus, the sum of co-interior angles is 180° formed by lines AD, BC and transversal AB, therefore, AD ∥ BC. So, ABCD is a trapezium. Hence, the given statement is true.

Example 3 Three angles of a quadrilateral ABCD are equal. Is it a parallelogram? Why or why not?

Solution. It need not be a parallelogram; because we may have $∠A = ∠B = ∠C = 80°$, then $∠D = 360° − 3 × 80° = 120°$, so $∠B ≠ ∠D$ (opposite angles are not equal).

Example 4 Two opposite angles of a parallelogram are $(3x − 2)°$ and $(63 − 2x)°$. Find all the angles of the parallelogram.

Solution. As the opposite angles of a parallelogram are equal,

$(3x − 2)° = (63 − 2x)° ⇒ 3x − 2 = 63 − 2x$

⇒ $5x = 65 ⇒ x = 13.$

∴   One angle of the parallelogram $= (3 × 13 − 2)° = 37°$.

Then its adjacent angle $= 180° − 37° = 143°$.

So, all the angles of the parallelogram are 37°, 143°, 37°, 143°.

Example 5 In a quadrilateral ABCD, AO and BO are the bisectors of ∠A and ∠B respectively. Prove that ∠AOB = $\frac{1}{2}$(∠C + ∠D).

Solution. Given ABCD is a quadrilateral, OA and OB are the bisectors of ∠A and ∠B respectively. Mark the angles as shown in the figure given below.

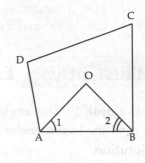

As OA and OB are bisectors of ∠A and ∠B respectively,

$$∠1 = \frac{1}{2}∠A \text{ and } ∠2 = \frac{1}{2}∠B \qquad ...(i)$$

$$∠AOB + ∠1 + ∠2 = 180°$$
$$\text{(sum of angles in } ∆OAB)$$

⇒ $\qquad ∠AOB = 180° - (∠1 + ∠2)$

⇒ $\qquad ∠AOB = 180° - \frac{1}{2}(∠A + ∠B) \qquad \text{(using } (i))$

⇒ $\qquad ∠AOB = 180° - \frac{1}{2}(360° - (∠C + ∠D))$

[∵ sum of angles in a quadrilateral is 360°, so ∠A + ∠B + ∠C + ∠D = 360°
⇒ ∠A + ∠B = 360° - (∠C + ∠D)]

⇒ $\qquad ∠AOB = \frac{1}{2}(∠C + ∠D)$.

Example 6 In the adjoining figure, bisectors of ∠A and ∠C of quadrilateral ABCD meet DC and BA produced at Y and X respectively. Prove that :

$$∠X + ∠Y = \frac{1}{2}(∠A + ∠C).$$

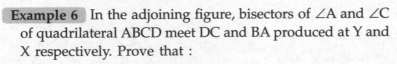

Solution. As AY is bisector of ∠A,

$$∠DAY = \frac{1}{2}∠A \qquad ...(i)$$

As CX is bisector of ∠C,

$$∠BCX = \frac{1}{2}∠C \qquad ...(ii)$$

In ∆ADY,
$$∠DAY + ∠D + ∠Y = 180° \qquad ...(iii) \text{ (sum of angles of a ∆)}$$

In ∆BCX,
$$∠BCX + ∠B + ∠X = 180° \qquad ...(iv)$$

On adding (iii) and (iv), we get

$$∠DAY + ∠D + ∠Y + ∠BCX + ∠B + ∠X = 360°$$

⇒ $\frac{1}{2}∠A + ∠D + ∠Y + \frac{1}{2}∠C + ∠B + ∠X = 360°$ $\qquad$ (using (i), (ii))

⇒ $\frac{1}{2}∠A + \frac{1}{2}∠C + ∠B + ∠D + ∠X + ∠Y = ∠A + ∠B + ∠C + ∠D$

$\qquad\qquad\qquad\qquad$ (∵ sum of angles of a quadrilateral = 360°)

⇒ $\qquad ∠X + ∠Y = \frac{1}{2}(∠A + ∠C)$.

Example 7 In a triangle ABC, median BM is produced to a point D such that DM = BM. Prove that ABCD is a parallelogram.

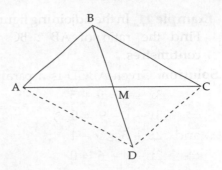

Solution. As BM is median, so M is mid-point of AC *i.e.* AM = CM.

In quadrilateral ABCD,

      AM = CM and BM = DM   (given)

Thus, we have a quadrilateral ABCD in which the diagonal AC and BD bisect each other, therefore, ABCD is a parallelogram (theorem 13.8).

Example 8 Diagonals of a quadrilateral ABCD bisect each other. If ∠A = 45°, determine ∠B.

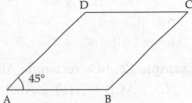

Solution. Since the diagonals AC and BD of quadrilateral ABCD bisect each other, ABCD is a parallelogram.

AD ∥ BC and AB is a transversal,

      ∠A + ∠B = 180° (sum of co-interior angle = 180°)

⇒   45° + ∠B = 180°

⇒   ∠B = 135°.

Example 9 The angle between two altitudes of a parallelogram through the vertex of an obtuse angle of the parallelogram is 60°. Find the angles of the parallelogram.

Solution. Let ABCD be parallelogram such that

      DM ⊥ AB, DN ⊥ BC and ∠MDN = 60°.

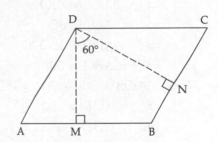

In quadrilateral DMBN,

      ∠MDN + ∠M + ∠N + ∠B = 360°

⇒   60° + 90° + 90° + ∠B = 360°

⇒   ∠B = 120°.

AD ∥ BC and AB is a transversal,

      ∠A + ∠B = 180°

⇒   ∠A + 120° = 180° ⇒ ∠A = 60°.

      ∠C = ∠A and ∠D = ∠B   (opp. ∠s of a ∥ gm are equal)

⇒   ∠C = 60° and ∠D = 120°.

Hence, the angles of ∥ gm ABCD are 60°, 120°, 60°, 120°.

Example 10 In the adjoining figure, ABCD is parallelogram. Find the values of *x*, *y* and *z*.

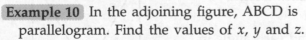

Solution. Given ABCD is a parallelogram,

      3*x* − 1 = 2*x* + 2   (opp. sides are equal)

⇒   *x* = 3.

      ∠D = ∠B = 102°   (opp. ∠s are equal)

For ΔACD, *y* = 50° + ∠D   (∵ ext. ∠ = sum of two int. opp. ∠s)

⇒   *y* = 50° + 102° = 152°

      ∠DAB + 102° = 180°   (AD ∥ BC, sum of co-int. ∠s = 180°)

⇒   ∠DAB = 180° − 102° = 78°.

From figure, *z* = ∠DAB − ∠DAC = 78° − 50° = 28°.

Example 11 In the adjoining figure, ABCD is a parallelogram. Find the ratio of AB : BC. All measurements are in centimetres.

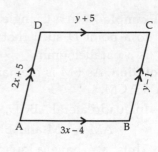

Solution. Given ABCD is a parallelogram,

$$3x - 4 = y + 5 \qquad \text{(opp. sides are equal)}$$
$$\Rightarrow \quad 3x - y - 9 = 0 \qquad\qquad\qquad …(i)$$
and $\quad 2x + 5 = y - 1 \qquad \text{(opp. sides are equal)}$
$$\Rightarrow \quad 2x - y + 6 = 0 \qquad\qquad\qquad …(ii)$$

On subtracting (ii) from (i), we get

$$x - 15 = 0 \Rightarrow x = 15.$$

On substituting this value of x in (i), we get

$$3 \times 15 - y - 9 = 0 \Rightarrow 36 - y = 0 \Rightarrow y = 36.$$
$$\therefore \quad AB = 3x - 4 = 3 \times 15 - 4 = 41$$

and $\quad BC = y - 1 = 36 - 1 = 35.$

Hence, AB : BC = 41 : 35.

Example 12 In a rectangle ABCD, diagonals intersect at O. If $\angle OAB = 30°$, find

(i) $\angle ACB$ (ii) $\angle ABO$ (iii) $\angle COD$ (iv) $\angle BOC$.

Solution. (i) $\angle ABC = 90°$ (each angle of a rectangle = 90°)

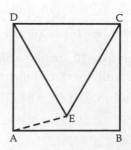

$$\angle ACB + 30° + 90° = 180° \text{ (sum of angles in } \triangle ABC)$$
$$\Rightarrow \quad \angle ACB = 180° - 30° - 90° = 60°.$$

(ii) $\qquad AC = BD \qquad$ (diagonals are equal)
$$\Rightarrow \quad 2AO = 2BO \qquad \text{(diagonals bisect each other)}$$
$$\Rightarrow \quad AO = BO$$
$$\Rightarrow \quad \angle ABO = \angle OAB \qquad \text{(angles opp. equal sides in } \triangle OAB)$$
$$\Rightarrow \quad \angle ABO = 30° \qquad\qquad (\because \angle OAB = 30° \text{ given})$$

(iii) $\angle AOB + 30° + 30° = 180° \qquad \text{(sum of angles in } \triangle OAB)$
$$\Rightarrow \quad \angle AOB = 180° - 30° - 30° = 120°.$$
But $\angle COD = \angle AOB \qquad\qquad\qquad\qquad\qquad$ (vert. opp. $\angle$s)
$$\Rightarrow \quad \angle COD = 120°.$$

(iv) $\angle BOC + 120° = 180° \qquad\qquad\qquad\qquad\qquad$ (linear pair)
$$\Rightarrow \quad \angle BOC = 180° - 120° = 60°.$$

Example 13 In the adjoining figure, ABCD is a square and CDE is an equilateral triangle. Find

(i) $\angle AED$ (ii) $\angle EAB$ (iii) reflex $\angle AEC$.

Solution. (i) From figure, $\angle ADE = 90° - 60°$

($\because$ each angle in a square = 90° and each angle in an equilateral triangle = 60°)

$$\Rightarrow \quad \angle ADE = 30°.$$
$$ED = DC \qquad \text{(sides of equilateral triangle)}$$
$$AD = DC \qquad\qquad \text{(sides of square)}$$
$$\Rightarrow \quad ED = AD \Rightarrow \angle AED = \angle EAD \qquad \text{(angles opp. equal sides in } \triangle AED)$$
But $\angle AED + \angle EAD + \angle ADE = 180° \qquad \text{(sum of angles in } \triangle AED)$
$$\Rightarrow \quad 2\angle AED + 30° = 180°$$
$$\Rightarrow \quad \angle AED = \frac{180° - 30°}{2} = 75°.$$

(ii) ∠EAB = 90° − 75° = 15°   (∵ ∠EAD = ∠AED = 75°)

(iii) Reflex ∠AEC = 360° − 75° − 60° = 225°.

Example 14 BEC is an equilateral triangle in the square ABCD. Find the value of x in the figure.

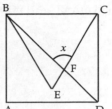

Solution. Since ABCD is a square and BD is a diagonal,

∴   ∠DBC = 45°.

As BEC is an equilateral triangle,

∠BCE = 60°.

In ΔBFC, x + 45° + 60° = 180°

⇒ x = 180° − 45° − 60° = 75°.

Example 15 In the adjoining figure, ABCD is a rhombus and ABE is an equilateral triangle. E and D lie on opposite sides of AB. If ∠BCD = 78°, calculate ∠ADE and ∠BDE.

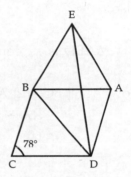

Solution. Since ABCD is a rhombus, ∠DAB = ∠BCD = 78°.

As ABE is an equilateral triangle, ∠BAE = 60°.

From figure,

∠DAE = ∠DAB + ∠BAE = 78° + 60° = 138°.

Also BA = AE   (Since ABE is equilateral triangle)

and BA = AD   (∵ ABCD is a rhombus)

⇒   AE = AD ⇒ ∠ADE = ∠AED   (∵ angles opp. equal sides in ΔAED)

∴   ∠ADE = $\frac{1}{2}$ (180° − 138°) = $\frac{1}{2}$ × 42° = 21°.

In ΔBCD, BC = CD   (∵ ABCD is a rhombus)

⇒   ∠CBD = ∠CDB.

∴   ∠CBD = $\frac{1}{2}$ (180° − 78°) = $\frac{1}{2}$ (102°) = 51°.

But ∠BDA = ∠CBD   (BC ∥ AD, alt. ∠s are equal)

⇒   ∠BDA = 51°.

From figure, ∠BDE = ∠BDA − ∠EDA = 51° − 21° = 30°.

Example 16 In parallelogram ABCD, AB = 10 cm and AD = 6 cm. The bisector of ∠A meets DC in E. AE and BC produced meet at F. Find the length of CF.

Solution. Mark the angles as shown in the figure.

As AE is bisector of ∠A,

∠1 = ∠2   ...(i)

Since ABCD is a parallelogram, AD ∥ BC i.e. AD ∥ BF

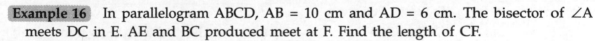

∠1 = ∠3   (alt. ∠s are equal)

⇒   ∠2 = ∠3   (using (i))

In ΔABF,   ∠2 = ∠3

⇒   BF = AB

(sides opp. equal angles are equal)

⇒   BC + CF = 10 cm

⇒   AD + CF = 10 cm   (BC = AD, opp. sides of a ∥ gm)

⇒   6 cm + CF = 10 cm ⇒ CF = 4 cm.

Example 17 ABCD is a rhombus in which altitude from D to side AB bisects AB. Find the angles of the rhombus.

Solution. ABCD is a rhombus in which DM ⊥ AB such that M is mid-point of AB. Join BD.

In ΔDAM and ΔDBM,

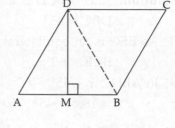

$$\angle AMD = \angle BMD \qquad (each = 90°)$$
$$AM = BM \qquad (M \text{ is mid-point of AB})$$
$$DM = DM \qquad (common)$$
∴   ΔDAM ≅ ΔDBM (SAS rule of congruency)
⇒   AD = BD
Also,   AD = AB   (∵ ABCD is a rhombus)
⇒   AD = BD = AB
⇒   ΔABD is an equilateral triangle
⇒   ∠A = 60°.

Now, AD ∥ BC and AB is a transversal,

∴   ∠A + ∠B = 180°   (sum of co-interior ∠s)
⇒   60° + ∠B = 180° ⇒ ∠B = 120°
          ∠C = ∠A and ∠D = ∠B   (opp. ∠s in a ∥ gm are equal)
⇒   ∠C = 60° and ∠D = 120°.

Hence, the angles of the rhombus are 60°, 120°, 60°, 120°.

Example 18 In the adjoining figure, ABCD is a parallelogram. E and F are points on the sides AB and CD respectively such that AE = CF. Prove that EF and BD bisect each other.

Solution.
$$AB = CD$$
$$\qquad\qquad (opp. \text{ sides of a } \parallel gm)$$
$$AE = CF \qquad (given)$$
∴   AB − AE = CD − CF ⇒ EB = DF.

In ΔOEB and ΔOFD,

$$EB = DF \qquad\qquad (proved\ above)$$
$$\angle EOB = \angle FOD \qquad\qquad (vert.\ opp.\ \angle s)$$
$$\angle OEB = \angle OFD \qquad (alt.\ \angle s,\ AB \parallel DC\ and\ EF\ is\ transversal)$$
∴   ΔOEB ≅ ΔOFD   (AAS rule of congruency)
⇒   OB = OD and OE = OF   (c.p.c.t.)
⇒   EF and BD bisect each other.

Example 19 ABCD is a parallelogram. AM and BN are perpendicular on DC and DC (produced) respectively. Prove that AM = BN.

Solution. In ΔADM and ΔBCN,

$$AD = BC\ (opp.\ \text{sides of a } \parallel gm)$$
$$\angle AMD = \angle BND \qquad (each = 90°)$$
$$\angle ADM = \angle BCN$$
$$\qquad (corres.\ \angle s,\ AD \parallel BC\ and\ DC\ is\ transversal)$$
∴   ΔADM ≅ ΔBCN   (AAS rule of congruency)
⇒   AM = BN   (c.p.c.t.)

Example 20 ABCD is a parallelogram. AB is produced to E such that BE = AB. Prove that ED bisects BC.

Solution.

	AB = DC	(opp. sides of a ∥ gm)
	BE = AB	(given)
∴	BE = DC.	

In ΔOBE and ΔOCD,

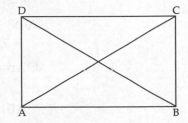

	BE = DC	(proved above)
	∠BOE = ∠COD	(vert. opp. ∠s)
	∠OEB = ∠ODC	(alt. ∠s, AD ∥ BC and DE is transversal)
∴	ΔOBE ≅ ΔOCD	(AAS rule of congruency)

Example 21 Prove that the diagonals of a rectangle are equal.

Solution. Let ABCD be a rectangle. We need to prove that AC = BD.

In ΔABC and ΔBAD,

BC = AD   (opp. sides of a rectangle are equal)

AB = BA   (common)

∠ABC − ∠BAD (each angle of a rectangle = 90°)

ΔABC ≅ ΔBAD   (SAS rule of congruency)

∴   AC = BD   (c.p.c.t.)

Example 22 If the diagonals of a parallelogram are equal, then prove that it is a rectangle.

Solution. Let ABCD be a parallelogram in which AC = BD. We need to prove that ∠A = 90°.

In ΔABC and ΔBAD,

	BC = AD	(opp. sides of a ∥ gm)
	AB = AB	(common)
	AC = BD	(given, diagonals are equal)
∴	ΔABC ≅ ΔBAD	(SSS rule of congruency)
∴	∠B = ∠A	(c.p.c.t.)

As AD ∥ BC and AB is a transversal,

∠A + ∠B = 180°   (sum of co-int. ∠s)

⇒   ∠A + ∠A = 180° ⇒ 2∠A = 180° ⇒ ∠A = 90°.

∴ ABCD is a rectangle.

Example 23 Show that the diagonals of a rhombus bisect each other at right angles.

Solution. Let ABCD be a rhombus and let its diagonals AC and BD meet at O.

We need to prove that OA = OC, OB = OD and ∠AOB = 90°. As every rhombus is a ∥ gm, therefore, the diagonals bisect each other *i.e.* OA = OC and OB = OD.

Thus, the diagonals of a rhombus bisect each other.

In ΔOAB and ΔOCB,

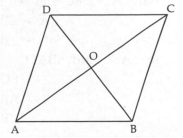

	OA = OC	(proved above)
	OB = OB	(common)
	AB = BC	(sides of a rhombus)
∴	ΔOAB ≅ ΔOCB	(SSS rule of congruency)

$$\therefore \qquad \angle AOB = \angle BOC \qquad\qquad\qquad \text{(c.p.c.t.)}$$

But $\quad \angle AOB + \angle BOC = 180° \qquad\qquad\qquad$ (linear pair)

$\Rightarrow \qquad \angle AOB + \angle AOB = 180° \Rightarrow \angle AOB = 90°.$

Hence, the diagonals of a rhombus bisect each other at right angles.

Example 24 If the diagonals of a quadrilateral bisect each other at right angles, then prove that the quadrilateral is a rhombus.

Solution. Let ABCD be a quadrilateral in which the diagonals AC and BD bisect each other at O and are at right angles *i.e.* OA = OC, OB = OD and AC ⊥ BD. We need to prove that ABCD is a rhombus.

As the diagonals of the quadrilateral ABCD bisect each other, ABCD is a parallelogram.

In ΔOAB and ΔOCB,

$$OA = OC \qquad\qquad \text{(from given)}$$
$$OB = OB \qquad\qquad \text{(common)}$$
$$\angle AOB = \angle COB$$

(each = 90°, because AC ⊥ BD given)

$$\therefore \qquad \Delta OAB \cong \Delta OCB$$

(by SAS rule of congruency)

$$\therefore \qquad\qquad AB = BC \qquad\qquad\qquad\qquad \text{(c.p.c.t.)}$$

Thus, ABCD is a parallelogram in which two adjacent sides are equal, therefore, ABCD is a rhombus.

Example 25 Prove that the diagonals of a square are equal and bisect each other at right angles.

Solution. Let ABCD is a square and let its diagonals AC and BD meet at O. We need to prove that OA = OC, OB = OD, ∠AOB = 90° and AC = BD.

As ABCD is a square, so it is a parallelogram. Therefore, its diagonals bisect each other

i.e. $\qquad\qquad OA = OC$ and $OB = OD.$

Thus, the diagonals of a square bisect each other.

In ΔOAB and ΔOCB,

$$OA = OC \qquad\qquad\qquad \text{(proved above)}$$
$$AB = BC \qquad\qquad\qquad \text{(sides of a square)}$$
$$OB = OB \qquad\qquad\qquad\qquad \text{(common)}$$

$$\therefore \qquad \Delta OAB \cong \Delta OCB \quad \text{(by SSS rule of congruency)}$$

$$\therefore \qquad \angle AOB = \angle BOC \qquad\qquad\qquad\qquad \text{(c.p.c.t.)}$$

But $\quad \angle AOB + \angle BOC = 180° \qquad\qquad\qquad$ (linear pair)

$\Rightarrow \qquad \angle AOB + \angle AOB = 180° \Rightarrow \angle AOB = 90°$

As ABCD is a square, so one of its angle is 90°. Let ∠A = 90°.

Now AD ∥ BC and AB is a transversal

$$\angle A + \angle B = 180° \qquad\qquad\qquad \text{(sum of co-int. } \angle s)$$

$\Rightarrow \qquad 90° + \angle B = 180° \Rightarrow \angle B = 90°.$

In ΔABC and ΔBAD,

$$BC = AD \qquad\qquad\qquad\qquad \text{(sides of a square)}$$
$$AB = BA \qquad\qquad\qquad\qquad \text{(common)}$$
$$\angle B = \angle A \qquad\qquad\qquad\qquad \text{(each = 90°)}$$

$$\therefore \qquad \triangle ABC \cong \triangle BAD$$
$$\therefore \qquad AC = BD \qquad\qquad \text{(c.p.c.t.)}$$

Hence, the diagonals of a square are equal and bisect each other at right angles.

Example 26 In the adjoining figure, ABC is an isosceles triangle in which AB = AC. AD bisects exterior angle PAC and CD ∥ BA. Show that

(*i*) ∠DAC = ∠BCA

(*ii*) ABCD is a parallelogram.

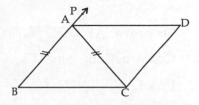

Solution. (*i*) AB = AC ⇒ ∠ABC = ∠BCA   (∠s opp. equal sides)

Also,   ∠PAC = ∠ABC + ∠BCA   (ext. ∠ = sum of two int. opp. ∠s)

⇒   ∠PAC = 2 ∠BCA   ...(1)

As AD bisects ∠PAC,

∠PAC = 2 ∠DAC   ...(2)

From (1) and (2), we get

2∠DAC = 2 ∠BCA ⇒ ∠DAC = ∠BCA.

(*ii*) We note that the line segments BC and AD are intersected by the transversal AC, so ∠DAC and ∠BCA form a pair of alternate interior angles and these angles are equal (from (*i*)),

∴   BC ∥ AD

Also   BA ∥ CD   (given)

Thus, both pairs of opposite sides of a quadrilateral ABCD are parallel, therefore, ABCD is a parallelogram.

Example 27 In the adjoining figure, ABCD is a parallelogram and AP, CQ are perpendiculars from the vertices A, C respectively on the diagonal BD. Show that

(*i*) △APB ≅ △CQD

(*ii*) AP = CQ.

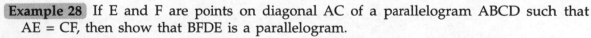

Solution. (*i*) In △APB and △CQD,

AB = CD   (opp. sides of a ∥ gm)

∠P = ∠Q   (each = 90°)

∠ABP = ∠CDQ   (alt. ∠s, AB ∥ DC and BD is a transversal)

∴   △APB ≅ △CQD   (by AAS rule of congruency)

(*ii*) AP = CQ   (c.p.c.t.)

Example 28 If E and F are points on diagonal AC of a parallelogram ABCD such that AE = CF, then show that BFDE is a parallelogram.

Solution. As ABCD is a parallelogram, its diagonals bisect each other *i.e.* OA = OC and OB = OD.

Given   AE = CF

∴   OA – AE = OC – CF

⇒   OE = OF

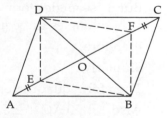

Thus, in quadrilateral BFDE, OE = OF and OB = OD *i.e.* its diagonals EF and BD bisect each other, therefore, BFDE is a parallelogram.

Example 29 ABCD is a parallelogram. If the bisectors of ∠A and ∠C meet the diagonal BD at P and Q respectively, prove that the quadrilateral PCQA is a parallelogram.

Solution. Given. ABCD is a ∥gm, AP bisects ∠A and CQ bisects ∠C.

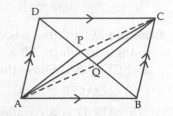

To prove. AP ∥ QC and PC ∥ AQ.

Construction. Join AC.

Proof.

Statements	Reasons
1. $\angle BAP = \dfrac{1}{2} \angle A$	1. AP is bisector of ∠A.
2. $\angle DCQ = \dfrac{1}{2} \angle C$	2. CQ is bisector of ∠C.
3. ∠BAP = ∠DCQ	3. ∠A = ∠C, since ABCD is a ∥gm.
4. ∠BAC = ∠DCA	4. Alt. ∠s, since AB ∥ DC.
5. ∠BAP − ∠BAC = ∠DCQ − ∠DCA	5. Subtracting 4 from 3.
6. ∠CAP = ∠ACQ	6. From figure.

7. AP ∥ QC
    Similarly, PC ∥ AQ.
    Hence, PCQA is a parallelogram.
            Q.E.D
	7. Alt. ∠s are equal.

Example 30 In the adjoining figure, two parallel lines l and m are intersected by a transversal p. Show that the quadrilateral formed by the bisectors of interior angles is a rectangle.

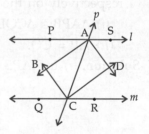

Solution. It is given that the lines l and m are parallel *i.e.* PS ∥ QR and transversal p intersects them at points A and C respectively.

The bisectors of ∠PAC and ∠QCA intersect at B, and the bisectors of ∠ACR and ∠CAS intersect at D. We need to show that quadrilateral ABCD is a rectangle.

Now,   ∠PAC = ∠ACR   (alt. ∠s, l ∥ m and p is a transversal)

⇒ $\dfrac{1}{2} \angle PAC = \dfrac{1}{2} \angle ACR \Rightarrow \angle BAC = \angle ACD.$

But these angles form a pair of alternate angles for lines AB and DC with AC as transversal and these angles are equal,

therefore,   AB ∥ DC.

Similarly,   BC ∥ AD   (∠ACB = ∠CAD, why?)

Therefore, quadrilateral ABCD is a parallelogram.

Also,   ∠PAC + ∠CAS = 180°   (linear pair)

⇒ $\dfrac{1}{2} \angle PAC + \dfrac{1}{2} \angle CAS = \dfrac{1}{2} \times 180° = 90°$

$\Rightarrow$ $\angle BAC + \angle CAD = 90° \Rightarrow \angle BAD = 90°.$

Thus, ABCD is a parallelogram in which one angle is 90°.

Therefore, ABCD is a rectangle.

Example 31 Show that the bisectors of the angles of a parallelogram form a rectangle.

Solution. Let ABCD be a parallelogram and let P, Q, R and S be the points of intersection of the bisectors of $\angle A$ and $\angle B$, $\angle B$ and $\angle C$, $\angle C$ and $\angle D$, and $\angle D$ and $\angle A$ respectively. We need to show that PQRS is a rectangle.

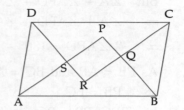

As ABCD is a || gm, AD || BC and AB is a transversal.

$\therefore$ $\angle A + \angle B = 180°$ (sum of co-int. $\angle$s = 180°)

$\Rightarrow$ $\dfrac{1}{2}\angle A + \dfrac{1}{2}\angle B = 90°$

$\Rightarrow$ $\angle PAB + \angle PBA = 90°$ ($\because$ AP is bisector of $\angle A$ and BP is bisector of $\angle B$)

In $\triangle PAB$, $\angle APB + \angle PAB + \angle PBA = 180°$ (sum of angles in a $\triangle$)

$\Rightarrow$ $\angle APB + 90° = 180° \Rightarrow \angle APB = 90° \Rightarrow \angle SPQ = 90°.$

Similarly, $\angle PQR = 90°, \angle QRS = 90°$ and $\angle RSP = 90°.$

So, PQRS is a quadrilateral in which each angle is 90°.

Now, $\angle SPQ = \angle QRS$ (each = 90°)

and $\angle PQR = \angle RSP$ (each = 90°)

Thus, PQRS is a quadrilateral in which both pairs of opposite angles are equal, therefore, PQRS is a parallelogram. Also, in this parallelogram one angle (in fact all angles) is 90°. Therefore, PQRS is a rectangle.

Example 32 In the adjoining figure, P is mid-point of the side BC of a parallelogram ABCD such that $\angle BAP = \angle DAP$. Prove that AD = 2CD.

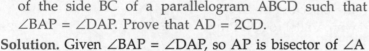
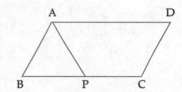

Solution. Given $\angle BAP = \angle DAP$, so AP is bisector of $\angle A$

$\Rightarrow$ $\angle A = 2 \angle BAP$ ...(i)

As ABCD is a parallelogram, BC || AD

                         $\angle A + \angle B = 180°$ (sum of co-interior angles)

$\Rightarrow$ $2 \angle BAP + \angle B = 180°$ ...(ii) (using (i))

          $\angle BAP + \angle B + \angle APB = 180°$ (sum of $\angle$s in a $\triangle$)

$\Rightarrow$ $2 \angle BAP + \angle B = \angle BAP + \angle B + \angle APB$ (using (ii))

$\Rightarrow$ $\angle BAP = \angle APB$

$\Rightarrow$ $AB = BP$ (in $\triangle ABP$, sides opp. equal angles are equal)

$\Rightarrow$ $AB = \dfrac{1}{2} BC$ ($\because$ P is mid-point of BC)

$\Rightarrow$ $2AB = BC \Rightarrow 2\,CD = AD$

($\because$ In || gm ABCD, AB = CD and BC = AD, opp. sides are equal).

Example 33 In the adjoining figure, ABCD is a parallelogram. If AB = 2AD and P is mid-point of AB, prove that $\angle DPC = 90°$.

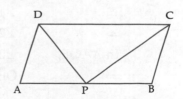

Solution. Given P is mid-point of AB

$\Rightarrow$ $AP = PB = \dfrac{1}{2} AB.$

Also AB = 2AD ⇒ AD = $\frac{1}{2}$ AB.

∴   AP = AD.

In △APD, AP = AD

⇒   ∠APD = ∠ADP   (angles opp. equal sides)

But   ∠A + ∠APD + ∠ADP = 180°   (sum of angles in a △ = 180°)

⇒   ∠A + ∠APD + ∠APD = 180°   (∵ ∠ADP = ∠APD)

⇒   2 ∠APD = 180° – ∠A ⇒ ∠APD = $\frac{180° – ∠A}{2}$ ...(i)

As PB = AP and BC = AD   (opp. sides of ∥ gm ABCD)

⇒   PB = BC   (∵ AP = AD)

In △BPC, PB = BC ⇒ ∠CPB = ∠BCP.

But   ∠B + ∠CPB + ∠BCP = 180°

⇒   ∠B + ∠CPB + ∠CPB = 180°

⇒   2 ∠CPB = 180° – ∠B ⇒ ∠CPB = $\frac{180° – ∠B}{2}$ ...(ii)

Adding (i) and (ii), we get

$$∠APD + ∠CPB = 180° – \frac{1}{2}(∠A + ∠B)$$

$$= 180° – \frac{1}{2}(180°)$$

(∵ ABCD is a ∥gm, AD ∥ BC, so ∠A + ∠B = 180°)

⇒   ∠APD + ∠CPB = 90°   ...(iii)

But   ∠APD + ∠DPC + ∠CPB = 180°   (∵ APB is a line)

⇒   (∠APD + ∠CPB) + ∠DPC = 180°

⇒   90° + ∠DPC = 180°

⇒   ∠DPC = 90°   (using (iii))

Example 34 In the adjoining figure, ABCD is a parallelogram. OA and OB are the bisectors of ∠A and ∠B respectively. Line EOF is drawn parallel to AB. Prove that:

(i) AE = BF

(ii) OE = OF.

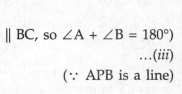

Solution. (i) Mark the angles as shown in the given figure.

As ABCD is a parallelogram,

AD ∥ BC *i.e.* AE ∥ BF.

EF ∥ AB   (given)

∴ ABFE is a parallelogram,

⇒   AE = BF   (opp. sides of a ∥ gm)

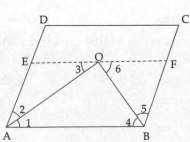

(ii) As OA is bisector of ∠A, ∠1 = ∠2.

EF ∥ AB *i.e.* EO ∥ AB

and OA is a transversal,

∴   ∠1 = ∠3   (alt. ∠s)

⇒   ∠2 = ∠3   (∵ ∠1 = ∠2)

In △AOE,   ∠2 = ∠3

⇒   OE = AE   (sides opp. equal angles are equal)

As OB is bisector of ∠B, ∠4 = ∠5.

EF ∥ AB *i.e.* OF ∥ AB and OB is a transversal

∴   ∠4 = ∠6   (alt. ∠s)

⇒   ∠5 = ∠6   (∵ ∠4 = ∠5)

In ΔOBF,   ∠5 = ∠6

⇒   OF = BF   (sides opp. equal angles are equal)

Thus,   OE = AE and OF = BF but AE = BF   (proved in (*i*))

⇒   OE = OF.   (∵ ∠4 = ∠5)

Example 35 In the parallelogram ABCD, M is mid-point of AC, and X, Y are points on AB and DC respectively such that AX = CY. Prove that

(*i*) triangle AXM is congruent to triangle CYM.

(*ii*) XMY is a straight line.

Solution. Given. ABCD is a ∥gm, M is mid-point of AC, X, Y are points on AB, CD such that AX = CY.

To prove. (*i*) ΔAXM ≅ ΔCYM

         (*ii*) XMY is a straight line.

Construction. Join XM and MY.

Proof.

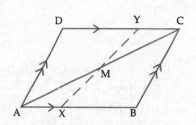

Statements	Reasons
In Δs AXM and CYM	
1. AX = CY	1. Given.
2. AM = MC	2. M is mid-point of AC.

3. ∠XAM = ∠MCY
  ∴ (*i*) ΔAXM ≅ ΔCYM
	3. Alt. ∠s, since AB ∥ DC.
	  SAS rule of congruency.

4. ∠CMY = ∠AMX	4. 'c.p.c.t.'
5. ∠XMC = ∠XAM + ∠AXM	5. Ext. ∠ = sum of two int. opp. ∠s.
6. ∠CMY + ∠XMC = ∠AMX + ∠XAM + ∠AXM	6. Adding 4 and 5.

7. ∠CMY + ∠XMC = 180°
  (*ii*) XMY is a straight line
        Q.E.D.
	7. Sum of ∠s of a Δ = 180°.
	  Sum of adj. ∠s = 180°.

Example 36 In the adjoining figure, ABCD is a kite in which AB = AD and BC = CD. Prove that:

(*i*) AC is a bisector of ∠A and of ∠C.

(*ii*) AC is perpendicular bisector of BD.

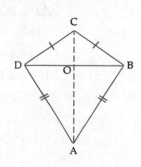

Solution. (*i*) In ΔABC and ΔADC,

AB = AD   (given)

BC = CD   (given)

CA = CA   (common)

∴   △ABC ≅ △ADC   (SSS rule of congruency)

        ∠BAC = ∠CAD and ∠BCA = ∠ACD.   (c.p.c.t.)

        Hence, AC is bisector of ∠A and of ∠C.

(ii) In △OBC and △ODC,

            BC = CD   (given)

            ∠BCO = ∠OCD   (proved above)

            OC = OC   (common)

∴   △OBC ≅ △ODC   (SAS rule of congruency)

∴   OB = OD and ∠BOC = ∠COD   (c.p.c.t.)

But   ∠BOC + ∠COD = 180°   (linear pair)

⇒   2∠BOC = 180° ⇒ ∠BOC = 90°.

        Hence, AC is perpendicular bisector of BD.

Example 37 In the adjoining kite, diagonals intersect at
O. If ∠ABO = 25° and ∠OCD = 40°, find

(i) ∠ABC   (ii) ∠ADC   (iii) ∠BAD.

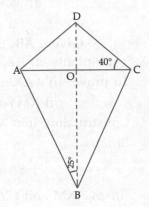

Solution. (i) Since the diagonal BD bisects ∠ABC, ∠ABC
= 2 ∠ABO = 2 × 25° = 50°.

(ii) ∠DOC = 90°   (diagonals intersect at right angles)

        ∠ODC + 40° + 90° = 180°

                        (sum of angles in △OCD)

⇒   ∠ODC = 180° − 40° − 90° = 50°.

        Since the diagonal BD bisects ∠ADC,

        ∠ADC = 2 ∠ODC = 2 × 50° = 100°.

(iii) Since the diagonal BD bisects ∠ADC, ∠ADB = ∠ODC = 50°.

        ∠BAD + 50° + 25° = 180°   (sum of angles in △ABD)

⇒   ∠BAD = 180° − 50° − 25° = 105°.

Example 38 In the adjoining figure, ABCD is an isosceles
trapezium and its diagonals meet at O. Prove that:

(i) ∠A = ∠B and ∠C = ∠D.

(ii) AC = BD.

(iii) OA = OB and OC = OD.

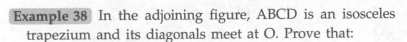

Solution. (i) From C and D, draw perpendiculars CN and DM on AB respectively.

        In △AMD and △BNC,

            AD = BC   (given)

            ∠AMD = ∠CNB

            (∵ DM ⊥ AB and CN ⊥ AB, by construction)

            MD = CN (distance between parallel lines)

∴   △AMD ≅ △BNC (RHS rule of congruency)

∴   ∠A = ∠B   (c.p.c.t.)

        Also ∠A + ∠D = 180° and ∠B + ∠C = 180°)

                        (∵ AB ∥ DC, sum of co-int. ∠s = 180°)

⇒   ∠A + ∠D = ∠B + ∠C

⇒   ∠D = ∠C   (∵ ∠A = ∠B, proved above)

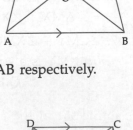

(ii) In △ABD and △BAC,

∠A = ∠B		(proved above)
AD = BC		(given)
AB = AB		(common)
∴ △ABD ≅ △BAC		(SAS rule of congruency)
∴ AC = BD		(c.p.c.t.)

(iii) In △OAD and △OBC,

AD = BC	(given)
∠AOD = ∠BOC	(vert. opp. ∠s)
∠ADO = ∠BCO	(∵ △ABD ≅ △BAC, so ∠ADB = ∠ACB)
∴ △OAD ≅ △OBC	(AAS rule of congruency)
∴ OA = OB and OC = OD.	(c.p.c.t.)

Example 39 In the adjoining figure, ABCD is a trapezium. If ∠AOB = 126° and ∠PDC = ∠QCD = 52°, find the values of x and y.

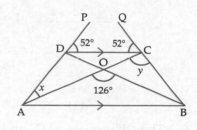

Solution. Produce AP and BQ to meet at R.

In △RDC, ∠RDC = ∠RCD   (each angle = 52°)

∴   DR = CR   (sides opp. equal angles are equal)

∠RAB = ∠RDC   (corres. ∠s, AB ∥ DC).

Similarly, ∠RBA = ∠RCD.

∴   ∠RAB = ∠RBA

⇒   AR = RB.

∴   AD = AR – DR = RB – CR = BC

⇒   ABCD is an isosceles trapezium.

∴   OA = OB   (Example 38)

⇒   ∠OAB = ∠OBA.

∴   ∠OAB = $\dfrac{180° - 126°}{2}$ = 27°.

∠DAC = ∠DAB – ∠OAB = 52° – 27° = 25°

∴ x = 25°.

∠ACB + ∠CAB + ∠ABC = 180°   (sum of angle in △ABC)

⇒ y + 27° + 52° = 180° ⇒ y = 180° – 27° – 52°

⇒ y = 101°.

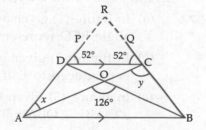

EXERCISE 13.1

1 If two angles of a quadrilateral are 40° and 110° and the other two are in the ratio 3 : 4, find these angles.

2 If the angles of a quadrilateral, taken in order, are in the ratio 1 : 2 : 3 : 4, prove that it is a trapezium.

3 If an angle of a parallelogram is two-thirds of its adjacent angle, find the angles of the parallelogram.

4   (a) In figure (1) given below, ABCD is a parallelogram in which ∠DAB = 70°, ∠DBC = 80°. Calculate angles CDB and ADB.

(b) In figure (2) given below, ABCD is a parallelogram. Find the angles of the △AOD.

(c) In figure (3) given below, ABCD is a rhombus. Find the value of x.

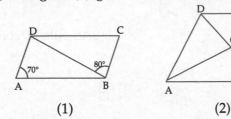

(1)　　　　　　(2)　　　　　　(3)

5　(a) In figure (1) given below, ABCD is a parallelogram with perimeter 40. Find the values of x and y.

(b) In figure (2) given below, ABCD is a parallelogram. Find the values of x and y.

(c) In figure (3) given below, ABCD is a rhombus. Find x and y.

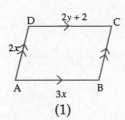 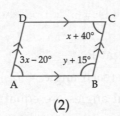 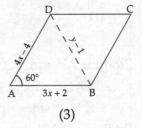

(1)　　　　　　(2)　　　　　　(3)

6 The diagonals AC and BD of a rectangle ABCD intersect each other at P. If ∠ABD = 50°, find ∠DPC.

7　(a) In figure (1) given below, equilateral triangle EBC surmounts square ABCD. Find angle BED represented by x.

(b) In figure (2) given below, ABCD is a rectangle and diagonals intersect at O. AC is produced to E. If ∠ECD = 146°, find the angles of the △AOB.

(c) In figure (3) given below, ABCD is a rhombus and diagonals intersect at O. If ∠OAB : ∠OBA = 3 : 2, find the angles of the △AOD.

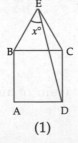 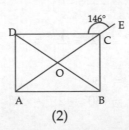 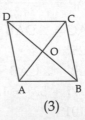

(1)　　　　　　(2)　　　　　　(3)

8　(a) In figure (1) given below, ABCD is a trapezium. Find the values of x and y.

(b) In figure (2) given below, ABCD is an isosceles trapezium. Find the values of x and y.

(c) In figure (3) given below, ABCD is a kite and diagonals intersect at O. If ∠DAB = 112° and ∠DCB = 64°, find ∠ODC and ∠OBA.

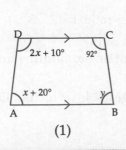 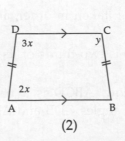 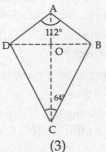

(1)　　　　　　(2)　　　　　　(3)

9 (*i*) Prove that each angle of a rectangle is 90°.

(*ii*) If the angle of a quadrilateral are equal, prove that it is a rectangle.

(*iii*) If the diagonals of a rhombus are equal, prove that it is a square.

(*iv*) Prove that every diagonal of a rhombus bisects the angles at the vertices.

10 ABCD is parallelogram. If the diagonal AC bisects $\angle A$, then prove that:
(*i*) AC bisects $\angle C$ (*ii*) ABCD is a rhombus   (*iii*) AC $\perp$ BD.

11 (*i*) Prove that bisectors of any two adjacent angles of a parallelogram are at right angles.

(*ii*) Prove that bisectors of any two opposite angles of a parallelogram are parallel.

(*iii*) If the diagonals of a quadrilateral are equal and bisect each other at right angles, then prove that it is a square.

12 (*i*) If ABCD is a rectangle in which the diagonal BD bisects $\angle B$, then show that ABCD is a square.

(*ii*) Show that if the diagonals of a quadrilateral are equal and bisect each other at right angles, then it is a square.

13 P and Q are points on opposite sides AD and BC of a parallelogram ABCD such that PQ passes through the point of intersection O of its diagonals AC and BD. Show that PQ is bisected at O.

Hint. Show that $\triangle$OAP $\cong$ $\triangle$OCQ.

14 (*a*) In figure (1) given below, ABCD is a parallelogram and X is mid-point of BC. The line AX produced meets DC produced at Q. The parallelogram ABPQ is completed. Prove that

(*i*) the triangles ABX and QCX are congruent.

(*ii*) DC = CQ = QP

(*b*) In figure (2) given below, points P and Q have been taken on opposite sides AB and CD respectively of a parallelogram ABCD such that AP = CQ. Show that AC and PQ bisect each other.

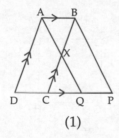

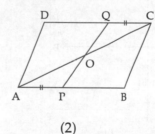

              (1)   (2)

15 ABCD is a square. A is joined to a point P on BC and D is joined to a point Q on AB. If AP = DQ, prove that AP and DQ are perpendicular to each other.

Hint. $\triangle$ ABP $\cong$ $\triangle$ DAQ $\Rightarrow$ $\angle$BAP = $\angle$ADQ. But $\angle$BAD = 90°
$\Rightarrow$ $\angle$PAD + $\angle$ADQ = 90°.

16 If P and Q are points of trisection of the diagonal BD of a parallelogram ABCD, prove that CQ $\parallel$ AP.

Hint. $\triangle$ ABP $\cong$ $\triangle$CDQ.

17 A transversal cuts two parallel lines at A and B. The two interior angles at A are bisected and so are the two interior angles at B; the four bisectors form a quadrilateral ACBD. Prove that

(*i*) ACBD is a rectangle.

(*ii*) CD is parallel to the original parallel lines.

18 In a parallelogram ABCD, the bisector of ∠A meets DC in E and AB = 2AD. Prove that

(i) BE bisects ∠B

(ii) ∠AEB = a right angle.

19 ABCD is a parallelogram, bisectors of angles A and B meet at E which lies on DC. Prove that AB = 2AD.

20 ABCD is a square and the diagonals intersect at O. If P is a point on AB such that AO = AP, prove that 3∠POB = ∠AOP.

21 ABCD is a square. E, F, G and H are points on the sides AB, BC, CD and DA respectively such that AE = BF = CG = DH. Prove that EFGH is a square.

Hint. Given AE = BF = CG = DH

⇒   EB = FC = GD = HA.

In ∆s AEH and BFE,

AE = BF, AH = EB,

∠A = ∠B   (each ∠ = 90°)

∴   ∆AEH ≅ ∆BFE

⇒   EH = EF and ∠4 = ∠2.

But ∠1 + ∠4 = 90° ⇒ ∠1 + ∠2 = 90°

⇒   ∠HEF = 90°.

(∵ ∠4 = ∠2)

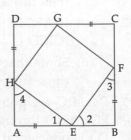

22 (a) In the figure (1) given below, ABCD and ABEF are parallelograms. Prove that
(i) CDFE is a parallelogram (ii) FD = EC (iii) ∆AFD ≅ ∆BEC.

(b) In the figure (2) given below, ABCD is a parallelogram, ADEF and AGHB are two squares. Prove that FG = AC.

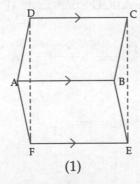

(1)

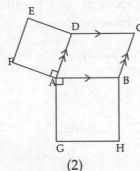

(2)

Hint. (a) AB ∥ DC, AB ∥ FE ⇒ DC ∥ FE, AB = DC, AB = FE ⇒ DC = FE.

(b) ∆AFG ≅ ∆BCA, for, AF = BC, AG = AB,

∠FAG = 360° − 90° − 90° − ∠A = 180° − ∠A = ∠B.

23 ABCD is a rhombus in which ∠A = 60°. Find the ratio AC : BD.
Hint. As ∠A = 60°, ABD is an equilateral triangle.

Let AB = a, then BD = a ⇒ OB = $\frac{a}{2}$. In ∆AOB, ∠AOB = 90°.

By Pythagoras theorem, AO² = AB² − OB² = $a^2 - \left(\frac{1}{2}a\right)^2 = \frac{3}{4}a^2$

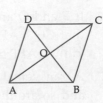

⇒ AO = $\frac{\sqrt{3}}{2}a$ ⇒ AC = $\sqrt{3}\,a$.

13.2 CONSTRUCTION OF QUADRILATERALS

Quadrilaterals are constructed by splitting the figure into suitable triangles. Students are advised to draw a rough *free hand* sketch before constructing the actual figure.

Construction 13.1. To construct quadrilaterals.

(*i*) *To construct a quadrilateral when its four sides and one angle are given.*

Given. Let AB = 3·8 cm, BC = 3·2 cm, CD = 4·6 cm, DA = 2·9 cm and ∠BAD = 60°.

Required. To construct quad. ABCD.

Steps of construction.

1. Draw AB = 3·8 cm.

2. At A, construct ∠BAP = 60°.

3. From AP, cut off AD = 2·9 cm.

4. With B as centre and radius 3·2 cm, draw an arc.

5. With D as centre and radius 4·6 cm, draw an arc to meet the previous arc at C.

6. Join BC and DC. Then, ABCD is the required quadrilateral.

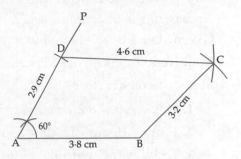

(*ii*) *To construct a quadrilateral when its three sides and two angles are given.*

Given. Let AB = 4 cm, BC = 2·8 cm, AD = 4·1 cm, ∠A = 90° and ∠B = 120°.

Required. To construct quadrilateral ABCD.

Steps of construction.

1. Draw AB = 4 cm.

2. At A, construct ∠BAP = 90° and cut off AD = 4·1 cm.

3. At B, construct ∠ABQ = 120° and cut off BC = 2·8 cm.

4. Join CD. Then, ABCD is the required quadrilateral.

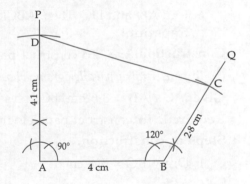

(*iii*) *To construct a quadrilateral whose four sides and one diagonal are given.*

Given. Let AB = 3·6 cm, BC = 3·1 cm, CD = 2·4 cm, DA = 3 cm and BD = 3·4 cm.

Required. To construct quad. ABCD.

Steps of construction.

1. Construct △ABD.

2. Construct △BCD.

Then, ABCD is the required quadrilateral.

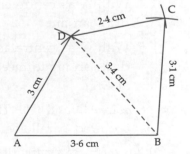

(*iv*) *To construct a quadrilateral whose three sides and two diagonals are given.*

Given. Let AB = 2·7 cm, BC = 1·9 cm, AD = 3·6 cm, AC = 3·5 cm and BD = 5·3cm.

Required. To construct quad. ABCD.

Steps of construction.

    1. Construct △ABC.

    2. Construct △ABD.

    3. Join CD.

Then, ABCD is the required quadrilateral.

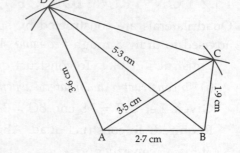

Construction 13.2. To construct trapezium.

To construct a trapezium whose four sides are given.

Given. Let AB = 5·2 cm, BC = 3·1 cm, CD = 3·4 cm, DA = 2·7 cm and AB ∥ DC.

Required. To construct trapezium ABCD.

Steps of construction.

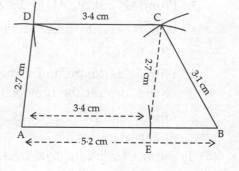

    1. Draw AB = 5·2 cm.

    2. From AB, cut off AE = 3·4 cm.

    3. Draw △EBC with EC = 2·7 cm and BC = 3·1 cm.

    4. With A as centre and radius = 2·7 cm, draw an arc.

    5. With C as centre and radius 3·4 cm, draw an arc to meet the previous arc at D.

    6. Join AD and DC. Then, ABCD is the required trapezium.

Construction 13.3. To construct parallelograms.

(i) To construct a parallelogram whose two adjacent sides and the included angle are given.

Given. Let AB = 3·6 cm, BC = 5·4 cm and ∠ABC = 60°.

Required. To construct parallelogram ABCD.

Steps of construction.

    1. Draw BC = 5·4 cm.

    2. At B, construct ∠PBC = 60°.

    3. From BP, cut off AB = 3·6 cm.

    4. With A as centre and radius 5·4 cm, draw an arc.

    5. With C as centre and radius 3·6 cm, draw an arc to meet the previous arc at D.

    6. Join AD and CD. Then, ABCD is the required parallelogram.

(ii) To construct a parallelogram whose two adjacent sides and one diagonal are given.

Given. Let AB = 5·6 cm, AD = 4 cm and BD = 5·2 cm.

Required. To construct parallelogram ABCD.

Steps of construction.

1. Draw AB = 5·6 cm.

2. With A as centre and radius 4 cm, draw an arc.

3. With B as centre and radius 5·2 cm, draw an arc to meet the previous arc at D.

4. With D as centre and radius 5·6 cm, draw an arc.

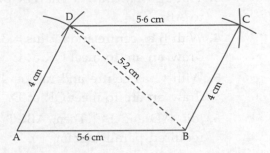

5. With B as centre and radius 4 cm, draw an arc to meet the previous arc at C.

6. Join AD, BC and DC. Then ABCD is the required parallelogram.

(iii) To construct a parallelogram whose one side and both diagonals are given.

Given. Let AB = 5·1 cm, AC = 6·4 cm and BD = 5 cm.

Required. To construct ∥gm ABCD.

Steps of construction.

1. Draw ΔOAB with AB = 5·1 cm,

   OA = $\frac{1}{2}$. AC = $\left(\frac{1}{2} \times 6\cdot4\right)$ cm = 3·2 cm,

   and OB = $\frac{1}{2}$. BD = $\left(\frac{1}{2} \times 5\right)$ cm = 2·5 cm

   (∵ Diagonals of a ∥ gm bisect each other)

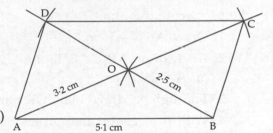

2. Produce AO to C such that OC = OA.

3. Produce BO to D such that OD = OB.

4. Join CD. Then, ABCD is the required parallelogram.

(iv) To construct a parallelogram whose two diagonals and the included angle are given.

Given. Let AC = 6 cm, BD = 4·6 cm and ∠COD = 60°.

Required. To construct ∥gm ABCD.

Steps of construction.

1. Draw AO = $\frac{1}{2}$ AC = $\left(\frac{1}{2} \times 6\right)$ cm = 3 cm, and produce AO to C such that OC = OA.

2. At O, construct ∠COP = 60°.

3. From OP, cut off OD = $\frac{1}{2}$ BD = $\left(\frac{1}{2} \times 4\cdot6\right)$ cm = 2·3 cm, produce DO to B such that OB = OD.

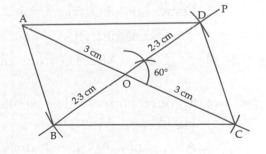

4. Join AB, BC, CD and DA. Then, ABCD is the required parallelogram.

(v) To construct a parallelogram whose two adjacent sides and one height are given.

Given. Let AB = 4·9 cm, BC = 3·4 cm and height from AB = 2·7 cm.

Required. To construct ∥ gm ABCD.

Steps of construction.

1. Draw AB = 4·9 cm.

2. At B, draw BP ⊥ AB. From BP, cut off BN = 2·7 cm.

3. Through N, draw a line QR parallel to AB.

4. With B as centre and radius = 3.4 cm, draw an arc to meet QR at C.

5. With C as centre and radius 4.9 cm, draw an arc to meet QR at D.

6. Join AD and BC. Then, ABCD is the required parallelogram.

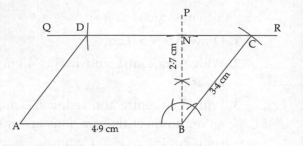

Note With the given data, two parallelograms are possible. However, if ∠A is acute, then only one parallelogram can be constructed.

(vi) To construct a parallelogram whose one side, one diagonal and one height are given.

Given. Let AB = 4.5 cm, AC = 3.8 cm and height from AB = 2.5 cm.

Required. To construct ‖ gm ABCD.

Steps of construction.

1. Draw AB = 4.5 cm.

2. At A, draw AP ⊥ AB. From AP, cut off AN = 2.5 cm.

3. Through N, draw a line QR parallel to AB.

4. With A as centre and radius = 3.8 cm, draw an arc to meet QR at C.

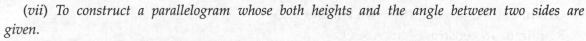

5. With C as centre and radius = 4.5 cm, draw an arc to meet QR at D.

6. Join BC and AD. Then, ABCD is the required parallelogram.

(vii) To construct a parallelogram whose both heights and the angle between two sides are given.

Given. Let ∠BAD = 60°, heights be 2.3 cm and 4 cm from AB and BC respectively.

Required. To construct ‖ gm ABCD.

Steps of construction.

1. Draw a line PQ, take a point A on it.

2. At A, construct ∠QAF = 60°.

3. At A, draw AE ⊥ PQ, from AE cut off AN = 2.3 cm.

4. Through N draw a line parallel to PQ to meet AF at D.

5. At A, draw AG ⊥ AD, from AG cut off AM = 4 cm.

6. Through M, draw a line parallel to AD to meet AQ at B and ND at C. Then, ABCD is the required parallelogram.

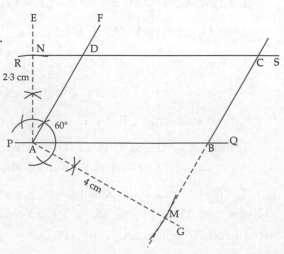

Construction 13.4. To construct rectangles.

(*i*) *To construct a rectangle whose adjacent sides are given.*

Since every angle of a rectangle is 90°, therefore, to construct the required rectangle proceed as in construction 13.1 (*i*).

(*ii*) *To construct a rectangle whose one side and one diagonal are given.*

Given. Let AB = 5·2 cm and AC = 5·7 cm.

Required. To construct rectangle ABCD.

Steps of construction.

1. Draw AB = 5·2 cm.

2. At B, draw BP ⊥ AB.

3. With A as centre and radius = 5·7 cm, draw an arc to meet BP at C.

4. With C as centre and radius = 5·2 cm, draw an arc.

5. With B as centre and radius = 5·7 cm, draw an arc to meet the previous arc at D.

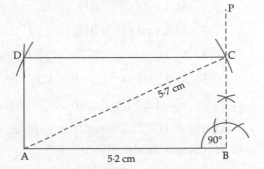

6. Join AD and DC. Then, ABCD is the required rectangle.

Construction 13.5. To construct squares.

(*i*) *To construct a square whose one side is given.*

Since all the sides of a square are equal and each angle is 90°, therefore, to construct the required square proceed as in construction 13.1 (*i*).

(*ii*) *To construct a square whose one diagonal is given.*

Since both the diagonals of a square are equal and they intersect at right angles, therefore, to construct the required square proceed as in construction 13.3 (*iv*).

Construction 13.6. To construct rhombi.

(*i*) *To construct a rhombus whose one side and an angle are given.*

Since all the sides of a rhombus are equal, therefore, to construct the required rhombus proceed as in construction 13.1 (*i*).

(*ii*) *To construct a rhombus whose diagonals are given.*

Given. Let AC = 5 cm and BD = 6·8 cm.

Required. To construct rhombus ABCD.

Steps of construction.

1. Draw AC = 5 cm.

2. Draw perpendicular bisector PQ of AC to meet it at O.

3. From POQ, cut off OB and OD such that

$$OB = OD = \left(\frac{1}{2} \times 6\cdot8\right) \text{ cm} = 3\cdot4 \text{ cm}.$$

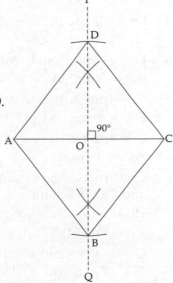

4. Join AB, BC, CD and DA. Then, ABCD is the required rhombus.

13.4 CONSTRUCTION OF REGULAR HEXAGON

Construction 13.7. *To construct a regular hexagon whose side is given.*

Given. Let AB = 2 cm.

Required. To construct regular hexagon ABCDEF.

Method I. (Each interior angle of a regular hexagon = 120°)

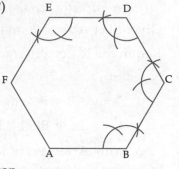

Steps of construction.

    1. Draw AB = 2 cm.

    2. At B, draw ∠ABC = 120° and BC = 2 cm.

    3. At C, draw ∠BCD = 120° and CD = 2 cm.

    4. At D, draw ∠CDE = 120° and DE = 2 cm.

    5. At E, draw ∠DEF = 120° and EF = 2 cm.

    6. Join FA. Then, ABCDEF is the required regular hexagon.

Method II. (The length of side of regular hexagon = radius of its *circumcircle*).

Steps of construction.

    1. Draw a circle of radius 2 cm.

    2. Take any point A on the circumference. With A as centre and radius = 2 cm, draw two arcs to cut the circle at B and F.

    3. With B as centre and radius = 2 cm, draw an arc to cut the circle at C.

    4. With C as centre and radius = 2 cm, draw an arc to cut the circle at D.

    5. With D as centre and radius = 2 cm, draw an arc to cut the circle at E.

    6. Join AB, BC, CD, DE, EF and FA. Then, ABCDEF is the required regular hexagon.

EXERCISE 13.2

1 Using ruler and compasses only, construct the quadrilateral ABCD in which ∠BAD = 45°, AD = AB = 6 cm, BC = 3·6 cm, CD = 5 cm. Measure ∠BCD.

2 Draw a quadrilateral ABCD with AB = 6 cm, BC = 4 cm, CD = 4 cm and ∠ABC = ∠BCD = 90°.

3 Using ruler and compasses only, construct the quadrilateral ABCD given that AB = 5 cm, BC = 2·5 cm, CD = 6 cm, ∠BAD = 90° and the diagonal AC = 5·5 cm.

4 Construct a quadrilateral ABCD in which AB = 3·3 cm, BC = 4·9 cm, CD = 5·8 cm, DA = 4 cm and BD = 5·3 cm.

5 Construct a trapezium ABCD in which AD ∥ BC, AB = CD = 3 cm, BC = 5·2 cm and AD = 4 cm.

6 Construct a trapezium ABCD in which AD ∥ BC, ∠B = 60°, AB = 5 cm, BC = 6·2 cm and CD = 4·8 cm.

    Hint. Draw BC = 6·2 cm. At B, construct ∠CBP = 60°. From BP, cut off AB = 5 cm. Through A, draw a line parallel to BC.

7 Using ruler and compasses only, construct a parallelogram ABCD with AB = 5·1 cm, BC = 7 cm and ∠ABC = 75°.

8 Using ruler and compasses only, construct a parallelogram ABCD in which AB = 4·6 cm, BC = 3·2 cm and AC = 6·1 cm.

9 Using ruler and compasses, construct a parallelogram ABCD given that AB = 4 cm, AC = 10 cm, BD = 6 cm. Measure BC.

10 Using ruler and compasses only, construct a parallelogram ABCD such that BC = 4 cm, diagonal AC = 8·6 cm and diagonal BD = 4·4 cm. Measure the side AB.

11 Use ruler and compasses to construct a parallelogram with diagonals 6 cm and 8 cm in length having given the acute angle between them is 60°. Measure one of the longer sides.

12 Using ruler and compasses only, draw a parallelogram whose diagonals are 4 cm and 6 cm long and contain an angle of 75°. Measure and write down the length of one of the shorter sides of the parallelogram.

13 Using ruler and compasses only, construct a parallelogram ABCD with AB = 6 cm, altitude = 3·5 cm and side BC = 4 cm. Measure the acute angles of the parallelogram.

14 The perpendicular distances between the pairs of opposite sides of a parallelogram ABCD are 3 cm and 4 cm and one of its angles measures 60°. Using ruler and compasses only, construct ABCD.

15 Using ruler and compasses, construct a rectangle ABCD with AB = 5 cm and AD = 3 cm.

16 Using ruler and compasses only, construct a rectangle each of whose diagonals measures 6 cm and the diagonals intersect at an angle of 45°.

17 Using ruler and compasses only, construct a square having a diagonal of length 5 cm. Measure its sides correct to the nearest millimetre.

18 Using ruler and compasses only, construct a rhombus ABCD, given that AB = 5 cm, AC = 6 cm. Measure ∠BAD.

19 Using ruler and compasses only, construct rhombus ABCD with sides of length 4 cm and diagonal AC of length 5 cm. Measure ∠ABC.

20 Construct a rhombus PQRS whose diagonals PR, QS are 8 cm and 6 cm respectively.

21 Construct a rhombus ABCD of side 4·6 cm and ∠BCD = 135°, by using ruler and compasses only.

22 Construct a trapezium in which AB ∥ CD, AB = 4·6 cm, ∠ABC = 90°, ∠DAB = 120° and the distance between parallel sides is 2·9 cm.

23 Construct a trapezium ABCD when one of parallel sides AB = 4·8 cm, height = 2·6 cm, BC = 3·1 cm and AD = 3·6 cm.
   Hint. Draw a line PQ parallel to AB at a distance = 2·6 cm.

24 Construct a regular hexagon of side 2·5 cm.

Multiple Choice Questions

Choose the correct answer from the given four options (1 to 12):

1 Three angles of a quadrilateral are 75°, 90° and 75°. The fourth angle is
   (a) 90°   (b) 95°   (c) 105°   (d) 120°

2 A quadrilateral ABCD is a trapezium if
   (a) AB = DC   (b) AD = BC
   (c) ∠A + ∠C = 180°   (d) ∠B + ∠C = 180°

3 If PQRS is a parallelogram, then $\angle Q - \angle S$ is equal to

    (*a*) 90°   (*b*) 120°   (*c*) 0°   (*d*) 180°

4 A diagonal of a rectangle is inclined to one side of the rectangle at 25°. The acute angle between the diagonals is

    (*a*) 55°   (*b*) 50°   (*c*) 40°   (*d*) 25°

5 ABCD is a rhombus such that $\angle ACB = 40°$. Then $\angle ADB$ is

    (*a*) 40°   (*b*) 45°   (*c*) 50°   (*d*) 60°

6 The diagonals AC and BD of a parallelogram ABCD intersect each other at the point O. If $\angle DAC = 32°$ and $\angle AOB = 70°$, then $\angle DBC$ is equal to

    (*a*) 24°   (*b*) 86°   (*c*) 38°   (*d*) 32°

7 If the diagonals of a square ABCD intersect each other at O, then $\triangle OAB$ is

    (*a*) an equilateral triangle

    (*b*) a right angled but not an isosceles triangle

    (*c*) an isosceles but not right angled triangle

    (*d*) an isosceles right angled triangle.

8 If the diagonals of a quadrilateral PQRS bisect each other, then the quadrilateral PQRS must be a

    (*a*) parallelogram   (*b*) rhombus   (*c*) rectangle   (*d*) square

9 If the diagonals of a quadrilateral PQRS bisect each other at right angles, then the quadrilateral PQRS must be a

    (*a*) parallelogram   (*b*) rectangle   (*c*) rhombus   (*d*) square

10 Which of the following statement is true for a parallelogram?

    (*a*) Its diagonals are equal.

    (*b*) Its diagonals are perpendicular to each other.

    (*c*) The diagonals divide the parallelogram into four congruent triangles.

    (*d*) The diagonals bisect each other.

11 Which of the following is not true for a parallelogram?

    (*a*) opposite sides are equal

    (*b*) opposite angles are equal

    (*c*) opposite angles are bisected by the diagonals

    (*d*) diagonals bisect each other.

12 A quadrilateral in which the diagonals are equal and bisect each other at right angles is a

    (*a*) rectangle which is not a square

    (*b*) rhombus which is not a square

    (*c*) kite which is not a square

    (*d*) square

Summary

- A simple closed plane figure made up entirely of line segments is called a **polygon**.
- A polygon is called **regular polygon** if all its sides have equal lengths and all its angles have equal size.
- A simple closed plane figure bounded by four line segments is called a **quadrilateral**.
- Sum of interior angles of a quadrilateral is 360°.

❏ **Types of quadrilaterals**

    (*i*) *A quadrilateral in which one pair of opposite sides is parallel is called a **trapezium**. If non-parallel sides of a trapezium are equal, then it is called an **isosceles trapezium**.*

    (*ii*) *A quadrilateral in which both pairs of opposite sides are parallel is called a **parallelogram**.*

    (*iii*) *If one of the angles of a parallelogram is a right angle, then it is called a **rectangle**.*

    (*iv*) *If all the sides of a quadrilateral are equal, then it is called a **rhombus**.*

    (*v*) *A quadrilateral in which all sides are equal and one angle is a right angle, then it is called a **square**.*

    (*vi*) *A quadrilateral in which two pairs of adjacent sides are equal is called a **kite**.*

❏ **Properties of parallelograms**

    (*i*) *A diagonal of a parallelogram divides it into two congruent triangles.*

    (*ii*) *In a parallelogram, opposite sides are equal. **Conversely**, if each pair of opposite sides of a quadrilateral is equal then it is a parallelogram.*

    (*iii*) *In a parallelogram, opposite angles are equal. **Conversely**, if each pair of opposite angles of a quadrilateral is equal then it is a parallelogram.*

    (*iv*) *If a pair of opposite sides of a quadrilateral is equal and parallel, then it is a parallelogram.*

    (*v*) *The diagonals of a parallelogram bisect each other. **Conversely,** if the diagonals of a quadrilateral bisect each other then it is a parallelogram.*

❏ **Properties of a rectangle**

Since every rectangle is a parallelogram, therefore, it has all the properties of a parallelogram. Additional properties of a rectangle are:

    (*i*) *All the (interior) angles of a rectangle are right angles.*

    (*ii*) *The diagonals of a rectangle are equal.*

❏ **Properties of a rhombus**

Since every rhombus is a parallelogram, therefore, it has all the properties of a parallelogram. Additional properties of a rhombus are :

    (*i*) *All the sides of a rhombus are equal.*

    (*ii*) *The diagonals of a rhombus intersect at right angles.*

    (*iii*) *The diagonals bisect the angles of a rhombus.*

❏ **Properties of a square**

Since every square is a parallelogram, therefore, it has all the properties of a parallelogram. Additional properties of a square are :

    (*i*) *All the interior angles of a square are right angles.*

    (*ii*) *All the sides of a square are equal.*

    (*iii*) *The diagonals of a square are equal.*

    (*iv*) *The diagonals of a square intersect at right angles.*

    (*v*) *The diagonals bisect the angles of a square.*

In fact, a square is a rectangle as well as a rhombus, so it has all the properties of a rectangle as well as that of a rhombus.

1 In the adjoining figure, ABCD is a parallelogram. CB is produced to E such that BE = BC. Prove that AEBD is a parallelogram.

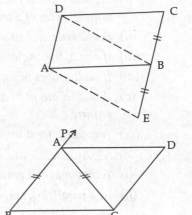

2 In the adjoining figure, ABC is an isosceles triangle in which AB = AC. AD bisects exterior angle PAC and CD ∥ BA. Show that

    (i) ∠DAC = ∠BCA

    (ii) ABCD is a parallelogram.

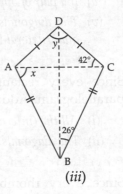

3 Prove that the quadrilateral obtained by joining the mid-points of an isosceles trapezium is a rhombus.

4 Find the size of each lettered angle in the following figures:

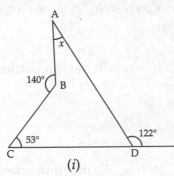

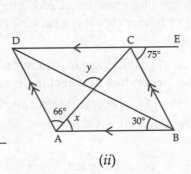

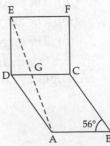

    (i)   (ii)   (iii)

5 Find the size of each lettered angle in the following figures :

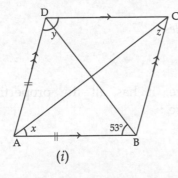

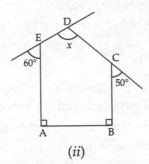

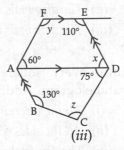

    (i)   (ii)   (iii)

6 In the adjoining figure, ABCD is a rhombus and DCFE is a square. If ∠ABC = 56°, find

    (i) ∠DAG

    (ii) ∠FEG

    (iii) ∠GAC

    (iv) ∠AGC.

7 If one angle of a rhombus is 60° and the length of a side is 8 cm, find the lengths of its diagonals.

8 Using ruler and compasses only, construct a parallelogram ABCD with AB = 5 cm, AD = 2·5 cm and ∠BAD = 45°. If the bisector of ∠BAD meets DC at E, prove that ∠AEB is a right angle.

14 Theorems on Area

INTRODUCTION

We know that Geometry originated from the need of measuring land or recasting/refixing its boundaries in the process of distribution of certain land or field among different people. You may recall that the part of the plane enclosed by a simple closed curve is called a *planar region* corresponding to that figure and the magnitude (or measure) of this plane region is called the *area* of that figure. This magnitude of measure is always expressed with the help of a number (in some unit) such as 15 cm^2, 32 m^2, 3·5 hectares etc. So, we can say that the area of a simple closed plane figure is a number (in some unit) associated with the part of the plane enclosed by the figure.

In earlier classes, we have learnt some formulae for finding the areas of some different simple closed plane figures such as triangle, rectangle, square, parallelogram etc. In this chapter, we shall consolidate the knowledge about these formulae by studying some relationship between the areas of these geometric figures under the condition when they lie on the same base (or equal bases) and between the same parallel lines.

14.1 AXIOMS OF AREA

❑ **Congruence area axiom**

If two figures are congruent, then the areas enclosed by these figures are equal.

Thus, if two figures A and B are congruent, then area enclosed by A = area enclosed by B.

This is known as **congruence area axiom**.

In the adjoining figure, $\triangle ABC \cong \triangle PQR$.

So, area of $\triangle ABC$ = area of $\triangle PQR$.

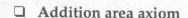

Note that by area of $\triangle ABC$ we mean the area of the region enclosed by the triangle ABC.

❑ **Addition area axiom**

If a planar region R consists of two non-overlapping planar regions R_1 and R_2, then area of region R = area of region R_1 + area of region R_2.

This is known as **addition area axiom**.

In the adjoining figure, planar regions R_1 and R_2 are non-overlapping. If R is the total region *i.e.* the region made up of regions R_1 and R_2, then

area of region R = area of region R_1 + area of region R_2.

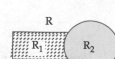

14.2 EQUAL FIGURES

Two figures are called equal if and only if they have equal area.

As two congruent figures have equal area, therefore, two congruence figures are always equal figures. However, the converse may not be true *i.e.* two equal figures may not be congruent.

For example, consider the two right triangles ABC and PQR given below:

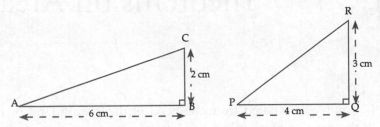

Area of $\triangle ABC = \left(\dfrac{1}{2} \times 6 \times 2\right)$ cm² = 6 cm².

Area of $\triangle PQR = \left(\dfrac{1}{2} \times 4 \times 3\right)$ cm² = 6 cm².

∴   Area of $\triangle ABC$ = area of $\triangle PQR$

⇒ $\triangle ABC$ and $\triangle PQR$ are equal figures.

Clearly, these triangles are not congruent.

14.3 THEOREMS ON AREA

Theorem 14.1

A diagonal of a parallelogram divides it into two triangles of equal areas.

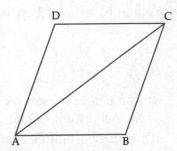

Given. ABCD is a parallelogram and AC is its one diagonal.

To prove. Area of $\triangle ABC$ = area of $\triangle ACD$.

Proof.

Statements	Reasons
In $\triangle ABC$ and $\triangle CDA$	
1. AB = DC	1. Opp. sides of ‖ gm ABCD.
2. BC = AD	2. Opp. sides of ‖ gm ABCD.
3. AC = AC	3. Common.
4. $\triangle ABC \cong \triangle CDA$	4. SSS rule of congruency.
5. Area of $\triangle ABC$ = area of $\triangle ACD$ Q.E.D.	5. Congruence area axiom.

Theorem 14.2

Parallelograms on the same base and between the same parallel lines are equal in area.

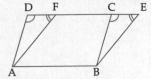

Given. Two parallelograms ABCD and ABEF on the same base AB and between the same parallel lines AB and DE.

To prove. Area of ‖ gm ABCD = area of ‖ gm ABEF.

Proof.

Statements	Reasons
In △ADF and △BCE	
1. ∠ADF = ∠BCE	1. Corres. ∠s, AD ∥ BC and DE is a transversal.
2. ∠AFD = ∠BEC	2. Corres. ∠s, AF ∥ BE and DE is a transversal.
3. AD = BC	3. Opp. sides of ∥ gm ABCD.
4. △ADF ≅ △BCE	4. AAS rule of congruency.
5. Area of △ADF = area of △BCE	5. Congruent figures have equal area.
6. Area of △ADF + area of quad. ABCF = area of △BCF + area of quad. ABCF	6. Adding same area on both sides.
7. Area of ∥ gm ABCD = area of ∥ gm ABEF	7. Addition area axiom.

Corollary 1. *A parallelogram and a rectangle on the same base and between the same parallel lines are equal in area.*

Proof. Let a parallelogram ABCD and a rectangle ABEF be on the same base AB and between the same parallel lines AB and FC (as shown in the adjoining figure).

We want to prove that area of ∥ gm ABCD = area of rect. ABEF.

Since a rectangle is also a parallelogram, therefore,

area of ∥ gm ABCD = area of rect. ABEF (Theorem 14.2).

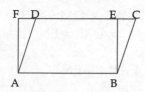

Hence, a parallelogram and a rectangle on the same base and between the same parallel lines are equal in area.

Corollary 2. *Area of a parallelogram = base × height.*

Proof. By corollary 1, we have

area of parallelogram ABCD = area of rectangle ABEF ...(*i*)

(see figure of corollary 1)

Also area of rectangle ABEF = AB × BE ...(*ii*)

From (*i*) and (*ii*), we get

area of parallelogram ABCD = AB × BE = base × height.

Hence, the area of a parallelogram = base × height.

Corollary 3. *Parallelograms with equal bases and between the same parallels are equal in area.*

Proof. Let ABCD and EFGH be two parallelograms with equal bases *i.e.* AB = EF and between the same parallel lines EB and HC.

From B, draw BM ⊥ DC and from E, draw EN ⊥ HG, then BM = EN

(∵ EBMN is a rectangle (why?)), so opp. sides are equal *i.e.* BM = EN)

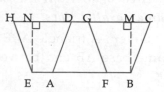

By corollary 2,

area of parallelogram ABCD = base × height = AB × BM

= EF × EN (∵ AB = EF and BM = EN)

= area of parallelogram EFGH.

Hence, parallelograms with equal bases and between the same parallel lines are equal in area.

❑ **Converse of theorem 14.2**

The converse of the above theorem 14.2 is also true. In fact, we have:

Theorem 14.3

Parallelograms on the same base and having equal areas lie between same parallel lines.

Given. Two parallelograms ABCD and ABEF on the same base AB and area of ‖ gm ABCD = area of ‖ gm ABEF.

To prove. AB ‖ FC.

Construction. From D, draw DM ⊥ AB and from E, draw EN ⊥ AB.

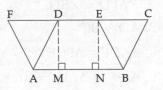

Proof.

Statements	Reasons
1. Area of ‖ gm ABCD = AB × DM	1. Area of a ‖ gm = base × height.
2. Area of ‖ gm ABEF = AB × EN	2. Area of a ‖ gm = base × height.
3. AB × DM = AB × EN ⇒ DM = EN	3. Area of ‖ gm ABCD = area of ‖ gm ABEF (given)
4. DM ‖ EN	4. DM and EN are both perpendicular to the same line AB.
5. DMNE is a parallelogram.	5. Two sides DM and EN of quad. DMNE are equal and parallel.
6. MN ‖ DE *i.e.* AB ‖ FC	6. By definition of a ‖ gm.

Corollary 1. *Parallelograms on equal bases and having equal areas have equal corresponding altitudes.*

(In the above proof of the theorem, we obtained DM = EN, so ‖ gm ABCD and ‖ gm ABEF have equal corresponding altitudes.)

Corollary 2. *Parallelograms on equal bases and having equal areas lie between same parallel lines.*

Theorem 14.4

Area of a triangle is half that of a parallelogram on the same base and between the same parallel lines.

Given. A triangle ABE and a parallelogram ABCD on the same base AB and between the same parallel lines AB and DC.

To prove. Area of ΔABE = $\frac{1}{2}$ area of ‖ gm ABCD.

Construction. Through B, draw BF ‖ AE to meet DC (produced) at F.

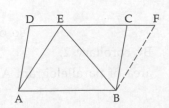

Proof.

Statements	Reasons
1. ABFE is a parallelogram	1. By construction.
2. Area of $\triangle$ABE = $\frac{1}{2}$ area of $\parallel$ gm ABFE	2. BE is a diagonal of $\parallel$ gm ABFE, and a diagonal divides it into two triangles of equal areas.
3. Area of $\parallel$ gm ABCD = area of $\parallel$ gm ABFE	3. Parallelograms on the same base and between the same parallels are equal in area.
4. Area of $\triangle$ABE = $\frac{1}{2}$ area of $\parallel$ gm ABCD	4. From 2 and 3.

Corollary 1. *Area of a triangle = $\frac{1}{2}$ base × height*

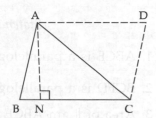

Proof. Let ABC be a triangle with base BC and AN $\perp$ BC, then height of $\triangle$ABC = AN. Through A and C draw lines parallel to BC and BA to meet at D, then ABCD is a parallelogram.

Thus, $\triangle$ABC and parallelogram ABCD are on the same base BC and between same parallel lines BC and AD.

Area of $\triangle$ABC $= \frac{1}{2}$ area of parallelogram ABCD   (Theorem 14.4)

$= \frac{1}{2}$ BC × AN   (area of $\parallel$ gm = base × height)

$= \frac{1}{2}$ base × height.

Corollary 2. *A median of a triangle divides it into two triangles of equal areas.*

Proof. Let ABC be any triangle and AD be one of its medians (shown in the adjoining figure).

We need to show that area of $\triangle$ABD = area of $\triangle$ACD.

From A, draw AN $\perp$ BC.

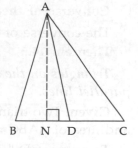

Now, area ($\triangle$ABD) $= \frac{1}{2}$ base × corresponding height

$= \frac{1}{2}$ BD × AN $= \frac{1}{2}$ DC × AN

($\because$ D is mid-point of BC, so BD = DC)

$=$ area of $\triangle$ACD.

Hence, a median of a triangle divides it into two triangles of equal area.

Corollary 3. *Area of a trapezium = $\frac{1}{2}$ (sum of parallel sides) × height.*

Proof. Let ABCD be a trapezium in which AB $\parallel$ DC. Join AC. From C, draw CN $\perp$ AB and from A, draw AM $\perp$ CD (produced).

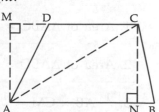

Then   CN = AM = height of trapezium

$= h$ (say).

Area of trapezium ABCD = area of $\triangle$ABC + area of $\triangle$ACD

$= \frac{1}{2}$ AB × CN $+ \frac{1}{2}$ DC × AM

$$= \frac{1}{2}(AB \times h + DC \times h) = \frac{1}{2}(AB + DC) \times h$$

$$= \frac{1}{2}(\text{sum of parallel sides}) \times \text{height}.$$

Theorem 14.5

Triangles on the same base (or equal bases) and between the same parallel lines are equal in area.

Given. Two triangles ABC and BCD on the same BC and between the same parallel lines BC and *l*.

To prove. Area of △ABC = area of △BCD.

Construction. Through C, draw CE ∥ BA and CF ∥ BD to meet line *l* at E and F respectively.

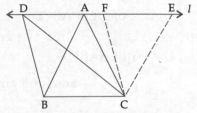

Proof.

Statements	Reasons
1. ABCE is a parallelogram.	1. BC ∥ AE (given), CE ∥ BA (Const.)
2. BCFD is a parallelogram	2. BC ∥ DF (given), CF ∥ BD (Const.)
3. Area of ∥ gm ABCE = area of ∥ gm BCFD.	3. Parallelogram on same base and between same parallel lines.
4. Area of △ABC = $\frac{1}{2}$ area of ∥ gm ABCE	4. Area of a △ is half that of a ∥ gm on the same base and between same parallels.
5. Area of △BCD = $\frac{1}{2}$ area of ∥ gm BCFD	5. Area of a △ is half that of a ∥ gm on the same base and between same parallels.
6. Area of △ABC = area of △BCD	6. From 3, 4 and 5.

❑ **Converse of theorem 14.5**

The converse of the above theorem 14.5 is also true. In fact, we have:

Theorem 14.6

Triangles on the same base (or equal bases) and having equal areas lie between the same parallel lines.

Given. Two triangles ABC and ABD on the same base AB, and area of △ABC = area of △ABD.

To prove. CD ∥ AB.

Construction. From C and D, draw perpendiculars CM and DN on AB respectively.

Proof.

Statements	Reasons
1. Area of △ABC = $\frac{1}{2}$ AB × CM	1. Area of a triangle = $\frac{1}{2}$ base × height.
2. Area of △ABD = $\frac{1}{2}$ AB × DN	2. Same as above.
3. $\frac{1}{2}$ AB × CM = $\frac{1}{2}$ AB × DN	3. Area of △ABC = area of △ABD (given)
4. CM = DN	4. From 3, cancelling $\frac{1}{2}$ AB.

5. CM ∥ DN	5. CM and DN are both perpendiculars to the same line AB.
6. CMND is a parallelogram.	6. Two sides CM and DN of quad. CMND are equal and parallel.
7. CD ∥ MN *i.e.* CD ∥ AB	7. By definition of a ∥ gm.

Corollary 1. *Triangles on the same base (or equal bases) and having equal areas have equal corresponding altitudes.*

(In the above proof of the theorem, we obtained CM = DN. So, ∆ABC and ∆ABD have equal corresponding altitudes.)

Corollary 2. *If two triangles lie between the same parallels (i.e. have equal altitudes), then the ratio of their areas equals the ratio of their bases.*

Corollary 3. *If two triangles have equal bases, then the ratio of their areas equals the ratio of their altitudes.*

Illustrative Examples

Example 1 P and Q are any two points lying on the sides DC and AD respectively of a parallelogram ABCD. Show that area of ∆APB = area of ∆BQC.

Solution. Given a parallelogram ABCD, and P and Q are points lying on the sides DC and AD respectively as shown in the adjoining figure.

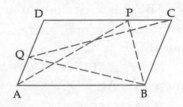

As ∆APB and ∥ gm ABCD are on the same base and between the same parallels AB and DC,

$$\text{area of } \triangle APB = \frac{1}{2} \text{ area of } \parallel \text{gm ABCD} \qquad …(i)$$

Also, as ∆BQC and ∥ gm ABCD are on the same BC and between the same parallels AD and BC,

$$\text{area of } \triangle BQC = \frac{1}{2} \text{ area of } \parallel \text{gm ABCD} \qquad …(ii)$$

From (*i*) and (*ii*), we get

area of ∆APB = area of ∆BQC.

Example 2 In the adjoining figure, ABCD is a rectangle with sides AB = 8 cm and AD = 5 cm. Compute

(*i*) area of parallelogram ABEF

(*ii*) area of ∆EFG.

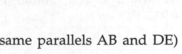

Solution. (*i*) Area of ∥ gm ABEF

= area of rectangle ABCD

(on the same base AB and between the same parallels AB and DE)

= (8 × 5) cm² = 40 cm².

(*ii*) Area of ∆EFG = $\frac{1}{2}$ area of ∥ gm ABEF

(on the same base FE and between the same parallels FE and AG)

= $\left(\frac{1}{2} \times 40\right)$ cm² = 20 cm².

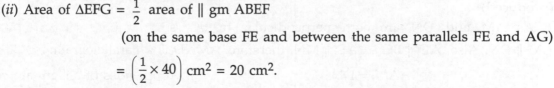

Example 3 In the adjoining figure, ABCD and ABEF are parallelograms and P is any point on DC. If area of ∥gm ABCD = 90 cm², find:

(i) area of ∥gm ABEF

(ii) area of ΔABP

(iii) area of ΔBEF.

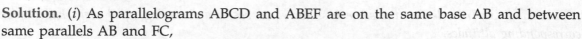

Solution. (i) As parallelograms ABCD and ABEF are on the same base AB and between same parallels AB and FC,

area of ∥gm ABEF = area of ∥gm ABCD = 90 cm²   (given)

(ii) As ΔABP and ∥gm ABCD are on the same base AB and between same parallels AB and DC,

area of ΔABP = $\frac{1}{2}$ area of ∥gm ABCD = $\left(\frac{1}{2} \times 90\right)$ cm² = 45 cm²

(iii) As a diagonals of a ∥gm divides it into two congruent triangles of equal area,

area of ΔBEF = $\frac{1}{2}$ area of ∥gm ABEF = $\left(\frac{1}{2} \times 90\right)$ cm² = 45 cm². (using part (i))

Example 4 In the adjoining figure, ABCD is a quadrilateral with BD as one of its diagonals and AB = CD = 2·5 cm, ∠ABD = ∠CDB = 90° and BD = 4 cm. Show that quad. ABCD is a parallelogram and find its area.

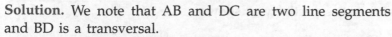

Solution. We note that AB and DC are two line segments and BD is a transversal.

Given ∠ABD = ∠CDB, which a pair of alternate angles, therefore, AB ∥ DC.

Also   AB = CD   (given)

Thus, in quadrilateral ABCD, AB ∥ DC and AB = CD, therefore, ABCD is a parallelogram.

If we take AB as base, then BD is the corresponding height

(∵ ∠ABD = 90°, so BD ⊥ AB).

Area of ∥gm ABCD = base × height

= (2·5 cm) × (4 cm) = 10 cm².

Example 5 In the adjoining figure, ABCD is a parallelogram. Points P and Q on BC trisect BC in three equal parts. Prove that area of ΔAPQ = area of ΔDPQ = $\frac{1}{6}$ area of ∥gm ABCD.

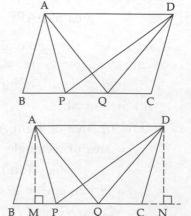

Solution. Given points P and Q on BC trisect BC, so BP = PQ = QC

⇒   PQ = $\frac{1}{3}$ BC.

From A, draw AM ⊥ BC and from D, draw DN ⊥ BC (produced).

As AM and DN are both perpendicular to BC, so AM ∥ DN. Also, AD ∥ BC i.e. AD ∥ MN, therefore, AMND is a parallelogram.

∴   AM = DN   (opp. sides of a ∥ gm are equal)

Now area of $\triangle APQ = \frac{1}{2} PQ \times AM = \frac{1}{2} \left(\frac{1}{3} BC\right) \times AM$

$$= \frac{1}{6} BC \times AM = \frac{1}{6} \text{ area of } \|\text{gm ABCD}\qquad\qquad ...(i)$$

and area of $\triangle DPQ = \frac{1}{2} PQ \times DN = \frac{1}{2} \left(\frac{1}{3} BC\right) \times AM$

$$= \frac{1}{6} BC \times AM = \frac{1}{6} \text{ area of } \|\text{gm ABCD}\qquad\qquad ...(ii)$$

From (i) and (ii), we get

$$\text{area of } \triangle APQ = \text{area of } \triangle DPQ = \frac{1}{6} \text{ area of } \|\text{gm ABCD}.$$

Example 6 In the adjoining figure, BD = 2DC. If area of $\triangle ABC = 60 \text{ cm}^2$, find area of $\triangle ADC$.

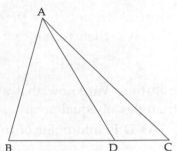

Solution. Given BD = 2DC

$\Rightarrow$ $\qquad$ BC − DC = 2DC $\Rightarrow$ BC = 2DC

$\Rightarrow$ $\qquad\qquad DC = \frac{1}{3} BC\qquad\qquad ...(i)$

Note that $\triangle ABC$ and $\triangle ADC$ have same height.

$$\text{area of } \triangle ADC = \frac{1}{2} \text{ base} \times \text{height}$$

$$= \frac{1}{2} DC \times \text{height}$$

$$= \frac{1}{2} \times \left(\frac{1}{3} BC\right) \times \text{height}\qquad\qquad \text{(using (i))}$$

$$= \frac{1}{3} \left(\frac{1}{2} BC \times \text{height}\right) = \frac{1}{3} \text{ area of } \triangle ABC.$$

Example 7 A point E is taken on the side BC of a parallelogram ABCD. AE and DC are produced to meet at F. Prove that area of $\triangle ADF$ = area of quad. ABFC.

Solution. Join AC and BF.

As triangles ACF and BCF have same base CF and are between the same parallels AB and CF ($\because$ AB $\|$ DC),

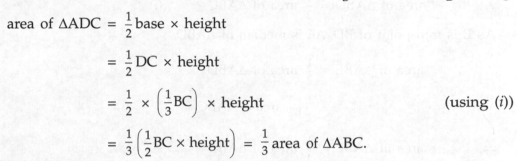

$\qquad$ area of $\triangle ACF$ = area of $\triangle BCF\qquad\qquad ...(i)$

As diagonal AC divides $\|$ gm ABCD into two triangles of equal area,

$\qquad$ area of $\triangle DAC$ = area of $\triangle ABC\qquad\qquad ...(ii)$

On adding (i) and (ii), we get

$\qquad$ area of $\triangle ACF$ + area of $\triangle DAC$ = area of $\triangle BCF$ + area of $\triangle ABC$

$\Rightarrow$ $\qquad$ area of $\triangle ADF$ = area of quad. ABFC.

Example 8 In a triangle ABC, E is mid-point of median AD. Show that

$$\text{area of } \triangle BED = \frac{1}{4} \text{ area of } \triangle ABC.$$

Solution. We know that a median of a triangle divides it into two triangles of equal area.

As AD is median of $\triangle ABC$,

$\therefore$ $\qquad$ area of $\triangle ABD$ = ar$(\triangle ACD)$

$\Rightarrow$ $\qquad$ area of $\triangle ABD = \dfrac{1}{2}$ area of $\triangle ABC$ $\qquad$ ...(i)

Also E is mid-point of AD *i.e.* BE is a median of $\triangle ABD$,

$\therefore$ $\qquad$ area of $\triangle BED =$ area of $\triangle ABE$

$\Rightarrow$ $\qquad$ area of $\triangle BED = \dfrac{1}{2}$ area of $\triangle ABD$

$\qquad\qquad\qquad = \dfrac{1}{2}\left(\dfrac{1}{2}\text{ area of }\triangle ABC\right)$ $\qquad$ (using (i))

$\Rightarrow$ $\qquad$ area of $\triangle BED = \dfrac{1}{4}$ area of $\triangle ABC$

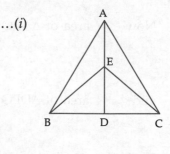

Example 9 In the adjoining figure, D is the mid-point of side BC of $\triangle ABC$ and E is the mid-point of BD. If O is the mid-point of AE, then prove that

$\qquad$ area of $\triangle OBE = \dfrac{1}{8}$ area of $\triangle ABC$.

Solution. We know that a median of a triangle divides it into two triangles of equal area.

As D is mid-point of the side BC, AD is a median of $\triangle ABC$,

$\therefore$ $\qquad$ area of $\triangle ABD = \dfrac{1}{2}$ area of $\triangle ABC$ $\qquad$ ...(i)

As E is mid-point of BD, AE is median of $\triangle ABD$,

$\therefore$ $\qquad$ area of $\triangle ABE = \dfrac{1}{2}$ area of $\triangle ABD$

$\qquad\qquad\qquad = \dfrac{1}{2}\left(\dfrac{1}{2}\text{ area of }\triangle ABC\right)$ $\qquad$ (using (i))

$\Rightarrow$ $\qquad$ area of $\triangle ABE = \dfrac{1}{4}$ area of $\triangle ABC$ $\qquad$ ...(ii)

As O is mid-point of AE, BO is median of $\triangle ABE$,

$\therefore$ $\qquad$ area of $\triangle OBE = \dfrac{1}{2}$ area of $\triangle ABE$

$\qquad\qquad\qquad = \dfrac{1}{2}\left(\dfrac{1}{4}\text{ area of }\triangle ABC\right)$ $\qquad$ (using (ii))

$\Rightarrow$ $\qquad$ area of $\triangle OBE = \dfrac{1}{8}$ area of $\triangle ABC$, as required.

Example 10 If the medians of a triangle ABC intersect at G, prove that

$\qquad$ area of $\triangle AGB =$ area of $\triangle BGC =$ area of $\triangle CGA = \dfrac{1}{3}$ area of $\triangle ABC$.

Solution. A triangle ABC such that its medians AD, BE and CF intersect at G.

We want to prove that

area of $\triangle AGB =$ area of $\triangle BGC =$ area of $\triangle CGA$

$\qquad = \dfrac{1}{3}$ area of $\triangle ABC$.

We know that a median of a triangle divides it into two triangles of equal area.

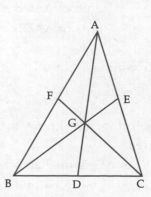

In ΔABC, AD is median

∴   area of ΔABD = area of ΔACD   ...(i)

In ΔBGC, GD is median

∴   area of ΔGBD = area of ΔGDC   ...(ii)

Subtracting (ii) from (i), we get

     area of ΔABD – area of ΔGBD = area of ΔACD – area of ΔGDC

⇒   area of ΔAGB = area of ΔCGA   ...(iii)

Similarly, area of ΔAGB = area of ΔBGC   ...(iv)

From (iii) and (iv), we get

⇒   area of ΔAGB = area of ΔBGC = area of ΔCGA   ...(v)

From fig., area of ΔAGB + area of ΔBGC = area of ΔCGA = area of ΔABC

⇒   3 area of ΔAGB = area of ΔABC ⇒ area of ΔAGB = $\frac{1}{3}$ area of ΔABC.

Hence, area of ΔAGB = area of ΔBGC = area of ΔCGA = $\frac{1}{3}$ area of ΔABC.

Example 11 In the adjoining figure, ABCD is a parallelogram with area 80 sq. cm. The diagonals AC and BD intersect at O. If P is the mid-point of OA, then find area of ΔBOP.

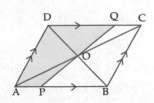

Solution. As P is mid-point of OA, BP is median of ΔOAB. As a median of a triangle divides it into two triangles of equal area,

∴   area of ΔBOP = $\frac{1}{2}$ area of ΔOAB   ...(i)

We know that the diagonals of a parallelogram bisect each other, O is mid-point of AC, therefore, OB is median of ΔABC,

∴   area of ΔOAB = $\frac{1}{2}$ area of ΔABC   ...(ii)

We know that a diagonal of a parallelogram divides it into two triangles of each area,

∴   area of ΔABC = $\frac{1}{2}$ area of ∥gm ABCD

                 = $\left(\frac{1}{2} \times 80\right)$ sq. cm   (∵ area of ∥gm ABCD = 80 sq. cm)

⇒   area of ΔABC = 40 sq. cm   ...(iii)

Using (i) and (ii), we have

      area of ΔBOP = $\frac{1}{2}$ area of ΔOAB = $\frac{1}{2}\left(\frac{1}{2}$ area of ΔABC$\right)$

                 = $\frac{1}{4}$ area of ΔABC = $\left(\frac{1}{4} \times 40\right)$ sq. cm   (using (iii)

⇒   area of ΔBOP = 10 sq. cm.

Example 12 The diagonals of a parallelogram ABCD intersect at O. A straight line through O meets AB at P and the opposite side CD at Q. Prove that area of quad. APQD = $\frac{1}{2}$ area of ∥ gm ABCD.

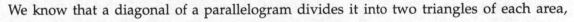

Proof.

Statements	Reasons
1. Area of $\triangle$ACD = $\frac{1}{2}$ area of $\parallel$ gm ABCD	1. Diagonal divides a $\parallel$gm into two $\triangle$s of equal area.
In $\triangle$OAP and $\triangle$OCQ	
2. $\angle$OAP = $\angle$OCQ	2. Alt. $\angle$s.
3. $\angle$AOP = $\angle$COQ	3. Vert. opp. $\angle$s.
4. AO = OC	4. Diagonals bisect each other.
5. $\triangle$OAP $\cong$ $\triangle$OCQ	5. ASA rule of congruency.
6. Area of $\triangle$OAP = area of $\triangle$OCQ	6. Congruence area axiom.
7. Area of $\triangle$OAP + area of quad. AOQD = area of $\triangle$OCQ + area of quad. AOQD	7. Adding same area on both sides.
8. Area of quad. APQD = area of $\triangle$ACD	8. Addition area axiom.
9. Area of quad. APQD $\quad = \frac{1}{2}$ area of $\parallel$ gm ABCD **Q.E.D.**	9. From 8 and 1.

Example 13 ABCD is a trapezium with AB $\parallel$ DC, and diagonals AC and BD meet at O. Prove that area of $\triangle$DAO = area of $\triangle$OBC.

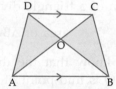

Proof.

Statements	Reasons
1. AB $\parallel$ DC	1. Given.
2. Area of $\triangle$ABD = area of $\triangle$ABC	2. $\triangle$s on the same base AB and between the same parallels AB and CD are equal in area.
3. Area of $\triangle$DAO + area of $\triangle$OAB = area of $\triangle$OBC + area of $\triangle$OAB	3. Addition area axiom.
4. Area of $\triangle$DAO = area of $\triangle$OBC **Q.E.D.**	4. Subtracting same area from both sides.

Example 14 The diagonals AC and BD of a quadrilateral ABCD intersect at O. If OB = OD, prove that the triangles ABC and ACD are equal in area.

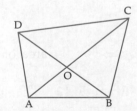

Proof.

Statements	Reasons
1. AO is median of $\triangle$ABD	1. OB = OD (given).
2. Area of $\triangle$OAB = area of $\triangle$OAD	2. Median divides a $\triangle$into two $\triangle$s of equal area.

Statements	Reasons
3. CO is median of △CBD	3. OB = OD (given)
4. Area of △OBC = area of △OCD	4. Median divides a △ into two △s of equal area.
5. Area of △OAB + area of △OBC = area of △OAD + area of △OCD	5. Adding 2 and 4
6. Area of △ABC = area of △ACD **Q.E.D.**	6. Addition area axiom.

Example 15 In quadrilateral ABCD, M is mid-point of the diagonal AC. Prove that area of quad. ABMD = area of quad. DMBC.

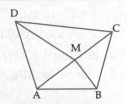

Proof.

Statements	Reasons
1. BM is median of △BCA	1. M is mid-point of AC (given).
2. Area of △ABM = area of △MBC	2. Median divides a △ into two △s of equal area.
3. DM is median of △DAC	3. M is mid-point of AC (given).
4. Area of △DAM = area of △DMC	4. Median divides a triangle into two △s of equal area.
5. Area of △ABM + area of △DAM = area of △MBC + area of △DMC	5. Adding 2 and 4.
6. Area of quad. ABMD = area of quad. DMBC **Q.E.D.**	6. Addition area axiom.

Example 16 In the adjoining figure, D is mid-point of AB and P is any point on side BC of △ABC. If CQ ∥ PD meets AB in Q, then prove that area of △BPQ = $\frac{1}{2}$ area of △ABC.

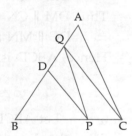

Solution. Join CD.

Triangles DPQ and DPC are on the same base PD and between same parallels CQ and PD,

∴   area of △PDQ = area of △DPC   ...(i)

As D is mid-point of AB, so CD is a median of △ABC. Since a median divides a triangle into two triangles of equal area,

      area of △BCD = $\frac{1}{2}$ area of △ABC

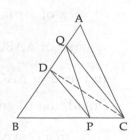

⇒   area of △BPD + area of △DPC = $\frac{1}{2}$ area of △ABC

⇒   area of △BPD + area of △DPQ = $\frac{1}{2}$ area of △ABC   (using (i))

⇒   area of △BPQ = $\frac{1}{2}$ area of △ABC.

Example 17 In the adjoining figure, ABCDE is any pentagon. BP drawn parallel to AC meets DC produced at P and EQ drawn parallel to AD meets CD produced at Q. Prove that area of ABCDE = area of △APQ.

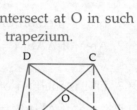

Solution. △PCA and △BCA are on the same base CA and between same parallels BP ∥ AC.

∴   area of △BCA = area of △PCA   ...(i)

△EAD and △QAD are on the same base AD and between same parallels EQ ∥ AD,

∴   area of △EAD = area of △QAD   ...(ii)

Also, area of △ACD = area of △ACD   ...(iii)

On adding (i), (iii) and (ii), we get

        area of △BCA + area of △ACD + area of △EAD

                = area of △PCA + area of △ACD + area of △QAD

⇒   area of ABCDE = area of △APQ.

Example 18 The diagonals AC and BD of a quadrilateral ABCD intersect at O in such a way that area of △OAD = area of △OBC. Prove that ABCD is a trapezium.

Solution. Draw DM ⊥ AB and CN ⊥ AB.

As DM and CN are both perpendiculars to AB, therefore, DM ∥ CN.

Given area of △OAD = area of △OBC

⇒   area of △OAD + area of △OAB

        = area of △OBC + area of △OAB   (adding same area on both sides)

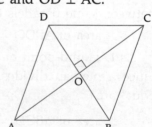

⇒   area of △ABD = area of △ABC

⇒ $\frac{1}{2}$ AB × DM = $\frac{1}{2}$ AB × CN

⇒   DM = CN.

Thus DM ∥ CN and DM = CN, therefore, DMNC is a parallelogram

⇒   DC ∥ MN *i.e.* DC ∥ AB.

Hence, ABCD is a trapezium.

Example 19 Prove that area of a rhombus = $\frac{1}{2}$ × product of diagonals.

Solution. Let ABCD be a rhombus, and let its diagonals intersect at O.

Since the diagonals of a rhombus cut at right angles, OB ⊥ AC and OD ⊥ AC.

As area of a triangle = $\frac{1}{2}$ base × height,

∴ area of △ABC = $\frac{1}{2}$ AC × OB   ...(i)

and area of △ACD = $\frac{1}{2}$ AC × OD   ...(ii)

On adding (i) and (ii), we get

        area of △ABC + area of △ACD = $\frac{1}{2}$ AC × OB + $\frac{1}{2}$ AC × OD

⇒   area of rhombus ABCD = $\frac{1}{2}$ AC × (OB + OD)

                = $\frac{1}{2}$ AC × BD

                = $\frac{1}{2}$ × product of diagonals.

Example 20 ABCD is a trapezium with AB ∥ DC. A line parallel to AC intersects AB at X and BC at Y. Prove that: area of △ADX = area of △ACY.

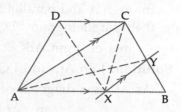

Solution. Join CX.

As triangles ADX and ACX have same base AX and are between the same parallels (AB ∥ DC given, so, AX ∥ DC),

∴   area of △ADX = area of △ACX   ...(i)

As triangles ACY and ACX have same base AC and are between the same parallels (XY ∥ AC given),

∴   area of △ACY = area of △ACX   ...(ii)

From (i) and (ii), we get

area of △ADX = area of △ACY.

Example 21 XY is a line parallel to side BC of a triangle ABC. If BE ∥ CA and FC ∥ AB meet XY at E and F respectively, show that area of △ABE = area of △ACF.

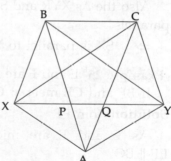

Solution. As △ABE and ∥ gm EBCY have the same base BE and are between the same parallels BE ∥ CA (given),

∴   area of △ABE = $\frac{1}{2}$ area of ∥ gm EBCY   ...(i)

As △ACF and ∥ gm XBCF have the same base CF and are between the same parallels CF ∥ BA (given),

∴   area of △ACF = $\frac{1}{2}$ area of ∥ gm XBCF   ...(ii)

But ∥ gm EBCY and ∥ gm XBCF have the same base BC and are between the same parallels (XY ∥ BC given),

∴   area of ∥ gm EBCY = area of ∥ gm XBCF

⇒ $\frac{1}{2}$ area of ∥ gm EBCY= $\frac{1}{2}$ area of ∥ gm XBCF

⇒   area of △ABE = area of △ACF   (using (i) and (ii))

Example 22 In the adjoining figure, BC ∥ XY, BX ∥ CA and AB ∥ YC. Prove that

area of △ABX = area of △AYC.

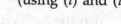

Solution. As △BCX and △BCY are on the same base BC and between the same parallels BC and XY,

area of △BCX = area of △BCY   ...(i)

Since △BCX and △ABX are on the same base BX and between same BX and CA,

∴   area of △BCX = area of △ABX   ...(ii)

As △BCY and △AYC are on the same base CY and between same parallels CY and BA,

∴   area of △BCY = area of △AYC   ...(iii)

From (i) and (ii), we get

area of △ABX = area of △BCY   ...(iv)

From (iii) and (iv), we get

area of △ABX = area of △AYC, as required.

Example 23 In the adjoining figure, the side AB of a parallelogram ABCD is produced to any point P. A line through A and parallel to CP meets CB produced at Q and then parallelogram PBQR is completed. Show that

area of || gm ABCD = area of || gm PBQR.

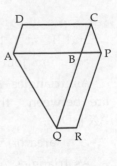

Solution. Join AC and PQ.

As AC is a diagonal of || gm ABCD,

area of || gm ABCD = 2 area of △ABC   ...(i)

As PQ is a diagonal of || gm PBQR,

area of || gm PBQR = 2 area of △PBQ   ...(ii)

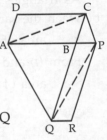

Now, triangles CAQ and PAQ have the same base AQ and are between the same parallels AQ || CP,

∴   area of △CAQ = area of △PAQ

⇒   area of △CAQ – area of △BAQ = area of △PAQ – area of △BAQ

                (subtracting same area from both sides)

⇒   area of △ABC = area of △PBQ

⇒   2 area of △ABC = 2 area of △PBQ

⇒   area of || gm ABCD = area of || gm PBQR   (using (i) and (ii))

Example 24 In the adjoining figure, PQRS and PXYZ are two parallelograms of equal area. Prove that SX is parallel to YR.

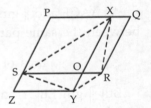

Solution. Join XR, SY.

Given area of || gm PQSR = area of || gm PXYZ.

Subtract area of || gm PSOX from both sides.

∴   Area of || gm XORQ = area of || gm SZYO

⇒   area of △ XOR = area of △SYO

                (because diagonal divides a || gm into two equal areas)

Adding area of △OYR to both sides, we get

area of △XYR = area of △SYR.

Also the △s XYR and SYR have the same base YR, therefore, these lie between the same parallels

⇒   SX is parallel to YR.

Example 25 E and F are mid-points of the sides AB and AC respectively of a triangle ABC. If BF and CE meet at O, prove that area of △OBC = area of quad. AEOF.

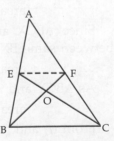

Solution. Join EF.

As E and F are mid-points of AB and AC respectively, EF || BC.

∴   Area of △EBC = area of △FBC.

(Triangles on the same base BC and between same parallels)

⇒   area of △EBC – area of △OBC

                = area of △FBC – area of △OBC

⇒   area of △BOE = area of △COF   ...(i)

As F is mid-point of AC, area of △FBC = area of △ABF

                (∵ A median divides a triangle into two triangles of equal area).

⇒   area of △FBC – area of △COF = area of △ABF – area of △BOE   (using (i))

⇒   area of △OBC = area of quad. AEOF   (from figure)

Example 26 In the adjoining figure, ABCD, DCFE and ABFE are parallelograms. Show that area of $\triangle$ADE = area of $\triangle$BCF.

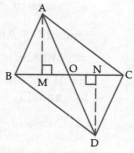

Solution. As ABCD is a parallelogram,

$$AD = BC \qquad \text{(opp. sides of a } \parallel \text{gm)}$$

Similarly, $\qquad$ DE = CF and AE = BF.

In $\triangle$ADE and $\triangle$BCF,

$$AD = BC, \; DE = CF \text{ and } AE = BF$$

$\therefore \qquad \triangle ADE \cong \triangle BCF \qquad$ (by SSS rule of congruency)

$\therefore \qquad$ area of $\triangle$ADE = area of $\triangle$BCF $\qquad$ (congruent figures have equal areas)

Example 27 Triangles ABC and DBC are on the same base BC with A, D on opposite sides of BC. If area of $\triangle$ABC = area of $\triangle$DBC, prove that BC bisects AD.

Solution. Let BC and AD intersect at O.

Draw AM $\perp$ BC and DN $\perp$ BC.

Given area of $\triangle$ABC = area of $\triangle$DBC

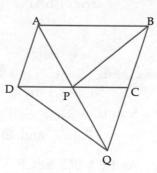

$$\Rightarrow \quad \frac{1}{2} BC \times AM = \frac{1}{2} BC \times DN$$

$$\Rightarrow \quad AM = DN.$$

In $\triangle$AMO and $\triangle$DNO,

$$\angle AOM = \angle DON \qquad \text{(vert. opp. } \angle s)$$

$$\angle AMO = \angle DNO \qquad \text{(each angle = 90°)}$$

$$AM = DN \qquad \text{(proved above)}$$

$\therefore \qquad \triangle AMO \cong \triangle DNO \qquad$ (AAS rule of congruency)

$\therefore \qquad AO = DO \qquad$ (c.p.c.t.)

Hence, BC bisects AD.

Example 28 In the adjoining figure, ABCD is a parallelogram and BC is produced to a point Q such that CQ = AD. If AQ intersects DC at P, show that area of $\triangle$BPC = area of $\triangle$DPQ.

Solution. Join AC.

As triangles BPC and APC have same base PC and are between the same parallels (AB $\parallel$ DC *i.e.* AB $\parallel$ PC),

$\therefore \qquad$ area of $\triangle$BPC = area of $\triangle$APC $\qquad$ ...(*i*)

In quad. ADQC, AD $\parallel$ CQ

$$(\because \text{ AD } \parallel \text{ BC, opp. sides of } \parallel \text{ gm ABCD})$$

$$AD = CQ \qquad \text{(given)}$$

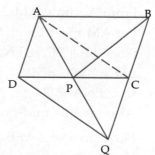

$\therefore$ ADQC is a parallelogram, so its diagonals AQ and DC bisect each other *i.e.* DP = PC and AP = PQ.

In $\triangle$APC and $\triangle$QPD,

$$PC = DP$$

$$AP = PQ$$

$$\angle APC = \angle QPD \qquad \text{(vert. opp. } \angle s)$$

$$\triangle APC \cong \triangle QPD$$

$\therefore \qquad$ area of $\triangle$APC = area of $\triangle$DPQ $\qquad$ ...(*ii*)

From (*i*) and (*ii*), we get

$$\text{area of } \triangle BPC = \text{area of } \triangle DPQ.$$

Example 29 In the adjoining figure, P is a point in the interior of a parallelogram ABCD. Show that:

(i) area of $\triangle$APB + area of $\triangle$PDC = $\frac{1}{2}$(area of $\parallel$ gm ABCD)

(ii) area of $\triangle$APD + area of $\triangle$PBC = area of $\triangle$APB + area of $\triangle$PDC

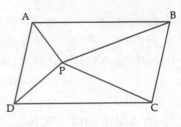

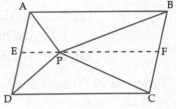

Solution. (i) Through P, draw a line parallel to AB to meet AD at E and BC at F.

Then AEFB is a parallelogram.

As $\triangle$APB and $\parallel$ gm AEFB are on the same base AB and between the same parallels AB and EF,

∴   area of $\triangle$APB = $\frac{1}{2}$(area of $\parallel$ gm AEFB)   ...(1)

Since EF $\parallel$ AB and AB $\parallel$ DC, so EF $\parallel$ DC

⇒   EDCF is a parallelogram.

As $\triangle$PDC and $\parallel$ gm EDCF are on the same base DC and between the same parallels DC and EF,

∴   area of $\triangle$PDC = $\frac{1}{2}$(area of $\parallel$ gm EDCF)   ...(2)

On adding (1) and (2), we get

area of $\triangle$APB + area of $\triangle$PDC = $\frac{1}{2}$(area of $\parallel$ gm AEFB + area of $\parallel$ gm EDCF)

= $\frac{1}{2}$(area of $\parallel$ gm ABCD)

(ii) Similarly, by drawing a line through P and parallel to AD, we get

area of $\triangle$APD + area of $\triangle$PBC = $\frac{1}{2}$(area of $\parallel$ gm ABCD)

= area of $\triangle$APB + area of $\triangle$PDC   (using part (i))

Example 30 ABC is a triangle whose area is 50 cm². E and F are mid-points of the sides AB and AC respectively. Prove that EBCF is a trapezium. Also find its area.

Solution. Since E and F are mid-points of the sides AB and AC respectively,

EF $\parallel$ BC and EF = $\frac{1}{2}$ BC.

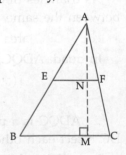

As EF $\parallel$ BC, EBCF is a trapezium.

From A, draw AM $\perp$ BC.

Let AM meet EF at N.

Since EF $\parallel$ BC, $\angle$ENA = $\angle$BMN.

But $\angle$BMN = 90°   (∵ AM $\perp$ BC)

so $\angle$ENA = 90° *i.e.* AN $\perp$ EF.

Also, as E is mid-point of AB and EN $\parallel$ BM, N is mid-point of AM.

Now, area of $\triangle$AEF = $\frac{1}{2}$ EF × AN = $\frac{1}{2}$($\frac{1}{2}$ BC × $\frac{1}{2}$ AM)

= $\frac{1}{4}$($\frac{1}{2}$ BC × AM) = $\frac{1}{4}$(area of $\triangle$ABC)

= $\frac{1}{4}$(50 cm²) = 12·5 cm².

∴   Area of trapezium EBCF = area of $\triangle$ABC − area of $\triangle$AEF

= 50 cm² − 12·5 cm² = 37·5 cm².

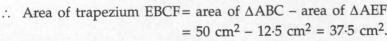

Example 31 Prove that the area of the quadrilateral formed by joining the mid-points of the adjacent sides of a quadrilateral is half the area of the given quadrilateral.

Given. A quadrilateral ABCD, and PQRS is the quadrilateral formed by joining mid-points of the sides AB, BC, CD and DA respectively.

To prove. Area of quad. PQRS = $\frac{1}{2}$ area of quad. ABCD.

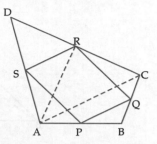

Construction. Join AC and AR.

Proof.

Statements	Reasons
1. Area of $\triangle$ARD = $\frac{1}{2}$ area of $\triangle$ACD	1. Median divides a triangle into two triangles of equal area.
2. Area of $\triangle$SRD = $\frac{1}{2}$ area of $\triangle$ARD	2. Same as in 1.
3. Area of $\triangle$SRD = $\frac{1}{4}$ area of $\triangle$ACD	3. From 1 and 2.
4. Area of $\triangle$PBQ = $\frac{1}{4}$ area of $\triangle$ABC	4. As in 3.
5. Area of $\triangle$SRD + area of $\triangle$PBQ = $\frac{1}{4}$ (area of $\triangle$ACD + area of $\triangle$ABC)	5. Adding 3 and 4.
6. Area of $\triangle$SRD + area of $\triangle$PBQ = $\frac{1}{4}$ area of quad. ABCD	6. Addition area axiom.
7. Area of $\triangle$APS + area of $\triangle$QCR = $\frac{1}{4}$ area of quad. ABCD	7. Same as in 6.
8. Area of $\triangle$APS + area of $\triangle$PBQ + area of $\triangle$QCR + area of $\triangle$SRD = $\frac{1}{2}$ area of quad. ABCD	8. Adding 6 and 7.
9. Area of $\triangle$APS + area of $\triangle$PBQ + area of $\triangle$QCR + area of $\triangle$SRD + area of quad. PQRS = area of quad. ABCD	9. Addition area axiom.
10. Area of quad. PQRS = $\frac{1}{2}$ area of quad. ABCD **Q.E.D.**	10. Subtracting 8 from 9.

EXERCISE 14

1 Prove that the line segment joining the mid-points of a pair of opposite sides of a parallelogram divides it into two equal parallelograms.

2 Prove that the diagonals of a parallelogram divide it into four triangles of equal area.

3 (a) In the figure (1) given below, AD is median of $\triangle$ABC and P is any point on AD. Prove that
    (i) area of $\triangle$PBD = area of $\triangle$PDC   (ii) area of $\triangle$ABP = area of $\triangle$ACP.

(b) In the figure (2) given below, DE ∥ BC. Prove that
   (i) area of ΔACD = area of ΔABE   (ii) area of ΔOBD = area of ΔOCE.

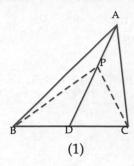

(1)

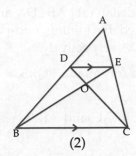

(2)

Hint. (b) (i) Area of ΔDEC = area of ΔDEB, add area of ΔADE to both sides.

4   (a) In the figure (1) given below, ABCD is a parallelogram and P is any point in BC. Prove that, area of ΔABP + area of ΔDPC = area of ΔAPD.

(b) In the figure (2) given below, O is any point inside a parallelogram ABCD. Prove that

   (i) area of ΔOAB + area of ΔOCD = $\frac{1}{2}$ area of ∥ gm ABCD.

   (ii) area of ΔOBC + area of ΔOAD = $\frac{1}{2}$ area of ∥ gm ABCD.

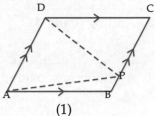

(1)

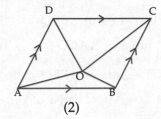

(2)

Hint. (b) (i) Through O, draw a straight line parallel to AB.

5   If E, F, G and H are mid-points of the sides AB, BC, CD and DA respectively of a parallelogram ABCD, prove that area of quad. EFGH = $\frac{1}{2}$ area of ∥gm ABCD.

Hint. Join HF. AH = $\frac{1}{2}$ AD and BF = $\frac{1}{2}$ BC ⇒ AH = BF and AH ∥ BF, so ABFH is a ∥gm.

∴   Area of ΔEFH = $\frac{1}{2}$ area of ∥ gm ABFH.

6   (a) In the figure (1) given below, ABCD is a parallelogram. P, Q are any two points on the sides AB and BC respectively. Prove that

   area of ΔCPD = area of ΔAQD.

(b) In the figure (2) given below, PQRS and ABRS are parallelograms and X is any point on the side BR. Show that

   area of ΔAXS = $\frac{1}{2}$ area of ∥ gm PQRS.

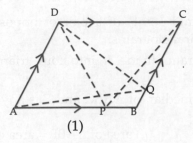

(1)

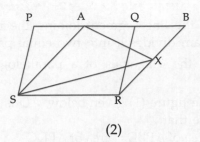

(2)

7 D, E and F are mid-points of the sides BC, CA and AB respectively of a $\triangle$ABC. Prove that

    (*i*) FDCE is a parallelogram   (*ii*) area of $\triangle$DEF = $\frac{1}{4}$ area of $\triangle$ABC

    (*iii*) area of || gm FDCE = $\frac{1}{2}$ area of $\triangle$ABC.

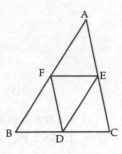

8 In the adjoining figure, D, E and F are mid-points of the sides BC, CA and AB respectively of $\triangle$ABC. Prove that BCEF is a trapezium and area of trap. BCEF = $\frac{3}{4}$ area of $\triangle$ABC.

9   (*a*) In the figure (1) given below, the point D divides the side BC of $\triangle$ABC in the ratio *m* : *n*. Prove that
        area of $\triangle$ABD : area of $\triangle$ADC = *m* : *n*.

  (*b*) In the figure (2) given below, P is a point on the side BC of $\triangle$ABC such that PC = 2BP, and Q is a point on AP such that QA = 5PQ, find area of $\triangle$AQC : area of $\triangle$ABC.

  (*c*) In the figure (3) given below, AD is a median of $\triangle$ABC and P is a point in AC such that area of $\triangle$ADP : area of $\triangle$ABD = 2 : 3. Find
    (*i*) AP : PC   (*ii*) area of $\triangle$PDC : area of $\triangle$ABC

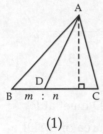 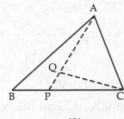 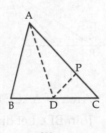

       (1)   (2)   (3)

Hint. (*b*) PC = 2BP $\Rightarrow$ PC = $\frac{2}{3}$ BC $\Rightarrow$ area of $\triangle$APC = $\frac{2}{3}$ area of $\triangle$ABC. QA = 5PQ

            $\Rightarrow$ AQ = $\frac{5}{6}$ AP $\Rightarrow$ area of $\triangle$AQC = $\frac{5}{6}$ area of $\triangle$APC

            = $\frac{5}{6} \cdot \frac{2}{3}$ area of $\triangle$ABC = $\frac{5}{9}$ area of $\triangle$ABC.

    (*c*) AD is median of $\triangle$ABC $\Rightarrow$ area of ABD = area of $\triangle$ADC.
       Given area of $\triangle$ADP : area of $\triangle$ABD = 2 : 3
       $\Rightarrow$ area of $\triangle$ADP : area of $\triangle$ADC = 2 : 3 $\Rightarrow$ AP : AC = 2 : 3
       $\Rightarrow$ AP : PC = 2 : 1.

10   (*a*) In the figure (1) given below, area of parallelogram ABCD is 29 cm². Calculate the height of parallelogram ABEF if AB = 5·8 cm.

  (*b*) In the figure (2) given below, area of $\triangle$ABD is 24 sq. units. If AB = 8 units, find the height of $\triangle$ABC.

  (*c*) In the figure (3) given below, E and F are mid-points of sides AB and CD respectively of parallelogram ABCD. If the area of parallelogram ABCD is 36 cm², (*i*) state the area of ΔAPD.

(*ii*) name the parallelogram whose area is equal to the area of ΔAPD.

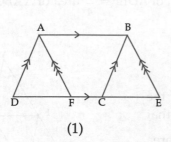

(1)

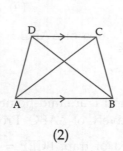

(2)

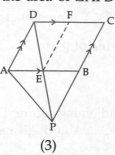

(3)

11 (*a*) In the figure (1) given below, ABCD is a parallelogram. Points P and Q on BC trisect BC into three equal parts. Prove that:

area of ΔAPQ = area of ΔDPQ = $\frac{1}{6}$ (area of ∥ gm ABCD)

(*b*) In the figure (2) given below, DE is drawn parallel to the diagonal AC of the quadrilateral ABCD to meet BC produced at the point E. Prove that area of quad. ABCD = area of ΔABE.

(*c*) In the figure (3) given below, ABCD is a parallelogram. O is any point on the diagonal AC of the parallelogram. Show that the area of ΔAOB is equal to the area of ΔAOD.

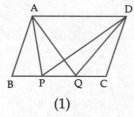

(1)

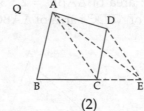

(2)

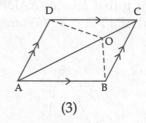

(3)

Hint. (*b*) Area of ΔACE = area of ΔACD

(*c*) Join BD. Let diagonals AC and BD of ∥ gm ABCD meet at P.

Then AP is median of ΔABD ⇒ area of ΔABP = area of ΔADP.

Similarly, area of ΔPBO = area of ΔPDO.

12 (*a*) In the figure (1) given below, ABCD and AEFG are two parallelograms. Prove that area of ∥ gm ABCD = area of ∥ gm AEFG.

(*b*) In the figure (2) given below, the side AB of the parallelogram ABCD is produced to E. A straight line through A is drawn parallel to CE to meet CB produced at F, and parallelogram BFGE is completed. Prove that

area of ∥ gm BFGE = area of ∥ gm ABCD.

(*c*) In the figure (3) given below, AB ∥ DC ∥ EF, AD ∥ BE and DE ∥ AF. Prove that the area of DEFH is equal to the area of ABCD.

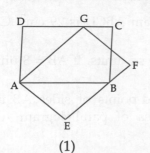

(1)

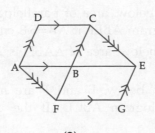

(2)

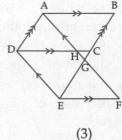

(3)

Hint. (a)   Join BG. Area of $\triangle ABG = \frac{1}{2}$ (area of || gm ABCD);

           area of $\triangle ABG = \frac{1}{2}$ (area of || gm AEFG).

    (b)   Join AC and EF. Area of $\triangle CAF$ = area of $\triangle EAF$.

13 Any point D is taken on the side BC of a $\triangle ABC$ and AD is produced to E such that AD = DE, prove that area of $\triangle BCE$ = area of $\triangle ABC$.

14 ABCD is a rectangle and P is mid-point of AB. DP is produced to meet CB at Q. Prove that area of rectangle ABCD = area of $\triangle DQC$.

Hint. $\triangle APD \cong \triangle PQB$.

15   (a) In the figure (1) given below, the perimeter of parallelogram is 42 cm. Calculate the lengths of the sides of the parallelogram.

    (b) In the figure (2) given below, the perimeter of $\triangle ABC$ is 37 cm. If the lengths of the altitudes AM, BN and CL are $5x$, $6x$ and $4x$ respectively, calculate the lengths of the sides of $\triangle ABC$.

    (c) In the figure (3) given below, ABCD is a parallelogram. P is a point on DC such that area of $\triangle DAP = 25$ cm^2 and area of $\triangle BCP = 15$ cm^2. Find

    (i) area of ||gm ABCD   (ii) DP : PC.

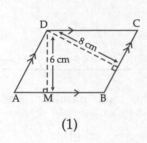
(1)

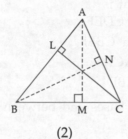
(2)

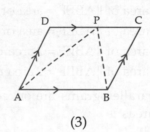
(3)

Hint.   (a) Let AB = p, then BC = $\frac{1}{2} \cdot 42 - p$. Also $6 \cdot p = 8 \cdot (21 - p)$.

        (b) Let BC = p, CA = q, then AB = $37 - p - q$.

            Also $\frac{1}{2}p \cdot 5x = \frac{1}{2}q \cdot 6x = \frac{1}{2}(37 - p - q) \cdot 4x$.

16 In the adjoining figure, E is mid-point of the side AB of a triangle ABC and EBCF is a parallelogram. If the area of $\triangle ABC$ is 25 sq. units, find the area of || gm EBCF.

Hint. Let EF meet AC at G. As E is mid-point of AB and EF || BC, G is mid-point of AC *i.e.* AG = GC.

    Also $\angle EAG = \angle GCF$ and $\angle EGA = \angle CGF$

    $\Rightarrow$ $\triangle AEG \cong \triangle CFG$.

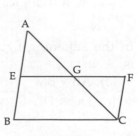

17   (a) In the figure (1) given below, BC || AE and CD || BE. Prove that

         area of $\triangle ABC$ = area of $\triangle EBD$.

    (b) In the figure (2) given below, ABC is right angled triangle at A. AGFB is a square on the side AB and BCDE is a square on the hypotenuse BC. If AN $\perp$ ED, prove that

(i) $\triangle BCF \cong \triangle ABE$.

(ii) area of square ABFG = area of rectangle BENM.

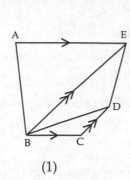

(1)

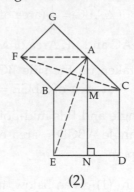

(2)

Hint. (a) Join CE. Area of $\triangle ABC$ = area of $\triangle EBC$. Area of $\triangle BCD$ = area of $\triangle ECD$.

(b) (ii) Area of $\triangle BCF = \dfrac{1}{2}$ area of square ABFG.

Multiple Choice Questions

Choose the correct answer from the given four options (1 to 8):

1 In the adjoining figure, if $l \parallel m$, AF $\parallel$ BE, FC $\perp m$ and ED $\perp m$, then the correct statement is

(a) area of $\parallel$ABEF = area of rect. CDEF

(b) area of $\parallel$ABEF = area of quad. CBEF

(c) area of $\parallel$ABEF = 2 area of $\triangle$ACF

(d) area of $\parallel$ABEF = 2 area of $\triangle$EBD

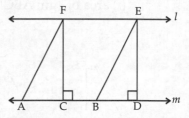

2 Two parallelograms are on equal bases and between the same parallels. The ratio of their areas is

(a) $1:2$ (b) $1:1$ (c) $2:1$ (d) $3:1$

3 If a triangle and a parallelogram are on the same base and between same parallels, then the ratio of area of the triangle to the area of parallelogram is

(a) $1:3$ (b) $1:2$ (c) $3:1$ (d) $1:4$

4 A median of a triangle divides it into two

(a) triangles of equal area   (b) congruent triangles

(c) right triangles   (d) isosceles triangles

5 In the adjoining figure, area of parallelogram ABCD is

(a) AB × BM   (b) BC × BN

(c) DC × DL   (d) AD × DL

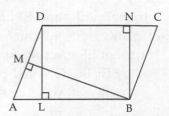

6 The mid-points of the sides of a triangle along with any of the vertices as the fourth point make a parallelogram of area equal to

(a) $\dfrac{1}{2}$ area of $\triangle$ABC   (b) $\dfrac{1}{3}$ area of $\triangle$ABC

(c) $\dfrac{1}{4}$ area of $\triangle$ABC   (d) area of $\triangle$ABC

7 In the adjoining figure, ABCD is a trapezium with parallel sides AB = a cm and DC = b cm. E and F are mid-points of the non-parallel sides. The ratio of area of ABFE and area of EFCD is

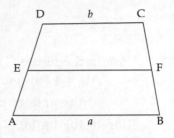

    (a) $a : b$

    (b) $(3a + b) : (a + 3b)$

    (c) $(a + 3b) : (3a + b)$

    (d) $(2a + b) : (3a + b)$

8 In the adjoining figure, AB ∥ DC and AB ≠ DC. If the diagonals AC and BD of the trapezium ABCD intersect at O, then which of the following statements is not true?

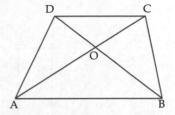

    (a) area of ΔABC = area of ΔABD

    (b) area of ΔACD = area of ΔBCD

    (c) area of ΔOAB = area of ΔOCD

    (d) area of ΔOAD = area of ΔOBC

Summary

....

☐ *Axioms of area*

    (i) *Congruence area axiom: If two figures are congruent, then the areas enclosed by these figures are equal.*

    (ii) *Addition area axiom: If a planar region R consists of two non-overlapping planar regions R_1 and R_2, then*

        area of region R = area of region R_1 + area of region R_2.

- Two figures are called equal if and only if they have equal area. Two congruent figures are always equal figures but equal figures may not be congruent.

☐ *Theorems on area*

- A diagonal of a parallelogram divides it into two triangles of equal areas.
- Parallelograms on the same base (or equal bases) and between the same parallel lines are equal in area.

  Conversely, parallelograms on the same base (or equal bases) and having equal areas lie between the same lines (*i.e.* have equal corresponding altitudes).

- Area of a triangle is half that of a parallelogram on the same base and between same parallel lines.
- A median of a triangle divides it into two triangles of equal areas.
- Triangles on the same base (or equal bases) and between the same parallel lines are equal in area.

  Conversely, triangles on the same base (or equal bases) and having equal areas lie between the same parallel lines (*i.e.* have equal corresponding altitudes).

1   (a) In the figure (1) given below, ABCD is a rectangle (not drawn to scale) with side AB = 4 cm and AD = 6 cm. Find

       (i) the area of parallelogram DEFC   (ii) area of ΔEFG.

    (b) In the figure (2) given below, PQRS is a parallelogram formed by drawing lines parallel to the diagonals of a quadrilateral ABCD through its corners. Prove that area of ‖ gm PQRS = 2 × area of quad. ABCD.

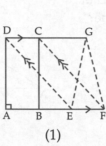
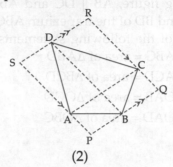

              (1)   (2)

2   In the parallelogram ABCD, P is a point on the side AB and Q is a point on the side BC. Prove that

      (i) area of ΔCPD = area of ΔAQD

      (ii) area of ΔADQ = area of ΔAPD + area of ΔCPB.

3   In the adjoining figure, X and Y are points on the side LN of triangle LMN. Through X, a line is drawn parallel to LM to meet MN at Z. Prove that area of ΔLZY = area of quad. MZYX.

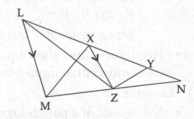

      Hint. As Δs LZX and MZX are on the same base ZX and between same parallels XZ and LM, area of ΔLZX = area of ΔMZX.

        Add same area of ΔXZY on both sides.

4   Perpendiculars are drawn from a point within an equilateral triangle to the three sides. Prove that the sum of the three perpendiculars is equal to the altitude of the triangle.

5   If each diagonal of a quadrilateral divides it into two triangles of equal areas, then prove that the quadrilateral is a parallelogram.

      Hint. Let ABCD be a quadrilateral such that each diagonal divide it into triangles of equal areas, then area of ΔABC = $\frac{1}{2}$ (area of quad. ABCD) and area of ΔABD = $\frac{1}{2}$ (area of quad. ABCD). So, area of Δ ABC = area of ΔABD. By Theorem 14.6, DC ‖ AB.

6   In the adjoining figure, ABCD is a parallelogram in which BC is produced to E such that CE = BC. AE intersects CD at F. If area of ΔDFB = 3 cm², find the area of parallelogram ABCD.

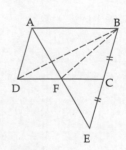

      Hint. Join AC and DE. ACED is a parallelogram (why?). Diagonals AE and DC of ‖gm ACED bisect each other, so F is mid-point of DC.

        Area of ΔBFC = area of ΔDBF = 3 cm² (given).

7 In the adjoining figure, ABCD is a square. E and F are mid-points of sides BC and CD respectively. If R is mid-point of EF, prove that

area of △AER = area of △AFR.

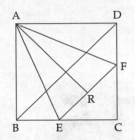

Hint. Show that △ABE ≅ △ADF.

⇒ AE = AF.

Now, show that △AER ≅ △AFR.

8 In the adjoining figure, X and Y are mid-points of the sides AC and AB respectively of △ABC. QP ∥ BC and CYQ and BXP are straight lines. Prove that area of △ABP = area of △ACQ.

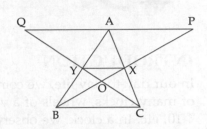

Hint. Since X and Y are mid-points of AC and AB, YX ∥ BC. But QP ∥ BC, so YX ∥ QP. In △BAP, Y is mid-point of AB and YX ∥ AP, so X is mid-point of BP and YX = $\frac{1}{2}$ AP.

Similarly, Y is mid-point of CQ and YX = $\frac{1}{2}$ QA ⇒ AP = QA.

Thus, ABP and ACQ are two triangles on equal bases AP, QA and are between same parallels BC and QP, therefore,

area of △ABP = area of △ACQ.

15 Circle

INTRODUCTION

In our day-to-day life, we come across many objects which are round in shape, such as dials of many clocks, wheels of a vehicle, bangles, key rings, coins of denomination ₹ 1, ₹ 2, ₹ 5, ₹ 10, etc. In a clock, we observe that second's hand goes round the dial of the clock rapidly and its tip moves in a round path. This path traced by the tip of the second's hand is called a **circle**. In this chapter, we shall study about circles, some terms related with a circle, chord properties of a circle, arc and chord properties of a circle.

15.1 CIRCLE

*A **circle** is the collection of all those points, say P, in a plane each of which is at a constant distance from a fixed point in that plane.*

In other words, a circle is the path of a point which moves in a plane so that it remains at a constant distance from a fixed point in the plane.

*The fixed point is called the **centre** and the constant distance is called the **radius** of the circle.*

The radius of a circle is always positive.

The adjoining figure shows a circle with O as its centre and r as its radius.

Note that the centre of a circle does not lie on the circle.

Let O be the centre of a circle and r its radius. If P is a point on the circle, then the line segment $\overline{OP}$ is a radius of the circle and its length is r. If Q is another point on the circle then $\overline{OQ}$ is another radius of the circle. Note that all radii (plural of radius) have one point in common, which is the centre of the circle. Also OP = OQ = r. Thus:

All radii of a circle are equal.

> **Note** The line segment joining the centre and any point on the circle is also called a radius of the circle. Thus, 'radius' is used in two senses — in the sense of a line segment and also in the sense of its length.

15.1.1 Some terms related with a circle

1. Circle-interior and exterior

A circle is a closed curve. It divides the plane region into three parts. They are:

(*i*) **Circle** —The collection of all points P of the plane such that OP = r form a circle with *centre* O and radius r ($r > 0$).

(*ii*) **Interior of a circle** —The collection of all points of the plane which lie inside the circle *i.e.* the collection of all points P of the plane such that OP < r form the **interior of the circle**.

The collection of all points of the plane which either lie on the circle or are inside the circle form the **circular region**.

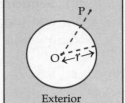

(*iii*) **Exterior of a circle** — The collection of all points of the plane which lie outside the circle *i.e.* the collection of all points of the plane such that OP > *r* form the **exterior of the circle**.

Exterior

2. Chord of a circle

A line segment joining any two points of a circle is called a **chord of the circle**.

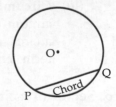

In the adjoining figure, PQ is a chord of the circle with centre O. The distance PQ is called the **length of the chord**.

3. Diameter of a circle

A chord of a circle which passes through its centre is called a **diameter of the circle**.

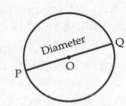

A diameter of a circle is the **longest chord** of the circle and all diameters have equal length.

In the adjoining figure, $\overline{PQ}$ is a diameter of the circle with centre O. Note that $\overline{OP}$ and $\overline{OQ}$ are both radii of the circle, so OP = OQ = *r*.

It follows that PQ = 2*r* = 2 × radius. Thus:

Length of a diameter = 2 × radius.

Note that there are infinitely many lines passing through the point O (centre of circle), so a circle has infinitely many diameters.

4. Secant of a circle

A line which meets a circle in two points is called a **secant** of the circle. In the adjoining figure, line PQ is a secant of the circle with centre O.

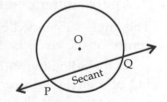

5. Arc of a circle

A (continuous) part of a circle is called an **arc of the circle**.

The arc of a circle is denoted by the symbol "⌢".

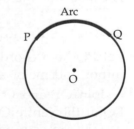

Arc

In the adjoining figure, $\overset{\frown}{PQ}$ denotes the arc PQ of the circle with centre O.

Arc of a circle is divided into following categories:

(*i*) **Minor and major arc** — An arc less than one-half of the whole arc of a circle is called a **minor arc** of the circle and an arc greater than one-half of the whole arc is called a **major arc** of the circle. Here, $\overset{\frown}{PQ}$ is the minor arc and $\overset{\frown}{PRQ}$ is the major arc.

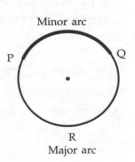

Minor arc

R
Major arc

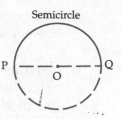
Semicircle

(ii) **Semicircle**—When PQ is a diameter, then both arcs are equal and each is called a **semicircle**. Thus, one-half of the whole arc of a circle is called a semicircle.

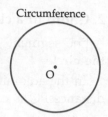
Circumference

(iii) **Circumference**—The whole arc of a circle is called the **circumference** of the circle. The length of the circumference of a circle is the length of the whole arc. However, in general, the term **'circumference of a circle'** refers to its length.

6. Sector of a circle

The part of the plane region enclosed by an arc of a circle and its two bounding radii is called a **sector of the circle**.

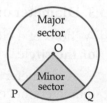

The part containing the minor arc is called **minor sector** and the part containing the major arc is called **major sector**.

7. Segment of a circle

A chord of a circle divides its circular region into two parts. Each part of the circular region is called a segment of the circle.

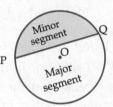

The part of the circular region containing the minor arc is called a **minor segment** and the part containing the major arc is called a **major segment**.

8. Angle subtended by an arc

The angle subtended by the two bounding radii of an arc of a circle at the centre of the circle is called the **angle subtended by the arc**.

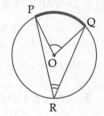

In the adjoining figure, $\angle POQ$ is the angle subtended by the minor arc PQ of a circle with centre O and the reflex $\angle POQ$ is the angle subtended by the major arc PQ at O. If R is any point on the major arc, then $\angle PRQ$ is called the angle subtended by the minor arc PQ at the point R.

9. Angle subtended by a chord

Let PQ be a chord of a circle with centre O and R, S be points on the minor and major arcs of the circle (as shown in the adjoining figure).

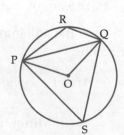

Join OP and OQ, then $\angle POQ$ is the angle subtended by the chord PQ at the centre O.

Join PR, QR, PS and QS, then $\angle PRQ$ and $\angle PSQ$ are the angles subtended by the chord PQ at the points R and S respectively on the minor and major arcs.

10. Concentric circles

Two or more circles are called concentric circles if and only if they have same centre but different radii.

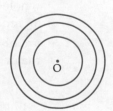

11. Equal (or congruent) circles

Two or more circles are called **equal (or congruent)** circles if and only if they have same radius.

In the adjoining figures, two circles with centres A and B have equal radius (= r), so, these are equal circles.

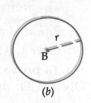

(a)   (b)

15.2 CHORD PROPERTIES OF CIRCLES

Theorem 15.1

The straight line drawn from the centre of a circle to bisect a chord, which is not a diameter, is perpendicular to the chord.

Given. A chord AB of a circle with centre O, and OM bisects the chord AB.

To prove. OM ⊥ AB.

Construction. Join OA and OB.

Proof.

Statements	Reasons
In Δs OAM and OBM	
1. OA = OB	1. Radii of same circle.
2. AM = MB	2. M is mid-point of AB.
3. OM = OM	3. Common.
4. ΔOAM ≅ ΔOBM	4. S.S.S. rule of congruency.
5. ∠AMO = ∠OMB	5. 'c.p.c.t.'.
6. ∠AMO + ∠OMB = 180°	6. AMB is a straight line.
7. ∠AMO = 90° Hence OM ⊥ AB. **Q.E.D.**	7. From 5 and 6.

Theorem 15.2 (*Converse of theorem 15.1*)

The perpendicular to a chord from the centre of the circle bisects the chord.

Given. A chord AB of a circle with centre O, and OM is perpendicular to the chord AB.

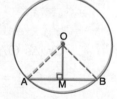

To prove. AM = MB.

Construction. Join OA and OB.

Proof.

Statements	Reasons
In Δs OAM and OBM	
1. OA = OB	1. Radii of same circle.
2. ∠AMO = ∠OMB	2. Each = 90°, since OM ⊥ AB.
3. OM = OM	3. Common.
4. Δ OAM ≅ Δ OBM	4. R.H.S. rule of congruency.
5. AM = MB	5. 'c.p.c.t.'.
Q.E.D.	

Theorem 15.3

Equal chords of a circle are equidistant from the centre.

Given. AB and CD are chords of a circle with centre O, and AB = CD.

To prove. AB and CD are equidistant from O *i.e.* if OM ⊥ AB and ON ⊥ CD, then OM = ON.

Construction. Join OA and OC.

Proof.

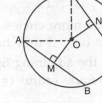

Statements	Reasons
1. AM = $\frac{1}{2}$ AB	1. Perpendicular from centre bisects the chord (Theorem 15.2).
2. CN = $\frac{1}{2}$ CD	2. Same as above.
3. AM = CN In Δs OAM and OCN	3. AB = CD (given).
4. AM = CN	4. From 3.
5. ∠AMO = ∠CNO	5. Each = 90°, OM ⊥ AB and ON ⊥ CD.
6. OA = OC	6. Radii of same circle.
7. ΔOAM ≅ ΔOCN	7. R.H.S. rule of congruency.
8. OM = ON **Q.E.D.**	8. 'c.p.c.t.'.

Theorem 15.4 (*Converse of theorem 15.3*)

Chords of a circle that are equidistant from the centre of the circle are equal.

Given. AB and CD are chords of a circle with centre O; OM ⊥ AB, ON ⊥ CD and OM = ON.

To prove. AB = CD.

Construction. Join OA and OC.

Proof.

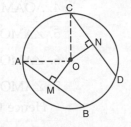

Statements	Reasons
In Δs OAM and OCN	
1. OM = ON	1. Given.
2. OA = OC	2. Radii of same circle.
3. ∠AMO = ∠CNO	3. Each = 90°, OM ⊥ AB and ON ⊥ CD.
4. Δ OAM ≅ Δ OCN	4. R.H.S. rule of congruency.
5. AM = CN	5. 'c.p.c.t.'.
6. AM = $\frac{1}{2}$ AB	6. Perpendicular from centre bisects the chord.
7. CN = $\frac{1}{2}$ CD	7. Same as above.
8. $\frac{1}{2}$ AB = $\frac{1}{2}$ CD ⇒ AB = CD. **Q.E.D.**	8. AM = CN, from 5.

Theorem 15.5

There is one and only one circle passing through three given non-collinear points.

Given. Three non-collinear points A, B and C.

To prove. One and only one circle can be drawn passing through the points A, B and C.

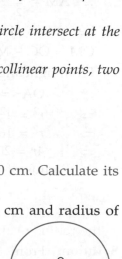

Construction. Join AB and BC.

Draw perpendicular bisectors of line segments AB and BC, say PQ and RS respectively. Let these bisectors meet at O. Join OA, OB and OC.

Proof.

Statements	Reasons
1. OA = OB	1. O lies on the perpendicular bisector PQ of AB and every point on the perpendicular bisector of a line segment is equidistant from its end points.
2. OB = OC	2. O lies on the perpendicular bisector RS of BC and every point on the perpendicular bisector of a line segment is equidistant from its end points.
3. OA = OB = OC	3. From 1 and 2.
4. If a circle is drawn with O as centre and radius = OA, it passes through the points B and C.	4. From 3, O is equidistant from points A, B and C.
5. There is only one circle passing through the points A, B and C.	5. Since two lines can intersect at only one point, the perpendicular bisectors of AB and BC meet at only one point O.
Hence, one and only one circle can be drawn passing through three given non-collinear points.	

Corollary 1. *In the plane of a circle, the perpendicular bisector of a chord of a circle passes through its centre.*

Corollary 2. *The perpendicular bisectors of two (non-parallel) chords of a circle intersect at the centre of the circle.*

Corollary 3. *As there is one and only one circle passing through three non-collinear points, two different circles can meet atmost in two different points.*

Illustrative Examples

Example 1 A chord of length 16 cm is drawn in a circle of diameter 20 cm. Calculate its distance from the centre of the circle.

Solution. Let AB be a chord of a circle with centre O such that AB = 16 cm and radius of

the circle = OA = $\frac{1}{2}$. diameter = $\frac{1}{2}$. 20 cm = 10 cm.

From O, draw OM ⊥ AB.

Since OM ⊥ AB, AB is bisected at M (Theorem 15.2)

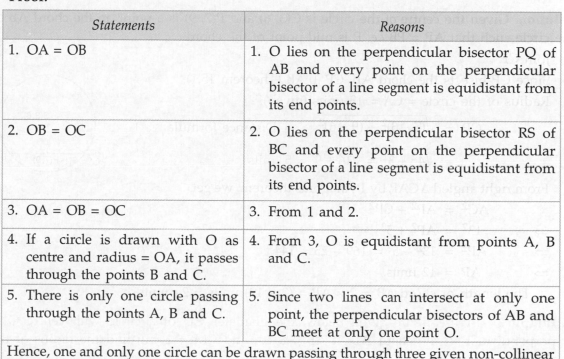

∴   AM = $\frac{1}{2}$ AB = $\frac{1}{2}$. 16 cm = 8 cm.

From right angled ΔOAM, by Pythagoras theorem, we get

$$OA^2 = OM^2 + AM^2$$

$$\Rightarrow \quad 10^2 = OM^2 + 8^2$$

$$\Rightarrow \quad OM^2 = 10^2 - 8^2 = 100 - 64 = 36$$

$$\Rightarrow \quad OM = 6 \text{ cm}.$$

Hence, the given chord is at a distance of 6 cm from the centre of the circle.

Example 2 The centre of a circle of radius 13 units is the point (3, 6). P(7, 9) is a point inside the circle. APB is a chord of the circle such that AP = PB. Calculate the length of AB.

Solution. Given the centre of the circle is C(3, 6) and P(7, 9) is a point on the chord AB of the circle such that AP = PB *i.e.* P is mid-point of the chord.

Join CP.

Since CP bisects the chord AB, CP ⊥ AB (Theorem 15.1).

Radius of the circle = CA = 13 units (given).

$$CP = \sqrt{(7-3)^2 + (9-6)^2} \quad | \text{ Distance formula}$$

$$= \sqrt{4^2 + 3^2} = \sqrt{16+9} = 5 \text{ units}$$

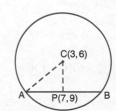

From right angled ΔCAP, by Pythagoras theorem, we get

$$AC^2 = AP^2 + CP^2$$

$$\Rightarrow \quad 13^2 = AP^2 + 5^2$$

$$\Rightarrow \quad AP^2 = 13^2 - 5^2 = 169 - 25 = 144$$

$$\Rightarrow \quad AP = 12 \text{ units}.$$

∴ The length of chord AB = 2 × AP = (2 × 12) units = 24 units.

Example 3 In the figure given below, the diameter CD of a circle with centre O is perpendicular to the chord AB. If AB = 8 cm and CM = 2 cm, find the radius of the circle.

Solution. Since CD ⊥ AB *i.e.* OM ⊥ AB, AB is bisected at M (Theorem 15.2),

$$\therefore \quad AM = \frac{1}{2} AB = \frac{1}{2} . 8 \text{ cm} = 4 \text{ cm}.$$

Let radius of circle = r cm, then

OM = OC - MC = $(r - 2)$.

From right angled Δ OAM, by Pythagoras theorem, we get

$$OA^2 = AM^2 + OM^2$$

$$\Rightarrow \quad r^2 = 4^2 + (r-2)^2$$

$$\Rightarrow \quad r^2 = 16 + r^2 - 4r + 4$$

$$\Rightarrow \quad 4r = 20 \quad \Rightarrow \quad r = 5.$$

∴ Radius of the circle = 5 cm.

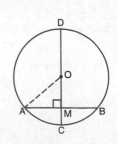

Example 4 In the adjoining figure, AB and CD are two chords of a circle with centre O at distances of 6 cm and 8 cm respectively. If the radius of the circle is 10 cm, find the lengths of the chords.

Solution. From O, draw OM ⊥ AB and ON ⊥ CD, then OM = 6 cm and ON = 8 cm (given)

Join OA and OC.

Since OM ⊥ AB, AB is bisected at M.

∴ $\qquad\qquad$ AB = 2 AM.

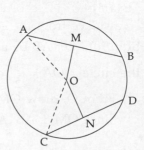

As ON ⊥ CD, CD is bisected at N.

$\therefore$ CD = 2 CN.

                  OA = OC = radius of circle = 10 cm   (given)

In $\triangle OAM$, $\angle M = 90°$. By Pythagoras theorem, we get

         $AM^2 + OM^2 = OA^2 \Rightarrow AM^2 = OA^2 = OM^2 = 10^2 - 6^2 = 64$

$\Rightarrow$ AM = 8 cm.

$\therefore$ AB = 2 AM = (2 × 8) cm = 16 cm.

In $\triangle OCN$, $\angle N = 90°$. By Pythagoras theorem, we get

         $CN^2 + ON^2 = OC^2 \Rightarrow CN^2 = OC^2 - ON^2 = 10^2 - 8^2 = 36$

$\Rightarrow$ CN = 6 cm.

$\therefore$ CD = 2 CN = (2 × 6) cm = 12 cm.

Example 5 The lengths of two parallel chords of a circle are 6 cm and 8 cm. If the smaller chord is at a distance of 4 cm from the centre, find the distance of the other chord from the centre.

Solution. Let AB = 6 cm, CD = 8 cm and O be the centre of the circle and r cm be its radius.

From O, draw OM ⊥ AB and ON ⊥ CD.

As OM ⊥ AB, OM bisects AB

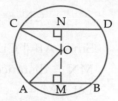

$\therefore$ $AM = \dfrac{1}{2} × 6$ cm = 3 cm.

Given OM = 4 cm.

In $\triangle OAM$, $\angle M = 90°$, by Pythagoras theorem,

         $OA^2 = AM^2 + OM^2 \Rightarrow r^2 = 3^2 + 4^2 \Rightarrow r^2 = 25 \Rightarrow r = 5$.

As ON ⊥ CD, ON bisects CD

$\therefore$ $CN = \dfrac{1}{2} × 8$ cm = 4 cm.

In $\triangle OCN$, $\angle N = 90°$, by Pythagoras theorem,

         $OC^2 = ON^2 + CN^2 \Rightarrow 5^2 = ON^2 + 4^2$ ($\because$ OC = radius = 5 cm)

$\Rightarrow$ $ON^2 = 25 - 16 = 9 \Rightarrow ON = 3$ cm.

Note   In the above problem, if the chords AB and CD are not parallel, even then we obtain the same answer.

Example 6 Two chords AB and CD of lengths 5 cm and 11 cm respectively of a circle are parallel to each other and are on the opposite sides of its centre. If the distance between AB and CD is 6 cm, find the radius of the circle.

Solution. Let O be the centre of the circle.

From O, draw OM ⊥ AB and ON ⊥ CD.

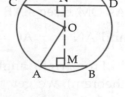

$\therefore$ $AM = \dfrac{1}{2} AB = \dfrac{1}{2} × 5$ cm $= \dfrac{5}{2}$ cm and

        $CN = \dfrac{1}{2} CD = \dfrac{1}{2} × 11$ cm $= \dfrac{11}{2}$ cm.

Since AB ∥ CD, points M, O and N are collinear.

Let   OM = x cm, then ON = $(6 - x)$ cm   ($\because$ MN = 6 cm, given)

Let the radius of the circle be r cm.

From right angled triangles OMA and ONC (by Pythagoras theorem), we get

         $OA^2 = AM^2 + OM^2$ and $OC^2 = CN^2 + ON^2$

$$\Rightarrow \quad r^2 = \left(\frac{5}{2}\right)^2 + x^2 \quad \text{...(i)} \qquad \text{and } r^2 = \left(\frac{11}{2}\right)^2 + (6-x)^2 \quad \text{...(ii)}$$

$$\Rightarrow \quad \left(\frac{5}{2}\right)^2 + x^2 = \left(\frac{11}{2}\right)^2 + (6-x)^2 \Rightarrow \frac{25}{4} + x^2 = \frac{121}{4} + 36 - 12x + x^2$$

$$\Rightarrow \quad 12x = 60 \Rightarrow x = 5.$$

Putting $x = 5$ in (i), we get

$$r^2 = \left(\frac{5}{2}\right)^2 + 5^2 = \frac{25}{4} + 25 = \frac{125}{4} \Rightarrow r = \frac{5\sqrt{5}}{2} \text{ cm.}$$

Example 7 Two chords AB, CD of lengths 24 cm, 10 cm respectively of a circle are parallel. If the chords lie on the same side of centre and the distance between them is 7 cm, find the length of a diameter of the circle.

Solution. Let O be the centre of the circle.

Draw OM ⊥ AB and ON ⊥ CD.

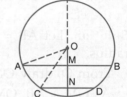

∴ $\quad$ AM = $\frac{1}{2}$ AB = $\frac{1}{2}$. 24 cm = 12 cm and

$\quad$ CN = $\frac{1}{2}$ CD = $\frac{1}{2}$. 10 cm = 5 cm.

Since AB ∥ CD, points O, M and N are collinear.

MN = distance between AB and CD = 7 cm (given).

Let OM = x cm, then ON = OM + MN = $(x + 7)$ cm.

Let the radius of the circle be r cm.

From right angled Δs OAM and OCN (by Pythagoras theorem), we get

$$OA^2 = AM^2 + OM^2 \text{ and } OC^2 = CN^2 + ON^2$$

$$\Rightarrow \quad r^2 = (12)^2 + x^2 \quad \text{...(i)}$$

and $\quad r^2 = 5^2 + (x+7)^2 \quad \text{...(ii)}$

From (i) and (ii), we get

$$5^2 + (x+7)^2 = (12)^2 + x^2$$

$$\Rightarrow \quad 25 + x^2 + 14x + 49 = 144 + x^2$$

$$\Rightarrow \quad 14x = 70 \quad \Rightarrow \quad x = 5.$$

∴ From (i), $r^2 = (12)^2 + 5^2 = 144 + 25 = 169 \quad \Rightarrow \quad r = 13.$

∴ The length of a diameter of the circle = $2r$ = 26 cm.

Example 8 AB and AC are two chords of a circle of radius r such that AB = 2 AC. If p and q are the distances of AB and AC from the centre, prove that $4q^2 = p^2 + 3r^2$.

Solution. Let O be the centre of circle and AC = $2x$, then AB = 2AC = 2 × 2x = 4x. From O, draw OM ⊥ AB and ON ⊥ AC.

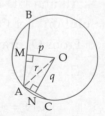

As OM bisects AB and ON bisects AC, AM = $\frac{1}{2}$ AB = $\frac{1}{2}$ × 4x = 2x
and AN = $\frac{1}{2}$ AC = $\frac{1}{2}$ × 2x = x.

From right angled triangles OAM and OAN (by Pythagoras theorem), we get

$$OA^2 = AM^2 + OM^2 \text{ and } OA^2 = AN^2 + ON^2$$

$$\Rightarrow \quad r^2 = (2x)^2 + p^2 \text{ and } r^2 = x^2 + q^2$$

$$\Rightarrow \quad r^2 = 4x^2 + p^2 \text{ and } x^2 = r^2 - q^2$$

$$\Rightarrow \quad r^2 = 4(r^2 - q^2) + p^2 \Rightarrow 4q^2 = p^2 + 3r^2.$$

Example 9 ABC is an isosceles triangle inscribed in a circle. If AB = AC = 25 cm and BC = 14 cm, find the radius of the circle.

Solution. Let O be the centre of the circle.

From A, draw AM ⊥ BC.

Since ΔABC is isosceles with AB=AC, M is the mid-point of BC *i.e.* AM is perpendicular bisector of BC, therefore, O lies on AM.

$$BM = \frac{1}{2}BC = \frac{1}{2}.14 \text{ cm} = 7 \text{ cm}.$$

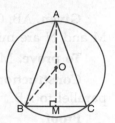

From right angled ΔABM, by Pythagoras theorem, we get

$$AM^2 = AB^2 - BM^2 = (25)^2 - 7^2 = 625 - 49 = 576$$

⇒   AM = 24 cm.

Let r cm be the radius of the circle, then

OM = AM − AO = (24 − r) cm.

From right angled Δ OBM, by Pythagoras theorem, we get

$$OB^2 = BM^2 + OM^2$$

⇒ $r^2 = 7^2 + (24 - r)^2$

⇒ $r^2 = 49 + 576 + r^2 - 48r$

⇒ $48r = 625 \Rightarrow r = \frac{625}{48} = 13\frac{1}{48}.$

Hence, the radius of the circle = $13\frac{1}{48}$ cm.

Example 10 In a circle of radius 5 cm, AB and AC are two chords such that AB = AC = 6 cm. Find the length of the chord BC.

Solution. Let O be the centre of the circle.

Let the bisector of ∠BAC meet the chord BC at M.

In Δs BAM and CAM

1. ∠BAM = ∠MAC   (by const.)

2. AB = AC   (given)

3. AM = AM   (common)

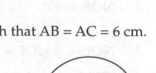

∴ Δ BAM ≅ Δ CAM   (S.A.S. rule of congruency)

∴ BM = MC and ∠BMA = ∠AMC   ('c.p.c.t.')

But   ∠BMA + ∠AMC = 180°   (∵ BMC is a straight line)

⇒   ∠BMA = 90°.

Therefore, AM is perpendicular bisector of BC, and hence it passes through the centre O of the circle.

Let   BM = y cm and OM = x cm, then

MA = OA − OM = (5 − x) cm   [∵ radius = 5 cm]

From right angled ΔOBM, $y^2 + x^2 = 5^2$ ...(i)

From right angled ΔBAM, $y^2 + (5 - x)^2 = 6^2$

i.e. $y^2 + x^2 - 10x = 11$ ...(ii)

Subtracting (ii) from (i), we get

$$10x = 25 - 11 \Rightarrow 10x = 14 \Rightarrow x = \frac{7}{5}.$$

Substituting this value of x in (i), we get

$$y^2 + \frac{49}{25} = 25 \implies y^2 = 25 - \frac{49}{25} = \frac{625 - 49}{25} \implies y^2 = \frac{576}{25} \implies y = \frac{24}{5}$$

∴   Length of chord BC = 2BM = $2 \cdot \frac{24}{5}$ cm = $\frac{48}{5}$ cm = 9·6 cm.

Example 11 Prove that the line joining mid-points of two parallel chords of a circle passes through the centre of the circle.

Given. AB, CD are two chords of a circle with centre O. AB ∥ CD, M and N are mid-points of AB and CD respectively.

To prove. MN passes through O.

Construction. Join OM, ON and through O draw a straight line parallel to AB.

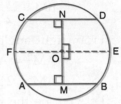

Proof.

Statements	Reasons
1. OM ⊥ AB	1. M is mid-point of AB, and the line drawn from the centre of circle to bisect a chord is perpendicular to it.
2. ∠AMO = 90°	2. OM ⊥ AB.
3. ∠MOE = 90°	3. OE ∥ AB, alternate angles are equal.
4. ∠NOE = 90°	4. Similarly, N is mid-point of CD and same reasons as above.
5. ∠NOE + ∠MOE = 180°	5. Adding 3 and 4.
6. MON is a straight line. Hence, MN passes through O. **Q.E.D.**	6. Sum of adjacent angles is 180°.

Example 12 If two equal chords of a circle intersect, prove that their segments will be equal.

Given. AB and CD are chords of a circle with centre O. AB and CD intersect at P and AB = CD.

To prove. (i) AP = PD   (ii) PB = CP.

Construction. Draw OM ⊥ AB, ON ⊥ CD. Join OP.

Proof.

Statements	Reasons
1. AM = MB = $\frac{1}{2}$ AB	1. Perpendicular from centre bisects the chord.
2. CN = ND = $\frac{1}{2}$ CD	2. Same as above.
3. AM = ND and MB = CN In ∆s OMP and ONP	3. AB = CD (given).
4. OM = ON	4. Equal chords of a circle are equidistant from the centre. (Theorem 15.3)

5. ∠OMP = ∠ONP	5. Each = 90°.
6. OP = OP	6. Common.
7. ΔOMP ≅ Δ ONP	7. R.H.S. rule of congruency.
8. MP = PN	8. 'c.p.c.t.'.
9. AM + MP = ND + PN ⇒ AP = PD.	9. From 3 and 8, adding.
10. MB – MP = CN – PN ⇒ PB = CP. Hence (i) AP = PD and (ii) PB = CP. **Q.E.D.**	10. From 3 and 8, subtracting.

Example 13 Of two unequal chords of a circle, prove that greater chord is nearer to the centre of the circle.

Given. AB and CD are chords of a circle with centre O. AB > CD, and OM ⊥ AB, ON ⊥ CD.

To prove. OM < ON.

Construction. Join OA and OC.

Proof.

Statements	Reasons
1. AM = $\frac{1}{2}$ AB	1. Perpendicular from centre bisects the chord.
2. CN = $\frac{1}{2}$ CD	2. Same as above.
3. AM > CN	3. AB > CD (given).
4. $OA^2 = AM^2 + OM^2$	4. In ΔOAM, ∠AMO = 90°.
5. $OC^2 = CN^2 + ON^2$	5. In ΔOCN, ∠CNO = 90°.
6. $AM^2 + OM^2 = CN^2 + ON^2$ ⇒ $OM^2 – ON^2 = – (AM^2 – CN^2)$	6. OA = OC, radii of same circle.
7. $OM^2 – ON^2 < 0$ ⇒ $OM^2 < ON^2$ ⇒ OM < ON. **Q.E.D.**	7. From 3, AM > CN ⇒ $AM^2 > CN^2$ ⇒ $AM^2 – CN^2$ is +ve.

Example 14 If two circles intersect in two points, then prove that the line through their centres is perpendicular bisector of the common chord.

Given. Two circles with centres C, D, and intersecting at points A, B so that AB is their common chord.

To prove. CD is perpendicular bisector of AB i.e. AM = MB and ∠CMA = 90°.

Construction. Join CA, CB, AD and BD.

 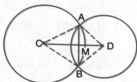

Proof.

Statements	Reasons
In Δs ACD and BCD	
1. CA = CB	1. Radii of same circle.
2. AD = BD	2. Radii of same circle.
3. CD = CD	3. Common.
4. Δ ACD $\cong$ Δ BCD	4. S.S.S. rule of congruency.
5. $\angle$ACM = $\angle$MCB In Δs ACM and BCM	5. 'c.p.c.t.'.
6. $\angle$ACM = $\angle$MCB	6. From 5.
7. CA = CB	7. Radii of same circle.
8. CM = CM	8. Common.
9. Δ ACM $\cong$ Δ BCM	9. S.A.S. rule of congruency.
10. AM = MB and $\angle$CMA = $\angle$CMB	10. 'c.p.c.t.'.
11. $\angle$CMA + $\angle$CMB = 180°	11. AMB is a straight line
12. $\angle$CMA = 90° Hence, CD is perpendicular bisector of AB. **Q.E.D.**	12. From 10 and 11.

Example 15 Two circles of radii 5 cm and 3 cm intersect at two points and the distance between their centres is 4 cm. Find the length of the common chord.

Solution. Let O, O' be the centres of circles with radii 5 cm, 3 cm respectively and AB be the common chord. As the line of centres is the perpendicular bisector of the common chord, OO' $\perp$ AB and M is mid-point of AB. Let AM = y cm and OM = x cm.

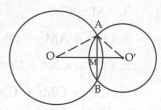

As OO' = 4 cm (given), so MO' = $(4 - x)$ cm.

In ΔOMA, $\angle$M = 90°, by Pythagoras theorem,
$$OA^2 = OM^2 + AM^2 \Rightarrow 5^2 = x^2 + y^2 \qquad \qquad \text{...}(i)$$

In ΔO'MA, $\angle$M = 90°, by Pythagoras theorem,
$$O'A^2 = OM'^2 + AM^2 \Rightarrow 3^2 = (4 - x)^2 + y^2 \qquad \text{...}(ii)$$

Subtracting (ii) from (i), we get
$$25 - 9 = x^2 - (4 - x^2) \Rightarrow 16 = 8x - 16 \Rightarrow x = 4.$$

Putting $x = 4$ in (ii), we get
$$3^2 = 0^2 + y^2 \Rightarrow y^2 = 9 \Rightarrow y = 3 \qquad \qquad (\because y > 0)$$

$\therefore$ Length of common chord AB = 2 × AM = (2 × 3) cm = 6 cm.

Note In the above question, we observe that $x = 4 \Rightarrow$ MO' = 0 $\Rightarrow$ the points M and O' coincide $\Rightarrow$ the centre of the smaller circle lies on the common chord $\Rightarrow$ the common chord is a diameter of the smaller circle.

1. Calculate the length of a chord which is at a distance 12 cm from the centre of a circle of radius 13 cm.

2. A chord of length 48 cm is drawn in a circle of radius 25 cm. Calculate its distance from the centre of the circle.

3. A chord of length 8 cm is at a distance 3 cm from the centre of the circle. Calculate the radius of the circle.

4. Calculate the length of a chord which is at a distance 6 cm from the centre of a circle of diameter 20 cm.

5. A chord of length 16 cm is at a distance 6 cm from the centre of the circle. Find the length of the chord of the same circle which is at a distance 8 cm from the centre.

6. In a circle of radius 5 cm, AB and CD are two parallel chords of length 8 cm and 6 cm respectively. Calculate the distance between the chords, if they are on

      (*i*) the same side of the centre.   (*ii*) the opposite sides of the centre.

7. (*a*) In the figure (*i*) given below, O is the centre of the circle. AB and CD are two chords of the circle. OM is perpendicular to AB and ON is perpendicular to CD. AB = 24 cm, OM = 5 cm, ON = 12 cm. Find the:

      (*i*) radius of the circle   (*ii*) length of chord CD.

   (*b*) In the figure (*ii*) given below, CD is a diameter which meets the chord AB in E such that AE = BE = 4 cm. If CE = 3 cm, find the radius of the circle.

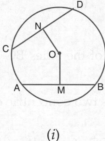

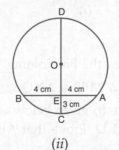

   (*i*)   (*ii*)

8. In the adjoining figure, AB and CD are two parallel chords and O is the centre. If the radius of the circle is 15 cm, find the distance MN between the two chords of length 24 cm and 18 cm respectively.

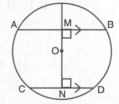

9. AB and CD are two parallel chords of a circle of lengths 10 cm and 4 cm respectively. If the chords lie on the same side of the centre and the distance between them is 3 cm, find the diameter of the circle.

10. ABC is an isosceles triangle inscribed in a circle. If AB = AC = $12\sqrt{5}$ cm and BC = 24 cm, find the radius of the circle.

11. An equilateral triangle of side 6 cm is inscribed in a circle. Find the radius of the circle.

12. AB is a diameter of a circle. M is a point in AB such that AM = 18 cm and MB = 8 cm. Find the length of the shortest chord through M.

13. A rectangle with one side of length 4 cm is inscribed in a circle of diameter 5 cm. Find the area of the rectangle.

14 The length of the common chord of two intersecting circles is 30 cm. If the radii of the two circles are 25 cm and 17 cm, find the distance between their centres.

15 The line joining mid-points of two chords of a circle passes through its centre. Prove that the chords are parallel.

16 If a diameter of a circle is perpendicular to one of two parallel chords of the circle, prove that it is perpendicular to the other and bisects it.

17 In an equilateral triangle, prove that the centroid and the circumcentre of the triangle coincide.

Hint.

Prove that medians are perpendicular bisectors of the sides of triangle.

18 (a) In the figure (i) given below, OD is perpendicular to the chord AB of a circle whose centre is O. If BC is a diameter, show that CA = 2 OD.

(b) In the figure (ii) given below, O is the centre of a circle. If AB and AC are chords of the circle such that AB = AC and OP ⊥ AB, OQ ⊥ AC, prove that PB = QC.

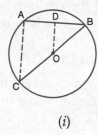
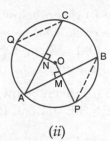

(i)   (ii)

Hint.

(a) OD becomes the line joining the mid-points of the sides BC and AB of △ABC.

(b) Prove that △ MPB ≅ △NQC.

19 (a) In the figure (i) given below, a line *l* intersects two concentric circles at the points A, B, C and D. Prove that AB = CD.

(b) In the figure (ii) given below, chords AB and CD of a circle with centre O intersect at E. If OE bisects ∠AED, prove that AB = CD.

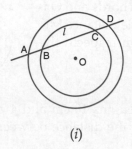
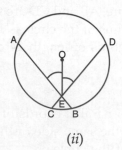

(i)   (ii)

Hint.

(a) Draw OM ⊥ *l*.

(b) Draw OM ⊥ AB and ON ⊥ CD. △OME ≅ △ONE   (A.A.S. rule of congruency)
    ⇒ OM = ON.

20 (a) In the figure (i) given below, AD is a diameter of a circle with centre O. If AB ∥ CD, prove that AB = CD.

(b) In the figure (ii) given below, AB and CD are equal chords of a circle with centre O. If AB and CD meet at E (outside the circle) prove that

(i) AE = CE   (ii) BE = DE.

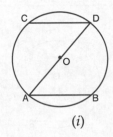

(i)

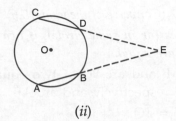

(ii)

Hint.

(a) Draw OM ⊥ AB and ON ⊥ CD, ΔOAM ≅ ΔODN.

(b) Draw OM ⊥ AB and ON ⊥ CD, ΔOME ≅ ΔONE.

15.3 ARC AND CHORD PROPERTIES OF CIRCLES

15.3.1 Axiom of equal arcs

In equal circles (or in the same circle), if two arcs subtend equal angles at the centres (or centre) then they are equal.

In the adjoining figure, arc AB and arc PQ of two equal circles (having equal radii) with centres O and O' respectively subtend equal angles at the centres *i.e.*

∠AOB = ∠PO'Q, then

arc AB = arc PQ.

Conversely. *In equal circles (or in the same circle), if two arcs are equal then they subtend equal angles at the centres (or centre).*

In the adjoining figure, arc AB and arc PQ of equal circles (having equal radii) with centres O and O' respectively are equal *i.e.*

arc AB = arc PQ, then

∠AOB = ∠PO'Q.

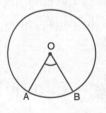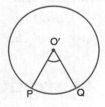

Theorem 15.6

In equal circles (or in the same circle), equal chords cut off equal arcs.

Given. AB and PQ are chords of two equal circles with centres O and O' respectively, and AB = PQ.

To prove. Arc AB = Arc PQ.

Construction. Join OA, OB, O'P and O'Q.

Proof.

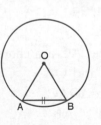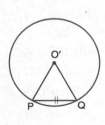

Statements	Reasons
In Δs OAB and O'PQ	
1. OA = O'P	1. Radii of equal circles.
2. OB = O'Q	2. Radii of equal circles.
3. AB = PQ	3. Given.
4. Δ OAB ≅ Δ O'PQ	4. S.S.S. rule of congruency.

5. ∠AOB = ∠PO'Q	5. 'c.p.c.t.'.
6. Arc AB = Arc PQ **Q.E.D.**	6. Axiom of equal arcs.

Theorem 15.7 (*Converse of theorem 15.6*).

In equal circles (or in same circle), if two arcs are equal then their chords are equal.

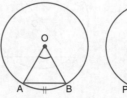

Given. Arc AB and arc PQ of two equal circles with centres O and O' respectively, and arc AB = arc PQ.

To prove. AB = PQ.

Construction. Join OA, OB, O'P and O'Q.

Proof.

Statements	Reasons
1. Arc AB = arc PQ	1. Given.
2. ∠AOB = ∠PO'Q In Δs OAB and O'PQ	2. Axiom of equal arcs.
3. OA = O'P	3. Radii of equal circles.
4. OB = O'Q	4. Radii of equal circles.
5. ∠AOB = ∠PO'Q	5. From 2.
6. Δ OAB ≅ ΔO'PQ	6. S.A.S. rule of congruency.
7. AB = PQ **Q. E. D.**	7. 'c.p.c.t.'.

Corollary 1. *Equal chords of the same circle (or of equal circles) subtend equal angles at the centre (or centres) of the circle (or circles).*

Corollary 2. *In equal circles (or on the same circle), equal angles at the centres (or centre) make equal chords.*

Illustrative Examples

Example 1 AB and AC are equal chords of a circle with centre O. Prove that OA bisects ∠BAC.

Solution. AB and AC are chords of a circle with centre O such that AB = AC.

Join OB, OC and OA.

In ΔOAB and ΔOAC,

$$AB = AC \qquad \text{(given)}$$
$$OB = OC \qquad \text{(radii of same circle)}$$
$$OA = OA \qquad \text{(common)}$$
∴   ΔOAB ≅ ΔOAC   (SSS rule of congruency)
∴   ∠OAB = ∠OAC

Example 2 Two chords AB and AC of a circle with centre O are equal. Prove that the centre of the circle lies on the bisector of ∠BAC.

Solution. Given chords AB and AC of a circle with centre O are equal *i.e.* AB = AC. We want to prove that O lies on the bisector of ∠BAC.

Join BC and let the bisector of ∠BAC meet BC at M.

In ΔABM and ΔACM,

	AB = AC	(given)
	∠BAM = ∠CAM	
		(∵ AM is bisector of ∠BAC)
	AM = AM	(common)
∴	ΔABM ≅ ΔACM	(SAS rule of congruency)
∴	BM = CM	(c.p.c.t.)
	∠AMB = ∠AMC	(c.p.c.t.)

But   ∠AMB + ∠AMC = 180°   (linear pair)

⇒   ∠AMB + ∠AMB = 180° ⇒ ∠AMB = 90°

⇒   AM ⊥ BC.

Thus, AM is the perpendicular bisector of the chord BC and we know that a perpendicular bisector of a chord of a circle passes through its centre, so AM passes through the centre O of the circle.

Hence, the centre O of the circle lies on the bisector of ∠BAC.

Example 3 If two chords AB and AC of a circle with centre O are such that the centre O lies on the bisector of ∠BAC, then prove that the chords are equal.

Solution. Given AB and AC are chords of a circle with centre O such that ∠BOA = ∠CAO.

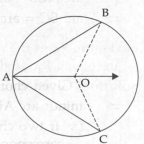

We want to prove that AB = AC.

Join OB and OC.

In ΔOAB,   OA = OB   (radii of same circle)

⇒   ∠ABO = ∠BAO

                (∠s opp. equal sides of a Δ are equal)

In ΔOAC,   OA = OC   (radii of same circle)

⇒   ∠ACO = ∠CAO   (∠s opp. equal sides of a Δ are equal)

But   ∠BAO = ∠CAO

∴   ∠ABO = ∠ACO.

In ΔAOB and ΔAOC,

	∠ABO = ∠ACO	(proved above)
	∠BAO = ∠CAO	(given)
	OA = OA	(common)
∴	ΔAOB ≅ ΔAOC	(AAS rule of congruency)
∴	AB = AC	(c.p.c.t.)

Example 4 Prove that the line of centres of two intersecting circles subtend equal angles at the two points of intersection.

Solution. Given two circles with centres O and O', and intersecting at the points A and B. Join OO'.

We need to prove that ∠OAO' = ∠OBO'.

In ΔOAO' and ΔOBO',

	OA = OB	(radii of same circle)
	O'A = O'B	(radii of same circle)
	OO' = OO'	(common)
∴	ΔOAO' ≅ ΔOBO'	(by SSS rule of congruency)
∴	∠OAO' = ∠OBO'	(c.p.c.t.)

Example 5 In a circle with centre O, chord SR = chord SM. Radius OS intersects the chord RM at P. Prove that RP = PM.

Solution. Join OR and OM.

Given SR = SM and we know that equal chords of a circle subtend equal angles at the centre of the circle, therefore,

$$\angle SOR = \angle SOM \ i.e. \ \angle POR = \angle POM.$$

In $\triangle ORP$ and $\triangle OMP$,

$\angle POR = \angle POM$		(proved above)
OR = OM		(radii of same circle)
OP = OP		(common)
$\therefore$	$\triangle ORP \cong \triangle OMP$	(SAS rule of congruency)
$\therefore$	RP = PM	(c.p.c.t.)

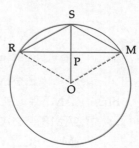

Example 6 In the adjoining figure, AB is a diameter of a circle with centre O. If chord AC = chord AD, prove that arc BC = arc DB.

Solution. Given chord AC = chord AD

$\Rightarrow$ arc AC = arc AD (Theorem 15.6)

Since AB is a diameter of the given circle, arc ACB = arc ADB.

$\therefore$ arc ACB – arc AC = arc ADB – arc AD

$\Rightarrow$ arc BC = arc DB.

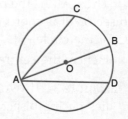

Example 7 In the adjoining figure, chords AB and CD of a circle are equal. Prove that AD = CB.

Solution. Given chord AB = chord CD

$\Rightarrow$ minor arc AB = minor arc CD

($\because$ If two chords of a circle are equal, then their corresponding arcs are equal)

$\Rightarrow \quad \overset{\frown}{AB} = \overset{\frown}{CD}$

$\Rightarrow \quad \overset{\frown}{AB} - \overset{\frown}{BD} = \overset{\frown}{CD} - \overset{\frown}{BD}$ (subtracting $\overset{\frown}{BD}$ from both sides)

$\Rightarrow \quad \overset{\frown}{AD} = \overset{\frown}{CB}$

$\Rightarrow$ chord AD = chord CB   (Theorem 15.7)

$\Rightarrow$ AB = CB.

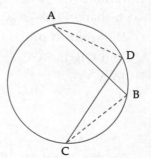

Example 8 In the adjoining figure, AOC is a diameter of the circle and arc AXB = $\frac{1}{2}$ arc BYC. Find $\angle BOC$.

Solution. As arc AXB = $\frac{1}{2}$ arc BYC,

$$\angle AOB = \frac{1}{2} \angle BOC \qquad \qquad \ldots(i)$$

Since AOC is a diameter, $\angle AOB + \angle BOC = 180°$

$\Rightarrow \quad \frac{1}{2} \angle BOC + \angle BOC = 180°$ (using (i))

$\Rightarrow \quad \frac{3}{2} \angle BOC = 180° \Rightarrow \angle BOC = \frac{2}{3} \times 180° = 120°.$

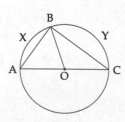

Example 9 In the adjoining figure, arc AB = arc CD.

Prove that $\angle A = \angle B$.

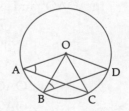

Solution. Given arc AB = arc CD

$\Rightarrow \quad \angle AOB = \angle COD$

$(\because$ equal arcs of a circle subtend equal angles at the centre of the circle)

$\Rightarrow \quad \angle AOB + \angle BOC = \angle COD + \angle BOC$ (adding $\angle BOC$ to both sides)

$\Rightarrow \quad \angle AOC = \angle BOD.$

In $\triangle AOC$ and $\triangle BOD$,

OA = OB	(radii of same circle)
OC = OD	(radii of same circle)
$\angle AOC = \angle BOD$	(proved above)
$\therefore \quad \triangle AOC \cong \triangle BOD$	(SAS rule of congruency)
$\Rightarrow \quad \angle A = \angle B$	(c.p.c.t.)

EXERCISE 15.2

1 If arcs APB and CQD of a circle are congruent, then find the ratio of AB : CD.

(Ans. 1 : 1)

2 A and B are points on a circle with centre O. C is a point on the circle such that OC bisects $\angle AOB$, prove that OC bisects the arc AB.

3 Prove that the angle subtended at the centre of a circle is bisected by the radius passing through the mid-point of the arc.

4 In the adjoining figure, two chords AB and CD of a circle intersect at P. If AB = CD, prove that arc AD = arc CB.

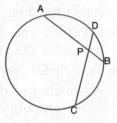

Hint.

Minor arc AB = minor arc CD. Subtract minor arc BD from both sides.

Multiple Choice Questions

Choose the correct answer from the given four options (1 to 6) :

1 If P and Q are any two points on a circle, then the line segment PQ is called a
    (*a*) radius of the circle   (*b*) diameter of the circle
    (*c*) chord of the circle   (*d*) secant of the circle

2 If P is a point in the interior of a circle with centre O and radius r, then
    (*a*) $OP = r$ (*b*) $OP > r$ (*c*) $OP \geq r$ (*d*) $OP < r$

3 The circumference of a circle must be
    (*a*) a positive real number   (*b*) a whole number
    (*c*) a natural number   (*d*) an integer

4 AD is a diameter of a circle and AB is a chord. If AD = 34 cm and AB = 30 cm, then the distance of AB from the centre of circle is
    (*a*) 17 cm   (*b*) 15 cm   (*c*) 4 cm   (*d*) 8 cm

5 If AB = 12 cm, BC = 16 cm and AB is perpendicular to BC, then the radius of the circle passing through the points A, B and C is
    (*a*) 6 cm   (*b*) 8 cm   (*c*) 10 cm   (*d*) 12 cm

6 In the adjoining figure, O is the centre of the circle. If OA = 5 cm, AB = 8 cm and OD ⊥ AB, then length of CD is equal to

    (a) 2 cm   (b) 3 cm

    (c) 4 cm   (d) 5 cm

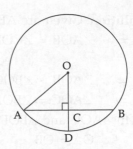

S ummary

....

○ A circle is the collection of all those points in a plane each of which is at a constant distance from a fixed point in the plane.

○ The fixed point is called the centre and constant distance is called radius.

○ All radii of a circle are equal.

○ The centre of the circle lies in the interior of the circle.

○ A line segment joining any two points of a circle is called a chord of the circle.

○ A chord of the circle passing through its centre is called a diameter of the circle.

○ The length of a diameter of a circle is twice its radius.

○ A (continuous) part of a circle is called an arc of the circle.

○ The whole arc of a circle is called its circumference. The length of the circumference is the length of the whole arc.

○ One-half of the whole arc of the circle is called a semicircle.

○ Let P and Q be two points on a circle with centre O, then join OP and OQ. ∠POQ is called the angle subtended by the arc PQ at the centre.

○ If PQ is a chord of a circle with centre O, then ∠POQ is called the angle subtended by the chord PQ at the centre O of the circle.

○ Two circles are called equal (or congruent) if and only if they have same radius.

○ A straight line drawn from the centre of a circle to bisect a chord, which is not a diameter, is at right angles to the chord.

○ The perpendicular to a chord from the centre bisects the chord.

○ Equal chords are equidistant from the centre and conversely, chords equidistant from the centre are equal.

○ There is one and only one circle that passes through three given non-collinear points.

○ In the plane of circle, the perpendicular bisector of a chord of a circle passes through its centre.

○ If two arcs subtend equal angles at the centre, then they are equal and conversely, equal arcs subtend equal angles at the centre.

○ Equal chord cut off equal arcs and conversely, if two arcs are equal then their chords are equal.

1 In the adjoining figure, a chord PQ of a circle with centre O and radius 15 cm is bisected at M by a diameter AB. If OM = 9 cm, find the lengths of :

    (i) PQ   (ii) AP   (iii) BP.

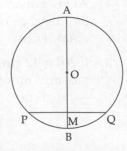

2 The radii of two concentric circles are 17 cm and 10 cm; a line PQRS cuts the larger circle at P and S and the smaller circle at Q and R. If QR = 12 cm, calculate PQ.

3 A chord of length 48 cm is at a distance of 10 cm from the centre of a circle. If another chord of length 20 cm is drawn in the same circle, find its distance from the centre of the circle.

4 (a) In the figure (i) given below, two circles with centres C, D intersect in points P, Q. If length of common chord is 6 cm and CP = 5 cm, DP = 4 cm, calculate the distance CD correct to two decimal places.

(b) In the figure (ii) given below, P is a point of intersection of two circles with centres C and D. If the st. line APB is parallel to CD, prove that AB = 2CD.

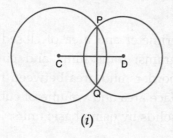

(i)

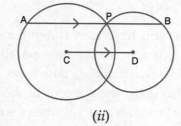

(ii)

Hint.

(b) From C, D draw CM, DN perpendiculars to AB. Then MCDN is a rectangle, so
MN = CD. MN = MP + PN = $\frac{1}{2}$AP + $\frac{1}{2}$PB = $\frac{1}{2}$AB.

5 (a) In the figure (i) given below, C and D are centres of two intersecting circles. The line APQB is perpendicular to the line of centres CD. Prove that
(i) AP = QB   (ii) AQ = BP.

(b) In the figure (ii) given below, two equal chords AB and CD of a circle with centre O intersect at right angles at P. If M and N are mid-points of the chords AB and CD respectively, prove that NOMP is a square.

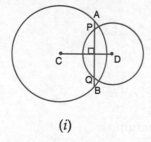

(i)

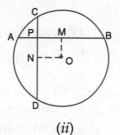

(ii)

6 In the adjoining figure, AD is diameter of a circle. If the chord AB and AC are equidistant from its centre O, prove that AD bisects ∠BAC and ∠BDC.

Hint.

As the chords AB and AC are equidistant from the centre, so AB = AC.

Since angle in a semi circle is 90°,

∠B = ∠C (each = 90°)

△ABD ≅ △ACD (Why?)

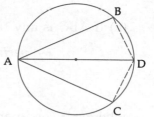

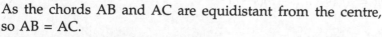

16 Mensuration

INTRODUCTION

In previous classes, you have learnt about the perimeter and area of closed plane figures such as triangles, squares, rectangles, parallelograms, trapeziums and circles; the area between two rectangles *i.e.* area of pathways or borders and area between two concentric circles. You have also learnt the concept of the surface area and volume of cube and cuboid, measurement of surface area and volume of such solids by using basic units. In this chapter, we shall review and strengthen all these.

16.1 PERIMETER AND AREA OF PLANE FIGURES

*The **perimeter** of a closed plane figure is the length of its boundary i.e. the sum of lengths of its sides.*

The unit of measurement of perimeter is the unit of length.

*The **area** of a closed plane figure is the measurement of the region (surface) enclosed by its boundary (sides).*

It is measured in *square units i.e.* square centimetres (abbreviated cm^2) or square metres (abbreviated m^2) etc.

16.2 PERIMETER AND AREA OF TRIANGLES

(*i*) *Area of a triangle* = $\frac{1}{2}$ *base* × *height*.

Any side of the triangle can be taken as its **base**, then the length of perpendicular (altitude) from the vertex opposite to this side is called its **corresponding height**.

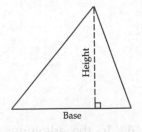

(*ii*) If ABC is any triangle with sides *a*, *b* and *c*, then

$$perimeter = a + b + c, \text{ and}$$

$$area = \sqrt{s(s-a)(s-b)(s-c)}$$

where *s* = semi-perimeter = $\frac{a+b+c}{2}$.

(This is known as **Heron's formula**.)

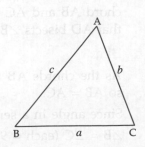

16.2.1 Some special types of triangles

(i) Right-angled triangle:

If ABC is a triangle in which $\angle B = 90°$,

then its area $= \dfrac{1}{2} BC \times AB$

$= \dfrac{1}{2}$ (product of sides containing right angle).

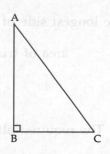

(ii) Equilateral triangle:

Let ABC be an equilateral triangle with side a and AD be the perpendicular from A to BC, then D is the mid-point of BC i.e. $BD = \dfrac{a}{2}$.

In $\triangle ABD$, $AD^2 = AB^2 - BD^2$ (Pythagoras theorem)

$\Rightarrow \qquad AD^2 = a^2 - \left(\dfrac{a}{2}\right)^2 = \dfrac{3}{4}a^2 \Rightarrow AD = \dfrac{\sqrt{3}}{2}a.$

$\therefore \qquad$ Area of $\triangle ABC = \dfrac{1}{2} BC \times AD$

$= \dfrac{1}{2}a \times \dfrac{\sqrt{3}}{2}a = \dfrac{\sqrt{3}}{4}a^2.$

Perimeter of $\triangle ABC = 3a$.

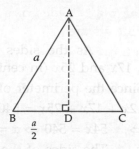

(iii) Isosceles triangle:

Let ABC be an isosceles triangle with $AB = AC = a$ and $BC = b$, and AD be the perpendicular from A to BC, then D is mid-point of BC i.e. $BD = \dfrac{b}{2}$.

In $\triangle ABD$, $AD^2 = AB^2 - BD^2$ (Pythagoras theorem)

$= a^2 - \left(\dfrac{b}{2}\right)^2 = a^2 - \dfrac{b^2}{4} = \dfrac{4a^2 - b^2}{4}$

$\Rightarrow \qquad AD = \dfrac{\sqrt{4a^2 - b^2}}{2}.$

$\therefore \qquad$ Area of $\triangle ABC = \dfrac{1}{2} BC \times AD = \dfrac{1}{2}b \times \dfrac{\sqrt{4a^2 - b^2}}{2}$

$= \dfrac{1}{4}b\sqrt{4a^2 - b^2}.$

Perimeter of $\triangle ABC = 2a + b$.

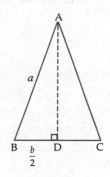

Illustrative Examples

Example 1 Calculate the area of a triangle whose sides are 13 cm, 5 cm and 12 cm. Hence, calculate the altitude using the longest side as base. Leave your answer as a fraction.

Solution. Since the sides of the triangle are 13 cm, 5 cm and 12 cm.

$\therefore \qquad\qquad s = \dfrac{13 + 5 + 12}{2}$ cm $= 15$ cm.

$\therefore \qquad$ Area of triangle $= \sqrt{s(s-a)(s-b)(s-c)}$

$= \sqrt{15(15-13)(15-5)(15-12)}$ cm^2

$= \sqrt{15 \times 2 \times 10 \times 3}$ cm$^2 = 30$ cm^2.

The longest side of the triangle is 13 cm, let h cm be the corresponding altitude, then

$$\text{area of triangle} = \frac{1}{2} \text{ base} \times \text{height}$$

$$\Rightarrow \qquad 30 = \frac{1}{2} \times 13 \times h \Rightarrow h = \frac{60}{13}.$$

$\therefore$ The required altitude of the triangle $= 4\frac{8}{13}$ cm.

Example 2 Sides of a triangle are in the ratio $12 : 17 : 25$ and its perimeter is 540 cm. Find its area.

Solution. As the sides of the triangle are in the ratio $12 : 17 : 25$, let the sides be $12x$, $17x$ and $25x$ (in centimetres).

Since the perimeter of the triangle is 540 cm, therefore,

$12x + 17x + 25x = 540$

$\Rightarrow \quad 54x = 540 \Rightarrow x = 10.$

$\therefore \qquad$ The sides of the triangle are (12×10) cm, (17×10) cm and (25×10) cm

i.e. 120 cm, 170 cm and 250 cm.

$$s = \text{semi-perimeter} = \frac{540}{2} \text{ cm} = 270 \text{ cm}.$$

Using Heron's formula,

$$\text{area of the triangle} = \sqrt{s(s-a)(s-b)(s-c)}$$

$$= \sqrt{270(270-120)(270-170)(270-250)} \text{ cm}^2$$

$$= \sqrt{270 \times 150 \times 100 \times 20} \text{ cm}^2 = 9000 \text{ cm}^2.$$

Example 3 The triangular side walls of a flyover have been used for advertisements. The sides of the walls are 122 m, 22 m and 120 m (shown in the adjoining figure). The advertisements yield an earning of ₹ 5000 per m² per year. A company hired one of its walls for 3 months. How much rent did it pay?

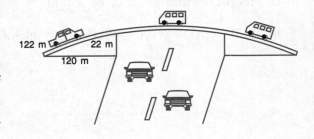

Solution. Here, $s = \dfrac{122 + 22 + 120}{2}$ m $= 132$ m.
Using Heron's formula,

$$\text{area of one triangular wall} = \sqrt{s(s-a)(s-b)(s-c)}$$

$$= \sqrt{132(132-122)(132-22)(132-120)} \text{ m}^2$$

$$= \sqrt{132 \times 10 \times 110 \times 12} \text{ m}^2 = 1320 \text{ m}^2.$$

Rent = ₹ 5000 per m² per year.

$\therefore$ Rent of one wall for 3 months $= ₹ \dfrac{1320 \times 5000 \times 3}{12} = ₹ 1650000.$

Example 4 The perimeter of a triangle is 50 cm. One side of a triangle is 4 cm longer than the smallest side and the third side is 6 cm less than twice the smallest side. Find the area of the triangle.

Solution. Let the smallest side of the triangle be x cm, then the other two sides are $(x + 4)$ cm and $(2x - 6)$ cm.

Given, perimeter of the triangle = 50 cm

$\Rightarrow \quad x + (x + 4) + (2x - 6) = 50$

$\Rightarrow \quad 4x = 52 \Rightarrow x = 13$

∴ The lengths of three sides of the triangle are 13 cm, (13 + 4) cm and (2 × 13 – 6) cm *i.e.* 13 cm, 17 cm and 20 cm.

Here, s = semi-perimeter = $\dfrac{50}{2}$ cm = 25 cm.

Using Heron's formula,

$$\text{area of the triangle} = \sqrt{s(s-a)(s-b)(s-c)}$$
$$= \sqrt{25(25-13)(25-17)(25-20)} \text{ cm}^2$$
$$= \sqrt{25 \times 12 \times 8 \times 5} \text{ cm}^2 = 20\sqrt{30} \text{ cm}^2.$$

Example 5 Find the area of a triangle whose perimeter is 22 cm, one side is 9 cm and the difference of the other two sides is 3 cm.

Solution. Let the other two sides of the triangle be a cm and b cm, $a > b$.

Then $9 + a + b = 22 \Rightarrow a + b = 13$ ...(i)

and $a - b = 3$ ...(ii)

On solving (i) and (ii), we get $a = 8$ and $b = 5$.

∴ The sides of the triangle are 9 cm, 8 cm and 5 cm.

s = semi-perimeter = $\dfrac{22}{2}$ cm = 11 cm.

∴ Area of the triangle $= \sqrt{s(s-a)(s-b)(s-c)}$

$$= \sqrt{11(11-9)(11-8)(11-5)} \text{ cm}^2$$

$$= \sqrt{11 \times 2 \times 3 \times 6} \text{ cm}^2 = 6\sqrt{11} \text{ cm}^2.$$

Example 6 From a point in the interior of an equilateral triangle, perpendiculars are drawn on the three sides. If the lengths of the perpendiculars are 14 cm, 10 cm and 6 cm, find the area of the triangle.

Solution. Let ABC be an equilateral triangle with length of each side = a cm.

O is a point in the interior of $\triangle$ABC, OD $\perp$ BC, OE $\perp$ CA and OF $\perp$ AB such that OD = 14 cm, OE = 10 cm and OF = 6 cm.

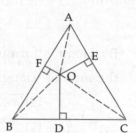

Area of equilateral triangle ABC = $\dfrac{\sqrt{3}}{4} a^2$ cm^2.

Also area of $\triangle$ABC = area of $\triangle$OBD + area of $\triangle$OCA + area of $\triangle$OAB

$$= \dfrac{1}{2} \text{ BC} \times \text{OD} + \dfrac{1}{2} \text{ CA} \times \text{OE} + \dfrac{1}{2} \text{ AB} \times \text{OF}$$

$\Rightarrow \quad \dfrac{\sqrt{3}}{4} a^2 \text{ cm}^2 = \dfrac{1}{2}(a \times 14 + a \times 10 + a \times 6) \text{ cm}^2$

$\Rightarrow \quad \dfrac{\sqrt{3}}{2} a^2 = 30a \Rightarrow \sqrt{3}\,a = 60$ ($\because a \neq 0$)

$\Rightarrow \quad a \Rightarrow 20\sqrt{3}$.

∴ Area of $\triangle$ABC = $\dfrac{\sqrt{3}}{4} \times (20\sqrt{3})^2$ cm^2 = $300\sqrt{3}$ cm^2.

Example 7 If the height of an equilateral triangle is 8 cm, calculate its area.

Solution. Let ABC be an equilateral triangle with side a cm. Let AD $\perp$ BC, then D is mid-point of BC and BD = $\dfrac{a}{2}$ cm.

In $\triangle$ABD, AD^2 = AB^2 – BD^2 (Pythagoras theorem)

$\Rightarrow \qquad 8^2 = a^2 - \left(\dfrac{a}{2}\right)^2$ ($\because$ height = AD = 8 cm given)

$$\Rightarrow \quad 64 = a^2 - \frac{a^2}{4} \Rightarrow \frac{3a^2}{4} = 64$$

$$\Rightarrow \quad a^2 = \frac{256}{3}.$$

$$\therefore \quad \text{Area of } \triangle ABC = \frac{\sqrt{3}}{4} a^2 \text{ cm}^2 = \frac{\sqrt{3}}{4} \times \frac{256}{3} \text{ cm}^2$$

$$= \frac{64\sqrt{3}}{3} \text{ cm}^2 = 36 \cdot 95 \text{ cm}^2.$$

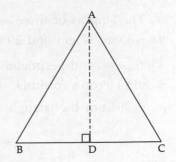

Example 8 The base of an isosceles triangle is 24 cm and its area is 192 sq. cm. Find its perimeter.

Solution. Let ABC be the isosceles triangle with base BC = 24 cm and area = 192 sq. cm. Let h cm be its height and AB = AC = a cm.

$$\text{Then area} = \frac{1}{2} \text{ base} \times \text{height}$$

$$\Rightarrow \quad 192 = \frac{1}{2} \times 24 \times h \Rightarrow h = 16.$$

In $\triangle ABD$, $AD^2 = AB^2 - BD^2$ (Pythagoras theorem)

$$\Rightarrow \quad (16)^2 = a^2 - (12)^2 \qquad \left(\because BD = \frac{1}{2} BC = 12 \text{ cm}\right)$$

$$\Rightarrow \quad 256 = a^2 - 144 \Rightarrow a^2 = 256 + 144$$

$$\Rightarrow \quad a^2 = 400 \Rightarrow a = 20.$$

$\therefore$ Perimeter of $\triangle ABC = 2a + b = (2 \times 20 + 24)$ cm = 64 cm.

Example 9 The base of an isosceles triangle measures 24 cm and its area is 60 cm². Find its perimeter (using Heron's formula).

Solution. Let each equal side of isosceles triangle be a cm, then

$$s = \frac{a + a + 24}{2} \text{ cm} = (a + 12) \text{ cm}.$$

By Heron's formula,

the area of triangle $= \sqrt{s(s-a)(s-b)(s-c)}$

$$\therefore \quad \sqrt{(a+12)(a+12-a)(a+12-a)(a+12-24)} = 60 \text{ (given)}$$

$$\Rightarrow \quad \sqrt{(a+12) \times 12 \times 12 \times (a-12)} = 60$$

$$\Rightarrow \quad 12\sqrt{(a+12)(a-12)} = 60$$

$$\Rightarrow \quad \sqrt{a^2 - 144} = 5$$

$$\Rightarrow \quad a^2 - 144 = 25 \Rightarrow a^2 = 169$$

$$\Rightarrow \quad a = 13 \qquad\qquad (\because a > 0)$$

$\therefore$ The perimeter of the triangle = 13 cm + 13 cm + 24 cm = 50 cm.

Example 10 Find the perimeter of an isosceles right-angled triangle whose area is 72 cm².

Solution. Let ABC be an isosceles right-angled triangle with $\angle B = 90°$ and AB = BC = a cm.

Then,

$$\text{area of } \triangle ABC = \frac{1}{2} BC \times AB$$

$$\Rightarrow \quad 72 = \frac{1}{2} a \times a \Rightarrow a^2 = 144$$

$$\Rightarrow \quad a = 12.$$

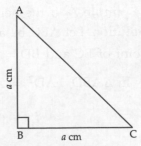

In $\triangle ABC$, $\angle B = 90°$. By Pythagoras theorem, we have
$$AC^2 = AB^2 + BC^2 = a^2 + a^2 = 2a^2$$
$\Rightarrow$ $AC = \sqrt{2}\, a$ cm

$\therefore$ Perimeter of $\triangle ABC = AB + BC + CA = (a + a + \sqrt{2}\, a)$ cm
$$= (2 + \sqrt{2})a \text{ cm} = (2 + \sqrt{2}) \times 12 \text{ cm}$$
$$= (2 + 1.414) \times 12 \text{ cm} = 40.97 \text{ cm.}$$

Example 11 In the adjoining figure, find the area of the shaded region (using Heron's formula).

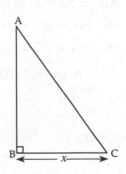

Solution. In $\triangle ABD$, $\angle D = 90°$.

By Pythagoras theorem,
$$AB^2 = AD^2 + BD^2 = 12^2 + 16^2$$
$$= 144 + 256 = 400$$
$\Rightarrow$ $AB = 20$ cm.

$\therefore$ Area of $\triangle ABD = \dfrac{1}{2} \times$ base $\times$ height $= \left(\dfrac{1}{2} \times 16 \times 12\right)$ cm^2 = 96 cm^2.

In $\triangle ABC$, the lengths of the sides are:
$a = 52$ cm, $b = 48$ cm and $c = 20$ cm,
$$s = \text{semi-perimeter} = \frac{52 + 48 + 20}{2} \text{ cm} = 60 \text{ cm.}$$

By Heron's formula,
$$\text{area of } \triangle ABC = \sqrt{s(s - a)(s - b)(s - c)}$$
$$= \sqrt{60(60 - 52)(60 - 48)(60 - 20)} \text{ cm}^2$$
$$= \sqrt{60 \times 8 \times 12 \times 40} \text{ cm}^2 = 10\sqrt{48 \times 48} \text{ cm}^2$$
$$= (10 \times 48) \text{ cm}^2 = 480 \text{ cm}^2.$$

$\therefore$ The area of shaded region = area of $\triangle ABC$ − area of $\triangle ABD$
$$= 480 \text{ cm}^2 - 96 \text{ cm}^2 = 384 \text{ cm}^2.$$

Example 12 If the difference between the two sides of a right angled-triangle is 2 cm and the area of the triangle is 24 cm^2, find the perimeter of the triangle.

Solution. Let ABC be a right-angled triangle with $\angle B = 90°$. Let $BC = x$ cm, then $AB = (x + 2)$ cm.

Area of $\triangle ABC = \dfrac{1}{2} BC \times AB$

$\Rightarrow$ $24 = \dfrac{1}{2} x(x + 2)$

$\Rightarrow$ $x(x + 2) = 48$

$\Rightarrow$ $x^2 + 2x - 48 = 0$

$\Rightarrow$ $(x + 8)(x - 6) = 0$

$\Rightarrow$ $x = -8$ or $x = 6$, but x cannot be negative

$\therefore$ $x = 6$.

$\therefore$ $BC = 6$ cm, then $AB = (6 + 2)$ cm = 8 cm.

In $\triangle ABC$, $AC^2 = AB^2 + BC^2$ (Pythagoras theorem)

$\Rightarrow$ $AC^2 = (8)^2 + (6)^2 = 64 + 36 = 100$

$\Rightarrow$ $AC = 10$ cm.

$\therefore$ Perimeter of $\triangle ABC = (8 + 6 + 10)$ cm = 24 cm.

Example 13 The perimeter of a right-angled triangle is 60 cm. If its hypotenuse is 26 cm, find the area of the triangle.

Solution. Let ABC be a right-angled triangle with $\angle B$ = 90°, then its hypotenuse AC = 26 cm   (given).

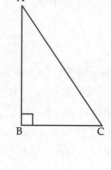

Let base BC = x cm, then

perimeter of $\triangle ABC$ = AB + BC + CA

$\Rightarrow$ 60 cm = AB + x cm + 26 cm $\Rightarrow$ AB = $(34 - x)$ cm.

In $\triangle ABC$, $\angle B$ = 90°,

      $AB^2 + BC^2 = AC^2$ (Pythagoras theorem)

$\Rightarrow$ $(34 - x)^2 + x^2 = 26^2$

$\Rightarrow$ $1156 - 68x + x^2 + x^2 = 676$

$\Rightarrow$ $2x^2 - 68x + 480 = 0 \Rightarrow x^2 - 34x + 240 = 0$

$\Rightarrow$ $(x - 24)(x - 10) = 0 \Rightarrow x = 24, 10$.

If $x = 24$, then BC = 24 cm and AB = $(34 - 24)$ cm = 10 cm.

$\therefore$ Area of $\triangle ABC = \frac{1}{2} \times BC \times AB = \frac{1}{2} \times 24 \times 10$ cm^2

                = 120 cm^2.

If $x = 10$, then BC = 10 cm and AB = $(34 - 10)$ cm = 24 cm.

$\therefore$ Area of $\triangle ABC = \frac{1}{2} \times BC \times AB = \frac{1}{2} \times 10 \times 24$ cm^2

                = 120 cm^2.

Hence, the area of $\triangle ABC$ = 120 cm^2.

Example 14 Each of equal sides of an isosceles triangle is 2 cm greater than its height. If the base of the triangle is 12 cm, find the area of triangle.

Solution. Let ABC be an isosceles triangle with base BC = 12 cm. Let its height AD be x cm, then D is mid-point of BC, therefore, BD = 6 cm.

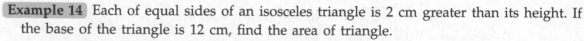

According to given, AB = AC = $(x + 2)$ cm.

From right angle $\triangle ABD$, by Pythagoras theorem, we get

AB^2 = AD^2 + BD^2

$\Rightarrow$ $(x + 2)^2 = x^2 + 6^2 \Rightarrow x^2 + 4x + 4 = x^2 + 36$

$\Rightarrow$ $4x = 32 \Rightarrow x = 8$.

$\therefore$ Area of $\triangle ABC = \frac{1}{2}$ BC $\times$ AD

              = $\frac{1}{2} \times 12 \times 8$ cm^2 = 48 cm^2.

Example 15 If the area of an isosceles triangle is 120 cm^2 and the length of each of its equal sides is 17 cm, find its base.

Solution. Let ABC be an isosceles triangle with AB = AC = 17 cm and its area = 120 cm^2.

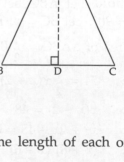

Let base BC = $2x$ cm.

Draw AD $\perp$ BC, then D is mid-point of BC.

$\therefore$ BD = DC = x cm.

In $\triangle ABD$, $\angle D = 90°$,

$\therefore \quad AD^2 + BD^2 = AB^2$ (Pythagoras theorem)

$\Rightarrow \quad AD^2 = AB^2 - BD^2 = 17^2 - x^2$

$\Rightarrow \quad AD = \sqrt{289 - x^2}$ cm.

Area of $\triangle ABC = \dfrac{1}{2} \times BC \times AD$

$\Rightarrow \quad 120 = \dfrac{1}{2} \times 2x \times \sqrt{289 - x^2} = x\sqrt{289 - x^2}$

$\Rightarrow \quad (120)^2 = x^2(289 - x^2) \Rightarrow x^4 - 289x^2 + 14400 = 0$

$\Rightarrow \quad (x^2 - 225)(x^2 - 64) = 0 \Rightarrow x^2 = 225, 64$

$\Rightarrow \quad x = 15, 8.$ ($\because$ x cannot be negative)

$\therefore \quad$ Base $= BC = 2x$ cm $= 30$ cm or 16 cm.

Example 16 In the adjoining figure, ABC is an isosceles triangle with base BC = 8 cm and AB = AC = 12 cm. AD is perpendicular to BC and O is a point on AD such that $\angle BOC = 90°$. Find the area of the shaded region.

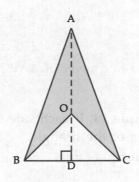

Solution. As AD $\perp$ BC, D is mid-point of BC.

$\therefore \quad BD = \dfrac{1}{2}$ of 8 cm = 4 cm.

From $\triangle ABD$, by Pythagoras theorem,

$\quad AD^2 = AB^2 - BD^2 = 12^2 - 4^2 = 144 - 16$

$\Rightarrow \quad AD = \sqrt{128}$ cm $= 8\sqrt{2}$ cm.

$\therefore \quad$ Area of $\triangle ABC = \dfrac{1}{2} BC \times AD$

$\qquad\qquad = \dfrac{1}{2} \times 8 \times 8\sqrt{2}$ cm^2

$\qquad\qquad = 32\sqrt{2}$ cm^2.

$\quad \triangle OBD \cong \triangle OCD$ (SAS rule of congruency)

$\Rightarrow \quad OB = OC.$

Let $\quad OB = OC = x$ cm.

From $\triangle OBC$, by Pythagoras theorem,

$\quad OB^2 + OC^2 = BC^2 \Rightarrow x^2 + x^2 = 8^2$

$\Rightarrow \quad 2x^2 = 64 \Rightarrow x^2 = 32.$

$\therefore \quad$ Area of $\triangle OBC = \dfrac{1}{2} OB \times OC = \dfrac{1}{2} x \times x$ cm^2

$\qquad\qquad = \dfrac{1}{2} x^2$ cm$^2 = \dfrac{1}{2} \times 32$ cm$^2 = 16$ cm^2.

$\therefore \quad$ Area of the shaded region = area of $\triangle ABC$ – area of $\triangle OBC$

$\qquad\qquad = 32\sqrt{2}$ cm$^2 - 16$ cm$^2 = 16(2\sqrt{2} - 1)$ cm^2

$\qquad\qquad = 29{\cdot}25$ cm^2.

Example 17 In the adjoining figure, $\angle B = 90°$ and D is mid-point of AC. If AB = 20 cm and BD = 14·5 cm, find the area and the perimeter of $\triangle ABC$.

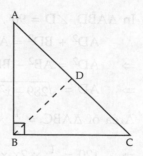

Solution. We know that the mid-point of hypotenuse of a right-angled triangle is equidistance from its vertices,

$$AD = DC = BD$$

$\Rightarrow \quad AD = DC = 14·5 \qquad (\because BD = 14·5 \text{ cm, given})$

$\therefore \quad AC = 2AD = (2 \times 14·5) \text{ cm} = 29 \text{ cm}$

In $\triangle ABD$, $\angle B = 90°$,

$\therefore \quad AC^2 = AB^2 + BC^2$ (Pythagoras theorem)

$\Rightarrow \quad 29^2 = 20^2 + BC^2$

$\Rightarrow \quad BC^2 = 29^2 - 20^2 = 841 - 400 = 441$

$\Rightarrow \quad BC = 21 \text{ cm}$

Area of $\triangle ABC = \dfrac{1}{2} \text{base} \times \text{height} = \left(\dfrac{1}{2} \times 21 \times 20\right) \text{ cm}^2$

$$= 210 \text{ cm}^2$$

and perimeter of $\triangle ABC = AB + BC + AC$

$$= (20 + 21 + 29) \text{ cm} = 70 \text{ cm}.$$

Example 18 If each side of a triangle is doubled, then find the percentage increase in the area of the triangle.

Solution. Let a, b, c be the sides of given triangle and s be its semi-perimeter, then

$$s = \frac{a + b + c}{2}$$

$\Rightarrow \quad 2s = a + b + c$

Area of the given triangle $= \sqrt{s(s - a)(s - b)(s - c)}$ ...(i)

As the sides of the given triangle are doubled, the sides of new triangle are $2a$, $2b$ and $2c$. Let S be the semi-perimeter of new triangle, then

$$S = \frac{2a + 2b + 2c}{2} = a + b + c = 2s$$ ...(ii)

Area of new triangle $= \sqrt{S(S - 2a)(S - 2b)(S - 2c)}$

$$= \sqrt{2s(2s - 2a)(2s - 2b)(2s - 2c)} \qquad \text{(using (ii))}$$

$$= \sqrt{16s(s - a)(s - b)(s - c)}$$

$$= 4\sqrt{s(s - a)(s - b)(s - c)}$$

$$= 4 \times \text{area of given triangle} \qquad \text{(using (i))}$$

Increase in area = area of new triangle – area of given triangle

$$= 4 \times \text{area of given triangle} - \text{area of given triangle}$$

$$= 3 \times \text{area of given triangle}.$$

The percentage increase in the area of given triangle

$$= \left(\frac{\text{increase in area}}{\text{area of given triangle}} \times 100\right)\%$$

$$= \left(\frac{3 \times \text{area of given triangle}}{\text{area of given triangle}} \times 100\right)\% = 300\%$$

EXERCISE 16.1

1 Find the area of a triangle whose base is 6 cm and corresponding height is 4 cm.

2 Find the area of a triangle whose sides are :

    (*i*) 3 cm, 4 cm and 5 cm.

    (*ii*) 29 cm, 20 cm and 21 cm.

    (*iii*) 12 cm, 9·6 cm and 7·2 cm.

3 Find the area of a triangle whose sides are 34 cm, 20 cm and 42 cm. Hence, find the length of the altitude corresponding to the shortest side.

4 The sides of a triangular field are 975 m, 1050 m and 1125 m. If this field is sold at the rate of ₹ 1000 per hectare, find its selling price.   [1 hectare = 10000 m²]

5 The base of a right angled triangle is 12 cm and its hypotenuse is 13 cm long. Find its area and the perimeter.

6 Find the area of an equilateral triangle whose side is 8 m. Give your answer correct to two decimal places.

7 If the area of an equilateral triangle is $81\sqrt{3}$ cm², find its perimeter.

8 If the perimeter of an equilateral triangle is 36 cm, calculate its area and height.

9 (*i*) If the lengths of the sides of a triangle are in the ratio 3 : 4 : 5 and its perimeter is 48 cm, find its area.

    (*ii*) The sides of a triangular plot are in the ratio 3 : 5 : 7 and its perimeter is 300 m. Find its area. Take $\sqrt{3}$ = 1·732.

10 ABC is a triangle in which AB = AC = 4 cm and ∠A = 90°. Calculate the area of △ABC. Also find the length of perpendicular from A to BC.

    Hint. By Pythagoras theorem, BC² = AB² + AC² = 4² + 4² = 32 ⟹ BC = $4\sqrt{2}$ cm.

11 Find the area of an isosceles triangle whose equal sides are 12 cm each and the perimeter is 30 cm.

12 Find the area of an isosceles triangle whose base is 6 cm and perimeter is 16 cm.

13 The sides of a right-angled triangle containing the right angle are 5*x* cm and (3*x* − 1) cm. Calculate the length of the hypotenuse of the triangle if its area is 60 cm².

14 In △ABC, ∠B = 90°, AB = (2*x* + 1) cm and BC = (*x* + 1) cm. If the area of the △ABC is 60 cm², find its perimeter.

15 If the perimeter of a right angled triangle is 60 cm and its hypotenuse is 25 cm, find its area.

16 The perimeter of an isosceles triangle is 40 cm. The base is two-third of the sum of equal sides. Find the length of each side.

17 If the area of an isosceles triangle is 60 cm² and the length of each of its equal sides is 13 cm, find its base.

18 The base of a triangular field is 3 times its height. If the cost of cultivating the field at the rate of ₹25 per 100 m² is ₹60000, find its base and height.

19 A triangular park ABC has sides 120 m, 80 m and 50 m (as shown in the adjoining figure). A gardner Dhania has to put a fence around it and also plant grass inside. How much area does she need to plant? Find the cost of fencing it with barbed wire at the rate of ₹ 20 per metre leaving a space 3 m wide for a gate on one side.

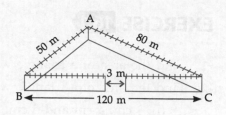

20 An umbrella is made by stitching 10 triangular pieces of cloth of two different colours (shown in the adjoining figure), each piece measuring 20 cm, 50 cm and 50 cm. How much cloth of each colour is required for the umbrella?

21 (a) In the figure (*i*) given below, ABC is an equilateral triangle with each side of length 10 cm. In △BCD, ∠D = 90° and CD = 6 cm. Find the area of the shaded region. Give your answer correct to one decimal place.

(b) In the figure (*ii*) given below, ABC is an isosceles right-angled triangle and DEFG is a rectangle. If AD = AE = 3 cm and DB = EC = 4 cm, find the area of the shaded region.

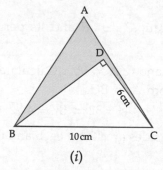

(*i*)

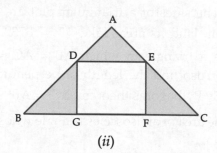

(*ii*)

Hint. (*b*) Area of △ADE = $\frac{1}{2} \times 3 \times 3$ cm² = $\frac{9}{2}$ cm².

△DBG is an isosceles triangle with BG = DG = x cm (say).

From △DBG, by Pythagoras theorem, $x^2 + x^2 = 4^2 \Rightarrow x^2 = 8$.

Area of △DBG = area of △EFC = $\frac{1}{2} x \times x$ cm² = $\frac{1}{2} \times 8$ cm² = 4 cm².

16.3 PERIMETER AND AREA OF QUADRILATERALS

Perimeter of a quadrilateral. If a, b, c and d are the lengths of the four sides of a quadrilateral, then its perimeter = $a + b + c + d$.

Area of a quadrilateral. Divide the given quadrilateral into two triangles and then find the areas of these triangles.

(*i*) *When one diagonal and the perpendiculars from the remaining vertices to this diagonal are given.*

In quad. ABCD, AC is diagonal and BM, DN are perpendiculars to AC from the remaining vertices B, D respectively.

Area of quad. ABCD = area of $\triangle$ABC + area of $\triangle$ACD

$$= \frac{1}{2} \text{ AC} \times \text{BM} + \frac{1}{2} \text{ AC} \times \text{DN}$$

$$= \frac{1}{2} \text{ AC (BM + DN)}$$

$$= \frac{1}{2} \times \text{ one diagonal} \times \text{ sum of lengths of}$$
perpendiculars drawn on it from the remaining two vertices.

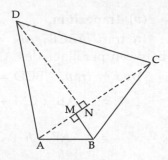

(ii) *When diagonals of a quadrilateral intersect at right angles.*

Area of quad. ABCD = area of $\triangle$ABC + area of $\triangle$ACD

$$= \frac{1}{2} \text{ AC} \times \text{OB} + \frac{1}{2} \text{ AC} \times \text{OD}$$

$$= \frac{1}{2} \text{ AC (OB + OD)} = \frac{1}{2} \text{ AC} \times \text{BD}$$

$$= \frac{1}{2} \times \text{ product of diagonals.}$$

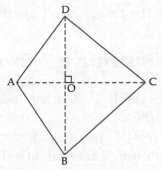

16.3.1 Some special types of quadrilaterals

(i) **Rectangle.**

In rectangle ABCD,

let AB = l (length) and BC = b (breadth), then its

$$\textbf{\textit{area}} = \text{AB} \times \text{BC} = l \times b,$$
$$\textbf{\textit{perimeter}} = 2(l + b).$$

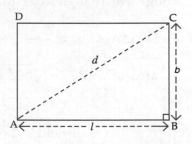

If d is the length of diagonal, then

$$d = \sqrt{l^2 + b^2}\,.$$

(ii) **Square.**

In square ABCD, let AB = a (side),

$$\textbf{\textit{area}} = (\text{AB})^2 = a^2,$$
$$\textbf{\textit{perimeter}} = 4a.$$

If d is the length of diagonal, then

$$d = \sqrt{a^2 + a^2} = \sqrt{2}\,a.$$

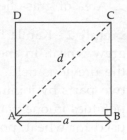

(iii) **Parallelogram.**

$$\textbf{\textit{Area}} = \textbf{\textit{base}} \times \textbf{\textit{height.}}$$

The height of a parallelogram is the distance between its base and the side parallel to base.

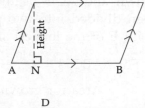

(iv) **Rhombus.**

Area of rhombus ABCD = base × height.

Since diagonals of a rhombus intersect at right angles,

area of rhombus

$$= \frac{1}{2} \times \text{ product of diagonals} = \frac{1}{2} \text{ AC} \times \text{BD.}$$

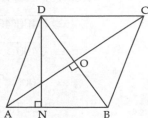

(v) **Trapezium.**

In trap. ABCD, AN = CM = h (each being distance between parallel sides AB and CD).

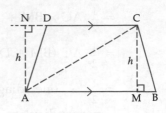

Area of trap. ABCD = area of △ABC + area of △ACD

$$= \frac{1}{2} AB \times CM + \frac{1}{2} CD \times AN$$

$$= \frac{1}{2} (AB \times h + CD \times h) = \frac{1}{2} (AB + CD) \times h$$

$$= \frac{1}{2} \text{(sum of parallel sides)} \times \text{height.}$$

The height of a trapezium is the distance between parallel sides.

Illustrative Examples

Example 1 A rhombus shaped field has green grass for 18 cows to graze. If each side of the rhombus is 30 m and its longer diagonal is 48 m, how much area of the grass field will each cow be getting?

Solution. Diagonal AC divides the rhombus ABCD into two congruent triangles of equal area.

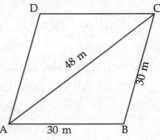

For △ABC, $s = \dfrac{30 + 30 + 48}{2}$ m = 54 m,

area of △ABC = $\sqrt{54(54 - 30)(54 - 30)(54 - 48)}$ m^2

$$= \sqrt{54 \times 24 \times 24 \times 6} \text{ m}^2 = 432 \text{ m}^2.$$

∴   Area of field = 2 × area of △ABC = (2 × 432) m^2 = 864 m^2.

∴ Area of grass field which each cow will be getting = $\dfrac{864}{18}$ m^2 = 48 m^2.

Example 2 Kamla has a triangular field with sides 240 m, 200 m and 300 m, where she grew wheat. In another triangular field with sides 240 m, 320 m and 400 m adjacent to the previous field, she wanted to grow potatoes and onions. She divided the field into two parts by joining the mid-point of the longest side to the opposite vertex and grew potatoes in one part and onions in the other part. How much area (in hectares) has been used for wheat, potatoes and onions? (1 hectare = 10000 m^2).

Solution. Let ABC be the triangular field where wheat is grown and ACD be the adjacent triangular field which has been divided into two parts by joining vertex C to the mid-point E of the longest side AD.

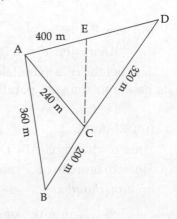

For △ABC, $s = \dfrac{240 + 200 + 360}{2}$ m = 400 m.

∴   Area for growing wheat = area of △ABC

$$= \sqrt{400(400 - 240)(400 - 200)(400 - 360)} \text{ m}^2$$

$$= \sqrt{400 \times 160 \times 200 \times 40} \text{ m}$$

$$= 16000\sqrt{2} \text{ m}^2 = \frac{16000\sqrt{2}}{10000} \text{ hectares}$$

$$= 2.26 \text{ hectares (approx.)}$$

For △ACD, $s = \dfrac{240 + 400 + 320}{2}$ m = 480 m.

Area of $\triangle ACD = \sqrt{480(480 - 240)(480 - 400)(480 - 320)}$ m²

$= \sqrt{480 \times 240 \times 80 \times 160}$ m² = 38400 m² = 3·84 hectares.

Note that the line segment EC divides $\triangle ACD$ into two triangles of equal area because $\triangle ACE$ and $\triangle DCE$ have equal bases AE, DE and have equal heights.

∴ Area for growing potatoes = area for growing onions = $\frac{1}{2}$ of 3·84 hectares = 1·92 hectares.

Example 3 Calculate the area of quadrilateral ABCD in which $\angle A = 90°$, AB = 32 cm, AD = 24 cm and BC = CD = 25 cm.

Solution. Join BD. Draw CE ⊥ BD.

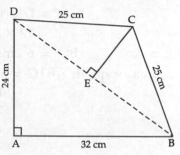

In $\triangle ABD$, $\angle A = 90°$,

∴ $BD^2 = AB^2 + AD^2 = (32)^2 + (24)^2$

              $= 1024 + 576 = 1600$

⇒ $BD = 40$ cm.

In $\triangle BCD$, BC = CD and CE ⊥ BD,

∴   E is mid-point of BD ⇒ DE = 20 cm.

In $\triangle CED$, $CE^2 = CD^2 - DE^2 = (25)^2 - (20)^2 = 625 - 400 = 225$

⇒   CE = 15 cm.

    Area of quad. ABCD = area of $\triangle ABD$ + area of $\triangle BCD$

$$= \frac{1}{2} AB \times AD + \frac{1}{2} BD \times CE$$

$$= \frac{1}{2} \times 32 \times 24 \text{ cm}^2 + \frac{1}{2} \times 40 \times 15 \text{ cm}^2$$

$$= (384 + 300) \text{ cm}^2 = 684 \text{ cm}^2.$$

Example 4 Calculate the area of a quadrilateral ABCD in which $\angle A = 90°$, AB = 30 cm, BC = 42 cm, CD = 20 cm and DA = 16 cm.

Solution. Join BD.

    Area of $\triangle ABD = \frac{1}{2} \times AB \times AD$

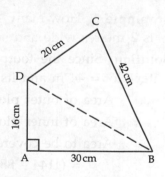

$$= \frac{1}{2} \times 30 \times 16 \text{ cm}^2 = 240 \text{ cm}^2$$

In $\triangle ABD$, $\angle A = 90°$.

By Pythagoras theorem, we get

    $BD^2 = AB^2 + AD^2 = 30^2 + 16^2$

          $= 900 + 256 = 1156$

⇒   BD = 34 cm

For area of $\triangle BCD$,

perimeter of $\triangle BCD$ = BC + CD + BD = (42 + 20 + 34) cm

                           = 96 cm

∴ $s = \frac{96}{2} = 48$ cm

Using Heron's formula, area of $\Delta = \sqrt{s(s-a)(s-b)(s-c)}$, we get

    area of $\triangle BCD = \sqrt{48(48-42)(48-20)(48-34)}$ cm²

$$= \sqrt{48 \times 6 \times 28 \times 14} \text{ cm}^2 = 336 \text{ cm}^2.$$

∴   Area of quad. ABCD = area of △ABC + area of △BCD

$$= (240 + 336) \text{ cm}^2 = 576 \text{ cm}^2.$$

Example 5 In the adjoining figure, triangle ABC is right-angled at B, AC = 7·5 cm and AB = 4·5 cm. TL is altitude of triangle BCT. Calculate TL, if the area of quadrilateral ABTC is 18 cm².

Solution. In △ABC, ∠B = 90°, by Pythagoras theorem, we get

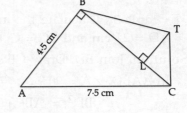

$$BC^2 = AC^2 - AB^2 = (7·5)^2 - (4·5)^2$$
$$= (7·5 + 4·5)(7·5 - 4·5)$$
$$= 12 \times 3 = 36$$

⇒   BC = 6 cm.

Area of quad. ABTC = area of △ABC + area of △BTC

$$= \frac{1}{2} \text{ BC} \times \text{AB} + \frac{1}{2} \text{ BC} \times \text{TL}$$

$$= \frac{1}{2} \times 6 \times 4·5 + \frac{1}{2} \times 6 \times \text{TL}$$

$$= 3 (4·5 + \text{TL}).$$

But area of quad. ABTC = 18 cm² (given)

∴   3(4·5 + TL) = 18 ⇒ 4·5 + TL = 6

⇒   TL = (6 − 4·5) cm = 1·5 cm.

Example 6 The perimeter of a rectangular plot is 120 m. If the length of the plot is twice its width, find the area of the plot.

Solution. Let the breadth of the plot be x metres, then its length = $2x$ metres.

∴ Perimeter of the plot = $2x + x + 2x + x = 6x$ metres.

According to given, $6x = 120 ⇒ x = 20 ⇒$ breadth = 20 m, length = 40 m.

∴ Area of the plot = length × breadth = (40×20) m² = 800 m².

Example 7 How many square tiles of side 20 cm will be needed to pave a footpath which is 2 metres wide and surrounds a rectangular plot 40 m long and 22 m wide?

Solution. Since the footpath is 2 m wide, length of the outer plot = 44 m and its breadth = 26 m.

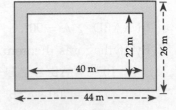

∴   Area of outer plot = (44×26) m² = 1144 m².

Area of inner plot = (40×22) m² = 880 m².

∴   Area to be covered with tiles

$$= (1144 - 880) \text{ m}^2 = 264 \text{ m}^2$$

$$= (264 \times 100 \times 100) \text{ cm}^2.$$

Area of one tile = (20×20) cm² = 400 cm².

∴ The number of tiles required to pave the footpath $= \dfrac{264 \times 100 \times 100}{400} = 6600.$

Example 8 The area of a square plot is 1764 m². Find the length of its one side and one diagonal.

Solution. Let a metres and d metres be the length of a side and a diagonal of the given square, then

$$a^2 = 1764 ⇒ a = 42 \text{ metres.}$$

In $\triangle ABC$, $\angle B = 90°$,

$\therefore \quad d^2 = a^2 + a^2 = 2a^2$

$\Rightarrow \quad d = \sqrt{2}\, a$

$\Rightarrow \quad d = (1\cdot414 \times 42)\,\text{m}$

$\qquad = 59\cdot39$ metres.

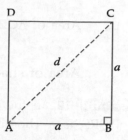

Example 9 Two adjacent sides of a parallelogram are 24 cm and 18 cm. If the distance between the longer sides is 12 cm, find the distance between shorter sides.

Solution. Let the distance between shorter sides be d cm, then

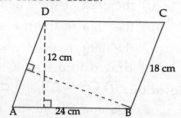

$\qquad 18 \times d = 24 \times 12$ (each = area of ‖ gm ABCD)

$\Rightarrow \quad d = 16.$

$\therefore$ The distance between shorter sides = 16 cm.

Example 10 A triangle and a parallelogram have the same base and the same area. If the sides of the triangle are 15 cm, 14 cm and 13 cm and the parallelogram stands on the base 15 cm, find the height of the parallelogram.

Solution. Let ABC be the triangle and BCDE be the parallelogram having same base BC (= 15 cm) and equal area.

Let h cm be the height (corresponding to the base BC) of ‖ gm BCDE.

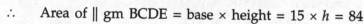

For $\triangle ABC$, $s = \dfrac{15 + 14 + 13}{2}$ cm = 21 cm.

$\therefore \quad$ Area of $\triangle ABC = \sqrt{s(s-a)(s-b)(s-c)}$

$\qquad\qquad = \sqrt{21(21-15)(21-14)(21-13)}$ cm^2

$\qquad\qquad = \sqrt{21 \times 6 \times 7 \times 8}$ cm^2 = 84 cm^2

$\therefore \quad$ Area of ‖ gm BCDE = base × height = 15 × h = 84

$\Rightarrow \quad 5h = 28 \Rightarrow h = \dfrac{28}{5} = 5\cdot6$ cm.

Example 11 A kite in the shape of a square with diagonal 32 cm and an isosceles triangle of base 8 cm and sides 6 cm each is to be made of three different shades as shown in the adjoining figure. How much paper of each shade has been used in it?

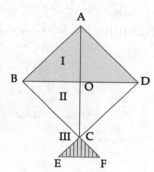

Solution. As the diagonals of a square bisect each other at right angles,

$\qquad AO = OC = \dfrac{1}{2} \times 32$ cm = 16 cm.

Area of shade I = $\dfrac{1}{2} \times BD \times AO = \dfrac{1}{2} \times 32 \times 16$ cm^2 = 256 cm^2,

Area of shade II = $\dfrac{1}{2} \times BD \times OC = \dfrac{1}{2} \times 32 \times 16$ cm^2 = 256 cm^2.

For $\triangle CEF$, $s = \dfrac{6 + 8 + 6}{2} = 10$ cm

$$\therefore \quad \text{Area of } \Delta CEF = \sqrt{10(10-6)(10-8)(10-6)} \text{ cm}^2 = \sqrt{10 \times 4 \times 2 \times 4} \text{ cm}^2$$

$$= 8\sqrt{5} \text{ cm}^2 = 17 \cdot 9 \text{ cm}^2 \text{ (approx.)}$$

$\therefore \quad$ Area of shade III = $17 \cdot 9$ cm^2 (approx.)

Example 12 In the given figure, ABCD is a rectangle and PQRS is a rhombus whose vertices are mid-points of the sides of the rectangle. Given that AB = 8 cm and AD = 6 cm, find

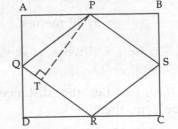

  (*i*) the area of the rhombus PQRS.

  (*ii*) the area of the triangle PBS.

  (*iii*) the length of PT, where PT is the perpendicular drawn from P to QR .

Solution. (*i*) QS = AB = 8 cm and PR = AD = 6 cm.

QS and PR are the diagonals of rhombus PQRS.

$$\therefore \quad \text{Area of rhombus PQRS} = \frac{1}{2} \text{QS} \times \text{PR} = \frac{1}{2} \times 8 \times 6 \text{ cm}^2 = 24 \text{ cm}^2.$$

(*ii*) Since P is mid-point of AB, PB = 4 cm.

Also S is mid-point of BC, BS = 3 cm. $\qquad$ (∵ BC = AD = 6 cm)

$$\therefore \quad \text{Area of } \Delta PBS = \frac{1}{2} \text{ PB} \times \text{BS} = \frac{1}{2} \times 4 \times 3 \text{ cm}^2 = 6 \text{ cm}^2.$$

(*iii*) In ΔPBS, $\angle B = 90°$,

$\therefore \qquad PS^2 = PB^2 + BS^2 = 4^2 + 3^2 = 16 + 9 = 25 \Rightarrow PS = 5$ cm.

$\therefore \qquad QR = 5$ cm $\qquad$ (∵ QR = PS side of rhombus)

Also area of rhombus PQRS = 24 cm^2 $\qquad\qquad$ (part (*i*))

$\therefore \qquad QR \times PT = 24 \Rightarrow 5 \times PT = 24$

$\Rightarrow \qquad PT = \dfrac{24}{5}$ cm $\Rightarrow PT = 4 \cdot 8$ cm.

Example 13 In the adjoining figure, AB and DC are parallel sides of a trapezium ABCD and $\angle ADC = 90°$. Given AB = 15 cm, CD = 40 cm and diagonal AC = 41 cm, calculate the area of trapezium ABCD.

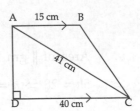

Solution. In ΔADC, $\angle D = 90°$,

$\therefore \qquad AD^2 = AC^2 - DC^2$

$\qquad\qquad = (41)^2 - (40)^2 = 1681 - 1600 = 81$

$\Rightarrow \qquad AD = 9$ cm.

$\therefore \quad$ Area of trap. ABCD = $\dfrac{1}{2}$ (sum of parallel sides) × height

$$= \frac{1}{2} (40 + 15) \times 9 \text{ cm}^2 = \frac{1}{2} \times 55 \times 9 \text{ cm}^2 = 247 \cdot 5 \text{ cm}^2.$$

Example 14 The parallel sides AB and DC of a trapezium ABCD are 51 cm and 30 cm respectively. If the sides AD and BC are 20 cm and 13 cm respectively. Find the distance between parallel sides and the area of the trapezium ABCD.

Solution. Draw CE parallel to DA and CN perpendicular to AB.

Then AECD is a parallelogram.

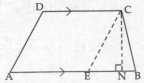

So $\quad$ EC = AD = 20 cm and AE = DC = 30 cm.

$\therefore \qquad$ EB = AB – AE = 51 cm – 30 cm = 21 cm.

Since the sides of $\triangle CEB$ are $CE = 20$ cm,
$EB = 21$ cm and $BC = 13$ cm,

$$s = \frac{20 + 21 + 13}{2} \text{ cm} = 27 \text{ cm}.$$

∴   The area of $\triangle CEB = \sqrt{s(s-a)(s-b)(s-c)}$

$$= \sqrt{27 \times 7 \times 6 \times 14} \text{ cm}^2 = \sqrt{81 \times 49 \times 4} \text{ cm}^2$$

$$= 9 \times 7 \times 2 \text{ cm}^2 = 126 \text{ cm}^2.$$

Also area of $\triangle CEB = \frac{1}{2} EB \times CN$

⇒ $126 = \frac{1}{2} \times 21 \times CN \Rightarrow CN = \frac{2 \times 126}{21} = 12.$

∴   The distance between parallel sides = 12 cm.

Area of trap. $ABCD = \frac{1}{2}$ (sum of parallel sides) × height

$$= \frac{1}{2} (51 + 30) \times 12 \text{ cm}^2 = \frac{1}{2} \times 81 \times 12 \text{ cm}^2 = 486 \text{ cm}^2.$$

Example 15 ABCD is a square with sides of length of 6 cm. Find point M on BC such that area of $\triangle ABM$: area of trap. ADCM = 1 : 3.

Solution. Let $BM = x$ cm, then $MC = (6 - x)$ cm.

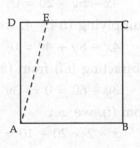

Area of $\triangle ABM = \frac{1}{2} \times 6 \times x \text{ cm}^2 = 3x \text{ cm}^2,$

area of trap. $ADCM = \frac{1}{2} [6 + (6 - x)] \times 6 \text{ cm}^2$

$$= 3(12 - x) \text{ cm}^2$$

According to given, $\frac{3x}{3(12 - x)} = \frac{1}{3}$

⇒ $3x = 12 - x \Rightarrow 4x = 12 \Rightarrow x = 3$

⇒   M is mid-point of BC.

Example 16 In the adjoining figure, ABCD is a square. E is a point on DC such that area of $\triangle AED$: area of the trap. ABCE = 1 : 5, find the ratio of the perimeters of $\triangle AED$ and trap. ABCE.

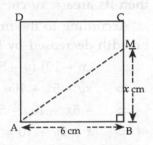

Solution. Let a side of the square ABCD be x units and $DE = y$ units, then $EC = (x - y)$ unit.

Area of $\triangle AED = \frac{1}{2} AD \times DE = \frac{1}{2} xy$ sq. units.

Area of trap. $ABCE = \frac{1}{2} [x + (x - y)] \times x$ sq. units.

According to given, $\dfrac{\frac{1}{2} xy}{\frac{1}{2} (2x - y)x} = \dfrac{1}{5}$

⇒ $\dfrac{y}{2x - y} = \dfrac{1}{5} \Rightarrow 2x - y = 5y$

⇒ $2x = 6y \Rightarrow x = 3y$ ...(i)

In $\triangle AED$, $\angle D = 90°$, by Pythagoras theorem, we get

$$AE^2 = AD^2 + DE^2 = x^2 + y^2 = (3y)^2 + y^2 = 10y^2 \qquad \text{(using (i))}$$

$\Rightarrow \quad AE = \sqrt{10}\, y$ units.

Perimeter of $\triangle AED = AD + DE + AE = (x + y + \sqrt{10}\, y)$ units

$$= (3y + y + \sqrt{10}\, y) \text{ units} \qquad \text{(using (i))}$$

$$= (4 + \sqrt{10})y \text{ units.}$$

Perimeter of trap. $ABCE = AB + BC + CE + AE$

$$= [x + x + (x - y) + \sqrt{10}\, y] \text{ units}$$

$$= (3x - y + \sqrt{10}\, y) \text{ units}$$

$$= (3 \times 3y - y + \sqrt{10}\, y) \text{ units} \qquad \text{(using (i))}$$

$$= (8 + \sqrt{10})y \text{ units.}$$

$\therefore$ Perimeter of $\triangle AEC$: perimeter of trap. $ABEC = (4 + \sqrt{10}) : (8 + \sqrt{10})$.

Example 17 If the length of a rectangle is increased by 10 cm and the breadth is decreased by 5 cm, the area is unaltered. If the length is decreased by 5 cm and the breadth is increased by 4 cm, even then the area is unaltered. Find the dimensions of the rectangle.

Solution. Let the length and the breadth of the rectangle be x cm and y cm respectively, then its area = xy cm^2.

According to the first condition of the question, when length is increased by 10 cm and breadth decreased by 5 cm, area of the rectangle remains unaltered.

$\therefore \quad (x + 10)(y - 5) = xy$

$\Rightarrow \quad xy - 5x + 10y - 50 = xy$

$\Rightarrow \quad -5x + 10y - 50 = 0$

$\Rightarrow \quad x - 2y + 10 = 0 \qquad \qquad \qquad \ldots(i)$

According to the second condition of the question, we get

$(x - 5)(y + 4) = xy$

$\Rightarrow \quad xy + 4x - 5y - 20 = xy$

$\Rightarrow \quad 4x - 5y - 20 = 0 \qquad \qquad \qquad \ldots(ii)$

Multiplying (i) by 4, we get

$4x - 8y + 40 = 0 \qquad \qquad \qquad \ldots(iii)$

Subtracting (iii) from (ii), we get

$3y - 60 = 0 \Rightarrow 3y = 60 \Rightarrow y = 20$.

From (i), we get

$x - 2 \times 20 + 10 = 0 \Rightarrow x - 40 + 10 = 0 \Rightarrow x = 30$.

Hence, the length of the rectangle = 30 cm and its breadth = 20 cm.

Example 18 The side of a square exceeds the side of another square by 3 cm and the sum of the areas of the two squares is 549 cm^2. Find the perimeters of the squares.

Solution. Let the side of one square be x cm then the side of the other square is $(x + 3)$ cm.

Then the area of the two squares are x^2 cm^2 and $(x + 3)^2$ cm^2.

According to given,

$x^2 + (x + 3)^2 = 549$

$\Rightarrow \quad x^2 + x^2 + 6x + 9 = 549$

$\Rightarrow$ $2x^2 + 6x - 540 = 0 \Rightarrow x^2 + 3x - 270 = 0$

$\Rightarrow$ $(x - 15)(x + 18) = 0$

$\Rightarrow$ $x = 15, -18$ (but x cannot be negative)

$\Rightarrow$ $x = 15$.

$\therefore$ The sides of two squares are 15 cm and 18 cm.

$\therefore$ Perimeters of the two squares are 60 cm and 72 cm.

EXERCISE 16.2

1   (i) Find the area of a quadrilateral whose one diagonal is 20 cm long and the perpendiculars to this diagonal from other vertices are of length 9 cm and 15 cm.

(ii) Find the area of a quadrilateral whose diagonals are of length 18 cm and 12 cm, and they intersect each other at right angles.

2   Find the area of the quadrilateral field ABCD whose sides AB = 40 m, BC = 28 m, CD = 15 m, AD = 9 m and $\angle A = 90°$.

3   Find the area of quadrilateral ABCD in which $\angle BCA = 90°$, AB = 13 cm and ACD is an equilateral triangle of side 12 cm.

4   Find the area of quadrilateral ABCD in which $\angle B = 90°$, AB = 6 cm, BC = 8 cm and CD = AD = 13 cm.

5   The perimeter of a rectangular cardboard is 96 cm; if its breadth is 18 cm, find the length and the area of the cardboard.

6   The length of a rectangular hall is 5 m more than its breadth. If the area of the hall is 594 m², find its perimeter.

7   (a) The diagram (i) given below shows two paths drawn inside a rectangular field 50 m long and 35 m wide. The width of each path is 5 metres. Find the area of the shaded portion.

(b) In the diagram (ii) given below, calculate the area of the shaded portion. All measurements are in centimetres.

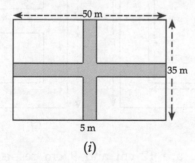

(i)

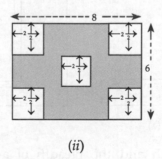

(ii)

8   A rectangular plot 20 m long and 14 m wide is to be covered with grass leaving 2 m all around. Find the area to be laid with grass.

9   The shaded region of the given diagram represents the lawn in front of a house. On three sides of the lawn there are flower-beds of width 2 m.

(i) Find the length and the breadth of the lawn.

(ii) Hence, or otherwise, find the area of the flower-beds.

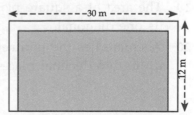

10 A footpath of uniform width runs all around the inside of a rectangular field 50 m long and 38 m wide. If the area of the path is 492 m², find its width.

11 The cost of enclosing a rectangular garden with a fence all around at the rate of ₹15 per metre is ₹5400. If the length of the garden is 100 m, find the area of the garden.

12 A rectangular floor which measures 15 m × 8 m is to be laid with tiles measuring 50 cm × 25 cm. Find the number of tiles required. Further, if a carpet is laid on the floor so that a space of 1 m exists between its edges and the edges of the floor, what fraction of the floor is uncovered?

13 The width of a rectangular room is $\frac{3}{5}$ of its length x metres. If its perimeter is y metres, write an equation connecting x and y. Find the floor area of the room if its perimeter is 32 m.

14 A rectangular garden 10 m by 16 m is to be surrounded by a concrete walk of uniform width. Given that the area of the walk is 120 square metres, assuming the width of the walk to be x, form an equation in x and solve it to find the value of x.

15 A rectangular room is 6 m long, 4·8 m wide and 3·5 m high. Find the inner surface area of the four walls.

16 A rectangular plot of land measures 41 metres in length and 22·5 metres in width. A boundary wall 2 metres high is built all around the plot at a distance of 1·5 m from the plot. Find the inner surface area of the boundary wall.

17 (a) Find the perimeter and area of the figure (i) given below in which all corners are right angles.

  (b) Find the perimeter and area of the figure (ii) given below in which all corners are right angles.

  (c) Find the area and perimeter of the figure (iii) given below in which all corners are right angles and all measurement in centimetres.

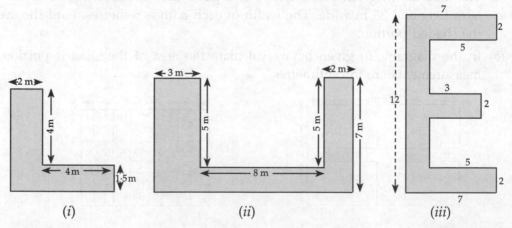

(i)   (ii)   (iii)

18 The length and the breadth of a rectangle are 12 cm and 9 cm respectively. Find the height of a triangle whose base is 9 cm and whose area is one-third that of rectangle.

19 The area of a square plot is 484 m². Find the length of its one side and the length of its one diagonal.

20 A square has the perimeter 56 m. Find its area and the length of one diagonal correct up to two decimal places.

21 A wire when bent in the form of an equilateral triangle encloses an area of $36\sqrt{3}$ cm². Find the area enclosed by the same wire when bent to form:

    (*i*) a square, and

    (*ii*) a rectangle whose length is 2 cm more than its width.

22 Two adjacent sides of a parallelogram are 15 cm and 10 cm. If the distance between the longer sides is 8 cm, find the area of the parallelogram. Also find the distance between shorter sides.

23 ABCD is a parallelogram with sides AB = 12 cm, BC = 10 cm and diagonal AC = 16 cm. Find the area of the parallelogram. Also find the distance between its shorter sides.

    Hint. Find area of △ABC. Area of ‖ gm ABCD = 2 area of △ABC.

24 Diagonals AC and BD of a parallelogram ABCD intersect at O. Given that AB = 12 cm and perpendicular distance between AB and DC is 6 cm. Calculate the area of the triangle AOD.

    Hint. Area of △AOD = $\frac{1}{4}$ (area of parallelogram ABCD).

25 ABCD is a parallelogram with side AB = 10 cm. Its diagonals AC and BD are of length 12 cm and 16 cm respectively. Find the area of the parallelogram ABCD.

    Hint. If diagonals intersect at O, find area of △OAB.

            Area of parallelogram ABCD = 4 (area of △OAB).

26 The area of a parallelogram is p cm² and its height is q cm. A second parallelogram has equal area but its base is r cm more than that of the first. Obtain an expression in terms of p, q and r for the height h of the second parallelogram.

27 What is the area of a rhombus whose diagonals are 12 cm and 16 cm?

28 The area of a rhombus is 98 cm². If one of its diagonal is 14 cm, what is the length of the other diagonal?

29 The perimeter of a rhombus is 45 cm. If its height is 8 cm, calculate its area.

30 PQRS is a rhombus. If it is given that PQ = 3 cm and the height of the rhombus is 2·5 cm, calculate its area.

31 If the diagonals of a rhombus are 8 cm and 6 cm, find its perimeter.

32 If the sides of a rhombus are 5 cm each and one diagonal is 8 cm, calculate

(*i*) the length of the other diagonal, and   (*ii*) the area of the rhombus.

33   (*a*) The figure (*i*) given below is a trapezium. Find the length of BC and the area of the trapezium. Assume AB = 5 cm, AD = 4 cm, CD = 8 cm.

    (*b*) The figure (*ii*) given below is a trapezium. Find

        (*i*) AB   (*ii*) area of trapezium ABCD.

    (*c*) The cross-section of a canal is shown in figure (*iii*) given below. If the canal is 8 m wide at the top and 6 m wide at the bottom and the area of the cross-section is 16·8 m², calculate its depth.

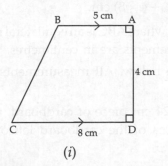

(*i*)

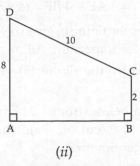

(*ii*)

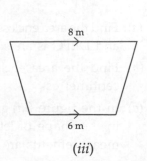

(*iii*)

34 The distance between parallel sides of a trapezium is 12 cm and the distance between mid-points of other sides is 18 cm. Find the area of the trapezium.

   Hint. Let ABCD be the given trapezium in which AB ∥ DC. Let E and F be mid-points of sides AD and BC respectively, then EF = 18 cm.

   Area of trap. ABCD = $\frac{1}{2}$ (AB + DC) × height = EF × height.

35 The area of a trapezium is 540 cm². If the ratio of parallel sides is 7 : 5 and the distance between them is 18 cm, find the length of parallel sides.

36 The parallel sides of an isosceles trapezium are in the ratio 2 : 3. If its height is 4 cm and area is 60 cm², find the perimeter.

37 The area of a parallelogram is 98 cm². If one altitude is half the corresponding base, determine the base and the altitude of the parallelogram.

38 The length of a rectangular garden is 12 m more than its breadth. The numerical value of its area is equal to 4 times the numerical value of its perimeter. Find the dimensions of the garden.

39 If the perimeter of a rectangular plot is 68 m and length of its diagonal is 26 m, find its area.

40 A rectangle has twice the area of a square. The length of the rectangle is 12 cm greater and the width is 8 cm greater than a side of a square. Find the perimeter of the square.

41 The perimeter of a square is 48 cm. The area of a rectangle is 4 cm² less than the area of the square. If the length of the rectangle is 4 cm greater than its breadth, find the perimeter of the rectangle.

   Hint. Area of square = 144 cm².

   Let breadth of rectangle be x cm, then $x(x + 4) = 144 - 4$.

42 In the adjoining figure, ABCD is a rectangle with sides AB = 10 cm and BC = 8 cm. HAD and BFC are equilateral triangles; AEB and DCG are right angled isosceles triangles. Find the area of the shaded region and the perimeter of the figure.

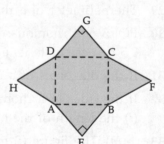

   Hint. Let AE = EB = x cm, then from right angled △AEB,

   $$x^2 + x^2 = 10^2 \Rightarrow x^2 = 50 \Rightarrow x = 5\sqrt{2}$$

   Area of △AEB = area of △DCG = $\frac{1}{2} x \times x$ cm² = 25 cm².

   Area of △BFC = area of △HAD = $\frac{\sqrt{3}}{4} \times 8^2$ cm² = $16\sqrt{3}$ cm².

   Area of shaded region = area of rect. ABCD + 2 × area of △AEB + 2 × area of △BFC.
   Perimeter of the figure = AE + EB + BF + FC + CG + GD + DH + HA

   $$= 4\,AE + 4\,BF = (4 \times 5\sqrt{2} + 4 \times 8) \text{ cm}.$$

43 (a) Find the area enclosed by the figure (i) given below, where ABC is an equilateral triangle and DEFG is an isosceles trapezium. All measurements are in centimetres.

   (b) Find the area enclosed by the figure (ii) given below. All measurements are in centimetres.

   (c) In the figure (iii) given below, from a 24 cm × 24 cm piece of cardboard, a block in the shape of letter M is cut off. Find the area of the cardboard left over, all measurements are in centimetres.

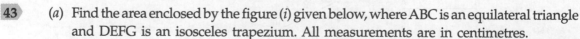

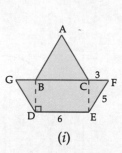

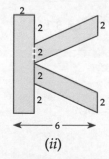

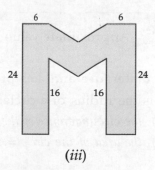

(i)   (ii)   (iii)

44 (a) The figure (i) given below shows the cross-section of the concrete structure with the measurements as given. Calculate the area of cross-section.

(b) The figure (ii) given below shows a field with the measurements given in metres. Find the area of the field.

(c) Calculate the area of the pentagon ABCDE shown in figure (iii) below, given that AX = BX = 6 cm, EY = CY = 4 cm, DE = DC = 5 cm, DX = 9 cm and DX is perpendicular to EC and AB.

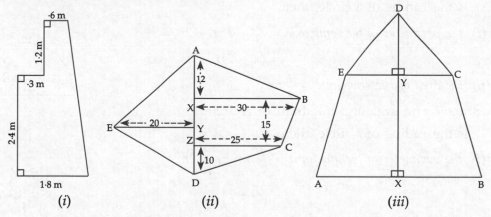

(i)   (ii)   (iii)

45 If the length and the breadth of a room are increased by 1 metre, the area is increased by 21 square metres. If the length is increased by 1 metre and breadth is decreased by 1 metre, the area is decreased by 5 square metres. Find the perimeter of the room.

46 A triangle and a parallelogram have the same base and same area. If the sides of the triangle are 26 cm, 28 cm and 30 cm, and the parallelogram stands on the base 28 cm, find the height of the parallelogram.

47 A rectangle of area 105 cm^2 has its length equal to x cm. Write down its breadth in terms of x. Given that its perimeter is 44 cm, write down an equation in x and solve it to determine the dimensions of the rectangle.

48 The perimeter of a rectangular plot is 180 m and its area is 1800 m^2. Take the length of the plot as x m. Use the perimeter 180 m to write the value of the breadth in terms of x. Use the value of length, breadth and the area to write an equation in x. Solve the equation to calculate the length and breadth of the plot.

16.4 CIRCUMFERENCE AND AREA OF A CIRCLE

The ratio of circumference of any circle to its diameter is constant, and this constant ratio is denoted by π (Pi, a Greek letter) *i.e.*

$$\frac{\text{circumference}}{\text{diameter}} = \pi$$

⇒ circumference = π × d, where d is diameter of the circle.

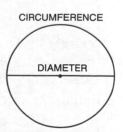

> **Note** Approximate value of π is $\frac{22}{7}$ or 3·14.

1. **Circumference and area of a circle.**

   If r is the radius of a circle, then

   (i) *the circumference of the circle = $2\pi r$.*

   (ii) *the area of the circle = πr^2.*

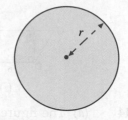

2. **Area of a circular ring.**

   If R and r are the radii of the bigger and smaller (concentric) circles, then

   area of ring (shaded portion) = $\pi(R^2 - r^2)$.

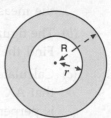

3. **Perimeter and area of a semicircle.**

   If r is the radius of a circle, then

   (i) *the perimeter of the semicircle = $\frac{1}{2} \times 2\pi r + 2r$*

   $\qquad\qquad\qquad\qquad\qquad = (\pi + 2)r.$

   (ii) *the area of the semicircle = $\frac{1}{2}\pi r^2$.*

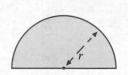

4. **Perimeter and area of a quadrant of a circle.**

   If r is the radius of a circle, then

   (i) *the perimeter of the quadrant = $\frac{1}{4} \times 2\pi r + 2r$*

   $\qquad\qquad\qquad\qquad\qquad = \left(\dfrac{\pi}{2} + 2\right)r.$

   (ii) *the area of the quadrant = $\frac{1}{4}\pi r^2$.*

Illustrative Examples

Example 1 How many times will the wheel of a car rotate in a journey of 88 km if it is known that the diameter of the wheel is 56 cm ? $\left(\text{Take } \pi = \dfrac{22}{7}\right)$

Solution. Given the diameter of the wheel = 56 cm,

$\therefore \qquad$ the radius of the wheel = $\dfrac{1}{2} \times 56$ cm = 28 cm.

$\therefore \qquad$ Circumference of the wheel = $2\pi r$

$\qquad\qquad\qquad\qquad\qquad = 2 \times \dfrac{22}{7} \times 28$ cm = 176 cm.

$\therefore$ Distance covered by the wheel in one revolution = 176 cm.

Since the distance covered = 88 km = 88 × 1000 × 100 cm,

$\therefore$ the number of times the wheel will rotate = $\dfrac{88 \times 1000 \times 100}{176}$ = 50000.

Example 2 There are two concentric circular tracks of radii 100 metres and 102 metres respectively. A runs on the inner track and goes once round the track in 1 minute 30 seconds; while B runs on the outer track in 1 minute 32 seconds. Who runs faster?

Solution. $\qquad$ Circumference of the inner track = $(2\pi \times 100)$ m = 200π m.

$\qquad\qquad\qquad$ Circumference of the outer track = $(2\pi \times 102)$ m = 204π m.

A covers a distance equal to circumference of the inner track in 1 minute 30 seconds *i.e.* in $\frac{3}{2}$ minutes.

So the distance travelled by A in $\frac{3}{2}$ minutes $= 200\pi$ m

$\therefore$ The distance travelled by A in 1 minute $= \left(\frac{3}{2} \times 200\pi\right)$ m $= 133 \cdot 33\pi$ m.

$\therefore$ Speed of A $= 133 \cdot 33\pi$ m/min.

B covers a distance equal to circumference of the outer track in 1 minute 32 seconds *i.e.*

in $\left(1 + \frac{32}{60}\right)$ min *i.e.* in $\frac{23}{15}$ min.

$\therefore$ The distance travelled by B in 1 minute $= \left(\frac{15}{23} \times 204\pi\right)$ m $= 133 \cdot 04\pi$ m.

$\therefore$ Speed of B $= 133 \cdot 04\pi$ m/min.

Since speed of A is greater than speed of B, therefore, A runs faster.

Example 3 A copper wire when bent in the form of a square encloses an area of 121 cm². If the same wire is bent into the form of a circle, find the area of the circle.

Solution. Let the side of the square be a cm.

Area of square $= a^2$ cm².

According to given, $a^2 = 121$

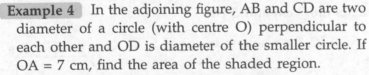
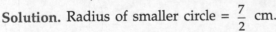

$\Rightarrow \quad a = \sqrt{121} = 11.$

$\therefore$ The length of the wire

$\quad$ = perimeter of the square

$\quad = 4a$ cm $= (4 \times 11)$ cm $= 44$ cm.

Let r cm be the radius of the circle.

Circumference of the circle $= 2\pi r$.

As the same wire is to be bent into the form of circle,

$\therefore \quad 2\pi r = 44 \Rightarrow 2 \times \frac{22}{7} \times r = 44$

$\Rightarrow \quad r = 7.$

$\therefore \quad$ The area of the circle $= \pi r^2 = \left(\frac{22}{7} \times 7 \times 7\right)$ cm² $= 154$ cm².

Example 4 In the adjoining figure, AB and CD are two diameter of a circle (with centre O) perpendicular to each other and OD is diameter of the smaller circle. If OA = 7 cm, find the area of the shaded region.

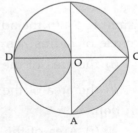

Solution. Radius of smaller circle $= \frac{7}{2}$ cm.

$\quad$ Area of $\triangle ABC = \frac{1}{2} \times$ base $\times$ height

$\qquad = \frac{1}{2} \times AB \times OC = \left(\frac{1}{2} \times 14 \times 7\right)$ cm²

$\qquad = 49$ cm²

$\therefore$ Required area = area of smaller circle + area of semicircle ABC – area of $\triangle$ABC

$\qquad = \left(\frac{22}{7} \times \left(\frac{7}{2}\right)^2 + \frac{1}{2} \times \frac{22}{7} \times 7^2 - 49\right)$ cm² $= \left(\frac{77}{2} + 77 - 49\right)$ cm²

$\qquad = (38 \cdot 5 + 28)$ cm² $= 66 \cdot 5$ cm²

Example 5 The area of a circular ring enclosed between two concentric circles is $286 \, cm^2$. Find the radii of the two circles, given that their difference is 7 cm. $\left(\text{Take } \pi = \dfrac{22}{7}\right)$

Solution. Let the radii of the outer and the inner circles be R cm and r cm respectively.

According to the given information,

$$R - r = 7 \qquad \qquad \text{...(i)}$$

and $\qquad \pi\,(R^2 - r^2) = 286$

$\Rightarrow \qquad \pi\,(R - r)\,(R + r) = 286$

$\Rightarrow \qquad \dfrac{22}{7} \times 7\,(R + r) = 286 \qquad \text{[using (i)]}$

$\Rightarrow \qquad \qquad R + r = 13 \qquad \qquad \text{...(ii)}$

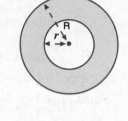

Adding (i) and (ii), we get

$$2R = 20 \; \Rightarrow \; R = 10.$$

Subtracting (i) from (ii), we get

$$2r = 6 \; \Rightarrow \; r = 3.$$

∴ The radii of the two circles are 10 cm and 3 cm.

Example 6 Two circles touch externally. The sum of their areas is $58\,\pi \, cm^2$ and the distance between their centres is 10 cm. Find the radii of the two circles.

Solution. Let R cm and r cm be the radii of two circles, then

$\qquad \quad R + r = 10$

$\Rightarrow \qquad r = 10 - R \qquad \qquad \text{...(i)}$

Also $\quad \pi R^2 + \pi r^2 = 58\,\pi$

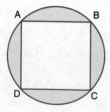

$\Rightarrow \qquad R^2 + r^2 = 58$

$\Rightarrow \qquad R^2 + (10 - R)^2 = 58 \qquad \text{(using (i))}$

$\Rightarrow \qquad R^2 + 100 + R^2 - 20\,R - 58 = 0$

$\Rightarrow \qquad 2R^2 - 20\,R + 42 = 0$

$\Rightarrow \qquad R^2 - 10R + 21 = 0 \Rightarrow (R - 7)\,(R - 3) = 0$

$\Rightarrow \qquad R - 7 = 0 \; \text{ or } \; R - 3 = 0 \; \Rightarrow \; R = 7 \; \text{ or } \; R = 3.$

When R = 7, then $r = 10 - 7 = 3$ and when R = 3, $r = 10 - 3 = 7$.

Hence, the radii of the two circles are 7 cm and 3 cm.

Example 7 In the adjoining figure, ABCD is a square inscribed in a circle of radius 7 cm. Calculate :

(i) the area of the circle.

(ii) the area of the shaded portion. $\left(\text{Take } \pi = \dfrac{22}{7}\right)$

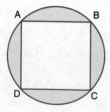

Solution.

(i) Area of the circle $= \pi r^2$

$$= \dfrac{22}{7} \times 7^2 \, cm^2 = 154 \, cm^2.$$

(ii) Let a cm be the side of the square ABCD inscribed in the given circle.

Join BD, then BD = diameter of circle = 2 × 7 cm = 14 cm.

From right angled △ BCD, by Pythagoras Th., we get

$BC^2 + CD^2 = BD^2$

$\Rightarrow \qquad \qquad a^2 + a^2 = (14)^2 \; \Rightarrow 2a^2 = 196 \; \Rightarrow a^2 = 98.$

$$\text{Area of the square ABCD} = a^2 \text{ cm}^2 = 98 \text{ cm}^2.$$

∴ The area of the shaded portion = area of circle – area of square ABCD

$$= 154 \text{ cm}^2 - 98 \text{ cm}^2 = 56 \text{ cm}^2.$$

Example 8 In the adjoining figure, O is the centre of the circle. If PQ = 24 cm and PR = 7 cm, find the area of the shaded region.

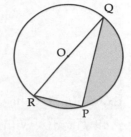

Solution. As O is the centre of the circle, so QR is a diameter.

We know that angle in a semicircle is 90°.

In $\triangle PQR$, $\angle QPR = 90°$.

By Pythagoras theorem,

$$QR^2 = PQ^2 + PR^2 = 24^2 + 7^2 = 576 + 49 = 625$$

$\Rightarrow$ QR = 25.

∴ Diameter of circle = 25 cm, so radius = $\dfrac{25}{2}$ cm.

$$\text{Area of semicircle} = \frac{1}{2}\,\pi r^2 = \left(\frac{1}{2} \times \frac{22}{7} \times \left(\frac{25}{2}\right)^2\right) \text{ cm}^2$$

$$= \frac{6875}{28} \text{ cm}^2.$$

$$\text{Area of } \triangle PQR = \frac{1}{2} \times \text{base} \times \text{height} = \frac{1}{2} \times PQ \times PR$$

$$= \left(\frac{1}{2} \times 24 \times 7\right) \text{ cm}^2 = 84 \text{ cm}^2.$$

Area of the shaded region = area of semicircle QORP – area of $\triangle PQR$

$$= \left(\frac{6875}{28} - 84\right) \text{ cm}^2 = \frac{4523}{28} \text{ cm}^2.$$

Example 9 The perimeter of a sheet of tin in the shape of a quadrant of a circle is 12·5 cm. Find its area. $\left(\text{Take } \pi = \dfrac{22}{7}\right)$

Solution. Let r cm be the radius of the circle, then perimeter of a quadrant of the circle

$$= \frac{1}{4} \times 2\pi r + 2r = \left(\frac{\pi}{2} + 2\right)r.$$

According to given, $\left(\dfrac{\pi}{2} + 2\right)r = 12\cdot5$

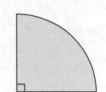

$\Rightarrow \qquad \left(\dfrac{1}{2} \times \dfrac{22}{7} + 2\right)r = \dfrac{25}{2}$

$\Rightarrow \qquad \dfrac{25}{7}r = \dfrac{25}{2} \Rightarrow r = \dfrac{7}{2}.$

∴ Area of quadrant $= \dfrac{1}{4}\pi r^2 \text{ cm}^2 = \dfrac{1}{4} \times \dfrac{22}{7} \times \left(\dfrac{7}{2}\right)^2 \text{ cm}^2$

$$= \frac{77}{8} \text{ cm}^2 = 9\cdot625 \text{ cm}^2.$$

Example 10 In the adjoining figure, ABCD is a square of side 14 cm. With centres A, B, C and D, four circles are drawn such that each circle touches externally two of the three remaining circles. Find the area of the shaded region.

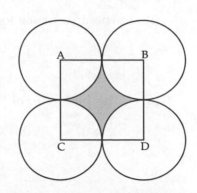

Solution. Side of square ABCD = 14 cm.

∴ Required area = area of a square of side 14 cm

– sum of areas of four quadrants of circles each of radius 7 cm

$$= \left((14)^2 - 4 \times \frac{1}{4} \times \frac{22}{7} \times 7^2 \right) \text{cm}^2$$

$$= (196 - 154) \text{cm}^2.$$

$$= 42 \text{cm}^2$$

Example 11 The area of an equilateral triangle is $49\sqrt{3}$ cm². With each vertex of the triangle as centre, a circle is described with radius equal to half the length of the side of the triangle as shown in the adjoining figure. Find the area of the shaded region.

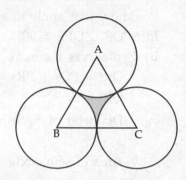

Solution. Let a cm be the side of equilateral triangle, then

$$\text{area of } \triangle ABC = \frac{\sqrt{3}}{4} a^2 = 49\sqrt{3} \text{ (given)}$$

$$\Rightarrow \quad a^2 = 196 \Rightarrow a = 14.$$

∴ Each side of triangle = 14 cm,

so, radius of each circle $= \left(\frac{1}{2} \times 14 \right)$ cm = 7 cm.

∴ Required area = area of $\triangle ABC$ – sum of areas of three sectors each

of central angle 60° and radius of circle 7 cm

= area of $\triangle ABC$ – area of a sector of radius 7 cm

and central angle as 60° + 60° + 60° *i.e.* 180°

= area of $\triangle ABC$ – area of semicircle of radius 7 cm

$$= \left(49\sqrt{3} - \frac{1}{2} \times \frac{22}{7} \times 7^2 \right) \text{cm}^2$$

$$= (49\sqrt{3} - 77) \text{cm}^2.$$

Example 12 The shape of the top of a table in a restaurant is that of a sector of a circle with centre O and ∠BOD = 90°. If BO = OD = 60 cm, find :

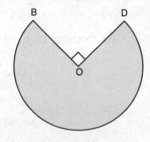

(*i*) the area of the top of the table

(*ii*) the perimeter of the table. Take π = 3·14

Solution. Given ∠BOD = 90°, so the top of the table is $\frac{3}{4}$ of a circle of radius 60 cm.

(*i*) The area of the top of the table $= \frac{3}{4} \pi \times 60^2$ cm²

$$= (3 \times 60 \times 15 \times 3·14) \text{cm}^2$$

$$= (2700 \times 3·14) \text{cm}^2 = 8478 \text{cm}^2.$$

(*ii*) The perimeter of the table $= \left(\frac{3}{4} \times 2\pi \times 60 \right)$ cm + (2 × 60) cm

$$= (90 \times 3·14) \text{cm} + 120 \text{cm}$$

$$= (282·6 + 120) \text{cm} = 402·6 \text{cm}.$$

Example 13 PS is a diameter of a circle of radius 6 cm. Q and R are points on the diameter that PQ, QR and RS are equal. Semicircles are drawn with PQ and QS as diameters, as shown in the figure. Find the perimeter and the area of the shaded region. $\pi = 3.14$.

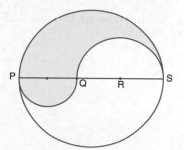

Also find the area of the shaded region.

Solution. PS = 2 × radius = (2 × 6) cm = 12 cm.

Given   PQ = QR = RS

$\Rightarrow$ PQ = $\frac{1}{3}$ of PS = $\frac{1}{3}$ of 12 cm = 4 cm

and   QS = 8 cm.

∴ The semicircles with PQ and QS as diameters have radii 2 cm and 4 cm respectively.

∴ Perimeter of the shaded region

$$= \left(\frac{1}{2} \times 2\pi \times 6 + \frac{1}{2} \times 2\pi \times 4 + \frac{1}{2} \times 2\pi \times 2\right) \text{ cm}$$

$$= \pi(6 + 4 + 2) \text{ cm} = 12\pi \text{ cm}$$

$$= (12 \times 3.14) \text{ cm} = 37.68 \text{ cm}.$$

Area of the shaded region

$$= \left(\frac{1}{2} \times \pi \times 6^2 - \frac{1}{2} \times \pi \times 4^2 + \frac{1}{2} \times \pi \times 2^2\right) \text{ cm}^2$$

$$= \frac{\pi}{2}(36 - 16 + 4) \text{ cm}^2 = 12\pi \text{ cm}^2$$

$$= (12 \times 3.14) \text{ cm}^2 = 37.68 \text{ cm}^2.$$

Example 14 A doorway is decorated as shown in the adjoining figure. There are four semicircles. BC, the diameter of the larger semicircle is of length 84 cm. The centres of the three equal semicircles lie on BC. ABC is an isosceles triangle with AB = AC.

If BO = OC, find the area of the shaded region. Take $\pi = \frac{22}{7}$.

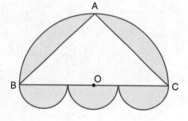

Solution. As angle in a semicircle is 90°, $\angle A = 90°$. From $\triangle ABC$, by Pythagoras theorem, we get

AB^2 + AC^2 = BC^2 $\Rightarrow$ AB^2 + AB^2 = (84)^2

$\Rightarrow$ 2AB^2 = 84 × 84 $\Rightarrow$ AB^2 = 84 × 42.

Area of $\triangle ABC$ = $\frac{1}{2}$ AB × AC = $\frac{1}{2}$ AB × AB = $\frac{1}{2}$ AB^2

$$= \frac{1}{2} \times 84 \times 42 \text{ cm}^2 = 1764 \text{ cm}^2.$$

Radius of semicircle with BC as diameter = $\frac{1}{2}$ × 84 cm = 42 cm.

Diameter of each of three equal semicircles = $\frac{1}{3}$ × 84 cm = 28 cm

$\Rightarrow$ radius of each of three equal semicircles = 14 cm.

The area of the shaded region = area of semicircle with 42 cm as radius + area of three equal semicircles of radius 14 cm − area of ΔABC

$$= \frac{1}{2}\pi \times 42^2 \text{ cm}^2 + 3 \times \frac{1}{2}\pi \times 14^2 \text{ cm}^2 - 1764 \text{ cm}^2$$

$$= \frac{1}{2}\pi (42^2 + 3 \times 14^2) \text{ cm}^2 - 1764 \text{ cm}^2$$

$$= \frac{1}{2} \times \frac{22}{7} \times 14^2 (9 + 3) \text{ cm}^2 - 1764 \text{ cm}^2$$

$$= (22 \times 14 \times 12) \text{ cm}^2 - 1764 \text{ cm}^2$$

$$= 3696 \text{ cm}^2 - 1764 \text{ cm}^2 = 1932 \text{ cm}^2.$$

Example 15 In the adjoining figure, OACB is a quadrant of a circle with centre O and radius 3·5 cm. If OD = 2 cm, find

(i) the area of the quadrant OACB

(ii) the area of the shaded region

(iii) the perimeter of the shaded region.

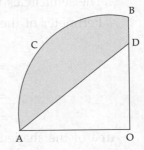

Solution. (i) Radius of circle = 3·5 cm = $\frac{7}{2}$ cm

∴ Area of the quadrant OACB = $\frac{1}{4} \times \pi r^2$

$$= \left(\frac{1}{4} \times \frac{22}{7} \times \left(\frac{7}{2}\right)^2\right) \text{ cm}^2 = \frac{77}{8} \text{ cm}^2$$

(ii) Area of ΔOAD = $\frac{1}{2} \times$ base × height

$$= \left(\frac{1}{2} \times \frac{7}{2} \times 2\right) \text{ cm}^2 = \frac{7}{2} \text{ cm}^2$$

∴ Area of shaded region

= area of quadrant OACB − area of ΔOAD

$$= \left(\frac{77}{8} - \frac{7}{2}\right) \text{ cm}^2 = \frac{49}{8} \text{ cm}^2$$

(iii) Length of arc ACB = $\frac{1}{4} \times 2\pi r$

$$= \left(\frac{1}{4} \times 2 \times \frac{22}{7} \times \frac{7}{2}\right) \text{ cm} = \frac{11}{2} \text{ cm}$$

In ΔOAD, ∠AOD = 90°.

By Pythagoras theorem,

$$AD^2 = OA^2 + OD^2 = \left(\frac{7}{2}\right)^2 + 2^2 = \frac{49}{4} + 4 = \frac{65}{4}$$

⇒ AD = $\frac{\sqrt{65}}{2}$ cm.

DB = OB − OD = $\left(\frac{7}{2} - 2\right)$ cm = $\frac{3}{2}$ cm

∴ Perimeter of shaded region

= length of arc ACB + AD + DB

$$= \left(\frac{11}{2} + \frac{\sqrt{65}}{2} + \frac{3}{2}\right) \text{ cm} = \left(7 + \frac{\sqrt{65}}{2}\right) \text{ cm.}$$

Example 16 In the adjoining figure, ABC is a quadrant of a circle of radius 28 cm and a semicircle is drawn with BC as diameter. Find the area of the shaded region.

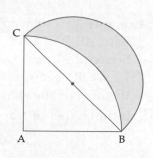

Solution. In $\triangle ABC$, $\angle CAB = 90$.

By Pythagoras theorem,

$$BC^2 = AB^2 + AC^2 = (28)^2 + (28)^2$$

$$\Rightarrow \quad BC = 28\sqrt{2} \text{ cm}$$

$\therefore$ Required area = area of semicircle with BC as diameter

$\qquad$ + area of $\triangle ABC$ – area of quadrant of a circle of radius 28 cm

$$= \left(\frac{1}{2} \times \frac{22}{7} \times \left(\frac{28\sqrt{2}}{2}\right)^2 + \frac{1}{2} \times 28 \times 28 - \frac{1}{4} \times \frac{22}{7} \times 28^2\right) \text{cm}^2$$

$$= (616 + 392 - 616) \text{ cm}^2$$

$$= 392 \text{ cm}^2.$$

Example 17 Calculate the area of the designed region (shown in the adjoining figure) between the two quadrants of circles of radius 8 cm each.

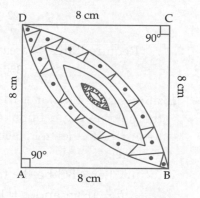

Solution. Join BD.

Required area $= 2$ (area of quadrant of a circle of radius 8 cm – area of $\triangle ABD$)

$$= 2\left[\frac{1}{4} \times \frac{22}{7} \times 8^2 - \frac{1}{2} \times 8 \times 8\right] \text{cm}^2$$

$$= 2\left(\frac{32 \times 11}{6} - 32\right) \text{cm}^2$$

$$= 64\left(\frac{11}{7} - 1\right) \text{cm}^2$$

$$= \frac{256}{7} \text{ cm}^2.$$

Example 18 In the adjoining figure, ABCD is a square of side 14 cm and semicircles are drawn with each side of the square as diameter. Find the area of the shaded region.

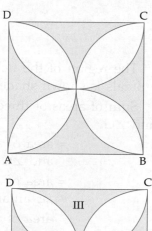

Solution. Mark the shaded regions as I, II, III and IV (shown in the adjoining figure).

Area of I + area of III

$\qquad$ = area of square ABCD

$\qquad\qquad$ – area of two semicircles each of radius 5 cm

$$= \left(14^2 - 2 \times \frac{1}{2} \times \frac{22}{7} \times 7^2\right)$$

$$= (196 - 154) \text{ cm}^2 = 42 \text{ cm}^2$$

Similarly, area of II + area of IV $= 42 \text{ cm}^2$

$\therefore$ Required area = sum of areas of regions I, II, III and IV

$$= (2 \times 42) \text{ cm}^2$$

$$= 84 \text{ cm}^2.$$

Example 19 In the adjoining figure, ABCD is a trapezium with AB ∥ DC, AB = 18 cm, DC = 32 cm and distance between AB and DC = 14 cm. If the arcs of equal radii 7 cm with centres A, B, C and D have drawn, then find the area of the shaded region.

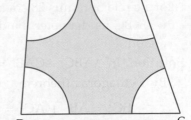

Solution. Area of trapezium ABCD

$$= \frac{1}{2}\,(\text{sum of parallel sides}) \times \text{height}$$

$$= \left(\frac{1}{2}(18 + 32) \times 14\right) \text{ cm}^2 = 350 \text{ cm}^2$$

Sum of areas of four sectors of radius 7 cm (each) and having central angles as ∠A, ∠B, ∠C and ∠D

= area of a sector of radius 7 cm and having central angle as sum of angles ∠A, ∠B, ∠C and ∠D

i.e. having central angle = ∠A + ∠B + ∠C + ∠D = 360°

= area of a circle of radius 7 cm

$$= \pi r^2 = \left(\frac{22}{7} \times 7^2\right) \text{cm}^2 = 154 \text{ cm}^2.$$

∴ Required area = area of trap. ABCD − area of four sectors

$$= (350 - 154) \text{ cm}^2 = 196 \text{ cm}^2$$

Example 20 Sides of a triangular field are 15 m, 16 m, 17 m. With the three corners of the field a cow, a buffalo and a horse are tied separately with ropes of length 7 m each to graze in the field. Find the area of the field which cannot be grazed by the three animals.

Solution. Let ABC be the triangular field with a = 15 m, b = 16 m and c = 17 m.

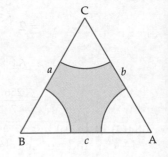

∴ $s = \dfrac{15 + 16 + 17}{2}\text{ m} = 24 \text{ m}$

∴ Area of △ABC = $\sqrt{s(s - a)(s - b)(s - c)}$

$$= \sqrt{24 \times 9 \times 8 \times 7} \text{ m}^2$$

$$= 24\sqrt{21} \text{ m}^2.$$

The region of the field left ungrazed by the three animals is shown shaded.

Sum of areas of three sectors of radius 7 m (each) and having central angles as ∠A, ∠B and ∠C

= area of a sector of radius 7 m and having central angle as sum of ∠A, ∠B and ∠C

= area of a sector of radius 7 m and having central angle as ∠A + ∠B + ∠C *i.e.* an angle of 180°

= area of a semicircle or radius 7 cm

$$= \left(\frac{1}{2} \times \frac{22}{7} \times 7^2\right) \text{ m}^2 = 77 \text{ m}^2$$

∴ Required area = area of triangular field − area of the field grazed by three animals

$$= (24\sqrt{21} - 77) \text{ m}^2.$$

Example 21 The adjoining figure shows a cross-section of a railway tunnel. The radius OA of the circular part is 2 m. If $\angle AOB = 90°$, calculate :

  (*i*) the height of the tunnel.

 (*ii*) the perimeter of the cross-section.

(*iii*) the area of the cross-section.

    (Leave the answer in π and surds.)

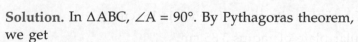

Solution. (*i*) Given $\angle AOB = 90°$.

$$OA = OB \text{ (radii of the same circle)} \Rightarrow \angle OAB = \angle OBA$$

$$\Rightarrow \qquad \angle OAB = \frac{1}{2}(180° - 90°) = 45°.$$

In $\triangle OAM$, $OM \perp AB$.

$$\therefore \qquad \angle AOM = 180° - (90° + 45°) = 45°.$$

Thus $\angle OAM = \angle AOM \Rightarrow OM = AM$.

From right triangle OAM, by Pythagoras theorem, we get

$$OA^2 = AM^2 + OM^2 \Rightarrow 2^2 = OM^2 + OM^2$$

$$\Rightarrow \qquad 2\,OM^2 = 4 \Rightarrow OM^2 = 2 \Rightarrow OM = \sqrt{2} \text{ m.}$$

$\therefore$ The height of the tunnel $= OC + OM = (2 + \sqrt{2})$ m.

(*ii*) Since $OM \perp AB$, M is mid-point of AB.

$$\therefore \qquad AB = 2\,AM = 2\,OM = 2\sqrt{2} \text{ m.}$$

Length of the major arc ACB $= \dfrac{3}{4}$ of circumference

$$= \left(\frac{3}{4} \times 2\pi \times 2\right) \text{m} = 3\pi \text{ m.}$$

$\therefore$ The perimeter of the cross-section $= (3\pi + 2\sqrt{2})$ m.

(*iii*) Area of $\triangle OAB = \dfrac{1}{2} \times AB \times OM = \left(\dfrac{1}{2} \times 2\sqrt{2} \times \sqrt{2}\right) \text{m}^2 = 2 \text{m}^2$.

Area of the sector OACB $= \dfrac{3}{4}$ of area of circle of radius 2 m

$$= \left(\frac{3}{4} \times \pi \times 2^2\right) \text{m}^2 = 3\pi \text{ m}^2.$$

$\therefore$ The area of the cross-section $= (3\pi + 2)$ m^2.

Example 22 In the adjoining figure, ABC is a right angled triangle at A. Find the area of the shaded region if AB = 6 cm, BC = 10 cm and I is the centre of incircle of $\triangle ABC$. Take $\pi = \dfrac{22}{7}$.

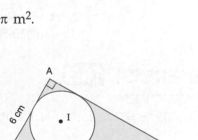

Solution. In $\triangle ABC$, $\angle A = 90°$. By Pythagoras theorem, we get

$$AC^2 = BC^2 - AB^2 = 10^2 - 6^2 = 64$$

$$\Rightarrow \qquad AC = 8 \text{ cm.}$$

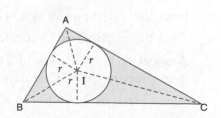

$\therefore$ Area of $\triangle ABC = \dfrac{1}{2} \times 6 \times 8 \text{ cm}^2$

$$= 24 \text{ cm}^2.$$

Let r cm be the radius of the incircle. From figure,

area of $\triangle$IBC + area of $\triangle$ICA + area of $\triangle$IAB = area of $\triangle$ABC

$\Rightarrow$ $\frac{1}{2} \times 10 \times r + \frac{1}{2} \times 8 \times r + \frac{1}{2} \times 6 \times r = 24$

$\Rightarrow$ $12r = 24 \Rightarrow r = 2$

$\therefore$ Radius of incircle = 2 cm.

Area of shaded region = area of $\triangle$ABC − area of incircle

$$= (24 - \pi \times 2^2)\,cm^2 = \left(24 - \frac{22}{7} \times 4\right) cm^2$$

$$= \frac{80}{7}\,cm^2 = 11\frac{3}{7}\,cm^2.$$

Example 23 In the adjoining figure, ABCD is a square drawn inside a circle with centre O. The centre of the square coincides with O and the diagonal AC is horizontal. If AP, DQ are vertical and AP = 45 cm, DQ = 25 cm, find

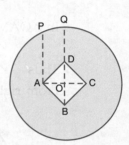

   (*i*) the radius of the circle.

   (*ii*) the side of the square.

   (*iii*) the area of the shaded region.

Take $\sqrt{2}$ = 1·41 and π = 3·14

Solution. (*i*) Let AO = x cm, then OD = x cm and radius of the circle

$$= OP = OQ = OD + DQ = (x + 25)\ cm.$$

Since $\triangle$ PAO is right angled at A, by Pythagoras theorem, we get

$$OP^2 = AP^2 + AO^2 \Rightarrow (x + 25)^2 = 45^2 + x^2$$

$\Rightarrow$ $x^2 + 50x + 625 = 2025 + x^2 \Rightarrow 50x = 2025 - 625$

$\Rightarrow$ $50x = 1400 \Rightarrow x = 28,$

$\therefore$ the radius of the circle = OP = (28 + 25) cm = 53 cm.

(*ii*) From right angled triangle AOD, by Pythagoras theorem, we get

$$AD^2 = AO^2 + OD^2 = x^2 + x^2 = 2x^2 = 2 \times 28^2$$

$\Rightarrow$ $AD = 28\sqrt{2}\ cm = 28 \times 1·41\ cm = 39·48\ cm.$

(*iii*) Area of the shaded region = area of the circle − area of the square

$$= (\pi \times 53^2 - (28\sqrt{2})^2)\ cm^2 = (3·14 \times 2809 - 1568)\ cm^2$$

$$= (8820·26 - 1568)\ cm^2 = 7252·26\ cm^2.$$

EXERCISE 16.3

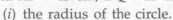

Take $\pi = \frac{22}{7}$, *unless stated otherwise.*

1 Find the length of the diameter of a circle whose circumference is 44 cm.

2 Find the radius and the area of a circle if its circumference is 18π cm.

3 Find the perimeter of semi-circular plate of radius 3·85 cm.

4 Find the radius and circumference of a circle whose area is 144π cm^2.

5 A sheet is 11 cm long and 2 cm wide. Circular pieces 0·5 cm in diameter are cut from it to prepare discs. Calculate the number of discs that can be prepared.

Hint. First we have to cut squares of side 0·5 cm.

6 If the area of a semi-circular region is 77 cm², find its perimeter.

7 (a) In the figure (i) given below, AC and BD are two perpendicular diameters of a circle ABCD. Given that the area of the shaded portion is 308 cm², calculate :

    (i) the length of AC and

    (ii) the circumference of the circle.

    (b) In the figure (ii) given below, AC and BD are two perpendicular diameters of a circle with centre O. If AC = 16 cm, calculate the area and perimeter of the shaded part. (Take π = 3·14)

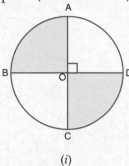

(i)

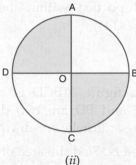

(ii)

8 A bucket is raised from a well by means of a rope which is wound round a wheel of diameter 77 cm. Given that the bucket ascends in 1 minute 28 seconds with a uniform speed of 1·1 m/sec, calculate the number of complete revolutions the wheel makes in raising the bucket.

9 The wheel of a cart is making 5 revolutions per second. If the diameter of the wheel is 84 cm, find its speed in km/h. Give your answer, correct to the nearest km.

10 The circumference of a circle is 123·2 cm. Calculate :

    (i) the radius of the circle in cm.

    (ii) the area of the circle in cm², correct to the nearest cm².

    (iii) the effect on the area of the circle if the radius is doubled.

11 (a) In the figure (i) given below, the area enclosed between the concentric circles is 770 cm². Given that the radius of the outer circle is 21 cm, calculate the radius of the inner circle.

    (b) In the figure (ii) given below, the area enclosed between the circumferences of two concentric circles is 346·5 cm². The circumference of the inner circle is 88 cm. Calculate the radius of the outer circle.

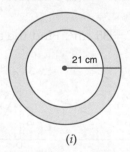

(i)

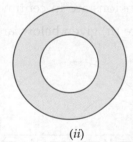

(ii)

12 A road 3·5 m wide surrounds a circular plot whose circumference is 44 m. Find the cost of paving the road at ₹50 per m².

13 The sum of diameters of two circles is 14 cm and the difference of their circumferences is 8 cm. Find the circumferences of the two circles.

14 Find the circumference of the circle whose area is equal to the sum of the areas of three circles with radius 2 cm, 3 cm and 6 cm.

15 A copper wire when bent in the form of a square encloses an area of 121 cm². If the same wire is bent into the form of a circle, find the area of the circle.

16 A copper wire when bent in the form of an equilateral triangle has area $121\sqrt{3}$ cm². If the same wire is bent into the form of a circle, find the area enclosed by the wire.

17 (a) Find the circumference of the circle whose area is 16 times the area of the circle with diameter 7 cm.

(b) In the given figure, find the area of the unshaded portion within the rectangle. (Take π = 3·14)

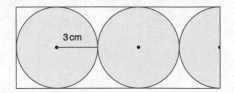

18 In the adjoining figure, ABCD is a square of side 21 cm. AC and BD are two diagonals of the square. Two semicircle are drawn with AD and BC as diameters. Find the area of the shaded region. Take π = $\frac{22}{7}$.

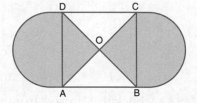

19 (a) In the figure (i) given below, ABCD is a square of side 14 cm and APD and BPC are semicircles. Find the area and the perimeter of the shaded region.

(b) In the figure (ii) given below, ABCD is a square of side 14 cm. Find the area of the shaded region.

(c) In the figure (iii) given below, the diameter of the semicircle is equal to 14 cm. Calculate the area of the shaded region.

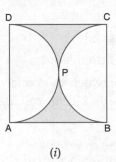
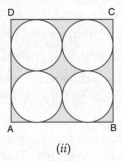
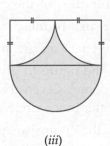

(i)   (ii)   (iii)

20 (a) Find the area and the perimeter of the shaded region in figure (i) given below. The diamensions are in centimetres.

(b) In the figure (ii) given below, area of ΔABC = 35 cm². Find the area of the shaded region.

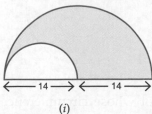
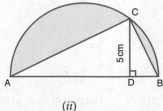

(i)   (ii)

21 (a) In the figure (i) given below, AOBC is a quadrant of a circle of radius 10 m. Calculate the area of the shaded portion. Take π = 3·14 and give your answer correct to two significant figures.

(b) In the figure (ii) given below, OAB is a quadrant of a circle. The radius OA = 7 cm and OD = 4 cm. Calculate the area of the shaded portion.

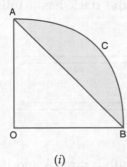

(i)

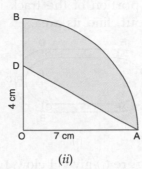

(ii)

22 A student takes a rectangular piece of paper 30 cm long and 21 cm wide. Find the area of the biggest circle that can be cut out from the paper. Also find the area of the paper left after cutting out the circle.

23 A rectangle with one side 4 cm is inscribed in a circle of radius 2·5 cm. Find the area of the rectangle.

24 (a) In the figure (i) given below, calculate the area of the shaded region correct to two decimal places. (Take π = 3·142).

(b) In the figure (ii) given below, ABC is an isosceles right angled triangle with ∠ABC = 90°. A semicircle is drawn with AC as diameter. If AB = BC = 7 cm, find the area of the shaded region. Take $\pi = \dfrac{22}{7}$.

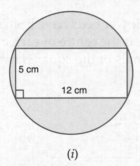

(i)

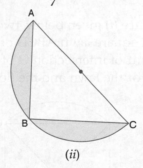

(ii)

25 A circular field has perimeter 660 m. A plot in the shape of a square having its vertices on the circumference is marked in the field. Calculate the area of the square field.

26 In the adjoining figure, ABCD is a square. Find the ratio between

(i) the circumferences

(ii) the areas of the incircle and the circumcircle of the square.

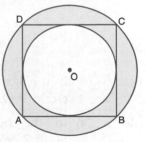

Hint.

Let a side of the square be $2a$ units, then radius of incircle = a units and radius of circumcircle = $\sqrt{2}\,a$ units (why?)

27 (a) The figure (i) given below shows a running track surrounding a grassed enclosure PQRSTU. The enclosure consists of a rectangle PQST with a semicircular region at each end. PQ = 200 m; PT = 70 m.

(i) Calculate the area of the grassed enclosure in m².

(ii) Given that the track is of constant width 7 m, calculate the outer perimeter ABCDEF of the track.

(b) In the figure (ii) given below, the inside perimeter of a practice running track with semi-circular ends and straight parallel sides is 312 m. The length of the straight portion of the track is 90 m. If the track has a uniform width of 2 m throughout, find its area.

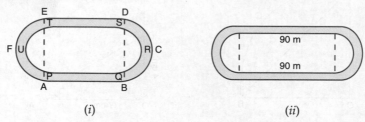

(i)　　　　　　　　　　(ii)

28 (a) In the figure (i) given below, two circles with centres A and B touch each other at the point C. If AC = 8 cm and AB = 3cm, find the area of the shaded region.

(b) The quadrants shown in the figure (ii) given below are each of radius 7 cm. Calculate the area of the shaded portion.

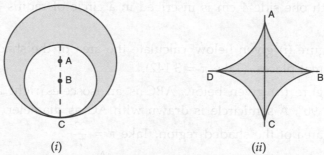

(i)　　　　　　　　　　(ii)

29 (a) In the figure (i) given below, two circular flower beds have been shown on the two sides of a square lawn ABCD of side 56 m. If the centre of each circular flower bed is the point of intersection O of the diagonals of the square lawn, find the sum of the areas of the lawn and the flower beds.

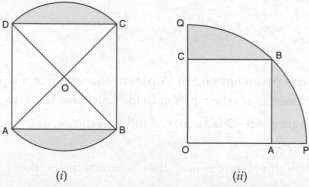

(i)　　　　　　　　　　(ii)

(b) In the figure (ii) given above, a square OABC is inscribed in a quadrant OPBQ of a circle. If OA = 20 cm, find the area of the shaded region. (Use π = 3·14)

30 (a) In the figure (i) given below, ABCD is a rectangle, AB = 14 cm and BC = 7 cm. Taking DC, BC and AD as diameters, three semicircles are drawn as shown in the figure. Find the area of the shaded portion.

(b) In the figure (ii) given below, O is the centre of a circle with AC = 24 cm, AB = 7 cm and ∠BOD = 90°. Find the area of the shaded region. (Use π = 3·14).

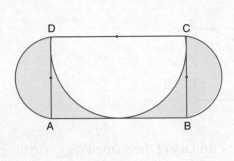

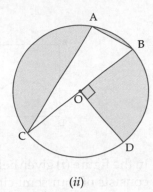

(i)   (ii)

31 (a) In the figure (i) given below, ABCD is a square of side 14 cm. A, B, C and D are centres of the equal circles which touch externally in pairs. Find the area of the shaded region.

(b) In the figure (ii) given below, the boundary of the shaded region in the given diagram consists of three semi-circular arcs, the smaller being equal. If the diameter of the larger one is 10 cm, calculate.

(i) the length of the boundary.

(ii) the area of the shaded region. (Take π to be 3·14)

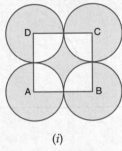

(i)

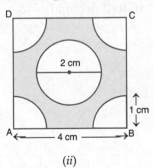

(ii)

32 (a) In the figure (i) given below, the points A, B and C are centres of arcs of circles of radii 5 cm, 3 cm and 2 cm respectively. Find the perimeter and the area of the shaded region. (Take π = 3·14)

(b) In the figure (ii) given below, ABCD is a square of side 4 cm. At each corner of the square a quarter circle of radius 1 cm, and at the centre a circle of diameter 2 cm are drawn. Find the area of the shaded region. Take π = 3·14.

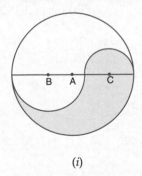

(i)

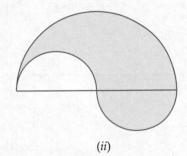

(ii)

33 (a) In the figure (i) given below, ABCD is a rectangle. AB = 14 cm, BC = 7 cm. From the rectangle, a quarter circle BFEC and a semicircle DGE are removed. Calculate the area of the remaining piece of the rectangle.

(b) The figure (ii) given below shows a kite, in which BCD is in the shape of a quadrant of a circle of radius 42 cm. ABCD is a square and $\triangle$CEF is an isosceles right angled triangle whose equal sides are 6 cm long. Find the area of the shaded region.

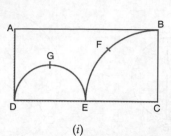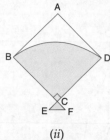

(i)   (ii)

34 (a) In the figure (i) given below, the boundary of the shaded region in the given diagram consists of four semi-circular arcs, the smallest two being equal. If the diameter of the largest is 14 cm and of the smallest is 3·5 cm, calculate

  (i) the length of the boundary.

  (ii) the area of the shaded region.

(b) In the figure (ii) given below, a piece of cardboard, in the shape of a trapezium ABCD, and AB ∥ DC and ∠BCD = 90°, quarter circle BFEC is removed. Given AB = BC = 3·5 cm and DE = 2 cm. Calculate the area of the remaining piece of the cardboard.

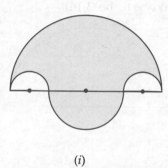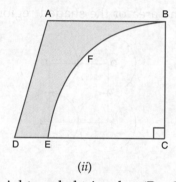

(i)   (ii)

35 (a) In the figure (i) given below, ABC is a right angled triangle, ∠B = 90°, AB = 28 cm and BC = 21 cm. With AC as diameter a semicircle is drawn and with BC as radius a quarter circle is drawn. Find the area of the shaded region correct to two decimal places.

(b) In the figure (ii) given below, ABC is an equilateral triangle of side 8 cm. A, B and C are the centres of circular arcs of equal radius. Find the area of the shaded region correct upto 2 decimal places.   (Take π = 3·142 and √3 = 1·732).

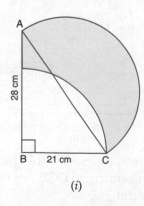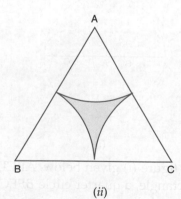

(i)   (ii)

36 A circle is inscribed in a regular hexagon of side $2\sqrt{3}$ cm. Find

  (i) the circumference of the inscribed circle.

  (ii) the area of the inscribed circle.

37 In the adjoining figure, a chord AB of a circle of radius 10 cm subtends a right angle at the centre O. Find the area of the sector OACB and of the major segment. Take π = 3·14.

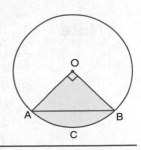

Hint.

Area of minor segment = area of sector OACB – area of ΔOAB.

16.5 SURFACE AREA AND VOLUME OF SOLIDS

Solid. *A figure which occupies a portion of space enclosed by plane or curved surfaces is called a solid.*

A solid has three dimensions—length, breadth and height.

Volume of a solid. The measurement of the space enclosed by a solid is called its **volume.** It is measured in cubic units.

Surface area of a solid. The sum of the areas of the plane or curved surfaces (faces) of a solid is called its **total surface area.** It is measured in square units.

16.5.1 Cuboid

*A solid in the shape of a box (or brick) is called a **cuboid.** It has six rectangular plane surfaces, called **faces**.*

The length, breadth and height of a cuboid are usually denoted by *l*, *b* and *h* respectively. A cuboid has 12 edges and 8 vertices (or corners).

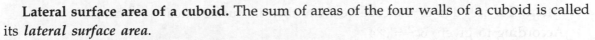

Surface area of a cuboid. The sum of areas of all the six faces of a cuboid is called its (total) *surface area.*

> *Surface area = 2 (lb + bh + lh) sq. units.*

Lateral surface area of a cuboid. The sum of areas of the four walls of a cuboid is called its *lateral surface area.*

> *Lateral surface area = 2 (l + b) h sq. units.*

Volume of a cuboid. The space enclosed by a cuboid is called its *volume.*

> *Volume = l × b × h cubic units.*

Diagonal of a cuboid. The line joining opposite corners of a cuboid is called its *diagonal.* A cuboid has four diagonals.

> *Length of a diagonal = $\sqrt{l^2 + b^2 + h^2}$ units.*
>
> [It is the length of the longest rod that can be placed in the cuboid.]

16.5.2 Cube

*A rectangular solid bounded by six squares is called a **cube.** It is a particular case of a cuboid, where l = b = h = a (say).*

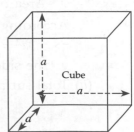

> *Surface area = 6a² sq. units.*
> *Lateral surface area = 4a² sq. units.*
> *Volume = a³ cubic units.*
> *Length of a diagonal = $\sqrt{3a^2}$ units or $\sqrt{3}$ a units.*

1. The capacity of a container = its internal volume.
2. The volume of material in a hollow body = its external volume – its internal volume.
3. If the external dimensions (length, breadth and height) of a box are l, b and h and if each side is of thickness x, then the internal dimensions of the
   (*i*) closed box are $l - 2x$, $b - 2x$ and $h - 2x$
   (*ii*) open box are $l - 2x$, $b - 2x$ and $h - x$.

16.5.3 Cross-section

*If a cut is made through a solid perpendicular to its length (breadth or height), then the surface so obtained is called its **cross-section**.*

If the surface made by the cut has the same shape and size at every point of its length (breadth or height), then it is called a **uniform cross-section**.

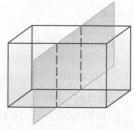

Cross-section
perpendicular to length

   (*i*) *volume = area of cross-section × length (breadth or height).*
   (*ii*) *lateral surface area = perimeter of cross-section × length (breadth or height).*

Illustrative   Examples

Example 1   The volume of a rectangular solid is 3600 cm³. If it is 20 cm long and 9 cm high, find its width.

Solution. Let its width be b cm, then $20 \times b \times 9 = 3600 \Rightarrow b = 20$.
   ∴ Width of solid = 20 cm.

Example 2   If the total surface area of a cube is 384 cm², find its volume.

Solution. Let an edge of the cube be a cm, then its surface area = $6a^2$ cm².
   According to given, $6a^2 = 384$

$\Rightarrow a^2 = \dfrac{384}{6} = 64 \Rightarrow a = 8$.

   ∴ Volume of the cube = $(8)^3$ cm³ = 512 cm³.

Example 3   The square on the diagonal of a cube has an area of 192 cm². Calculate

   (*i*) the side of the cube in cm.

   (*ii*) the total surface area of the cube in cm².

Solution. (*i*) Let a side of the cube be a cm, then length of a diagonal of the cube = $\sqrt{3}\, a$ cm.

   ∴   Area of the square whose side is $\sqrt{3}\, a$ cm = $(\sqrt{3}\, a)^2$ cm².

   According to given, $(\sqrt{3}\, a)^2 = 192$

   $\Rightarrow \quad 3a^2 = 192 \Rightarrow a^2 = 64 \Rightarrow a = 8$.

   ∴ The side of the cube = 8 cm.

   (*ii*) Total surface area of the cube = $6a^2$ cm²

   $= 6 \times 8^2$ cm² = 384 cm².

Example 4 Three cubes each of side 6 cm are joined together side-by-side (as shown in the adjoining figure) to form a cuboid. Find the volume and the surface area of the cuboid.

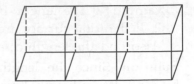

Solution. Length of the cuboid = (6 + 6 + 6) cm = 18 cm,

breadth = 6 cm and height = 6 cm.

∴ Volume of the cuboid = $18 \times 6 \times 6$ cm^3 = 648 cm^3.

Surface area of the cuboid = 2 ($18 \times 6 + 18 \times 6 + 6 \times 6$) cm^2

$$= (2 \times 252) \text{ cm}^2 = 504 \text{ cm}^2.$$

Example 5 The floor of a rectangular hall has a perimeter 250 m. If the cost of painting the four walls at the rate of ₹10 per m^2 is ₹ 15000, find the height of the hall.

Solution. As the cost of painting the walls at the rate of ₹10 per m^2 is ₹15000,

the painted area = $\dfrac{15000}{10}$ m^2 = 1500 m^2.

Let h metres be the height of the hall.

Area of four walls = perimeter × height.

∴ $250 \times h = 1500 \Rightarrow h = 6$.

Hence, the height of the hall = 6 metres.

Example 6 The length of a hall is 24 m and its width is 16 m. If the lateral surface area of the hall is two-third of the sum of the areas of the roof and the floor, find its height.

Solution. Length of the hall = l = 24 m and its width = b = 16 m.

Let h metres be the height of the hall, then

the lateral surface area of the hall = $2(l + b)h$

$$= 2(24 + 16)h \text{ m}^2 = 80h \text{ m}^2.$$

Sum of areas of the roof and the floor = $l \times b + l \times b$

$$= 2lb = 2 \times 24 \times 16 \text{ m}^2 = 768 \text{ m}^2.$$

According to given,

$$80h = \frac{2}{3} \times 768 \Rightarrow 80h = 512$$

$$\Rightarrow \quad h = \frac{512}{80} = \frac{32}{5} = 6{\cdot}4$$

Hence, the height of the hall = 6·4 m.

Example 7 A cuboid has length, breadth and diagonal as 4 m, 3 m and 13 m respectively. Find its volume.

Solution. Let the height of the cuboid be h metres.

Here, l = 4 m and b = 3 m.

As the length of diagonal of a cuboid = $\sqrt{l^2 + b^2 + h^2}$,

∴ $\sqrt{4^2 + 3^2 + h^2} = 13 \Rightarrow 16 + 9 + h^2 = 169$

$\Rightarrow \quad h^2 = 169 - 25 \Rightarrow h^2 = 144 \Rightarrow h = 12$ $\qquad (\because h > 0)$

∴ Height of cuboid = 12 m.

∴ Volume of cuboid = $l \times b \times h$ = $(4 \times 3 \times 12)$ m^3 = 144 m^3.

Example 8 The length, breadth and height of a rectangular solid are in the ratio $5 : 4 : 2$. If the total surface area is 1216 cm^2, find the length, breadth and height of the solid. Also find the length of a diagonal of the cuboid.

Solution. Since the length, breadth and height of a rectangular solid are in the ratio $5 : 4 : 2$, let its length, breadth and height be $5x$ cm, $4x$ cm and $2x$ cm respectively.

∴ Total surface area of the solid $= 2[5x \times 4x + 5x \times 2x + 4x \times 2x]$ cm$^2 = 76x^2$ cm^2.

According to given, $76\ x^2 = 1216$

$\Rightarrow x^2 = \dfrac{1216}{76} \Rightarrow x^2 = 16 \Rightarrow x = 4$.

∴ Length = 20 cm, breadth = 16 cm and height = 8 cm.

The length of a diagonal $= \sqrt{20^2 + 16^2 + 8^2}$ cm

$\qquad\qquad\qquad\qquad = \sqrt{400 + 256 + 64}$ cm $= \sqrt{720}$ cm $= 12\sqrt{5}$ cm.

Example 9 A solid piece of metal, cuboidal in shape, with dimensions 24 cm, 18 cm and 4 cm is recast into a cube. Calculate the lateral surface area of the cube.

Solution. Volume of the cuboid $= (24 \times 18 \times 4)$ cm^3.

Let a side of the cube be a cm, then its volume $= a^3$ cm^3.

Since the metal of the cuboid is to be recasted into a cube,

$\qquad$ volume of cube = volume of cuboid

$\Rightarrow \qquad a^3 = 24 \times 18 \times 4 = 24 \times 72 = 12 \times 144$

$\Rightarrow \qquad a^3 = (12)^3 \Rightarrow a = 12$.

$\qquad$ Lateral surface of the cube $= 4a^2$ cm^2

$\qquad\qquad\qquad\qquad\qquad = (4 \times 12 \times 12)$ cm$^2 = 576$ cm^2.

Example 10 Hameed has built a cubical water tank with lid for his house, with each outer edge 1·5 m long. He gets the outer surface of the tank excluding the base, covered with square tiles of side 25 cm (shown in the adjoining figure). Find how much he would spend for the tiles, if the cost of the tiles is ₹360 per dozen.

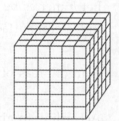

Solution. Each side (edge) of the tank = 1·5 m = 150 cm.

Outer surface area of the tank (excluding base) $= 5 \times 150 \times 150$ cm^2.

Area of each square tile $= 25 \times 25$ cm^2.

∴ $\qquad$ No. of tiles required $= \dfrac{5 \times 150 \times 150}{25 \times 25} = 180$.

Cost of one dozen *i.e.* 12 tiles = ₹360

∴ $\qquad$ Cost of one tile $= ₹\dfrac{360}{12} = ₹30$.

∴ $\qquad$ The cost of 180 tiles $= ₹(30 \times 180) = ₹5400$.

Example 11 The length of a room is 50% more than its breadth. The cost of carpeting the room at the rate of ₹38·50 m^2 is ₹924 and the cost of papering the walls at ₹3·30 m^2 is ₹214·50. If the room has one door of dimensions 1 m × 2 m and two windows each of dimensions 1 m × 1·5 m, find the dimensions of the room.

Solution. Let the breadth of the room be x metres.

As the length of the room is 50% more than its breadth,

$\qquad$ length of the room $= \left(1 + \dfrac{50}{100}\right)$ of x metres $= \dfrac{3}{2}x$ metres.

∴   The area of the floor of the room $= \left(\dfrac{3}{2} x \times x\right)$ m² $= \dfrac{3x^2}{2}$ m².

Cost of carpeting the room at the rate of ₹38·50 m² $= ₹\left(\dfrac{3x^2}{2} \times 38 \cdot 5\right)$.

According to given,

$$\dfrac{3x^2}{2} \times 38 \cdot 5 = 924 \Rightarrow x^2 = \dfrac{924 \times 2}{3 \times 38 \cdot 5} \Rightarrow x^2 = 16$$

$\Rightarrow$ $x = 4$ ($\because x$ cannot be negative)

Hence, the length of the room $= \dfrac{3}{2} x$ metres $= \dfrac{3}{2} \times 4$ metres = 6 metres

and   its breadth = x metres = 4 metres.

Let the height of the room be h metres, then

the surface area of all the walls of the room

                = 2(length + breadth) × height

                = 2(6 + 4) × h m² = 20h m².

Area of one door = 1 × 2 m² = 2 m²,

area of two windows = 2(1 × 1·5) m² = 3 m².

∴   Surface area to be papered

                = surface area of walls − surface area of door and windows

                = (20h − 2 − 3) m² = (20h − 5) m².

∴   Cost of papering the walls at the rate of ₹3·30 m² = ₹(20h − 5) × 3·30.

According to given,

    (20h − 5) × 3·30 = 214·50

$\Rightarrow$ $20h - 5 = \dfrac{214 \cdot 50}{3 \cdot 30} = 65$

$\Rightarrow$ $20h = 65 + 5 \Rightarrow 20h = 70 \Rightarrow h = 3 \cdot 5$

Hence, the height of the room = 3·5 metres.

Example 12 Shanti Sweets wants to place an order for cardboard boxes for packing sweets. They need two types of boxes, one with dimensions 25 cm × 20 cm × 5 cm and another with dimensions 15 cm × 12 cm × 5 cm. For all the overlaps, 5% of the total surface is required extra. If the cost of the cardboard is ₹4 for 1000 cm², find the cost of cardboard required for supplying 250 boxes of each type.

Solution. Surface area of 1 big box = 2(25 × 20 + 20 × 5 + 25 × 5) cm² = 1450 cm².

As 5% of total surface is required extra for overlaps,

∴   area of cardboard required for making one big box

           $= \left(1 + \dfrac{5}{100}\right) \times 1450$ cm² $= \dfrac{21}{20} \times 1450$ cm² = 1522·5 cm².

∴   Area of cardboard required for making 250 big boxes

           = 1522·5 × 250 cm² = 380625 cm².

Surface area of 1 small box = 2(15 × 12 + 12 × 5 + 15 × 5) cm² = 630 cm².

As 5% of total surface area is required for overlaps,

∴   area of cardboard required for making one small box

         $= \left(1 + \dfrac{5}{100}\right) \times 630$ cm² $= \dfrac{21}{20} \times 630$ cm² = 661·5 cm².

∴   Area of cardboard required for making 250 small boxes

$$= 661.5 \times 250 \text{ cm}^2 = 165375 \text{ cm}^2.$$

∴ Total area of cardboard required for supplying 250 big boxes and 250 small boxes

$$= (380625 + 165375) \text{ cm}^2 = 546000 \text{ cm}^2.$$

As cost of 1000 cm^2 of cardboard is ₹4,

∴   cost of 546000 cm^2 of cardboard = ₹ $\dfrac{546000 \times 4}{1000}$ = ₹2184.

Example 13 The volume of a cuboidal block of silver is 10368 cm^3. If its dimensions are in the ratio 3 : 2 : 1, find

(i) the dimensions of the block.

(ii) the cost of gold polishing its entire surface at ₹ 0·50 per cm^2.

Solution. (i) As the dimensions of the cuboidal block of silver are in the ratio 3 : 2 : 1, let its length, breadth and height be $3x$ cm, $2x$ cm and x cm respectively.

Volume of block = $(3x \times 2x \times x)$ cm^3 = 10368 cm^3

$\Rightarrow$ $6x^3 = 10368 \Rightarrow x^3 = 1728$

$\Rightarrow$ $x^3 = 12 \times 12 \times 12 \Rightarrow x = 12.$

∴   The dimensions of the block are $l = 3x$ cm = (3×12) cm = 36 cm,

$b = 2x$ cm = (2×12) cm = 24 cm and height = x cm = 12 cm.

(ii) Total surface area of the block of silver = $2(lb + lh + hb)$

$$= 2(36 \times 24 + 36 \times 12 + 24 \times 12) \text{ cm}^2$$

$$= 2(864 + 432 + 288) \text{ cm}^2 = (2 \times 1584) \text{ cm}^2 = 3168 \text{ cm}^2$$

Since the cost of gold polishing its surface is at the rate of ₹ 0·50 per cm^2 = ₹ $\dfrac{1}{2}$ per cm^2,

∴   the cost of gold polishing entire surface = ₹ $(\dfrac{1}{2} \times 3168)$ = ₹ 1584.

Example 14 A field is 102 m long and 25 m broad. A tank 10 m long, 5 m broad and 4 m deep is dug out from the middle of the field and the earth removed is evenly spread over the remaining part of the field. Find the rise in the level of the remaining part of the field in centimetres.

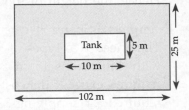

Solution. The volume of the earth dug out = $10 \times 5 \times 4$ m^3 = 200 m^3

The upper surface area of the tank = 10×5 m^2 = 50 m^2.

Total area of the field = 102×25 m^2 = 2550 m^2.

The remaining area of the field = $(2550 - 50)$ m^2 = 2500 m^2.

∴ The rise in the level of the remaining part of the field

$$= \frac{200}{2500} \text{ m} = \frac{2}{25} \text{ m} = \frac{2}{5} \times 100 \text{ cm} = 8 \text{ cm}.$$

Example 15 Squares each of side 6 cm are cut off from the four corners of a sheet of tin measuring 42 cm by 30 cm. The remaining portion of the tin sheet is made into an open box by folding up the flaps. Find the capacity of the box.

Solution. All measurements are in centimetres.

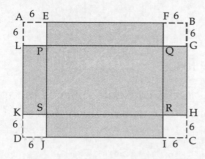 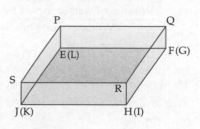

SR = PQ = EF = (42 – 6 – 6)cm = 30 cm,

RQ = SP = KL = (30 – 6 – 6)cm = 18 cm.

EP = LP = 6 cm.

Length of the open box = 30 cm, breadth = 18 cm and height = 6 cm.

∴ The capacity of the open box = 30 × 18 × 6 cm³ = 3240 cm³.

Example 16 A hollow square shaped tube open at both ends, is made of iron. The internal square is of 5 cm side and the length of the tube is 8 cm. There are 192 cm³ of iron in this tube. Find its thickness.

Solution. Since the internal square is of 5 cm side and the length of the tube is 8 cm.

∴ Its internal volume = 5 × 5 × 8 cm³ = 200 cm³.

Let the thickness of a side be x cm.

Then the external square is of $(5 + 2x)$ cm side.

As the tube is open at both ends, its length remains 8 cm.

∴ The external volume of the tube = $(5 + 2x)(5 + 2x) \times 8$ cm³.

Since the volume of iron in the tube is 192 cm³,

∴ $(5 + 2x)^2 \times 8 - 200 = 192$

⇒ $(5 + 2x)^2 \times 8 = 392$

⇒ $(5 + 2x)^2 = 49 \Rightarrow 5 + 2x = 7$

⇒ $2x = 7 - 5 \Rightarrow 2x = 2 \Rightarrow x = 1.$

∴ The thickness of the tube = 1 cm.

Example 17 To construct a wall 25 m long, 0·3 m thick and 6 m high, bricks of dimensions 25 cm × 15 cm × 10 cm, each are used. If mortar occupies $\frac{1}{10}$th of the volume of the wall, find the number of bricks used.

Solution. Length of wall = 25 m = 2500 cm, thickness = 0·3 m = 30 cm and height = 6 m = 600 cm.

∴ The volume of wall = $l \times b \times h$ = (2500 × 30 × 600) cm³.

Dimensions of each brick are 25 cm × 15 cm × 10 cm.

∴ Volume of each brick = (25 × 15 × 10) cm³.

Since $\frac{1}{10}$th of volume of wall is occupied by mortar,

so, the volume of wall occupied by bricks

$= \left(1 - \frac{1}{10}\right)$th of volume of wall

$= \left(\frac{9}{10} \times 2500 \times 30 \times 600\right)$ cm³ = (2500 × 27 × 600) cm³.

∴   The number of bricks required to construct the wall

$$= \frac{\text{Volume of wall occupied by bricks}}{\text{Volume of one brick}}$$

$$= \frac{2500 \times 27 \times 600}{25 \times 15 \times 10} = 100 \times 27 \times 4 = 10800.$$

Example 18 The area of cross-section of a pipe is 5·4 cm² and water is pumped out of it at the rate of 27 km/h. Find in litres the volume of water which flows out of the pipe in one minute.

Solution. Area of cross-section of the pipe = 5·4 cm² = $\dfrac{5·4}{100 \times 100}$ m².

Length of water which flows out of pipe in one minute

$$= \frac{27}{60} \text{km} = \frac{27}{60} \times 1000 \text{m}.$$

∴ Volume of water which flows out of pipe in one minute

$$= \frac{5·4}{100 \times 100} \times \frac{27}{60} \times 1000 \text{m}^3 = \frac{5·4 \times 27}{600} \text{m}^3$$

$$= \frac{5·4 \times 27}{600} \times 1000 \text{ litres} \qquad\qquad (\because 1 \text{ m}^3 = 1000 \text{ litres})$$

$$= 243 \text{ litres}.$$

Example 19 A solid cube of side 12 cm is cut into eight cubes of equal volume. What will be the side of the new cube? Also, find the ratio between their surface areas (surface area of original cube and of new 8 cubes).

Solution. Volume of given cube = (12 × 12 × 12) cm³

As the given cube is cut into 8 cubes of equal volume,

∴   volume of each new cube = $\dfrac{12 \times 12 \times 12}{8}$ cm³ = (6 × 6 × 6) cm³

⇒   side of each new cube = 6 cm.

Surface area of given cube = $6a^2$ = (6 × 12 × 12) cm².

Surface area of each new cube = $6a^2$ = (6 × 6²) cm²

Surface area of 8 new cubes = (8 × 8 × 6²) cm².

∴ $\dfrac{\text{Surface area of given cube}}{\text{Surface area of eight new cubes}} = \dfrac{6 \times 12 \times 12}{8 \times 6 \times 6 \times 6} = \dfrac{1}{2}.$

Hence, the required ratio = 1 : 2.

Example 20 The cross-section of a piece of metal 2 m in length is shown in figure (i) given below. Calculate

(i) the area of cross-section.

(ii) the volume of the piece of metal in cubic centimetres (cm³).

If 1 cm³ of the metal weighs 6·6 g, calculate the weight of the piece of metal to the nearest kg.

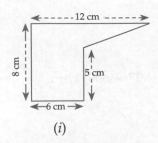

(i)

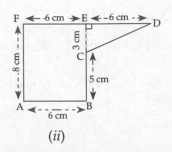

(ii)

Solution. Name the points as shown in figure (ii). Join CE.

From figure (ii), EC = 3 cm and ED = 6 cm.

(i) Area of cross-section = area of rectangle ABEF + area of ΔCED

$$= \left(6 \times 8 + \frac{1}{2} \times 6 \times 3\right) \text{ cm}^2 = 57 \text{ cm}^2.$$

(ii) Since the length of the piece of metal = 2 m = 200 cm.

∴ The volume of the piece of metal = 57 × 200 cm³ = 11400 cm³.

As the weight of 1 cm³ of metal is 6·6 g,

∴ the weight of the piece of metal = 11400 × 6·6 g

$$= \frac{11400 \times 6 \cdot 6}{1000} \text{ kg} = 75 \cdot 24 \text{ kg}$$

$$= 75 \text{ kg (nearest kg).}$$

EXERCISE 16.4

1 Find the surface area and volume of a cube whose one edge is 7 cm.

2 Find the surface area and the volume of a rectangular solid measuring 5 m by 4 m by 3 m. Also find the length of a diagonal.

3 The length and breadth of a rectangular solid are respectively 25 cm and 20 cm. If the volume is 7000 cm³, find its height.

4 A classroom is 10 m long, 6 m broad and 4 m high. How many students can it accommodate if one student needs 1·5 m² of floor area? How many cubic metres of air will each student have?

5 (a) The volume of a cuboid is 1440 cm³. Its height is 10 cm and the cross-section is a square. Find the side of the square.

   (b) The perimeter of one face of a cube is 20 cm. Find the surface area and the volume of the cube.

6 Mary wants to decorate her Christmas tree. She wants to place the tree on a wooden box covered with coloured papers with pictures of Santa Claus. She must know the exact quantity of paper to buy for this purpose. If the box has length 80 cm, breadth 40 cm and height 20 cm respectively, then how many square sheets of paper of side 40 cm would she require?

7 The volume of a cuboid is 3600 cm³ and its height is 12 cm. The cross-section is a rectangle whose length and breadth are in the ratio 4 : 3. Find the perimeter of the cross-section.

8 The volume of a cube is 729 cm³. Find its surface area and the length of a diagonal.

9 The length of the longest rod which can be kept inside a rectangular box is 17 cm. If the inner length and breadth of the box are 12 cm and 8 cm respectively, find its inner height.

10 A closed rectangular box has inner dimensions 90 cm by 80 cm by 70 cm. Calculate its capacity and the area of tin-foil needed to line its inner surface.

11 The internal measurements of a box are 20 cm long, 16 cm wide and 24 cm high. How many 4 cm cubes could be put into the box?

12 The internal measurements of a box are 10 cm long, 8 cm wide and 7 cm high. How many cubes of side 2 cm can be put into the box?

    Hint. Since height of box is 7 cm, only 3 cubes can be put height-wise.

13 A certain quantity of wood costs ₹250 per m³. A solid cubical block of such wood is bought for ₹182·25. Calculate the volume of the block and use the method of factors to find the length of one edge of the block.

14 A cube of 11 cm edge is immersed completely in a rectangular vessel containing water. If the dimensions of the base of the vessel are 15 cm × 12 cm, find the rise in the water level in centimetres correct to 2 decimal places, assuming that no water overflows.

15 A rectangular container, whose base is a square of side 6 cm, stands on a horizontal table and holds water up to 1 cm from the top. When a cube is placed in the water and is completely submerged, the water rises to the top and 2 cm³ of water overflows. Calculate the volume of the cube.

16 Two cubes, each with 12 cm edge, are joined end to end. Find the surface area of the resulting cuboid.

17 A cube of a metal of 6 cm edge is melted and cast into a cuboid whose base is 9 cm × 8 cm. Find the height of the cuboid.

18 The area of a playground is 4800 m². Find the cost of covering it with gravel 1 cm deep, if the gravel costs ₹260 per cubic metre.

19 A field is 30 m long and 18 m broad. A pit 6 m long, 4 m wide and 3 m deep is dug out from the middle of the field and the earth removed is evenly spread over the remaining area of the field. Find the rise in the level of the remaining part of the field in centimetres correct to two decimal places.

20 A rectangular plot is 24 m long and 20 m wide. A cubical pit of edge 4 m is dug at each of the four corners of the field and the soil removed is evenly spread over the remaining part of the plot. By what height does the remaining plot get raised?

21 The inner dimensions of a closed wooden box are 2 m, 1·2 m and ·75 m. The thickness of the wood is 2·5 cm. Find the cost of wood required to make the box if 1 m³ of wood costs ₹5400.

22 A cubical wooden box of internal edge 1 m is made of 5 cm thick wood. The box is open at the top. If the wood costs ₹9600 per cubic metre, find the cost of the wood required to make the box.

23 A square brass plate of side x cm is 1 mm thick and weighs 4725 g. If one cc of brass weighs 8·4 g, find the value of x.

24 Three cubes whose edges are x cm, 8 cm and 10 cm respectively are melted and recast into a single cube of edge 12 cm. Find x.

25 The area of cross-section of a pipe is 3·5 cm² and water is flowing out of pipe at the rate of 40 cm/s. How much water is delivered by the pipe in one minute?

26 (a) The figure (i) given below shows a solid of uniform cross-section. Find the volume of the solid. All measurements are in cm and all angles in the figure are right angles.

(b) The figure (ii) given below shows the cross-section of a concrete wall to be constructed. It is 2 m wide at the top, 3·5 m wide at the bottom and its height is 6 m, and its length is 400 m. Calculate (i) the cross-sectional area, and (ii) volume of concrete in the wall.

(c) The figure (iii) given below show the cross-section of a swimming pool 10 m broad, 2 m deep at one end and 3 m deep at the other end. Calculate the volume of water it will hold when full, given that its length is 40 m.

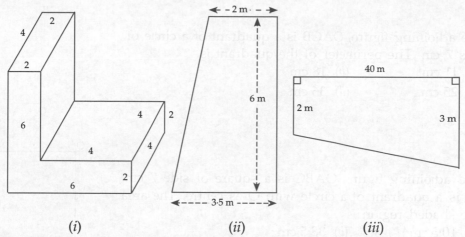

(i)   (ii)   (iii)

27 A swimming pool is 50 metres long and 15 metres wide. Its shallow and deep ends are $1\frac{1}{2}$ metres and $4\frac{1}{2}$ metres deep respectively. If the bottom of the pool slopes uniformly, find the amount of water required to fill the pool.

Multiple Choice Questions

Choose the correct answer from the given four options (1 to 24):

1 Area of a triangle is 30 cm². If its base is 10 cm, then its height is
   (a) 5 cm   (b) 6 cm   (c) 7 cm   (d) 8 cm

2 If the perimeter of a square is 80 cm, then its area is
   (a) 800 cm²   (b) 600 cm²   (c) 400 cm²   (d) 200 cm²

3 Area of a parallelogram is 48 cm². If its height is 6 cm then its base is
   (a) 8 cm   (b) 4 cm   (c) 16 cm   (d) None of these

4 If d is the diameter of a circle, then its area is
   (a) πd^2 (b) $\frac{\pi d^2}{2}$ (c) $\frac{\pi d^2}{4}$ (d) $2\pi d^2$

5 If the area of a trapezium is 64 cm² and the distance between parallel sides is 8 cm, then sum of its parallel sides is
   (a) 8 cm   (b) 4 cm   (c) 32 cm   (d) 16 cm

6 Area of a rhombus whose diagonals are 8 cm and 6 cm is
   (a) 48 cm²   (b) 24 cm²   (c) 12 cm²   (d) 96 cm²

7 If the lengths of diagonals of a rhombus is doubled, then area of rhombus will be
   (a) doubled   (b) tripled   (c) four times   (d) remains same.

8 If the length of a diagonal of a quadrilateral is 10 cm and lengths of the perpendiculars on it from opposite vertices are 4 cm and 6 cm, then area of quadrilateral is
   (a) 100 cm²   (b) 200 cm²   (c) 50 cm²   (d) None of these.

9 Area of a rhombus is 90 cm². If the length of one diagonal is 10 cm then the length of other diagonal is
   (a) 18 cm   (b) 9 cm   (c) 36 cm   (d) 4·5 cm

10 In the adjoining figure, OACB is a quadrant of a circle of radius 7 cm. The perimeter of the quadrant is
   (a) 11 cm   (b) 18 cm
   (c) 25 cm   (d) 36 cm

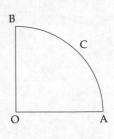

11 In the adjoining figure, OABC is a square of side 7 cm. OAC is a quadrant of a circle with O as centre. The area of the shaded region is
   (a) 10·5 cm²   (b) 38·5 cm²
   (c) 49 cm²   (d) 11·5 cm²

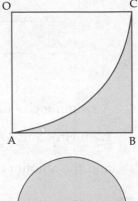

12 The adjoining figure shows a rectangle and a semicircle. The perimeter of the shaded region is
   (a) 70 cm   (b) 56 cm
   (c) 78 cm   (d) 46 cm

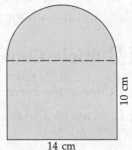

13 The area of the shaded region shown in Q. 12 (above) is
   (a) 140 cm²   (b) 77 cm²   (c) 294 cm²   (d) 217 cm²

14 In the adjoining figure, the boundary of the shaded region consists of semicircular arcs. The area of the shaded region is equal to
   (a) 616 cm²   (b) 385 cm²
   (c) 231 cm²   (d) 308 cm²

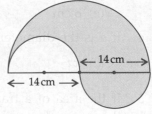

15 The perimeter of the shaded region shown in Q. 14 (above) is
   (a) 44 cm   (b) 88 cm   (c) 66 cm   (d) 132 cm

16 In the adjoining figure, ABC is a right angled triangle at B. A semicircle is drawn on AB as diameter. If AB = 12 cm and BC = 5 cm, then the area of the shaded region is
   (a) $(60 + 18\,\pi)$ cm²   (b) $(30 + 36\,\pi)$ cm²
   (c) $(30 + 18\,\pi)$ cm²   (d) $(30 + 9\,\pi)$ cm²

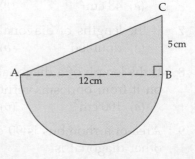

17 The perimeter of the shaded region shown in Q. 16 (above) is
   (a) $(30 + 6\,\pi)$ cm   (b) $(30 + 12\,\pi)$ cm   (c) $(18 + 12\,\pi)$ cm   (d) $(18 + 6\,\pi)$ cm

18 If the volume of a cube is 729 m³, then its surface area is
   (a) 486 cm²   (b) 324 cm²   (c) 162 cm²   (d) None of these.

19 If the total surface area of a cube is 96 cm², then the volume of the cube is

    (a) 8 cm³   (b) 512 cm³   (c) 64 cm³   (d) 27 cm³

20 The length of the longest pole that can be put in a room of dimensions (10 m × 10 m × 5 m) is

    (a) 15 m   (b) 16 m   (c) 10 m   (d) 12 m

21 The lateral surface area of a cube is 256 m². The volume of the cube is

    (a) 512 m³   (b) 64 m³   (c) 216 m³   (d) 256 m³

22 If the perimeter of one face of a cube is 40 cm, then the sum of lengths of its edge is

    (a) 80 cm   (b) 120 cm   (c) 160 cm   (d) 240 cm

23 A cuboid container has the capacity to hold 50 small boxes. If all the dimensions of the container are doubled, then it can hold (small boxes of same size)

    (a) 100 boxes   (b) 200 boxes   (c) 400 boxes   (d) 800 boxes

24 The number of planks of dimensions (4 m × 50 cm × 20 cm) that can be stored in a pit which is 16 m long, 12 m wide and 4 m deep is

    (a) 1900   (b) 1920   (c) 1800   (d) 1840

Summary

❏ **Area (of plane figures)**

    (i) Area of a triangle = $\frac{1}{2}$ base × height.

    (ii) Area of a triangle = $\sqrt{s(s-a)(s-b)(s-c)}$, where a, b, c are lengths of sides and $s = \frac{1}{2}(a+b+c)$ (Heron's formula)

    (iii) Area of an equilateral triangle = $\frac{\sqrt{3}}{4} a^2$, where a is its side.

    (iv) Area of an isosceles triangle = $\frac{b}{4}\sqrt{4a^2 - b^2}$, where b is the base and a is an equal side.

    (v) Area of a quadrilateral (when diagonals intersect at right angles)

                = $\frac{1}{2}$ × product of diagonals.

    (vi) Area of a rectangle = length × breadth.

    (vii) Area of a square = (side)².

    (viii) Area of a parallelogram = base × height.

    (ix) Area of a rhombus = $\frac{1}{2}$ × product of diagonals.

    (x) Area of a trapezium = $\frac{1}{2}$ × (sum of parallel sides) × height.

❏ **Length of diagonal**

    (i) Length of diagonal of a square = $\sqrt{2}\,a$, where a is its side.

    (ii) Length of diagonal of a rectangle = $\sqrt{l^2 + b^2}$, where l and b are its edges (sides).

    (iii) Length of diagonal of a cube = $\sqrt{3}\,a$, where a is its side.

    (iv) Length of diagonal of a cuboid = $\sqrt{l^2 + b^2 + h^2}$, where l, b and h are its edges (sides).

❏ **Circumference and area of a circle**

    If r is the radius of a circle, then

    (i) Circumference of circle = $2\pi r$.

    (ii) Area of circle = πr^2.

❏ **Area of a circular ring**

If R and r are the radii of the outer and inner circles, then area of circular ring $= \pi(R^2 - r^2)$.

❏ **Perimeter and area of a semicircle**

If r is the radius of a circle, then

    (i) Perimeter of semicircle $= (\pi + 2)r$.

    (ii) Area of semicircle $= \dfrac{1}{2}\pi r^2$.

❏ **Surface area and volume (of solids)**

Cuboid

    (i) Surface area of a cube $= 6a^2$, where a is its edge (side).

    (ii) Surface area of a cuboid $= 2(lb + bh + lh)$, where l, b and h are its edges (sides).

    (iii) Surface area of four walls (lateral surface area) of a cuboid $= 2h(l + b)$.

    (iv) Volume of a cube $= a^3$, where a is its edge (side).

    (v) Volume of a cuboid $=$ length $\times$ breadth $\times$ height $= l \times b \times h$.

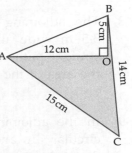

Chapter Test

Take $\pi = \dfrac{22}{7}$, unless stated otherwise.

1   (a) Calculate the area of the shaded region.

(b) If the sides of a square are lengthened by 3 cm, the area becomes 121 cm². Find the perimeter of the original square.

2   (a) Find the area enclosed by the figure (i) given below. All measurements are in centimetres.

(b) Find the area of the quadrilateral ABCD shown in figure (ii) given below. All measurements are in centimetres.

(c) Calculate the area of the shaded region shown in figure (iii) given below. All measurements are in metres.

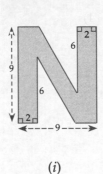

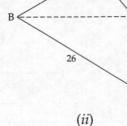

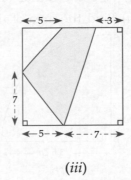

(i)   (ii)   (iii)

3   Asifa cut an aeroplane from a coloured chart paper (as shown in the adjoining figure). Find the total area of the chart paper used, correct to 1 decimal place.

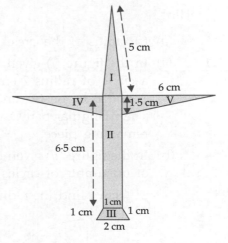

4   If the area of a circle is 78·5 cm², find its circumference. (Take $\pi = 3·14$)

5   From a square cardboard, a circle of biggest area was cut out. If the area of the circle is 154 cm², calculate the original area of the cardboard.

6   (a) From a sheet of paper of dimensions 2 m × 1·5 m, how many circles of radius 5 cm can be cut? Also find the area of the paper wasted. Take $\pi = 3·14$.

(b) If the diameter of a semi-circular protractor is 14 cm, then find its perimeter.

7 A road 3·5 m wide surrounds a circular park whose circumference is 88 m. Find the cost of paving the road at the rate of ₹60 per square metre.

8 The adjoining sketch shows a running track 3·5 m wide all around which consists of two straight paths and two semicircular rings. Find the area of the track.

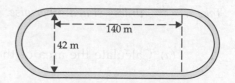
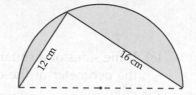

9 In the adjoining figure, O is the centre of a circular arc and AOB is a line segment. Find the perimeter and the area of the shaded region correct to one decimal place. (Take π = 3·142)

Hint. Angle in a semicircle is a right angle.

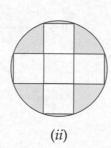

10 (a) In the figure (i) given below, the radius is 3·5 cm. Find the perimeter of the quarter of the circle.

(b) In the figure (ii) given below, there are five squares each of side 2 cm.

(i) Find the radius of the circle.

(ii) Find the area of the shaded region. (Take π = 3·14).

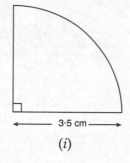

(i)

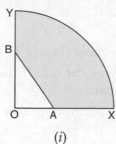

(ii)

Hint.

(b) (i) radius of the circle = $\sqrt{3^2 + 1}$ cm = $\sqrt{10}$ cm.

11 (a) In the figure (i) given below, a piece of cardbord in the shape of a quadrant of a circle of radius 7 cm is bounded by perpendicular radii OX and OY. Points A and B lie on OX and OY respectively such that OA = 3 cm and OB = 4 cm. The triangular part OAB is removed. Calculate the area and the perimeter of the remaining piece.

(b) In the figure (ii) given below, ABCD is a square. Points A, B, C and D are centres of quadrants of circles of the same radius. If the area of the shaded portion is $21\frac{3}{7}$ cm², find the radius of the quadrants.

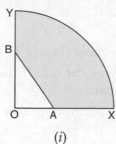

(i)

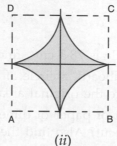

(ii)

12 In the adjoining figure, ABC is a right angled triangle right angled at B. Semicircles are drawn on AB, BC and CA as diameter. Show that the sum of areas of semicircles drawn on AB and BC as diameter is equal to the area of the semicircle drawn on CA as diameter.

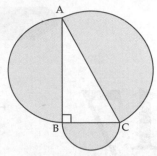

13 The length of minute hand of a clock is 14 cm. Find the area swept by the minute hand in 15 minutes.

14 Find the radius of a circle if a 90° arc has a length of 3·5π cm. Hence, find the area of the sector formed by this arc.

15 A cube whose each edge is 28 cm long has a circle of maximum radius on each of its face painted red. Find the total area of the unpainted surface of the cube.

16 Can a pole 6·5 m long fit into the body of a truck with internal dimensions of 3·5 m, 3 m and 4 m?

17 A car has a petrol tank 40 cm long, 28 cm wide and 25 cm deep. If the fuel consumption of the car averages 13·5 km per litre, how far can the car travel with a full tank of petrol?

18 An aquarium took 96 minutes to completely fill with water. Water was filling the aquarium at a rate of 25 litres every 2 minutes. Given that the aquarium was 2 m long and 80 cm wide, compute the height of the aquarium.

19 The lateral surface area of a cuboid is 224 cm². Its height is 7 cm and the base is a square. Find

    (*i*) a side of the square, and (*ii*) the volume of the cuboid.

20 If the volume of a cube is V m³, its surface area is S m² and the length of a diagonal is d metres, prove that $6\sqrt{3}\,V = Sd$.

21 The adjoining figure shows a victory stand, each face is rectangular. All measurements are in centimetres. Find its volume and surface area (the bottom of the stand is open).

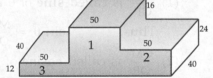

    Hint. Volume = $(50 \times 40 \times 12 + 50 \times 40 \times 40 + 50 \times 40 \times 24)\,\text{cm}^3$.

        Surface area = (area of front + area of back) + area of the vertical faces + area of top faces = $2\,(50 \times 12 + 50 \times 40 + 50 \times 24)\,\text{cm}^2$

                 $+ (12 \times 40 + 28 \times 40 + 16 \times 40 + 24 \times 40)\,\text{cm}^2 + 3\,(50 \times 40)\,\text{cm}^2$.

22 The external dimensions of an open rectangular wooden box are 98 cm by 84 cm by 77 cm. If the wood is 2 cm thick all around, find

    (*i*) the capacity of the box

    (*ii*) the volume of the wood used in making the box, and

    (*iii*) the weight of the box in kilograms correct to one decimal place, given that 1 cm³ of wood weighs 0·8 g.

23 A cuboidal block of metal has dimensions 36 cm by 32 cm by 0·25 m. It is melted and recast into cubes with an edge of 4 cm.

    (*i*) How many such cubes can be made?

    (*ii*) What is the cost of silver coating the surfaces of the cubes at the rate of ₹1·25 per square centimetre?

24 Three cubes of silver with edges 3 cm, 4 cm and 5 cm are melted and recast into a single cube. Find the cost of coating the surface of the new cube with gold at the rate of ₹3·50 per square centimetre.

17 Trigonometrical Ratios

INTRODUCTION

The word 'Trigonometry' is derived from the Greek words 'tri' (meaning three), 'gon' (meaning sides) and 'metron' (meaning measure). In fact, *trigonometry is the study of relationships between the sides and the angles of a triangle*.

Earlier, astronomers used trigonometry to find the distances of the planets and stars from the earth. Even today, most of the technologically advanced methods used in Physical sciences and Engineering are based on trigonometrical concepts.

In this chapter, we will study some ratios of the sides of a right triangle with respect to its acute angles, called *trigonometrical ratios of the angle* and *establish some relations between different trigonometrical ratios. We will also find the value of any trigonometrical ratio in terms of a given trigonometrical ratio.*

17.1 TRIGONOMETRICAL RATIOS

Let OMP be a right-angled triangle at M and $\angle MOP = \theta$ (theta), then the *trigonometrical ratios* (abbreviated *t-ratios*) are defined as

(1) $\dfrac{MP}{OP}$ is called **sine** of θ and is written as $\sin \theta$.

Thus, $\quad \sin \theta = \dfrac{MP}{OP}$.

(2) $\dfrac{OM}{OP}$ is called **cosine** of θ and is written as $\cos \theta$.

Thus, $\quad \cos \theta = \dfrac{OM}{OP}$.

(3) $\dfrac{MP}{OM}$ is called **tangent** of θ and is written as $\tan \theta$.

Thus, $\quad \tan \theta = \dfrac{MP}{OM}$.

(4) $\dfrac{OM}{MP}$ is called **cotangent** of θ and is written as $\cot \theta$.

Thus, $\quad \cot \theta = \dfrac{OM}{MP}$.

(5) $\dfrac{OP}{OM}$ is called **secant** of θ and is written as $\sec \theta$.

Thus, $\quad \sec \theta = \dfrac{OP}{OM}$.

(6) $\dfrac{OP}{MP}$ is called **cosecant** of θ and is written as $\operatorname{cosec} \theta$.

Thus, $\quad \operatorname{cosec} \theta = \dfrac{OP}{MP}$.

In reference to $\angle MOP$ in $\triangle OMP$, OM is called *base* or *adjacent side,* MP is called *height* or *opposite side* and OP is the *hypotenuse*. The *six trigonometrical ratios* can be defined as :

(1) $\sin \theta = \dfrac{\text{height}}{\text{hypotenuse}}$. $\qquad\qquad$ (2) $\cos \theta = \dfrac{\text{base}}{\text{hypotenuse}}$.

(3) $\tan \theta = \dfrac{\text{height}}{\text{base}}$.

(4) $\cot \theta = \dfrac{\text{base}}{\text{height}}$.

(5) $\sec \theta = \dfrac{\text{hypotenuse}}{\text{base}}$.

(6) $\operatorname{cosec} \theta = \dfrac{\text{hypotenuse}}{\text{height}}$.

Remarks

1. In right-angled triangle OMP, $\angle$MOP lies between $0°$ to $90°$ i.e. $\angle$MOP is acute angle i.e. θ is acute and all the six trigonometrical ratios are positive.

2. The symbol $\sin \theta$ is used as an abbreviation for 'sine of angle θ'. $\sin \theta$ is not the product of sin and θ. sin separated from θ has no meaning. Similar interpretations follow for other trigonometrical ratios (abbreviated t-ratios).

3. Trigonometrical ratios of an acute angle in a right angled triangle express the relationship between the angle and the lengths of its sides.

4. *Each trigonometrical ratio is a (unitless) real number.*

17.1.1 Reciprocal relations

From the right-angled triangle OMP, we get

(1) $\sin \theta = \dfrac{MP}{OP}$ and $\operatorname{cosec} \theta = \dfrac{OP}{MP}$

$\Rightarrow \quad \sin \theta = \dfrac{1}{\operatorname{cosec} \theta}$ and $\operatorname{cosec} \theta = \dfrac{1}{\sin \theta}$

$\Rightarrow \quad$ *$\sin \theta$ and $\operatorname{cosec} \theta$ are reciprocals of each other.*

(2) $\cos \theta = \dfrac{OM}{OP}$ and $\sec \theta = \dfrac{OP}{OM}$

$\Rightarrow \quad \cos \theta = \dfrac{1}{\sec \theta}$ and $\sec \theta = \dfrac{1}{\cos \theta}$

$\Rightarrow \quad$ *$\cos \theta$ and $\sec \theta$ are reciprocal of each other.*

(3) $\tan \theta = \dfrac{MP}{OM}$ and $\cot \theta = \dfrac{OM}{MP}$

$\Rightarrow \quad \tan \theta = \dfrac{1}{\cot \theta}$ and $\cot \theta = \dfrac{1}{\tan \theta}$

$\Rightarrow \quad$ *$\tan \theta$ and $\cot \theta$ are reciprocal of each other.*

From above, it follows that :

(*i*) $\sin \theta \times \operatorname{cosec} \theta = 1$

(*ii*) $\cos \theta \times \sec \theta = 1$

(*iii*) $\tan \theta \times \cot \theta = 1$.

17.1.2 Quotient relations

From the right-angled triangle OMP, we get

(1) $\dfrac{\sin \theta}{\cos \theta} = \dfrac{\dfrac{MP}{OP}}{\dfrac{OM}{OP}} = \dfrac{MP}{OP} \times \dfrac{OP}{OM} = \dfrac{MP}{OM} = \tan \theta$,

$\therefore \quad \mathbf{\tan \theta} = \dfrac{\sin \theta}{\cos \theta}$.

(2) $\dfrac{\cos \theta}{\sin \theta} = \dfrac{\dfrac{OM}{OP}}{\dfrac{MP}{OP}} = \dfrac{OM}{OP} \times \dfrac{OP}{MP} = \dfrac{OM}{MP} = \cot \theta$,

$\therefore \quad \mathbf{\cot \theta} = \dfrac{\cos \theta}{\sin \theta}$.

17.1.3 Square relations

From the right-angled triangle OMP, by Pythagoras theorem, we get

$$MP^2 + OM^2 = OP^2 \qquad \qquad \dots (i)$$

(1) Dividing both sides of (*i*) by OP^2, we get

$$\left(\frac{MP}{OP}\right)^2 + \left(\frac{OM}{OP}\right)^2 = 1$$

$$\Rightarrow \quad \sin^2 \theta + \cos^2 \theta = 1.$$

(2) Dividing both sides of (*i*) by OM^2, we get

$$\left(\frac{MP}{OM}\right)^2 + 1 = \left(\frac{OP}{OM}\right)^2$$

$$\Rightarrow \quad \tan^2 \theta + 1 = \sec^2 \theta \ i.e. \ \mathbf{1 + \tan^2 \theta = \sec^2 \theta.}$$

(3) Dividing both sides of (*i*) by MP^2, we get

$$1 + \left(\frac{OM}{MP}\right)^2 = \left(\frac{OP}{MP}\right)^2$$

$$\Rightarrow \quad \mathbf{1 + \cot^2 \theta = \operatorname{cosec}^2 \theta.}$$

From above, it follows that:

(*i*) $1 - \sin^2 \theta = \cos^2 \theta$ (*ii*) $1 - \cos^2 \theta = \sin^2 \theta$

(*iii*) $\sec^2 \theta - 1 = \tan^2 \theta$ (*iv*) $\sec^2 \theta - \tan^2 \theta = 1$

(*v*) $\operatorname{cosec}^2 \theta - 1 = \cot^2 \theta$ (*vi*) $\operatorname{cosec}^2 \theta - \cot^2 \theta = 1.$

Remark

$\sin^2 \theta$ means $(\sin \theta)^2$ and $\sin^2 \theta$ is read as *sine squared* θ. Similarly $\cos^2 \theta$ means $(\cos \theta)^2$ etc.

17.2 THE VALUE OF ANY T-RATIO IN TERMS OF A GIVEN T-RATIO

We shall explain the method of finding the value of any *t*-ratio in terms of a given *t*-ratio with the help of the following examples:

Illustrative Examples

Example 1 In $\triangle ABC$, right angled at B, AB = 24 cm and BC = 7 cm. Determine:

   (*i*) sin A, cos A   (*ii*) sin C, cos C.

Solution. In $\triangle ABC$, $\angle B = 90°$.

By Pythagoras Theorem, we get

$$AC^2 = AB^2 + BC^2$$

$$\Rightarrow \quad AC^2 = (24)^2 + 7^2 = 576 + 49 = 625$$

$$\Rightarrow \quad AC = 25 \text{ cm.}$$

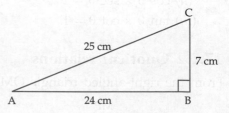

   (*i*) $\sin A = \dfrac{BC}{AC} = \dfrac{7}{25}$, $\cos A = \dfrac{AB}{AC} = \dfrac{24}{25}$.

   (*ii*) $\sin C = \dfrac{AB}{AC} = \dfrac{24}{25}$, $\cos C = \dfrac{BC}{AC} = \dfrac{7}{25}$.

Example 2 Given $\triangle ACB$ right angled at C, in which AB = 29 units, BC = 21 units and $\angle ABC = \theta$ (shown in the adjoining figure).

Determine the values of:

   (*i*) $\cos^2 \theta + \sin^2 \theta$ (*ii*) $\cos^2 \theta - \sin^2 \theta$

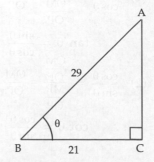

Solution. In $\triangle ACB$, $\angle C = 90°$.

By Pythagoras Theorem, we get

$$AB^2 = BC^2 + AC^2 \Rightarrow (29)^2 = (21)^2 + AC^2$$

$$\Rightarrow \quad AC^2 = 841 - 441 = 400 \Rightarrow AC = 20 \text{ units.}$$

$$\therefore \quad \sin \theta = \frac{AC}{AB} = \frac{20}{29} \text{ and } \cos \theta = \frac{BC}{AB} = \frac{21}{29}.$$

(i) $\cos^2 \theta + \sin^2 \theta = \left(\dfrac{21}{29}\right)^2 + \left(\dfrac{20}{29}\right)^2 = \dfrac{441 + 400}{841} = \dfrac{841}{841} = 1$

(ii) $\cos^2 \theta - \sin^2 \theta = \left(\dfrac{21}{29}\right)^2 - \left(\dfrac{20}{29}\right)^2 = \dfrac{441 - 400}{841} = \dfrac{41}{841}.$

Example 3 Given $\sec \theta = \dfrac{13}{12}$, calculate all other trigonometrical ratios.

Solution. Draw a right triangle OMP, right angled at M (as shown in the adjoining figure). Let $\angle MOP = \theta$, θ is an acute angle.

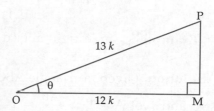

We know that $\sec \theta = \dfrac{OP}{OM} = \dfrac{13}{12}$ (given)

Let $OP = 13k$, then $OM = 12k$ where k is some positive real number.

By Pythagoras Theorem, we get

$$OP^2 = OM^2 + MP^2$$

$$\Rightarrow \quad (13k)^2 = (12k)^2 + MP^2 \Rightarrow MP^2 = 169k^2 - 144k^2 = 25k^2$$

$$\Rightarrow \quad MP = 5k. \qquad\qquad\qquad (\because MP \text{ is positive})$$

$$\therefore \quad \sin \theta = \frac{MP}{OP} = \frac{5k}{13k} = \frac{5}{13}, \quad \cos \theta = \frac{OM}{OP} = \frac{12k}{13k} = \frac{12}{13},$$

$$\tan \theta = \frac{MP}{OM} = \frac{5k}{12k} = \frac{5}{12}, \quad \cot \theta = \frac{OM}{MP} = \frac{12k}{5k} = \frac{12}{5}$$

and $\cosec \theta = \dfrac{OP}{MP} = \dfrac{13k}{5k} = \dfrac{13}{5}.$

Example 4 If $\sin \theta = \dfrac{5}{13}$ and θ is acute angle, find the value of $\tan \theta + \dfrac{1}{\cos \theta}$.

Solution. We know that $\sin \theta = \dfrac{MP}{OP}$ and $\sin \theta = \dfrac{5}{13}$ (given)

$$\Rightarrow \quad \frac{MP}{OP} = \frac{5}{13}.$$

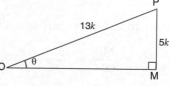

Draw a triangle OMP right-angled at M (shown in the adjoining figure) such that $\angle MOP = \theta$.

Let $MP = 5k$, then $OP = 13k$, where k is a positive real number.

From right-angled $\triangle OMP$, by Pythagoras theorem, we get

$$OP^2 = OM^2 + MP^2$$

$$\Rightarrow \quad OM^2 = OP^2 - MP^2$$

$$\Rightarrow \quad OM^2 = (13k)^2 - (5k)^2 = 169k^2 - 25k^2 = 144k^2$$

$$\Rightarrow \quad OM = 12k.$$

$$\therefore \quad \tan \theta = \frac{MP}{OM} = \frac{5k}{12k} = \frac{5}{12} \text{ and } \cos \theta = \frac{OM}{OP} = \frac{12k}{13k} = \frac{12}{13}.$$

$$\therefore \quad \tan \theta + \frac{1}{\cos \theta} = \frac{5}{12} + \frac{1}{\frac{12}{13}} = \frac{5}{12} + \frac{13}{12} = \frac{5 + 13}{12} = \frac{18}{12} = \frac{3}{2}.$$

Alternatively

We know that $\sin^2 \theta + \cos^2 \theta = 1$

$$\Rightarrow \qquad \cos^2 \theta = 1 - \sin^2 \theta = 1 - \left(\frac{5}{13}\right)^2 \qquad (\because \sin \theta = \frac{5}{13} \text{ given})$$

$$\Rightarrow \qquad \cos^2 \theta = 1 - \frac{25}{169} = \frac{169 - 25}{169} = \frac{144}{169}$$

$$\Rightarrow \qquad \cos \theta = \frac{12}{13}$$

(As θ is acute, $\cos \theta$ is +ve, so we take +ve value of the square root)

$$\therefore \qquad \tan \theta = \frac{\sin \theta}{\cos \theta} = \frac{5}{13} \div \frac{12}{13} = \frac{5}{13} \times \frac{13}{12} = \frac{5}{12}.$$

$$\therefore \quad \tan \theta + \frac{1}{\cos \theta} = \frac{5}{12} + \frac{1}{\frac{12}{13}} = \frac{5}{12} + \frac{13}{12} = \frac{5 + 13}{12} = \frac{18}{12} = \frac{3}{2}.$$

Example 5 In a right-angled triangle ABC, right-angled at B, if cot A = 1, prove that 2 sin A cos A = 1.

Solution. Given, a triangle ABC in which $\angle B = 90°$

and $\cot A = 1 \Rightarrow \dfrac{AB}{BC} = 1$

$\Rightarrow \quad AB = BC.$

Let $AB = BC = k$ units, where k is positive real number.

From right-angled $\triangle ABC$, by Pythagoras theorem, we get

$$AC^2 = AB^2 + BC^2 = k^2 + k^2 = 2k^2$$

$\Rightarrow \quad AC = \sqrt{2}\,k$ units.

$$\therefore \quad \sin A = \frac{BC}{AC} = \frac{k}{\sqrt{2}k} = \frac{1}{\sqrt{2}}$$

and $\cos A = \dfrac{AB}{AC} = \dfrac{k}{\sqrt{2}k} = \dfrac{1}{\sqrt{2}}.$

$$\therefore \quad 2 \sin A \cos A = 2 \times \frac{1}{\sqrt{2}} \times \frac{1}{\sqrt{2}} = \frac{2}{2} = 1.$$

Example 6 If $\tan \theta = \dfrac{5}{12}$, find $\sec \theta$ and $\sec \theta + \operatorname{cosec} \theta$, where θ is acute.

Solution. Given $\tan \theta = \dfrac{5}{12}$ but $\tan \theta = \dfrac{MP}{OM}$

$$\Rightarrow \qquad \frac{MP}{OM} = \frac{5}{12}.$$

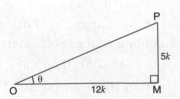

Draw a triangle OMP right angled at M (shown in the adjoining figure) such that MP = 5k, then OM = 12k, where k is a positive real number.

From right angled $\triangle OMP$, by Pythagoras theorem, we get

$$OP^2 = OM^2 + MP^2 = (12k)^2 + (5k)^2 = 144k^2 + 25k^2 = 169k^2$$

$\Rightarrow \quad OP = 13k.$

$$\therefore \quad \sec \theta = \frac{OP}{OM} = \frac{13k}{12k} = \frac{13}{12} \text{ and } \operatorname{cosec} \theta = \frac{OP}{MP} = \frac{13k}{5k} = \frac{13}{5}.$$

$$\therefore \quad \sec\theta + \operatorname{cosec}\theta = \frac{13}{12} + \frac{13}{5} = 13\left(\frac{1}{12} + \frac{1}{5}\right)$$

$$= 13 \cdot \frac{5+12}{60}$$

$$= \frac{13 \times 17}{60} = \frac{221}{60} = 3\frac{41}{60}.$$

Example 7 If θ is acute and $3\sin\theta = 4\cos\theta$, find the value of $4\sin^2\theta - 3\cos^2\theta + 2$.

Solution. Given $\ 3\sin\theta = 4\cos\theta \ \Rightarrow \ \dfrac{\sin\theta}{\cos\theta} = \dfrac{4}{3} \ \Rightarrow \ \tan\theta = \dfrac{4}{3}.$

But $\tan\theta = \dfrac{MP}{OM} \Rightarrow \dfrac{MP}{OM} = \dfrac{4}{3}.$

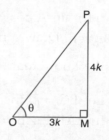

Draw a triangle OMP right angled at M (shown in the adjoining figure) such that $\angle MOP = \theta$. Let $MP = 4k$, then $OM = 3k$, where k is a positive real number.

From right-angled $\triangle OMP$, by Pythagoras theorem, we get
$$OP^2 = OM^2 + MP^2$$
$$\Rightarrow \qquad OP^2 = (3k)^2 + (4k)^2 = 9k^2 + 16k^2 = 25k^2$$
$$\Rightarrow \qquad OP = 5k.$$

$$\therefore \qquad \sin\theta = \frac{MP}{OP} = \frac{4k}{5k} = \frac{4}{5} \text{ and } \cos\theta = \frac{OM}{OP} = \frac{3k}{5k} = \frac{3}{5}.$$

$$\therefore \quad 4\sin^2\theta - 3\cos^2\theta + 2 = 4\times\left(\frac{4}{5}\right)^2 - 3\times\left(\frac{3}{5}\right)^2 + 2 = 4\times\frac{16}{25} - 3\times\frac{9}{25} + 2$$

$$= \frac{64 - 27 + 50}{25} = \frac{87}{25} = 3\frac{12}{25}.$$

Example 8 If $\cot B = \dfrac{12}{5}$, prove that $\tan^2 B - \sin^2 B = \sin^4 B \sec^2 B.$

Solution. Draw a right angled triangle ABC, right angled at A as shown in the adjoining figure.

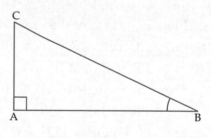

We know that $\cot B = \dfrac{AB}{AC} = \dfrac{12}{5}$ (given)

Let $AB = 12k$, then $AC = 5k$, where k is some positive real number.

By Pythagoras theorem, we get
$$BC^2 = AB^2 + AC^2 = (12k)^2 + (5k)^2 = 169k^2$$
$$\Rightarrow \qquad BC = 13k \qquad\qquad\qquad\qquad (\because BC \text{ is positive})$$

$$\therefore \quad \tan B = \frac{AC}{AB} = \frac{13k}{12k} = \frac{5}{12}, \ \sin B = \frac{AC}{BC} = \frac{5k}{13k} = \frac{5}{13} \text{ and}$$

$$\sec B = \frac{BC}{AB} = \frac{13k}{12k} = \frac{13}{12}.$$

$$\text{L.H.S.} = \tan^2 B - \sin^2 B = \left(\frac{5}{12}\right)^2 - \left(\frac{5}{13}\right)^2 = \frac{25}{144} - \frac{25}{169}$$

$$= 25\left(\frac{1}{144} - \frac{1}{169}\right) = 25\frac{169-144}{144\times169} = \frac{25\times25}{144\times169} \text{ and}$$

$$\text{R.H.S.} = \sin^4 B \sec^2 B = \left(\frac{5}{13}\right)^4 \times \left(\frac{13}{12}\right)^2 = \frac{5^4 \times 13^2}{13^4 \times 12^2}$$

$$= \frac{5^4}{13^2 \times 12^2} = \frac{25 \times 25}{169 \times 144}.$$

Hence, L.H.S. = R.H.S. *i.e.* $\tan^2 B - \sin^2 B = \sin^4 B \sec^2 B$.

Example 9 In a triangle ABC, right angled at B, if $\tan A = \dfrac{1}{\sqrt{3}}$ then find the values of:

    (*i*) $\sin A \cos C + \cos A \sin C$ (*ii*) $\cos A \cos C - \sin A \sin C$

Solution. Draw a right triangle ABC, right angled at B as shown in the figure given below.

We know that $\tan A = \dfrac{BC}{AB} = \dfrac{1}{\sqrt{3}}$ (given)

Let BC = k, then AB = $\sqrt{3}\,k$, where k is some positive real number.

In $\triangle ABC$, $\angle B = 90°$. By Pythagoras theorem, we get

$AC^2 = AB^2 + BC^2 = (\sqrt{3}\,k)^2 + k^2 = 3k^2 + k^2 = 4k^2 \Rightarrow AC = 2k$

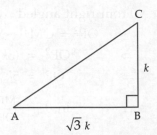

$\therefore$ $\sin A = \dfrac{BC}{AC} = \dfrac{k}{2k} = \dfrac{1}{2}$, $\cos A = \dfrac{AB}{AC} = \dfrac{\sqrt{3}k}{2k} = \dfrac{\sqrt{3}}{2}$;

      $\sin C = \dfrac{AB}{AC} = \dfrac{\sqrt{3}k}{2k} = \dfrac{\sqrt{3}}{2}$, $\cos C = \dfrac{BC}{AC} = \dfrac{k}{2k} = \dfrac{1}{2}$.

(*i*) $\sin A \cos C + \cos A \sin C = \dfrac{1}{2} \cdot \dfrac{1}{2} + \dfrac{\sqrt{3}}{2} \cdot \dfrac{\sqrt{3}}{2}$

$$= \dfrac{1}{4} + \dfrac{3}{4} = \dfrac{1+3}{4} = \dfrac{4}{4} = 1.$$

(*ii*) $\cos A \cos C - \sin A \sin C = \dfrac{\sqrt{3}}{2} \cdot \dfrac{1}{2} - \dfrac{1}{2} \cdot \dfrac{\sqrt{3}}{2} = \dfrac{\sqrt{3}}{4} - \dfrac{\sqrt{3}}{4} = 0.$

Example 10 In the adjoining figure, PQR is a right-angled triangle, right-angled at Q. If QR = 5 cm and PR − PQ = 1 cm, then find the values of sin P and sec P.

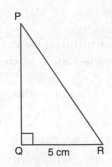

Solution. Given, QR = 5 cm and PR − PQ = 1 cm

$\Rightarrow$ PR = (1 + PQ) cm.

From right-angled $\triangle PQR$, by Pythagoras theorem, we get

    $PR^2 = PQ^2 + QR^2$

$\Rightarrow$ $(1 + PQ)^2 = PQ^2 + 5^2$

$\Rightarrow$ $1 + PQ^2 + 2PQ = PQ^2 + 25$

$\Rightarrow$ $2PQ = 25 - 1 \Rightarrow 2PQ = 24 \Rightarrow PQ = 12$ cm.

$\therefore$ PR = (1 + 12) cm = 13 cm

$\therefore$ $\sin P = \dfrac{QP}{PR} = \dfrac{5}{13}$ and $\sec P = \dfrac{PR}{PQ} = \dfrac{13}{12}$.

Example 11 In $\triangle PQR$, right angled at Q, PQ = 5 cm and PR + QR = 25 cm. Find the values of sin P, cos P and tan P.

Solution. Given PR + QR = 25 cm $\Rightarrow$ QR = (25 − PR) cm.

In $\triangle PQR$, $\angle Q = 90°$. By Pythagoras Theorem,

    $PR^2 = PQ^2 + QR^2$

$\Rightarrow \quad PR^2 = 5^2 + (25 - PR)^2$

$\Rightarrow \quad PR^2 = 25 + 625 - 50\ PR + PR^2$

$\Rightarrow \quad 50\ PR = 650 \Rightarrow PR = 13\ cm$

$\therefore \quad QR = (25 - 13)\ cm = 12\ cm.$

$\therefore \quad \sin P = \dfrac{QR}{PR} = \dfrac{12}{13},\ \cos P = \dfrac{PQ}{PR} = \dfrac{5}{13}$

and $\tan P = \dfrac{QR}{PQ} = \dfrac{12}{5}.$

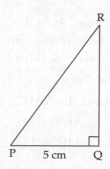

Example 12 If $\sin \theta = \dfrac{\sqrt{3}}{2}$ and $\cos \phi = \dfrac{1}{\sqrt{2}}$, find the value of $\dfrac{\tan \theta - \tan \phi}{1 + \tan \theta \tan \phi}$

(where θ and ϕ are acute).

Solution. We know that $\sin^2 \theta + \cos^2 \theta = 1$

$\Rightarrow \quad \cos^2 \theta = 1 - \sin^2 \theta = 1 - \left(\dfrac{\sqrt{3}}{2}\right) = 1 - \dfrac{3}{4} = \dfrac{1}{4}$

$\Rightarrow \quad \cos \theta = \dfrac{1}{2}$ \qquad\qquad ($\because \theta$ is acute, so $\cos \theta$ is +ve)

$\therefore \quad \tan \theta = \dfrac{\sin \theta}{\cos \theta} = \dfrac{\sqrt{3}}{2} \times \dfrac{2}{1} = \sqrt{3}.$

Also we know that $\sin^2 \phi + \cos^2 \phi = 1$

$\Rightarrow \quad \sin^2 \phi = 1 - \cos^2 \phi = 1 - \left(\dfrac{1}{\sqrt{2}}\right)^2 = 1 - \dfrac{1}{2} = \dfrac{1}{2}$

$\Rightarrow \quad \sin \phi = \dfrac{1}{\sqrt{2}}.$ \qquad\qquad ($\because \phi$ is acute, so $\sin \phi$ is +ve)

$\therefore \quad \tan \phi = \dfrac{\sin \phi}{\cos \phi} = \dfrac{1}{\sqrt{2}} \times \dfrac{\sqrt{2}}{1} = 1.$

$\therefore \quad \dfrac{\tan \theta - \tan \phi}{1 + \tan \theta \tan \phi} = \dfrac{\sqrt{3} - 1}{1 + \sqrt{3} \times 1} = \dfrac{\sqrt{3} - 1}{\sqrt{3} + 1} = \dfrac{\sqrt{3} - 1}{\sqrt{3} + 1} \times \dfrac{\sqrt{3} - 1}{\sqrt{3} - 1}$

$\qquad\qquad = \dfrac{(\sqrt{3} - 1)^2}{(\sqrt{3})^2 - 1^2} = \dfrac{3 + 1 - 2\sqrt{3}}{3 - 1} = \dfrac{4 - 2\sqrt{3}}{2} = 2 - \sqrt{3}.$

Example 13 From the adjoining figure, find

(i) $\sin x$ \qquad (ii) $\cos y$.

Solution. (i) From right-angled $\triangle BCD$, by
Pythagoras theorem, we get

$\qquad\qquad BD^2 = BC^2 + CD^2$

$\Rightarrow \qquad\qquad BD^2 = 4^2 + 3^2 = 16 + 9 = 25$

$\Rightarrow \qquad\qquad BD = 5.$

$\therefore \qquad\qquad \sin x = \dfrac{height}{hypotenuse} = \dfrac{4}{5}.$

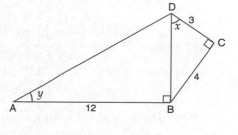

(ii) From right-angled $\triangle ABD$, by Pythagoras theorem, we get

$\qquad\qquad AD^2 = AB^2 + BD^2$

$\Rightarrow \qquad\qquad AD^2 = (12)^2 + 5^2 = 144 + 25 = 169 \Rightarrow AD = 13.$

$\therefore \qquad\qquad \cos y = \dfrac{base}{hypotenuse} = \dfrac{12}{13}.$

Example 14 In the adjoining figure, $\triangle ABC$ is right-angled at B, D is mid-point of BC, AC = 5 units, BC = 4 units and $\angle BAD = \theta$, find the values of:

    (i) $\tan \theta$ *(ii)* $\sin \theta$ *(iii)* $\sin^2 \theta + \cos^2 \theta$.

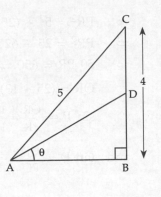

Solution. In $\triangle ABC$, $\angle B = 90°$.

$\therefore$ $AC^2 = AB^2 + BC^2 \Rightarrow 5^2 = AB^2 + 4^2$

$\Rightarrow$ $AB^2 = 25 - 16 = 9 \Rightarrow AB = 3$ units

As D is mid-point of BC, $BD = \dfrac{1}{2} BC = \left(\dfrac{1}{2} \times 4\right)$ units = 2 units.

In $\triangle ABD$, $\angle B = 90°$.

$\therefore$ $AD^2 = AB^2 + BD^2 \Rightarrow AD^2 = 3^2 + 2^2 = 13$

$\Rightarrow$ $AD = \sqrt{13}$ units.

     (i) $\tan \theta = \dfrac{BD}{AB} = \dfrac{2}{3}$.

     (ii) $\sin \theta = \dfrac{BD}{AD} = \dfrac{2}{\sqrt{13}}$.

     (iii) $\cos \theta = \dfrac{AB}{AD} = \dfrac{3}{\sqrt{13}}$,

$$\sin^2 \theta + \cos^2 \theta = \left(\dfrac{2}{\sqrt{13}}\right)^2 + \left(\dfrac{3}{\sqrt{13}}\right)^2 = \dfrac{4}{13} + \dfrac{9}{13} = 1.$$

Example 15 If $5 \tan \theta = 4$, find the value of $\dfrac{5\sin\theta - 3\cos\theta}{5\sin\theta + 2\cos\theta}$.

Solution. Given $5 \tan \theta = 4 \Rightarrow \tan \theta = \dfrac{4}{5}$ ... *(i)*

Now $\dfrac{5\sin\theta - 3\cos\theta}{5\sin\theta + 2\cos\theta} = \dfrac{5\dfrac{\sin\theta}{\cos\theta} - 3\dfrac{\cos\theta}{\cos\theta}}{5\dfrac{\sin\theta}{\cos\theta} + 2\dfrac{\cos\theta}{\cos\theta}}$

                         (Dividing the numerator and denominator by $\cos \theta$)

     $= \dfrac{5\tan\theta - 3}{5\tan\theta + 2}$ $\left(\because \tan\theta = \dfrac{\sin\theta}{\cos\theta}\right)$

     $= \dfrac{5.\dfrac{4}{5} - 3}{5.\dfrac{4}{5} + 2}$ (using *(i)*)

     $= \dfrac{4 - 3}{4 + 2} = \dfrac{1}{6}$.

Example 16 In the adjoining figure, $\triangle ABC$ is right-angled at B and $\tan A = \dfrac{4}{3}$. If AC = 15 cm, find the lengths of AB and BC.

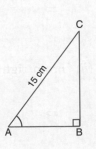

Solution. Given $\tan A = \dfrac{4}{3} \Rightarrow \dfrac{BC}{AB} = \dfrac{4}{3}$.

Let BC = $4x$ cm, then AB = $3x$ cm.

From right-angled $\triangle ABC$, by Pythagoras theorem, we get

     $AB^2 + BC^2 = AC^2 \Rightarrow (3x)^2 + (4x)^2 = 15^2$

$\Rightarrow \quad 9x^2 + 16x^2 = 225 \Rightarrow 25\, x^2 = 225$

$\Rightarrow \quad x^2 = 9 \Rightarrow x = 3.$

$\therefore \quad$ AB $= 3x$ cm $\Rightarrow (3 \times 3)$ cm $= 9$ cm and BC $= 4x$ cm $\Rightarrow (4 \times 3)$ cm $= 12$ cm.

Example 17 In the adjoining figure, AM is perpendicular to

BC. If tan B $= \dfrac{3}{4}$, tan C $= \dfrac{5}{12}$ and BC $= 56$ cm, calculate

the length of AM.

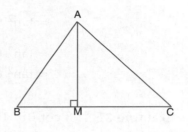

Solution. Given $\tan B = \dfrac{3}{4} \Rightarrow \dfrac{AM}{BM} = \dfrac{3}{4}.$

Let AM $= 3x$ cm, then BM $= 4x$ cm.

$\therefore \quad$ MC $=$ BC $-$ BM $= (56 - 4x)$ cm.

Also $\tan C = \dfrac{5}{12}$ (given) $\Rightarrow \dfrac{AM}{MC} = \dfrac{5}{12}$

$\Rightarrow \quad \dfrac{3x}{56 - 4x} = \dfrac{5}{12} \Rightarrow 36\,x = 280 - 20\,x$

$\Rightarrow \quad 56\,x = 280 \Rightarrow x = 5.$

$\therefore \quad$ AM $= 3x$ cm $= (3 \times 5)$ cm $= 15$ cm.

Example 18 ABCD is a rhombus whose diagonal AC makes an angle α with AB. If

$\cos \alpha = \dfrac{2}{3}$ and OB $= 3$ cm, then find the side and the diagonals of the rhombus.

Solution. We know that the diagonals of a rhombus bisects
each other at right angles.

From right-angled triangle OAB,

$$\cos \alpha = \frac{OA}{AB} = \frac{2}{3} \quad \text{(given).}$$

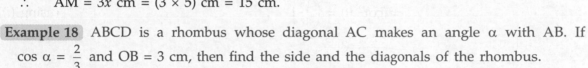

Let OA $= 2x$ cm , then AB $= 3x$ cm.

By Pythagoras theorem, AB$^2 =$ OA$^2 +$ OB^2

$\Rightarrow \quad (3x)^2 = (2x)^2 + 3^2 \Rightarrow 9x^2 = 4x^2 + 9$

$\Rightarrow \quad 5x^2 = 9 \Rightarrow x = \dfrac{3}{\sqrt{5}}.$

$\therefore \quad$ AB $= 3 \times \dfrac{3}{\sqrt{5}}$ cm $= \dfrac{9}{\sqrt{5}}$ cm and OA $= 2 \times \dfrac{3}{\sqrt{5}}$ cm $= \dfrac{6}{\sqrt{5}}$ cm.

$\therefore \quad$ BD $= 2 \times$ OB $= (2 \times 3)$ cm $= 6$ cm and AC $= 2 \times$ OA $= \left(2 \times \dfrac{6}{\sqrt{5}}\right)$ cm $= \dfrac{12}{\sqrt{5}}$ cm.

$\therefore \quad$ Each side $= \dfrac{9}{\sqrt{5}}$ cm, diagonal BD $= 6$ cm and diagonal AC $= \dfrac{12}{\sqrt{5}}$ cm.

Example 19 If tan $x +$ cot $x = 2$, find the value of tan^2 $x +$ cot^2 x.

Solution. Given $\tan x + \cot x = 2$, on squaring both sides, we get

$(\tan x + \cot x)^2 = 2^2$

$\Rightarrow \quad \tan^2 x + \cot^2 x + 2 \tan x \times \cot x = 4$

$\Rightarrow \quad \tan^2 x + \cot^2 x + 2 \times \tan x \times \dfrac{1}{\tan x} = 4 \qquad \left(\because \cot x = \dfrac{1}{\tan x} \right)$

$\Rightarrow \quad \tan^2 x + \cot^2 x + 2 = 4$

$\Rightarrow \quad \tan^2 x + \cot^2 x = 4 - 2$

$\Rightarrow \quad \tan^2 x + \cot^2 x = 2.$

Example 20 Prove that $\tan^2\theta - \dfrac{1}{\cos^2\theta} + 1 = 0$.

Solution.   L.H.S. $= \tan^2\theta - \dfrac{1}{\cos^2\theta} + 1$

$= \tan^2\theta - \sec^2\theta + 1$ $\left(\because \dfrac{1}{\cos\theta} = \sec\theta\right)$

$= \tan^2\theta - (1 + \tan^2\theta) + 1$ $(\because \sec^2\theta = 1 + \tan^2\theta)$

$= \tan^2\theta - 1 - \tan^2\theta + 1 = 0 = $ R.H.S.

Example 21 If $8\cot\theta = 15$, find the value of $\dfrac{(2 + 2\sin\theta)(1 - \sin\theta)}{(1 + \cos\theta)(2 - 2\cos\theta)}$.

Solution. Given $8\cot\theta = 15 \Rightarrow \cot\theta = \dfrac{15}{8}$ ...(i)

Now $\dfrac{(2 + 2\sin\theta)(1 - \sin\theta)}{(1 + \cos\theta)(2 - 2\cos\theta)} = \dfrac{2(1 + \sin\theta)(1 - \sin\theta)}{2(1 + \cos\theta)(1 - \cos\theta)}$

$= \dfrac{1 - \sin^2\theta}{1 - \cos^2\theta} = \dfrac{\cos^2\theta}{\sin^2\theta} = \left(\dfrac{\cos\theta}{\sin\theta}\right)^2$

$= (\cot^2\theta) = \left(\dfrac{15}{8}\right)^2$ (using (i))

$= \dfrac{225}{64} = 3\dfrac{33}{64}$.

Example 22 If $\tan\theta = \dfrac{1}{\sqrt{5}}$, find the value of $\dfrac{\csc^2\theta - \sec^2\theta}{\csc^2\theta + \sec^2\theta}$.

Solution. Given $\tan\theta = \dfrac{1}{\sqrt{5}} \Rightarrow \cot\theta = \sqrt{5}$.

Now $\sec^2\theta = 1 + \tan^2\theta = 1 + \left(\dfrac{1}{\sqrt{5}}\right)^2 = 1 + \dfrac{1}{5} = \dfrac{6}{5}$ and

$\csc^2\theta = 1 + \cot^2\theta = 1 + (\sqrt{5})^2 = 1 + 5 = 6$.

$\therefore$ $\dfrac{\csc^2\theta - \sec^2\theta}{\csc^2\theta + \sin^2\theta} = \dfrac{6 - \dfrac{6}{5}}{6 + \dfrac{6}{5}} = \dfrac{30 - 6}{30 + 6} = \dfrac{24}{36} = \dfrac{2}{3}$.

EXERCISE 17

1   (a) From the figure (1) given below, find the values of:

(i) $\sin\theta$ (ii) $\cos\theta$ (iii) $\tan\theta$ (iv) $\cot\theta$ (v) $\sec\theta$ (vi) $\csc\theta$.

(b) From the figure (2) given below, find the values of:

(i) $\sin A$ (ii) $\cos A$ (iii) $\sin^2 A + \cos^2 A$ (iv) $\sec^2 A - \tan^2 A$.

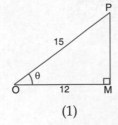

(1)

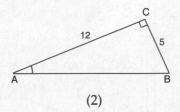

(2)

2   (a) From the figure (1) given below, find the values of:

(i) $\sin B$ (ii) $\cos C$ (iii) $\sin B + \sin C$ (iv) $\sin B \cos C + \sin C \cos B$.

(b) From the figure (2) given below, find the values of:

(i) $\tan x$ (ii) $\cos y$ (iii) $\operatorname{cosec}^2 y - \cot^2 y$ (iv) $\dfrac{5}{\sin x} + \dfrac{3}{\sin y} - 3\cot y$.

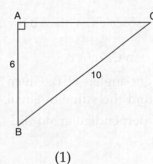

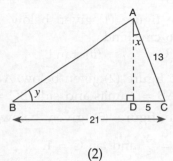

(1)   (2)

3   (a) From the figure (1) given below, find the value of $\sec\theta$.

(b) From the figure (2) given below, find the values of:

(i) $\sin x$ (ii) $\cot x$ (iii) $\cot^2 x - \operatorname{cosec}^2 x$ (iv) $\sec y$ (v) $\tan^2 y - \dfrac{1}{\cos^2 y}$.

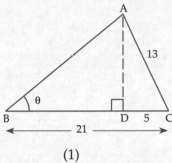

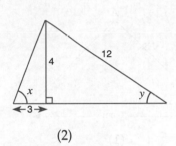

(1)   (2)

4   (a) From the figure (1) given below, find the values of:

(i) $2\sin y - \cos y$ (ii) $2\sin x - \cos x$

(iii) $1 - \sin x + \cos y$ (iv) $2\cos x - 3\sin y + 4\tan x$.

(b) In the figure (2) given below, $\triangle ABC$ is right-angled at B. If $AB = y$ units, BC = 3 units and CA = 5 units, find

(i) $\sin x°$ (ii) y.

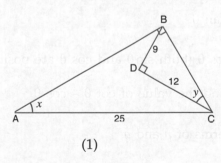

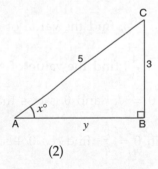

(1)   (2)

5 In a right-angled triangle, it is given that angle A is an acute angle and that $\tan A = \dfrac{5}{12}$. Find the values of:

(i) $\cos A$ (ii) $\operatorname{cosec} A - \cot A$.

6   (a) In $\triangle ABC$, $\angle A = 90°$. If $AB = 7$ cm and $BC - AC = 1$ cm, find :

(i) $\sin C$ (ii) $\tan B$

(b) In $\triangle PQR$, $\angle Q = 90°$. If $PQ = 40$ cm and $PR + QR = 50$ cm, find :

(i) $\sin P$ (ii) $\cos P$ (iii) $\tan R$.

7 In $\triangle ABC$, $AB = AC = 15$ cm, $BC = 18$ cm. Find (*i*) cos $\angle ABC$ (*ii*) sin $\angle ACB$.

Hint. Draw AD perpendicular to BC, then D is mid-point of BC, so BD = 9 cm. By Pythagoras theorem, AD = 12 cm.

8 (*a*) In the figure (1) given below, $\triangle ABC$ is isosceles with $AB = AC = 5$ cm and $BC = 6$ cm. Find

(*i*) sin C   (*ii*) tan B   (*iii*) tan C – cot B.

(*b*) In the figure (2) given below, $\triangle ABC$ is right-angled at B. Given that $\angle ACB = \theta$, side AB = 2 units and side BC = 1 unit, find the value of $\sin^2\theta + \tan^2\theta$.

(*c*) In the figure (3) given below, AD is perpendicular to BC, BD = 15 cm, $\sin B = \dfrac{4}{5}$ and $\tan C = 1$.

(*i*) Calculate the lengths of AD, AB, DC and AC.

(*ii*) Show that $\tan^2 B - \dfrac{1}{\cos^2 B} = -1$.

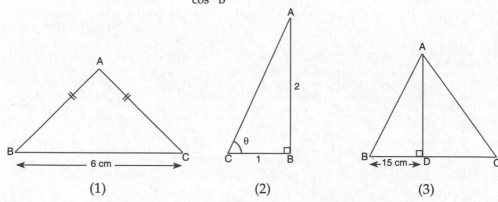

(1)   (2)   (3)

Hint. (*a*) Draw AD perpendicular to BC, then BD = DC = 3 cm and AD = 4 cm.

9 If $\sin \theta = \dfrac{3}{5}$ and θ is acute angle, find

(*i*) cos θ (*ii*) tan θ.

10 Given that $\tan \theta = \dfrac{5}{12}$ and θ is an acute angle, find sin θ and cos θ.

11 If $\sin \theta = \dfrac{6}{10}$, find the value of cos θ + tan θ.

12 If $\tan \theta = \dfrac{4}{3}$, find the value of sin θ + cos θ (both sin θ and cos θ are positive).

13 If cosec $\theta = \sqrt{5}$ and θ is less than 90°, find the value of cot θ – cos θ.

14 Given $\sin \theta = \dfrac{p}{q}$, find cos θ + sin θ in terms of p and q.

15 If θ is an acute angle and $\tan \theta = \dfrac{8}{15}$, find the value of sec θ + cosec θ.

16 Given A is an acute angle and 13 sin A = 5, evaluate :

$$\dfrac{5\sin A - 2\cos A}{\tan A}.$$

17 Given A is an acute angle and cosec A = $\sqrt{2}$, find the value of

$$\dfrac{2\sin^2 A + 3\cot^2 A}{\tan^2 A - \cos^2 A}.$$

18 The diagonals AC and BD of a rhombus ABCD meet at O. If AC = 8 cm and BD = 6 cm, find sin ∠OCD.

19 If $\tan \theta = \dfrac{5}{12}$, find the value of $\dfrac{\cos \theta + \sin \theta}{\cos \theta - \sin \theta}$.

20 Given $5 \cos A - 12 \sin A = 0$, find the value of $\dfrac{\sin A + \cos A}{2 \cos A - \sin A}$.

21 If $\tan \theta = \dfrac{p}{q}$, find the value of $\dfrac{p \sin \theta - q \cos \theta}{p \sin \theta + q \cos \theta}$.

22 If $3 \cot \theta = 4$, find the value of $\dfrac{5 \sin \theta - 3 \cos \theta}{5 \sin \theta + 3 \cos \theta}$.

23   (*i*) If $5 \cos \theta - 12 \sin \theta = 0$, find the value of $\dfrac{\sin \theta + \cos \theta}{2 \cos \theta - \sin \theta}$.

    (*ii*) If $\operatorname{cosec} \theta = \dfrac{13}{12}$, find the value of $\dfrac{2 \sin \theta - 3 \cos \theta}{4 \sin \theta - 9 \cos \theta}$.

Hint.   (*i*) $5 \cos \theta - 12 \sin \theta = 0 \Rightarrow 5 \cos \theta = 12 \sin \theta \Rightarrow \cot \theta = \dfrac{12}{5}$.

    (*ii*) $\cot^2 \theta = \operatorname{cosec}^2 \theta - 1 = \left(\dfrac{13}{12}\right)^2 - 1 = \dfrac{169}{144} - 1 = \dfrac{25}{144} \Rightarrow \cot \theta = \dfrac{5}{12}$.

24 If $5 \sin \theta = 3$, find the value of $\dfrac{\sec \theta - \tan \theta}{\sec \theta + \tan \theta}$.

25 If θ is an acute angle and $\sin \theta = \cos \theta$, find the value of
$$2 \tan^2 \theta + \sin^2 \theta - 1.$$

26 Prove the following:

(*i*) $\cos \theta \tan \theta = \sin \theta$ (*ii*) $\sin \theta \cot \theta = \cos \theta$ (*iii*) $\dfrac{\sin^2 \theta}{\cos \theta} + \cos \theta = \dfrac{1}{\cos \theta}$.

27 If in $\triangle$ ABC, $\angle C = 90°$ and $\tan A = \dfrac{3}{4}$, prove that
$$\sin A \cos B + \cos A \sin B = 1.$$

28   (*a*) In the figure (1) given below, $\triangle$ABC is right-angled at B and $\triangle$BRS is right-angled at R. If AB = 18 cm, BC = 7·5 cm, RS = 5 cm, $\angle$BSR = $x°$ and $\angle$SAB = $y°$, then find :

    (*i*) $\tan x°$ (*ii*) $\sin y°$.

   (*b*) In the figure (2) given below, $\triangle$ABC is right angled at B and BD is perpendicular to AC. Find

    (*i*) $\cos \angle$CBD   (*ii*) $\cot \angle$ABD.

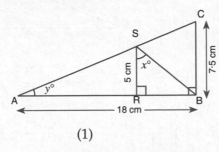
(1)

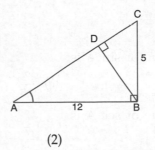
(2)

Hint.   (*a*) Δs ARS and ABC are similar,

$$\therefore \quad \frac{AR}{AB} = \frac{RS}{BC} \Rightarrow \frac{AR}{18} = \frac{5}{7·5} \Rightarrow AR = 12 \text{ cm}.$$

$$\therefore \quad RB = AB - AR = 18 \text{ cm} - 12 \text{ cm} = 6 \text{ cm}.$$

Also $AC^2 = AB^2 + BC^2 = 18^2 + (7.5)^2 = 380.25$

$\Rightarrow \quad AC = 19.5$ cm.

(b) $\angle CBD = \angle A$ and $\angle ABD = \angle C$.

29 In the adjoining figure, ABCD is a rectangle. Its diagonal AC = 15 cm and $\angle ACD = \alpha$. If $\cot \alpha = \dfrac{3}{2}$, find the perimeter and the area of the rectangle.

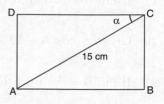
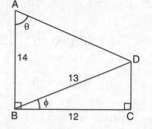

30 Using the measurements given in the figure alongside,
    (a) find the values of:
        (i) $\sin \phi$ (ii) $\tan \theta$.
    (b) write an expression for AD in terms of θ.
Hint. (b) CD = 5. Draw DE perpendicular to
           AB, BE = 5, EA = 9.

31 Prove the following :
    (i) $(\sin A + \cos A)^2 + (\sin A - \cos A)^2 = 2$

    (ii) $\cot^2 A - \dfrac{1}{\sin^2 A} + 1 = 0$

    (iii) $\dfrac{1}{1 + \tan^2 A} + \dfrac{1}{1 + \cot^2 A} = 1$

32 Simplify $\sqrt{\dfrac{1 - \sin^2 \theta}{1 - \cos^2 \theta}}$.

33 If $\sin \theta + \text{cosec } \theta = 2$, find the value of $\sin^2 \theta + \text{cosec}^2 \theta$.

34 If $x = a \cos \theta + b \sin \theta$ and $y = a \sin \theta - b \cos \theta$, prove that $x^2 + y^2 = a^2 + b^2$.
    Hint. Square and add. Use $\sin^2 \theta + \cos^2 \theta = 1$.

Multiple Choice Questions

Choose the correct answer from the given four options (1 to 13):

In the adjoining figure, ABC is a right angled triangle right angled at B; AB = 24 cm and BC = 7 cm. Using the figure answer (1 to 6) questions:

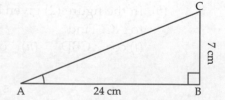

1 The value of sin A is
    (a) $\dfrac{7}{24}$ (b) $\dfrac{7}{25}$ (c) $\dfrac{25}{7}$ (d) $\dfrac{24}{25}$

2 The value of sec A is
    (a) $\dfrac{24}{7}$ (b) $\dfrac{7}{24}$ (c) $\dfrac{25}{24}$ (d) $\dfrac{25}{7}$

3 The value of tan C is
    (a) $\dfrac{24}{7}$ (b) $\dfrac{7}{24}$ (c) $\dfrac{7}{25}$ (d) $\dfrac{24}{25}$

4 The value of cosec C is

(a) $\dfrac{7}{24}$　　　　　(b) $\dfrac{24}{25}$　　　　　(c) $\dfrac{25}{7}$　　　　　(d) $\dfrac{25}{24}$

5 The value of tan A + cot C is

(a) $\dfrac{7}{12}$　　　　　(b) $\dfrac{12}{7}$　　　　　(c) $\dfrac{14}{25}$　　　　　(d) $\dfrac{25}{12}$

6 The value of 2 cos A − sin C is

(a) $\dfrac{25}{24}$　　　　　(b) $\dfrac{24}{25}$　　　　　(c) $\dfrac{41}{25}$　　　　　(d) $\dfrac{49}{25}$

7 In the adjoining figure, the value of sin B cos C + sin C cos B is

(a) 0　　　　　(b) 1

(c) $\dfrac{5}{3}$　　　　　(d) 2

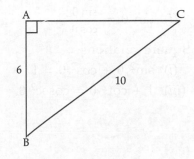

8 In the adjoining figure, the value of cos θ is

(a) $\dfrac{12}{13}$　　　　　(b) $\dfrac{13}{12}$

(c) $\dfrac{5}{12}$　　　　　(d) $\dfrac{5}{13}$

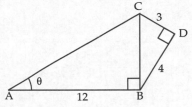

9 If cos A = $\dfrac{4}{5}$, then the value of tan A is

(a) $\dfrac{3}{5}$　　　　　(b) $\dfrac{3}{4}$　　　　　(c) $\dfrac{4}{3}$　　　　　(d) $\dfrac{5}{3}$

10 If sin A = $\dfrac{1}{2}$, then the value of cot A is

(a) $\sqrt{3}$　　　　　(b) $\dfrac{1}{\sqrt{3}}$　　　　　(c) $\dfrac{\sqrt{3}}{2}$　　　　　(d) 1

11 If cosec θ = $\dfrac{13}{12}$, then the value of tan θ is

(a) $\dfrac{12}{5}$　　　　　(b) $\dfrac{5}{12}$　　　　　(c) $\dfrac{5}{13}$　　　　　(d) $\dfrac{5}{12}$

12 If tan A = $\dfrac{x}{y}$, then cos A is equal to

(a) $\dfrac{x}{\sqrt{x^2 + y^2}}$　　　(b) $\dfrac{y}{\sqrt{x^2 + y^2}}$　　　(c) $\dfrac{x^2 - y^2}{\sqrt{x^2 + y^2}}$　　　(d) $\dfrac{x^2 - y^2}{x^2 + y^2}$

13 If sin θ = $\dfrac{a}{b}$, then cos θ is equal to

(a) $\dfrac{b}{\sqrt{b^2 - a^2}}$　　　(b) $\dfrac{b}{a}$　　　(c) $\dfrac{\sqrt{b^2 - a^2}}{b}$　　　(d) $\dfrac{a}{\sqrt{b^2 - a^2}}$

Summary

□ **Trigonometrical ratios**

Let OMP be a right angled triangle at M and $\angle MOP = \theta$ (theta), then

(i) $\sin \theta = \dfrac{\text{height}}{\text{hypotenuse}}$

(ii) $\cos \theta = \dfrac{\text{base}}{\text{hypotenuse}}$

(iii) $\tan \theta = \dfrac{\text{height}}{\text{base}}$

(iv) $\cot \theta = \dfrac{\text{base}}{\text{height}}$

(v) $\sec \theta = \dfrac{\text{hypotenuse}}{\text{base}}$

(vi) $\operatorname{cosec} \theta = \dfrac{\text{hypotenuse}}{\text{height}}$.

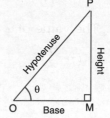

□ **Quotient relations**

(i) $\tan \theta = \dfrac{\sin \theta}{\cos \theta}$

(ii) $\cot \theta = \dfrac{\cos \theta}{\sin \theta}$.

□ **Square relations**

(i) $\sin^2 \theta + \cos^2 \theta = 1$

(ii) $1 + \tan^2 \theta = \sec^2 \theta$

(iii) $1 + \cot^2 \theta = \operatorname{cosec}^2 \theta$.

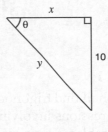

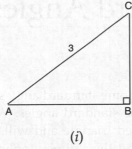

Chapter Test

1 (a) From the figure (i) given below, calculate all the six t-ratios for both acute angles.

   (b) From the figure (ii) given below, find the values of x and y in terms of t-ratios of θ.

(i)   (ii)

2 (a) From the figure (1) given below, find the values of :
   (i) sin ∠ABC   (ii) tan x – cos x + 3 sin x.

   (b) From the figure (2) given below, find the values of :
   (i) 5 sin x   (ii) 7 tan x   (iii) 5 cos x – 17 sin y – tan x.

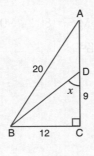

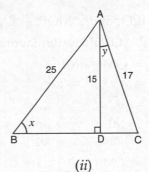

(i)   (ii)

3 If $q \cos θ = p$, find tan θ – cot θ in terms of p and q.

4 Given 4 sin θ = 3 cos θ, find the values of :
   (i) sin θ   (ii) cos θ   (iii) $\cot^2 θ - \csc^2 θ$.

5 If $2 \cos θ = \sqrt{3}$, prove that $3 \sin θ - 4 \sin^3 θ = 1$.

6 If $\dfrac{\sec θ - \tan θ}{\sec θ + \tan θ} = \dfrac{1}{4}$, find sin θ.

7 If $\sin θ + \csc θ = 3\dfrac{1}{3}$, find the value of $\sin^2 θ + \csc^2 θ$.

8 In the adjoining figure, AB = 4 m and ED = 3 m.

   If $\sin α = \dfrac{3}{5}$ and $\cos β = \dfrac{12}{13}$, find the length of BD.

   Hint. $\sin α = \dfrac{3}{5} \Rightarrow \tan α = \dfrac{3}{4}$.

   Also $\cos β = \dfrac{12}{13} \Rightarrow \tan β = \dfrac{5}{12}$.

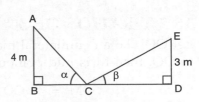

18 Trigonometrical Ratios of Standard Angles

INTRODUCTION

In this chapter, we shall find trigonometrical ratios of some standard angles and will evaluate trigonometrical expressions involving *t*-ratios of these standard angles. We shall also solve some simple 2-D problems involving one right angled triangle and will learn the concept of trigonometrical ratios of complementary angles and their direct applications.

18.1 T-RATIOS OF 45°

Let OMP be an isosceles triangle right-angled at M with sides OM = MP = a (say), then ∠MOP = 45°.

(∵ ∠MOP = ∠MPO, and ∠MOP + ∠MPO = 180° − ∠M = 180° − 90° = 90°)

From right-angled ΔOMP, by Pythagoras theorem, we get

$$OP^2 = OM^2 + MP^2$$
$$= a^2 + a^2 = 2a^2$$
$$\Rightarrow \qquad OP = \sqrt{2}\,a.$$

∴

$$\sin 45° = \frac{MP}{OP} = \frac{a}{\sqrt{2}a} = \frac{1}{\sqrt{2}},$$

$$\cos 45° = \frac{OM}{OP} = \frac{a}{\sqrt{2}a} = \frac{1}{\sqrt{2}},$$

$$\tan 45° = \frac{MP}{OM} = \frac{a}{a} = 1,$$

$$\cot 45° = \frac{OM}{MP} = \frac{a}{a} = 1,$$

$$\sec 45° = \frac{OP}{OM} = \frac{\sqrt{2}a}{a} = \sqrt{2} \text{ and}$$

$$\csc 45° = \frac{OP}{MP} = \frac{\sqrt{2}a}{a} = \sqrt{2}.$$

18.2 T-RATIOS OF 30° AND 60°

Let OQP be an equilateral triangle with each side = $2a$ (say), and let MP be perpendicular to OQ, then M is mid-point of OQ,

∴
$$OM = \frac{1}{2} OQ = \frac{1}{2} \times 2a = a.$$

Since each angle of an equilateral triangle is 60°,

∠MOP = 60° and

∠OPM = 180° − (60° + 90°) = 30°.

From right-angled ΔOMP, by Pythagoras theorem, we get

$$OP^2 = OM^2 + MP^2$$

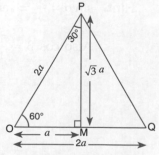

$$\Rightarrow \qquad MP^2 = OP^2 - OM^2 = (2a)^2 - a^2 = 4a^2 - a^2 = 3a^2$$
$$\Rightarrow \qquad MP = \sqrt{3}\,a.$$

(i) T-ratios of 30°.

In $\triangle OMP$, $\angle OMP = 90°$, $\angle MPO = 30°$, height = $OM = a$, base = $MP = \sqrt{3}\,a$ and hypotenuse = $OP = 2a$.

$$\therefore \qquad \sin 30° = \frac{\text{height}}{\text{hypotenuse}} = \frac{OM}{OP} = \frac{a}{2a} = \frac{1}{2},$$

$$\cos 30° = \frac{\text{base}}{\text{hypotenuse}} = \frac{MP}{OP} = \frac{\sqrt{3}a}{2a} = \frac{\sqrt{3}}{2},$$

$$\tan 30° = \frac{\text{height}}{\text{base}} = \frac{OM}{MP} = \frac{a}{\sqrt{3}a} = \frac{1}{\sqrt{3}},$$

$$\cot 30° = \frac{\text{base}}{\text{height}} = \frac{MP}{OM} = \frac{\sqrt{3}a}{a} = \sqrt{3},$$

$$\sec 30° = \frac{\text{hypotenuse}}{\text{base}} = \frac{OP}{MP} = \frac{2a}{\sqrt{3}a} = \frac{2}{\sqrt{3}} \quad \text{and}$$

$$\text{cosec}\ 30° = \frac{\text{hypotenuse}}{\text{height}} = \frac{OP}{OM} = \frac{2a}{a} = 2.$$

(ii) T-ratios of 60°.

In $\triangle OMP$, $\angle OMP = 90°$, $\angle MOP = 60°$, height = $MP = \sqrt{3}\,a$, base = $OM = a$ and hypotenuse = $OP = 2a$.

$$\therefore \qquad \sin 60° = \frac{\text{height}}{\text{hypotenuse}} = \frac{MP}{OP} = \frac{\sqrt{3}a}{2a} = \frac{\sqrt{3}}{2},$$

$$\cos 60° = \frac{\text{base}}{\text{hypotenuse}} = \frac{OM}{OP} = \frac{a}{2a} = \frac{1}{2},$$

$$\tan 60° = \frac{\text{height}}{\text{base}} = \frac{MP}{OM} = \frac{\sqrt{3}a}{a} = \sqrt{3},$$

$$\cot 60° = \frac{\text{base}}{\text{height}} = \frac{OM}{MP} = \frac{a}{\sqrt{3}a} = \frac{1}{\sqrt{3}},$$

$$\sec 60° = \frac{\text{hypotenuse}}{\text{base}} = \frac{OP}{OM} = \frac{2a}{a} = 2 \quad \text{and}$$

$$\text{cosec}\ 60° = \frac{\text{hypotenuse}}{\text{height}} = \frac{OP}{MP} = \frac{2a}{\sqrt{3}a} = \frac{2}{\sqrt{3}}.$$

18.3 T-RATIOS OF 0° AND 90°

Consider the arc APB of a circle with centre at O and radius = a (shown in the adjoining figure).

Let P (x, y) be any point on this arc. Draw MP perpendicular to OX, then OM = x, MP = y and OP = a. Let $\angle MOP = \theta$, then

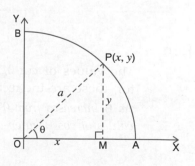

$$\sin \theta = \frac{y}{a}, \cos \theta = \frac{x}{a}, \tan \theta = \frac{y}{x},$$

$$\cot \theta = \frac{x}{y}, \sec \theta = \frac{a}{x}, \text{cosec}\ \theta = \frac{a}{y}.$$

(i) *T-ratios of 0°.*

When θ = 0°, P coincides with A so that $x = a$ and $y = 0$.

∴ $\sin 0° = \dfrac{0}{a} = 0$, $\cos 0° = \dfrac{a}{a} = 1$,

     $\tan 0° = \dfrac{0}{a} = 0$, $\cot 0° = \dfrac{a}{0}$, which is not defined,

     $\sec 0° = \dfrac{a}{a} = 1$, $\text{cosec } 0° = \dfrac{a}{0}$, which is not defined.

(ii) *T-ratios of 90°.*

When θ = 90°, P coincides with B so that $x = 0$ and $y = a$.

∴ $\sin 90° = \dfrac{a}{a} = 1$, $\cos 90° = \dfrac{0}{a} = 0$,

     $\tan 90° = \dfrac{a}{0}$, which is not defined, $\cot 90° = \dfrac{0}{a} = 0$,

     $\sec 90° = \dfrac{a}{0}$, which is not defined, $\text{cosec } 90° = \dfrac{a}{a} = 1$.

18.4 AID TO MEMORY

Trigonometrical ratios of 0°, 30°, 45°, 60° and 90° are given in the following table for ready reference:

Angle θ → Ratio ↓	0°	30°	45°	60°	90°
sin θ	0	$\dfrac{1}{2}$	$\dfrac{1}{\sqrt{2}}$	$\dfrac{\sqrt{3}}{2}$	1
cos θ	1	$\dfrac{\sqrt{3}}{2}$	$\dfrac{1}{\sqrt{2}}$	$\dfrac{1}{2}$	0
tan θ	0	$\dfrac{1}{\sqrt{3}}$	1	$\sqrt{3}$	not defined
cot θ	not defined	$\sqrt{3}$	1	$\dfrac{1}{\sqrt{3}}$	0
sec θ	1	$\dfrac{2}{\sqrt{3}}$	$\sqrt{2}$	2	not defined
cosec θ	not defined	2	$\sqrt{2}$	$\dfrac{2}{\sqrt{3}}$	1

Remarks

    * The values of cot θ, sec θ and cosec θ have not been written in the above table, for, these are the reciprocals of the values of tan θ, cos θ and sin θ respectively.

    * *As θ increases from 0° to 90°, the values of sin θ and tan θ go on increasing while the values of cos θ go on decreasing.*

18.5 EVALUATION OF TRIGONOMETRICAL EXPRESSIONS INVOLVING T-RATIOS OF THE STANDARD ANGLES

Illustrative Examples

Example 1 Find the value of

$$(\cos 0° + \sin 45° + \sin 30°)(\sin 90° - \cos 45° + \cos 60°).$$

Solution. $(\cos 0° + \sin 45° + \sin 30°)(\sin 90° - \cos 45° + \cos 60°)$

$$= \left(1 + \frac{1}{\sqrt{2}} + \frac{1}{2}\right)\left(1 - \frac{1}{\sqrt{2}} + \frac{1}{2}\right) = \left(\frac{3}{2} + \frac{1}{\sqrt{2}}\right)\left(\frac{3}{2} - \frac{1}{\sqrt{2}}\right)$$

$$= \left(\frac{3}{2}\right)^2 - \left(\frac{1}{\sqrt{2}}\right)^2 \qquad\qquad [\because (a+b)(a-b) = a^2 - b^2]$$

$$= \frac{9}{4} - \frac{1}{2} = \frac{9-2}{4} = \frac{7}{4} = 1\frac{3}{4}.$$

Example 2 Find the value of

$$\sin^2 30° \cos^2 45° + 4\tan^2 30° + \frac{1}{2}\sin^2 90° - 2\cos 90° + \frac{1}{24}.$$

Solution. $\sin^2 30° \cos^2 45° + 4\tan^2 30° + \frac{1}{2}\sin^2 90° - 2\cos 90° + \frac{1}{24}$

$$= \left(\frac{1}{2}\right)^2 \times \left(\frac{1}{\sqrt{2}}\right)^2 + 4 \times \left(\frac{1}{\sqrt{3}}\right)^2 + \frac{1}{2} \times (1)^2 - 2 \times 0 + \frac{1}{24}$$

$$= \frac{1}{4} \times \frac{1}{2} + 4 \times \frac{1}{3} + \frac{1}{2} \times 1 - 0 + \frac{1}{24} = \frac{1}{8} + \frac{4}{3} + \frac{1}{2} + \frac{1}{24}$$

$$= \frac{3 + 32 + 12 + 1}{24} = \frac{48}{24} = 2.$$

Example 3 Prove that: $(\sqrt{3} + 1)(3 - \cot 30°) = \tan^3 60° - 2\sin 60°.$

Solution. L.H.S. $= (\sqrt{3} + 1)(3 - \cot 30°)$

$$= (\sqrt{3} + 1)(3 - \sqrt{3}) = (\sqrt{3} + 1)\sqrt{3}(\sqrt{3} - 1)$$

$$= \sqrt{3}(\sqrt{3} + 1)(\sqrt{3} - 1) = \sqrt{3}((\sqrt{3})^2 - 1^2)$$

$$= \sqrt{3}(3 - 1) = 2\sqrt{3} \text{ and}$$

R.H.S. $= \tan^3 60° - 2\sin 60° = (\sqrt{3})^3 - 2.\frac{\sqrt{3}}{2}$

$$= 3\sqrt{3} - \sqrt{3} = 2\sqrt{3}.$$

Hence, $(\sqrt{3} + 1)(3 - \cot 30°) = \tan^3 60° - 2\sin 60°.$

Example 4 Show that: $\dfrac{2\tan 30°}{1 + \tan^2 30°} = \sin 60°.$

Solution. $\dfrac{2\tan 30°}{1 + \tan^2 30°} = \dfrac{2.\dfrac{1}{\sqrt{3}}}{1 + \left(\dfrac{1}{\sqrt{3}}\right)^2} = \dfrac{\dfrac{2}{\sqrt{3}}}{1 + \dfrac{1}{3}}$

$$= \dfrac{\dfrac{2}{\sqrt{3}}}{\dfrac{4}{3}} = \frac{2}{\sqrt{3}} \times \frac{3}{4} = \frac{\sqrt{3}}{2} = \sin 60°.$$

Example 5 Evaluate: $\dfrac{3\sin 3A + 2\cos(5A + 10°)}{\sqrt{3}\tan 3A - \mathrm{cosec}(5A - 20°)}$ when A = 10°.

Solution. When A = 10°,

$$\dfrac{3\sin 3A + 2\cos(5A + 10°)}{\sqrt{3}\tan 3A - \mathrm{cosec}(5A - 20°)} = \dfrac{3\sin 30° + 2\cos 60°}{\sqrt{3}\tan 30° - \mathrm{cosec}\ 30°}$$

$$= \dfrac{3\left(\dfrac{1}{2}\right) + 2\left(\dfrac{1}{2}\right)}{\sqrt{3}\left(\dfrac{1}{\sqrt{3}}\right) - 2} = \dfrac{\dfrac{3}{2} + 1}{1 - 2} = \dfrac{\dfrac{5}{2}}{-1} = -\dfrac{5}{2}.$$

Example 6 If 3θ is an acute angle and $\tan 3\theta - \sqrt{3} = 0$, find the value of θ.

Solution. Given $\tan 3\theta - \sqrt{3} = 0 \Rightarrow \tan 3\theta = \sqrt{3}$

$\Rightarrow \quad \tan 3\theta = \tan 60° \Rightarrow 3\theta = 60°$

$\Rightarrow \quad \theta = 20°.$

Hence, the value of θ is 20°.

Example 7 If $40° + x$ is an acute angle and $\cos(40° + x) = \sin 30°$, find the value of x.

Solution. Given $\cos(40° + x) = \sin 30° \Rightarrow \cos(40° + x) = \dfrac{1}{2}$

$\Rightarrow \quad \cos(40° + x) = \cos 60° \Rightarrow 40° + x = 60°$

$\Rightarrow \quad x = 60° - 40° \Rightarrow x = 20°.$

Hence, the value of x is 20°.

Example 8 If θ is an acute angle and $2\sin\theta = 1$, then find the value of θ and hence find the value of $4\sin^3\theta - 3\sin\theta$.

Solution. Given $2\sin\theta = 1 \Rightarrow \sin\theta = \dfrac{1}{2} \Rightarrow \theta = 30°$;

$$4\sin^3\theta - 3\sin\theta = \sin\theta\,(4\sin^2\theta - 3) = \sin 30°\,(4\sin^2 30° - 3)$$

$$= \dfrac{1}{2}\left(4 \cdot \left(\dfrac{1}{2}\right)^2 - 3\right) = \dfrac{1}{2}(1 - 3) = -1.$$

Example 9 If $2\sin(3x - 15)° = \sqrt{3}$, then find the value of $\sin^2(2x + 10)° + \tan^2(x + 5)°$.

Solution. Given $2\sin(3x - 15)° = \sqrt{3}$

$\Rightarrow \quad \sin(3x - 15)° = \dfrac{\sqrt{3}}{2} \Rightarrow \sin(3x - 15)° = \sin 60°$

$\Rightarrow \quad 3x - 15 = 60 \Rightarrow 3x = 75 \Rightarrow x = 25.$

$\therefore \quad \sin^2(2x + 10)° + \tan^2(x + 5)° = \sin^2 60° + \tan^2 30°$

$$= \left(\dfrac{\sqrt{3}}{2}\right)^2 + \left(\dfrac{1}{\sqrt{3}}\right)^2 = \dfrac{3}{4} + \dfrac{1}{3} = \dfrac{9 + 4}{12} = \dfrac{13}{12}.$$

Example 10 If $4\sin^2\theta - 1 = 0$ and θ is acute angle, find the value of θ and hence find the values of (i) $\cos^2\theta + \tan^2\theta$ (ii) $\cos 2\theta$ (iii) $\sin 3\theta$.

Solution. Given $4\sin^2\theta - 1 = 0$

$\Rightarrow \quad 4\sin^2\theta = 1 \quad \Rightarrow \quad \sin^2\theta = \dfrac{1}{4}$

$\Rightarrow \quad \sin\theta = \dfrac{1}{2} \qquad\qquad (\because \theta \text{ is acute angle, } \sin\theta \text{ is positive})$

$\Rightarrow$ $\qquad \sin \theta = \sin 30°$ $\qquad\qquad\qquad\qquad\qquad\qquad \left(\because \sin 30° = \dfrac{1}{2} \right)$

$\Rightarrow$ $\qquad\quad \theta = 30°.$

(i) $\cos^2 \theta + \tan^2 \theta = \cos^2 30° + \tan^2 30°$

$$= \left(\frac{\sqrt{3}}{2} \right)^2 + \left(\frac{1}{\sqrt{3}} \right)^2 = \frac{3}{4} + \frac{1}{3} = \frac{9+4}{12} = \frac{13}{12} = 1\frac{1}{12} .$$

(ii) $\qquad\qquad 2\theta = (2 \times 30)° = 60°.$

$\therefore \qquad \cos 2\theta = \cos 60° = \dfrac{1}{2} .$

(iii) $\qquad\qquad 3\theta = (3 \times 30)° = 90°.$

$\therefore \qquad \sin 3\theta = \sin 90° = 1.$

Example 11 If θ is an acute angle and $\sin \theta = \cos \theta$, find the value of

$2 \sin^2 \theta - 3 \cos^2 \theta + \dfrac{1}{2} \cot^2 \theta.$

Solution. Given, $\sin \theta = \cos \theta$

$\Rightarrow \qquad \dfrac{\sin \theta}{\cos \theta} = 1 \Rightarrow \tan \theta = 1$

$\Rightarrow \qquad \tan \theta = \tan 45°$ $\qquad\qquad\qquad\qquad\qquad\qquad (\because \tan 45° = 1)$

$\Rightarrow \qquad \theta = 45°.$

$\therefore \qquad 2 \sin^2 \theta - 3 \cos^2 \theta + \dfrac{1}{2} \cot^2 \theta = 2 \sin^2 45° - 3 \cos^2 45 + \dfrac{1}{2} \cot^2 45°$

$$= 2 \left(\frac{1}{\sqrt{2}} \right)^2 - 3 \left(\frac{1}{\sqrt{2}} \right)^2 + \frac{1}{2} (1)^2$$

$$= 2 \times \frac{1}{2} - 3 \times \frac{1}{2} + \frac{1}{2} \times 1 = 1 - \frac{3}{2} + \frac{1}{2} = 0.$$

Example 12 If θ is an acute angle and $\dfrac{\cos\theta + \sin\theta}{\cos\theta - \sin\theta} = \dfrac{1+\sqrt{3}}{1-\sqrt{3}}$, find the value of

$2 \sec^2 \theta - 3 \csc^2 \theta.$

Solution. Given, $\dfrac{\cos \theta + \sin \theta}{\cos \theta - \sin \theta} = \dfrac{1+\sqrt{3}}{1-\sqrt{3}} .$

Applying componendo and dividendo, we get

$$\frac{(\cos \theta + \sin \theta) + (\cos \theta - \sin \theta)}{(\cos \theta + \sin \theta) - (\cos \theta - \sin \theta)} = \frac{(1+\sqrt{3}) + (1-\sqrt{3})}{(1+\sqrt{3}) - (1-\sqrt{3})}$$

$\Rightarrow \qquad \dfrac{2\cos\theta}{2\sin\theta} = \dfrac{2}{2\sqrt{3}} \Rightarrow \dfrac{\cos\theta}{\sin\theta} = \dfrac{1}{\sqrt{3}}$

$\Rightarrow \qquad \dfrac{\sin\theta}{\cos\theta} = \sqrt{3} \Rightarrow \tan\theta = \sqrt{3}$

$\Rightarrow \qquad \tan \theta = \tan 60°$ $\qquad\qquad\qquad\qquad\qquad\qquad (\because \tan 60° = \sqrt{3})$

$\Rightarrow \qquad \theta = 60°.$

$\therefore \qquad 2 \sec^2 \theta - 3 \csc^2 \theta = 2 \sec^2 60° - 3 \csc^2 60°$

$$= 2 (2)^2 - 3 \left(\frac{2}{\sqrt{3}} \right)^2 = 2 \times 4 - 3 \times \frac{4}{3}$$

$$= 8 - 4 = 4.$$

Example 13 If A = 60° and B = 30°, verify that

$$\cos(A - B) = \cos A \cos B + \sin A \sin B.$$

Solution.   L.H.S. = cos (A – B)

$$= \cos(60° - 30°) = \cos 30° = \frac{\sqrt{3}}{2} \text{ and }$$

R.H.S. = cos A cos B + sin A sin B

$$= \cos 60° \cos 30° + \sin 60° \sin 30°$$

$$= \frac{1}{2} \cdot \frac{\sqrt{3}}{2} + \frac{\sqrt{3}}{2} \cdot \frac{1}{2}$$

$$= \frac{\sqrt{3}}{4} + \frac{\sqrt{3}}{4} = \frac{\sqrt{3} + \sqrt{3}}{4} = \frac{2\sqrt{3}}{4} = \frac{\sqrt{3}}{2}.$$

∴   L.H.S. = R.H.S.

Hence the result.

Example 14 If cos (A + B) = $\frac{1}{2}$ = sin (A – B), 0° < A + B ≤ 90°, A > B, find the values of A and B.

Solution. Given cos (A + B) = $\frac{1}{2}$

⇒   cos (A + B) = cos 60° $\left(\because \cos 60° = \frac{1}{2} \right)$

⇒   A + B = 60°   ...(i)

Also   sin (A – B) = $\frac{1}{2}$ (given)

⇒   sin (A – B) = sin 30° $\left(\because \sin 30° = \frac{1}{2} \right)$

⇒   A – B = 30°   ...(ii)

On adding (i) and (ii), we get 2A = 90° ⇒ A = 45°.

On subtracting (ii) from (i), we get 2B = 30° ⇒ B = 15°.

Hence, A = 45° and B = 15°.

Example 15 If tan (A + B) = $\sqrt{3}$, tan (A – B) = $\frac{1}{\sqrt{3}}$, 0° < A + B < 90°, A > B, find A and B. Also calculate tan A sin (A + B) + cos A tan (A – B).

Solution. Given tan (A + B) = $\sqrt{3}$ ⇒ tan (A + B) = tan 60°

⇒   A + B = 60°   ...(i)

Also tan (A – B) = $\frac{1}{\sqrt{3}}$

⇒   tan (A – B) = tan 30°

⇒   A – B = 30°   ...(ii)

Solving (i) and (ii), we get A = 45° and B = 15°.

tan A sin (A + B) + cos A tan (A – B)

$$= \tan 45° \sin 60° + \cos 45° \tan 30°$$

$$= 1 \times \frac{\sqrt{3}}{2} + \frac{1}{\sqrt{2}} \times \frac{1}{\sqrt{3}} = \frac{\sqrt{3}}{2} + \frac{1}{\sqrt{6}}$$

$$= \frac{\sqrt{3}}{2} + \frac{\sqrt{6}}{6} = \frac{3\sqrt{3} + \sqrt{6}}{6}.$$

Example 16 In a △ABC, right angled at A, if tan C = $\sqrt{3}$, find the value of sin B cos C + cos B sin C.

Solution. From right angled △ABC, we have

$\angle A + \angle B + \angle C = 180°$

$\Rightarrow \quad 90° + \angle B + \angle C = 180°$

$\Rightarrow \quad \angle B + \angle C = 90° \qquad\qquad …(i)$

Given tan C = $\sqrt{3}$ $\Rightarrow$ tan C = tan 60° $\Rightarrow$ C = 60°.

$\therefore \quad \angle B + 60° = 90°$ \qquad (using (i))

$\Rightarrow \quad \angle B = 30°.$

sin B cos C + cos B sin C = sin 30° cos 60° + cos 30° sin 60°

$$= \frac{1}{2} \times \frac{1}{2} + \frac{\sqrt{3}}{2} \times \frac{\sqrt{3}}{2} = \frac{1}{4} + \frac{3}{4} = 1.$$

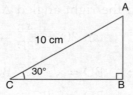

Example 17 In the right-angled triangle ABC, $\angle B = 90°$ and $\angle C = 30°$. If AC = 10 cm, find the lengths of the sides AB and BC.

Solution. In the right-angled △ABC,

$$\sin 30° = \frac{AB}{AC} \Rightarrow \frac{1}{2} = \frac{AB}{10 \text{ cm}}$$

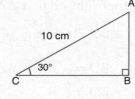

$\Rightarrow \qquad AB = \left(\frac{1}{2} \times 10\right) \text{ cm} = 5 \text{ cm.}$

$$\cos 30° = \frac{BC}{AC} \Rightarrow \frac{\sqrt{3}}{2} = \frac{BC}{10 \text{ cm}}$$

$\Rightarrow \qquad BC = \left(\frac{\sqrt{3}}{2} \times 10\right) \text{ cm} = 5\sqrt{3} \text{ cm.}$

Example 18 In the adjoining figure, PQR is a right angled triangle at Q. If PQ = 3 cm and PR = 6 cm, find $\angle QPR$ and $\angle PRQ$.

Solution. From right angled triangle PQR, we have

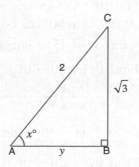

$$\cos \angle QPR = \frac{PQ}{PR} = \frac{3}{6} = \frac{1}{2} = \cos 60° \Rightarrow \angle QPR = 60°;$$

$$\sin \angle PRQ = \frac{PQ}{PR} = \frac{3}{6} = \frac{1}{2} = \sin 30° \Rightarrow \angle PRQ = 30°.$$

Example 19 In the figure given alongside, △ABC is right-angled at B. Given that AB = y units, BC = $\sqrt{3}$ units, AC = 2 units and $\angle A = x°$, find

(i) sin x°   (ii) x

(iii) tan x°

(iv) use cos x° to find the value of y.

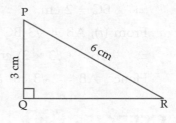

Solution. (i) From right-angled △ABC,

$$\sin x° = \frac{\text{height}}{\text{hypotenuse}} = \frac{\sqrt{3}}{2}.$$

(ii) From (i), sin x° = $\frac{\sqrt{3}}{2}$

$\Rightarrow \quad \sin x° = \sin 60°$

$\Rightarrow \quad x° = 60° \Rightarrow x = 60.$

$\left(\because \sin 60° = \frac{\sqrt{3}}{2}\right)$

(iii) From *(ii)*, $x = 60$,

$\therefore$ $\tan x° = \tan 60° = \sqrt{3}$.

(iv) From right-angled $\triangle$ABC, $\cos x° = \dfrac{\text{base}}{\text{hypotenuse}} = \dfrac{y}{2}$

$\cos 60° = \dfrac{y}{2}$ $\hspace{3cm}$ $(\because x = 60 \text{ from } (ii))$

$\Rightarrow$ $\dfrac{1}{2} = \dfrac{y}{2}$ $\hspace{3cm}$ $\left(\because \cos 60° = \dfrac{1}{2}\right)$

$\Rightarrow$ $y = 1$.

Example 20 In the adjoining figure, ABC is a right-angled triangle in which $\angle$ABC $= 90°$ and $\angle$ACB $= 60°$. BC is produced to D such that $\angle$ADB $= 30°$. If CD $= 4$ cm, find the lengths of AB and BC.

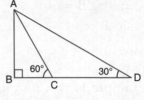

Solution. In the right-angled $\triangle$ABC,

$\tan 60° = \dfrac{AB}{BC} \Rightarrow \sqrt{3} = \dfrac{AB}{BC} \Rightarrow AB = \sqrt{3}\ BC$ $\hspace{2cm}$ ...*(i)*

In the right-angled $\triangle$ABD,

$\tan 30° = \dfrac{AB}{BD} \Rightarrow \dfrac{1}{\sqrt{3}} = \dfrac{AB}{BD} \Rightarrow BD = \sqrt{3}\ AB$

$\Rightarrow$ $BD = \sqrt{3}\ (\sqrt{3}\ BC)$ $\hspace{3cm}$ (using *(i)*)

$\Rightarrow$ $BD = 3\ BC$

$\Rightarrow$ $BC + CD = 3\ BC$ $\hspace{3cm}$ (from figure)

$\Rightarrow$ $CD = 3\ BC - BC$

$\Rightarrow$ $4\ \text{cm} = 2\ BC$ $\hspace{3cm}$ (CD = 4 cm, given)

$\Rightarrow$ $BC = 2\ \text{cm}$.

From *(i)*, $AB = \sqrt{3}\ BC$

$\Rightarrow$ $AB = (\sqrt{3} \times 2)\ \text{cm} = 2\sqrt{3}\ \text{cm}$.

Hence, $AB = 2\sqrt{3}$ cm and $BC = 2$ cm.

EXERCISE 18.1

1 Find the values of

    (i) $7 \sin 30° \cos 60°$ $\hspace{2cm}$ *(ii)* $3 \sin^2 45° + 2 \cos^2 60°$

    (iii) $\cos^2 45° + \sin^2 60° + \sin^2 30°$ $\hspace{1cm}$ *(iv)* $\cos 90° + \cos^2 45° \sin 30° \tan 45°$.

2 Find the values of

    (i) $\dfrac{\sin^2 45° + \cos^2 45°}{\tan^2 60°}$ $\hspace{2cm}$ *(ii)* $\dfrac{\sin 30° - \sin 90° + 2 \cos 0°}{\tan 30° \times \tan 60°}$

    (iii) $\dfrac{4}{3} \tan^2 30° + \sin^2 60° - 3 \cos^2 60° + \dfrac{3}{4} \tan^2 60° - 2 \tan^2 45°$.

3 Find the values of

    (i) $\dfrac{\sin 60°}{\cos^2 45°} - 3 \tan 30° + 5 \cos 90°$

    (ii) $2\sqrt{2} \cos 45° \cos 60° + 2\sqrt{3}\ \sin 30° \tan 60° - \cos 0°$

    (iii) $\dfrac{4}{5} \tan^2 60° - \dfrac{2}{\sin^2 30°} - \dfrac{3}{4} \tan^2 30°$.

4 Prove that

    (i) $\cos^2 30° + \sin 30° + \tan^2 45° = 2\frac{1}{4}$

    (ii) $4(\sin^4 30° + \cos^4 60°) - 3(\cos^2 45° - \sin^2 90°) = 2$

    (iii) $\cos 60° = \cos^2 30° - \sin^2 30°$.

5   (i) If $x = 30°$, verify that $\tan 2x = \dfrac{2 \tan x}{1 - \tan^2 x}$.

    (ii) If $x = 15°$, verify that $4 \sin 2x \cos 4x \sin 6x = 1$.

6 Find the values of

    (i) $\sqrt{\dfrac{1 - \cos^2 30°}{1 - \sin^2 30°}}$ (ii) $\dfrac{\sin 45° \cos 45° \cos 60°}{\sin 60° \cos 30° \tan 45°}$.

7 If $\theta = 30°$, verify that

    (i) $\sin 2\theta = 2 \sin \theta \cos \theta$ (ii) $\cos 2\theta = 2 \cos^2 \theta - 1$

    (iii) $\sin 3\theta = 3 \sin \theta - 4 \sin^3 \theta$ (iv) $\cos 3\theta = 4 \cos^3 \theta - 3 \cos \theta$.

8 If $\theta = 30°$, find the ratio $2 \sin \theta : \sin 2\theta$.

9 By means of an example, show that $\sin (A + B) \neq \sin A + \sin B$.

    Hint. Take $A = 30°$ and $B = 60°$.

10 If $A = 60°$ and $B = 30°$, verify that

    (i) $\sin (A + B) = \sin A \cos B + \cos A \sin B$

    (ii) $\cos (A + B) = \cos A \cos B - \sin A \sin B$

    (iii) $\sin (A - B) = \sin A \cos B - \cos A \sin B$

    (iv) $\tan (A - B) = \dfrac{\tan A - \tan B}{1 + \tan A \tan B}$.

11   (i) If 2θ is an acute angle and $2 \sin 2\theta = \sqrt{3}$, find the value of θ.

    (ii) If $20° + x$ is an acute angle and $\cos (20° + x) = \sin 60°$, then find the value of x.

    (iii) If $3 \sin^2 \theta = 2\frac{1}{4}$ and θ is less than $90°$, find the value of θ.

12 If θ is an acute angle and $\sin \theta = \cos \theta$, find the value of θ and hence, find the value of $2 \tan^2 \theta + \sin^2 \theta - 1$.

13 From the adjoining figure, find

    (i) $\tan x°$

    (ii) x

    (iii) $\cos x°$

    (iv) use $\sin x°$ to find y.

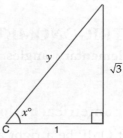

14 If 3θ is an acute angle, solve the following equations for θ:

    (i) $2 \sin 3\theta = \sqrt{3}$ (ii) $\tan 3\theta = 1$.

15 If $\tan 3x = \sin 45° \cos 45° + \sin 30°$, find the value of x.

16 If $4 \cos^2 x° - 1 = 0$ and $0 \leq x \leq 90$, find

    (i) x (ii) $\sin^2 x° + \cos^2 x°$ (iii) $\cos^2 x° - \sin^2 x°$.

17 (*i*) If $\sec \theta = \csc \theta$ and $0° \le \theta \le 90°$, find the value of θ.

(*ii*) If $\tan \theta = \cot \theta$ and $0° \le \theta \le 90°$, find the value of θ.

18 If $\sin 3x = 1$ and $0° \le 3x \le 90°$, find the values of

    (*i*) $\sin x$ (*ii*) $\cos 2x$ (*iii*) $\tan^2 x - \sec^2 x$.

19 If $3 \tan^2 \theta - 1 = 0$, find $\cos 2\theta$, given that θ is acute.

20 If $\sin x + \cos y = 1$, $x = 30°$ and y is acute angle, find the value of y.

21 If $\sin (A + B) = \dfrac{\sqrt{3}}{2} = \cos (A - B)$, $0° < A + B \le 90°$ ($A > B$), find the values of A and B.

22 If the length of each side of a rhombus is 8 cm and its one angle is 60°, then find the lengths of the diagonals of the rhombus.

23 In the right-angled triangle ABC, $\angle C = 90°$ and $\angle B = 60°$. If AC = 6 cm, find the lengths of the sides BC and AB.

24 In the adjoining figure, AP is a man of height 1·8 m and BQ is a building 13·8 m high. If the man sees the top of the building by focussing his binoculars at an angle of 30° to the horizontal, find the distance of the man from the building.

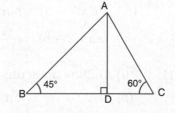

Hint. Let AB = d metres, then PC = d metres.

From right-angled $\triangle PCQ$,

$$\tan 30° = \frac{CQ}{PC} \Rightarrow \frac{1}{\sqrt{3}} = \frac{13\cdot8 - 1\cdot8}{d}.$$

25 In the adjoining figure, ABC is a triangle in which $\angle B = 45°$ and $\angle C = 60°$. If AD $\perp$ BC and BC = 8 m, find the length of the altitude AD.

Hint. In $\triangle ABD$, $\tan 45° = \dfrac{AD}{BD}$

$$\Rightarrow \quad 1 = \frac{AD}{BD} \Rightarrow BD = AD.$$

In $\triangle ADC$, $\tan 60° = \dfrac{AD}{DC} \Rightarrow \sqrt{3} = \dfrac{AD}{DC} \Rightarrow DC = \dfrac{AD}{\sqrt{3}}$.

But BD + DC = BC = 8 m $\Rightarrow AD + \dfrac{AD}{\sqrt{3}} = 8$.

18.6 TRIGONOMETRICAL RATIOS OF COMPLEMENTARY ANGLES

Complementary angles. *Two angles are called **complementary** if the sum of their measure is 90°.*

Trigonometrical ratios of complementary angles

Let OMP be a right angled triangle at M and $\angle MOP = \theta$, then

$$\angle MPO = 180° - (\angle OMP + \angle MOP)$$
$$= 180° - (90° + \theta) = 90° - \theta.$$

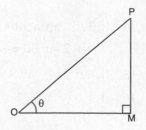

(1) $\sin (90° - \theta) = \dfrac{OM}{OP} = \cos \theta$.

(2) $\cos (90° - \theta) = \dfrac{MP}{OP} = \sin \theta$.

(3) $\tan (90° - \theta) = \dfrac{OM}{MP} = \cot \theta.$

(4) $\cot (90° - \theta) = \dfrac{MP}{OM} = \tan \theta.$

(5) $\sec (90° - \theta) = \dfrac{OP}{MP} = \operatorname{cosec} \theta.$

(6) $\operatorname{cosec} (90° - \theta) = \dfrac{OP}{OM} = \sec \theta.$

Hence, $\mathbf{sin\ (90° - \theta) = cos\ \theta}$

$\mathbf{cos\ (90° - \theta) = sin\ \theta}$

$\mathbf{tan\ (90° - \theta) = cot\ \theta}$

$\mathbf{cot\ (90° - \theta) = tan\ \theta}$

$\mathbf{sec\ (90° - \theta) = cosec\ \theta}$

$\mathbf{cosec\ (90° - \theta) = sec\ \theta.}$

Illustrative Examples

Example 1 Without using trigonometric tables, evaluate :

(i) $\dfrac{\sin 23°}{\cos 67°}$ (ii) $\dfrac{\tan 65°}{\cot 25°}$ (iii) $\dfrac{\operatorname{cosec} 31°}{\sec 59°}$.

Solution.

(i) $\dfrac{\sin 23°}{\cos 67°} = \dfrac{\sin 23°}{\cos (90° - 23°)} = \dfrac{\sin 23°}{\sin 23°}$ $(\because \cos (90° - \theta) = \sin \theta)$

$= 1$

(ii) $\dfrac{\tan 65°}{\cot 25°} = \dfrac{\tan 65°}{\cot (90° - 65°)} = \dfrac{\tan 65°}{\tan 60°}$ $(\because \cot (90° - \theta) = \tan \theta)$

$= 1$

(iii) $\dfrac{\operatorname{cosec} 31°}{\sec 59°} = \dfrac{\operatorname{cosec} (90° - 59°)}{\sec 59°} = \dfrac{\sec 59°}{\sec 59°}$ $(\because \operatorname{cosec} (90° - \theta) = \sec \theta)$

$= 1.$

Example 2 Without using trigonometric tables, evaluate :

(i) $\sin 18° - \cos 72°$

(ii) $\sin 35° \sin 55° - \cos 35° \cos 55°$

(iii) $3 \cos 80° \operatorname{cosec} 10° + 2 \sin 59° \sec 31°.$

Solution.

(i) $\sin 18° - \cos 72° = \sin 18° - \cos (90° - 18°)$

$= \sin 18° - \sin 18° = 0.$

(ii) $\sin 35° \sin 55° - \cos 35° \cos 55°$

$= \sin 35° \sin (90° - 35°) - \cos 35° \cos (90° - 35°)$

$= \sin 35° \cos 35° - \cos 35° \sin 35°$

$= 0.$

(iii) $3 \cos 80° \operatorname{cosec} 10° + 2 \sin 59° \sec 31°$

$= 3 \cos 80° \operatorname{cosec} (90° - 80°) + 2 \sin 59° \sec (90° - 59°)$

$= 3 \cos 80° \sec 80° + 2 \sin 59° \operatorname{cosec} 59°$

$$= 3 \cos 80° \times \frac{1}{\cos 80°} + 2 \sin 59° \times \frac{1}{\sin 59°}$$

$$= 3 \times 1 + 2 \times 1 = 3 + 2 = 5.$$

Example 3 Show that: $\tan 48° \tan 23° \tan 42° \tan 67° = 1$.

Solution. $\tan 48° \tan 23° \tan 42° \tan 67°$

$$= \tan (90° - 42°) \tan 23° \tan 42° \tan (90° - 23°)$$

$$= \cot 42° \tan 23° \tan 42° \cot 23°$$

$$= (\tan 42° \cot 42°)(\tan 23° \cot 23°)$$

$$= 1 \times 1 \qquad\qquad\qquad (\because \tan A \cot A = 1)$$

$$= 1.$$

Example 4 Find the values of the following:

(i) $\dfrac{\cot 35°}{\tan 55°} - \dfrac{1}{2}\left(\dfrac{\sec 25°}{\operatorname{cosec} 65°}\right) + 3 \sin 31° \sec 59°$ (ii) $\tan (45° - \theta) - \cot (45° + \theta)$.

Solution. (i) $\dfrac{\cot 35°}{\tan 55°} - \dfrac{1}{2}\left(\dfrac{\sec 25°}{\operatorname{cosec} 65°}\right) + 3 \sin 31° \sec 59°$

$$= \frac{\cot 35°}{\tan (90° - 35°)} - \frac{1}{2}\left(\frac{\sec 25°}{\operatorname{cosec}(90° - 25°)}\right) + 3 \sin 31° \sec (90° - 31°)$$

$$= \frac{\cot 35°}{\cot 35°} - \frac{1}{2}\left(\frac{\sec 25°}{\sec 25°}\right) + 3 \sin 31° \operatorname{cosec} 31°$$

$$= 1 - \frac{1}{2} \times 1 + 3 \times 1 \qquad\qquad (\because \sin A \operatorname{cosec} A = 1)$$

$$= 1 - \frac{1}{2} + 3 = 4 - \frac{1}{2} = 7\frac{1}{2}.$$

(ii) $\tan (45° - \theta) - \cot (45° + \theta) = \tan (45° - \theta) - \cot (90° - (45° - \theta))$

$$= \tan (45° - \theta) - \tan (45° - \theta)$$

$$\qquad\qquad (\because \cot (90° - A) = \tan A)$$

$$= 0.$$

Example 5 Evaluate the following:

(i) $2\left(\dfrac{\cos 58°}{\sin 32°}\right) - \sqrt{3}\left(\dfrac{\cos 38° \operatorname{cosec} 52°}{\tan 15° \tan 60° \tan 75°}\right)$

(ii) $\sec 41° \sin 49° + \cos 49° \operatorname{cosec} 41° - \dfrac{2}{\sqrt{3}} \tan 20° \tan 60° \tan 70°$

$$- 3(\cos^2 45° - \sin^2 90°).$$

Solution. (i) $2\left(\dfrac{\cos 58°}{\sin 32°}\right) - \sqrt{3}\left(\dfrac{\cos 38° \operatorname{cosec} 52°}{\tan 15° \tan 60° \tan 75°}\right)$

$$= 2\left(\frac{\cos(90° - 32°)}{\sin 32°}\right) - \sqrt{3}\,\frac{\cos 38° \operatorname{cosec} (90° - 38°)}{\tan 15°.\sqrt{3}.\tan(90° - 15°)} = 2\left(\frac{\sin 32°}{\sin 32°}\right) - \frac{\cos 38° \sec 38°}{\tan 15° \cot 15°}$$

$$= 2 \times 1 - \frac{1}{1} \qquad\qquad (\because \cos A \sec A = 1,\ \tan A \cot A = 1)$$

$$= 2 - 1 = 1.$$

(ii) $\sec 41° \sin 49° + \cos 49° \operatorname{cosec} 41° - \dfrac{2}{\sqrt{3}} (\tan 20° \tan 60° \tan 70°)$

$$- 3(\cos^2 45° - \sin^2 90°)$$

$$= \sec 41° \sin (90° - 41°) + \cos (90° - 41°) \operatorname{cosec} 41°$$

$$- \frac{2}{\sqrt{3}} (\tan 20°.\sqrt{3}.\tan (90° - 20°)) - 3\left(\left(\frac{1}{\sqrt{2}}\right)^2 - 1^2\right)$$

$$= \sec 41° \cos 41° + \sin 41° \operatorname{cosec} 41° - 2 (\tan 20° \cot 20°) - 3\left(\frac{1}{2}-1\right)$$

$$= 1 + 1 - 2 \times 1 - 3\left(-\frac{1}{2}\right)$$

$$(\because \sec A \cos A = 1, \sin A \operatorname{cosec} A = 1, \tan A \cot A = 1)$$

$$= 1 + 1 - 2 + \frac{3}{2} = \frac{3}{2}.$$

Example 6 Evaluate the following:

(i) $\dfrac{\sin^2 63° + \sin^2 27°}{\cos^2 17° + \cos^2 73°}$
(ii) $\sin 25° \cos 65° + \cos 25° \sin 65°$.

Solution. (i) As $\sin 63° = \sin (90° - 27°) = \cos 27°$ and

$$\cos 73° = \cos (90° - 17°) = \sin 17°,$$

$$\therefore \qquad \frac{\sin^2 63° + \sin^2 27°}{\cos^2 17° + \cos^2 73°} = \frac{\cos^2 27° + \sin^2 27°}{\cos^2 17° + \sin^2 17°}$$

$$= \frac{1}{1} \qquad\qquad (\because \sin^2 A + \cos^2 A = 1)$$

$$= 1.$$

(ii) $\sin 25° \cos 65° + \cos 25° \sin 65°$

$$= \sin 25° \cos (90° - 25°) + \cos 25° \sin (90° - 25°)$$

$$= \sin 25° \sin 25° + \cos 25° \cos 25°$$

$$= \sin^2 25° + \cos^2 25°$$

$$= 1 \qquad\qquad (\because \sin^2 A + \cos^2 A = 1)$$

Example 7 Without using trigonometrical tables, evaluate :

(i) $\dfrac{2}{3} \operatorname{cosec}^2 58° - \dfrac{2}{3} \cot 58° \tan 32° - \dfrac{5}{3} \tan 13° \tan 37° \tan 45° \tan 53° \tan 77°$

(ii) $\left(\dfrac{\tan 20°}{\operatorname{cosec} 70°}\right)^2 + \left(\dfrac{\cot 20°}{\sec 70°}\right)^2 + 2 \tan 15° \tan 45° \tan 75°$.

Solution.

(i) $\dfrac{2}{3} \operatorname{cosec}^2 58° - \dfrac{2}{3} \cot 58° \tan 32° - \dfrac{5}{3} \tan 13° \tan 37° \tan 45° \tan 53° \tan 77°$

$$= \frac{2}{3} \operatorname{cosec}^2 58° - \frac{2}{3} \cot 58° \tan (90° - 58°)$$

$$- \frac{5}{3} \tan 13° \tan 37° . 1 . \tan(90° - 37°) \tan (90° - 13°)$$

$$= \frac{2}{3} \operatorname{cosec}^2 58° - \frac{2}{3} \cot 58° \cot 58° - \frac{5}{3} \tan 13° \tan 37° \cot 37° \cot 13°$$

$$= \frac{2}{3} (\operatorname{cosec}^2 58° - \cot^2 58°) - \frac{5}{3} \tan 13° . 1 . \cot 13°$$

$$= \frac{2}{3} . 1 - \frac{5}{3} . 1 = \frac{2}{3} - \frac{5}{3} = -1.$$

(ii) $\left(\dfrac{\tan 20°}{\operatorname{cosec} 70°}\right)^2 + \left(\dfrac{\cot 20°}{\sec 70°}\right)^2 + 2 \tan 15° \tan 45° \tan 75°$

$$= \left(\frac{\tan 20°}{\operatorname{cosec} (90° - 20°)}\right)^2 + \left(\frac{\cot 20°}{\sec(90° - 20°)}\right)^2 + 2 \tan 15° . 1 . \tan (90° - 15°)$$

$$= \left(\frac{\tan 20°}{\sec 20°}\right)^2 + \left(\frac{\cot 20°}{\csc 20°}\right)^2 + 2 \tan 15° \cot 15°$$

$$= \left(\frac{\sin 20°}{\cos 20°} \cdot \cos 20°\right)^2 + \left(\frac{\cos 20°}{\sin 20°} \cdot \sin 20°\right)^2 + 2 \cdot 1$$

$$= \sin^2 20° + \cos^2 20° + 2$$

$$= 1 + 2 = 3.$$

Example 8 Express (sin 85° + cosec 85°) in terms of trigonometric ratios of angles between 0° and 45°.

Solution. sin 85° + cosec 85° = sin (90° − 5°) + cosec (90° − 5°)

$$= \cos 5° + \sec 5°.$$

Example 9 Express sin 67° + cos 75° in terms of trigonometric ratios of angles between 0° and 45°.

Solution. sin 67° + cos 75° = sin (90° − 23°) + cos (90° − 15°)

$$= \cos 23° + \sin 15°.$$

Example 10 If cos x = cos 40° sin 50° + sin 40° cos 50°, then find the value of x.

Solution. sin 50° = sin (90° − 40°) = cos 40° and

cos 50° = cos (90° − 40°) = sin 40°.

Given cos x = cos 40° sin 50° + sin 40° cos 50°

$\Rightarrow$ cos x = cos 40° cos 40° + sin 40° sin 40°

$\Rightarrow$ cos x = cos² 40° + sin² 40° = 1   ($\because$ cos² A + sin² A = 1)

$\Rightarrow$ cos x = cos 0° $\Rightarrow$ x = 0°.

Hence, x = 0°.

Example 11 If tan A = cot B, prove that A + B = 90°.

Solution. Given tan A = cot B

$\Rightarrow$ tan A = tan (90° − B)   ($\because$ cot B = tan (90° − B))

$\Rightarrow$ A = 90° − B $\Rightarrow$ A + B = 90°.

Example 12 If tan $\theta = \dfrac{15}{17}$ and $\theta + \alpha = 90°$, find the value of cot α.

Solution. Given $\theta + \alpha = 90° \Rightarrow \alpha = 90° − \theta$.

$\therefore$ cot α = cot (90° − θ) = tan θ

$\Rightarrow$ cot $\alpha = \dfrac{15}{17}$ ($\because$ tan $\theta = \dfrac{15}{17}$, given)

Example 13 Prove that: tan θ + tan (90° − θ) = sec θ sec (90° − θ).

Solution. L.H.S. = tan θ + tan (90° − θ) = tan θ + cot θ

$$= \frac{\sin\theta}{\cos\theta} + \frac{\cos\theta}{\sin\theta} = \frac{\sin^2\theta + \cos^2\theta}{\cos\theta\sin\theta} = \frac{1}{\cos\theta\sin\theta}$$

= sec θ cosec θ = sec θ sec (90° − θ) = R.H.S.

Example 14 Prove the following :

(i) $\dfrac{\sin(90° − A)\sin A}{\tan A} − 1 = − \sin^2 A$

(ii) $\dfrac{\sin A}{\sin(90° − A)} + \dfrac{\cos A}{\cos(90° − A)} = \sec A \csc A.$

Solution.

(i) L.H.S. $= \dfrac{\sin(90° - A)\sin A}{\tan A} - 1 = \dfrac{\cos A \sin A}{\dfrac{\sin A}{\cos A}} - 1 - 1$

$= \cos^2 A - 1 = -(1 - \cos^2 A)$

$= -\sin^2 A = $ R.H.S.

(ii) L.H.S. $= \dfrac{\sin A}{\sin(90° - A)} + \dfrac{\cos A}{\cos(90° - A)}$

$= \dfrac{\sin A}{\cos A} + \dfrac{\cos A}{\sin A} = \dfrac{\sin^2 A + \cos^2 A}{\cos A \sin A}$

$= \dfrac{1}{\cos A \sin A} = \sec A \operatorname{cosec} A = $ R.H.S.

Example 15 Find the value of A if:

sin 3A = cos (A – 26°), where 3A and A – 26° are acute angles.

Solution. Given sin 3A = cos (A – 26°)

$\Rightarrow$ cos (90° – 3A) = cos (A – 26°)

$\Rightarrow$ 90° – 3A = A – 26°

($\because$ 3A is an acute angle, so 90° – 3A is an acute angle, also A – 26° is an acute angle)

$\Rightarrow$ 116° = 4A $\Rightarrow$ A = 29°.

Hence, the value of A is 29°.

Example 16 If sin 54° cosec (90° – θ) = 1, find the value of θ, 0° < θ < 90°.

Solution. Given sin 54° cosec (90° – θ) = 1

$\Rightarrow$ sin 54° sec θ = 1 $\Rightarrow$ sin 54° $= \dfrac{1}{\sec \theta}$

$\Rightarrow$ sin 54° = cos θ $\Rightarrow$ sin (90° – 36°) = cos θ

$\Rightarrow$ cos 36° = cos θ $\Rightarrow$ θ = 36°.

Example 17 If A, B and C are the interior angles of a triangle ABC, show that:

(i) $\sin \dfrac{B+C}{2} = \cos \dfrac{A}{2}$ (ii) $\sec \dfrac{B+C}{2} = \operatorname{cosec} \dfrac{A}{2}$.

Solution. As A, B and C are the interior angles of $\triangle$ABC, A + B + C = 180°

$\Rightarrow$ B + C = 180° – A $\Rightarrow \dfrac{B+C}{2} = 90° - \dfrac{A}{2}$ ...(1)

(i) $\sin \dfrac{B+C}{2} = \sin\left(90° - \dfrac{A}{2}\right)$ (using (1))

$\Rightarrow \sin \dfrac{B+C}{2} = \cos \dfrac{A}{2}$ ($\because$ sin (90° – θ) = cos θ)

(ii) $\sec \dfrac{B+C}{2} = \sec\left(90° - \dfrac{A}{2}\right)$ (using (1))

$\Rightarrow \sec \dfrac{B+C}{2} = \operatorname{cosec} \dfrac{A}{2}$ ($\because$ cosec (90° – θ) = sec θ)

Example 18 In $\triangle$ABC, show that $\sin^2 \dfrac{A}{2} + \sin^2 \dfrac{B+C}{2} = 1$.

Solution. As sum of angles of a triangle is 180°, A + B + C = 180°

$\Rightarrow$ B + C = 180° – A $\Rightarrow \dfrac{B+C}{2} = 90° - \dfrac{A}{2}$.

$$\text{L.H.S.} = \sin^2 \frac{A}{2} + \sin^2 \frac{B+C}{2} = \sin^2 \frac{A}{2} + \sin^2\left(90° - \frac{A}{2}\right)$$

$$= \sin^2 \frac{A}{2} + \cos^2 \frac{A}{2} = 1 = \text{R.H.S.}$$

EXERCISE 18.2

Without using trigonometric tables, evaluate the following (1 to 5) :

1   (i) $\dfrac{\cos 18°}{\sin 72°}$ (ii) $\dfrac{\tan 41°}{\cos 49°}$ (iii) $\dfrac{\operatorname{cosec} 17° \, 30'}{\sec 72° \, 30'}$.

2   (i) $\dfrac{\cot 40°}{\tan 50°} - \dfrac{1}{2}\left(\dfrac{\cos 35°}{\sin 55°}\right)$ (ii) $\left(\dfrac{\sin 49°}{\cos 41°}\right)^2 + \left(\dfrac{\cos 41°}{\sin 49°}\right)^2$

    (iii) $\dfrac{\sin 72°}{\cos 18°} - \dfrac{\sec 32°}{\operatorname{cosec} 58°}$ (iv) $\dfrac{\cos 75°}{\sin 15°} + \dfrac{\sin 12°}{\cos 78°} - \dfrac{\cos 18°}{\sin 72°}$

    (v) $\dfrac{\sin 25°}{\sec 65°} + \dfrac{\cos 25°}{\operatorname{cosec} 65°}$.

3   (i) $\sin 62° - \cos 28°$ (ii) $\operatorname{cosec} 35° - \sec 55°$.

4   (i) $\cos^2 26° + \cos 64° \sin 26° + \dfrac{\tan 36°}{\cot 54°}$

    (ii) $\dfrac{\sec 17°}{\operatorname{cosec} 73°} + \dfrac{\tan 68°}{\cot 22°} + \cos^2 44° + \cos^2 46°$.

5   (i) $\dfrac{\cos 65°}{\sin 25°} + \dfrac{\cos 32°}{\sin 58°} - \sin 28° \sec 62° + \operatorname{cosec}^2 30°$

    (ii) $\dfrac{\sec 29°}{\operatorname{cosec} 61°} + 2 \cot 8° \cot 17° \cot 45° \cot 73° \cot 82° - 3\,(\sin^2 38° + \sin^2 52°)$.

6 Express each of the following in terms of trigonometric ratios of angles between 0° to 45° :

    (i) $\tan 81° + \cos 72°$ (ii) $\cot 49° + \operatorname{cosec} 87°$.

Without using trigonometric tables, prove that (7 to 11) :

7   (i) $\sin^2 28° - \cos^2 62° = 0$ (ii) $\cos^2 25° + \cos^2 65° = 1$
    (iii) $\operatorname{cosec}^2 67° - \tan^2 23° = 1$ (iv) $\sec^2 22° - \cot^2 68° = 1$.

8   (i) $\sin 63° \cos 27° + \cos 63° \sin 27° = 1$
    (ii) $\sec 31° \sin 59° + \cos 31° \operatorname{cosec} 59° = 2$.

9   (i) $\sec 70° \sin 20° - \cos 20° \operatorname{cosec} 70° = 0$
    (ii) $\sin^2 20° + \sin^2 70° - \tan^2 45° = 0$.

10   (i) $\dfrac{\cot 54°}{\tan 36°} + \dfrac{\tan 20°}{\cot 70°} - 2 = 0$

    (ii) $\dfrac{\sin 50°}{\cos 40°} + \dfrac{\operatorname{cosec} 40°}{\sec 50°} - 4 \cos 50° \operatorname{cosec} 40° + 2 = 0$.

11   (i) $\dfrac{\cos 70°}{\sin 20°} + \dfrac{\cos 59°}{\sin 31°} - 8 \sin^2 30° = 0$

    (ii) $\dfrac{\cos 80°}{\sin 10°} + \cos 59° \operatorname{cosec} 31° = 2$.

12 Without using trigonometrical tables, evaluate :

(i) $2\left(\dfrac{\tan 35°}{\cot 55°}\right)^2 + \left(\dfrac{\cot 55°}{\tan 35°}\right) - 3\left(\dfrac{\sec 40°}{\operatorname{cosec} 50°}\right)$ (ii) $\dfrac{\sin 35° \cos 55° + \cos 35° \sin 55°}{\operatorname{cosec}^2 10° - \tan^2 80°}.$

(iii) $\sin^2 34° + \sin^2 56° + 2 \tan 18° \tan 72° - \cot^2 30°.$

13 Prove the following :

(i) $\dfrac{\cos \theta}{\sin (90° - \theta)} + \dfrac{\sin \theta}{\cos (90° - \theta)} = 2$

(ii) $\cos \theta \sin (90° - \theta) + \sin \theta \cos (90° - \theta) = 1$

(iii) $\dfrac{\tan \theta}{\tan (90° - \theta)} + \dfrac{\sin (90° - \theta)}{\cos \theta} = \sec^2 \theta.$

14 Prove the following :

(i) $\dfrac{\cos (90° - A) \sin (90° - A)}{\tan (90° - A)} = 1 - \cos^2 A$

(ii) $\dfrac{\sin (90° - A)}{\operatorname{cosec} (90° - A)} + \dfrac{\cos (90° - A)}{\sec (90° - A)} = 1.$

15 Simplify the following :

(i) $\dfrac{\cos \theta}{\sin (90° - \theta)} + \dfrac{\cos (90° - \theta)}{\sec (90° - \theta)} - 3 \tan^2 30°$

(ii) $\dfrac{\operatorname{cosec} (90° - \theta) \sin (90° - \theta) \cot (90° - \theta)}{\cos (90° - \theta) \sec (90° - \theta) \tan \theta} + \dfrac{\cot \theta}{\tan (90° - \theta)}.$

16 Show that $\dfrac{\cos^2 (45° + \theta) + \cos^2 (45° - \theta)}{\tan (60° + \theta) \tan (30° - \theta)} = 1.$

17 Find the value of A if
(i) $\sin 3A = \cos (A - 6°)$, where 3A and A − 6° are acute angles
(ii) $\tan 2A = \cot (A - 18°)$, where 2A and A − 18° are acute angles.
(iii) If $\sec 2A = \operatorname{cosec} (A - 27°)$ where 2A is an acute angle, find the measure of $\angle A$.

18 Find the value of θ (0° < θ < 90°) if :
(i) $\cos 63° \sec (90° - \theta) = 1$
(ii) $\tan 35° \cot (90° - \theta) = 1.$

19 If A, B and C are the interior angles of a ΔABC, show that:

(i) $\cos \dfrac{A + B}{2} = \sin \dfrac{C}{2}$ (ii) $\tan \dfrac{C + A}{2} = \cot \dfrac{B}{2}.$

Multiple Choice Questions

Choose the correct answer from the given four options (1 to 15):

1 The value of $\dfrac{\tan 30°}{\cot 60°}$ is

(a) $\dfrac{1}{\sqrt{2}}$ (b) $\dfrac{1}{\sqrt{3}}$ (c) $\sqrt{3}$ (d) 1

2 The value of $(\sin 45° + \cos 45°)$ is

(a) $\dfrac{1}{\sqrt{2}}$ (b) $\sqrt{2}$ (c) $\dfrac{\sqrt{3}}{2}$ (d) 1

3 The value of $\tan^2 30° - 4 \sin^2 45°$ is

(a) 1   (b) $\dfrac{7}{3}$ (c) $-\dfrac{5}{3}$ (d) $-\dfrac{11}{3}$

4 If A = 30°, then the value of 2 sin A cos A is

(a) $\dfrac{1}{\sqrt{2}}$ 　　　　(b) $\dfrac{\sqrt{3}}{2}$ 　　　　(c) $\dfrac{1}{2}$ 　　　　(d) 1

5 The value of (sin 30° + cos 30°) − (sin 60° + cos 60°) is

(a) −1 　　　　(b) 0 　　　　(c) 1 　　　　(d) 2

6 The value of $\sqrt{3}$ cosec 60° − sec 60° is

(a) 0 　　　　(b) 1 　　　　(c) 2 　　　　(d) −1

7 The value of $\dfrac{1}{\sin 30°} - \dfrac{\sqrt{3}}{\cos 30°}$ is

(a) 2 　　　　(b) 1 　　　　(c) $\dfrac{1}{2}$ 　　　　(d) 0

8 If tan A = $\sqrt{3}$, then the value of cosec A is

(a) $\dfrac{1}{2}$ 　　　　(b) 2 　　　　(c) $\dfrac{2}{\sqrt{3}}$ 　　　　(d) $\dfrac{\sqrt{3}}{2}$

9 If sec θ . sin θ = 0, then the value of cos θ is

(a) 0 　　　　(b) $\dfrac{1}{\sqrt{2}}$ 　　　　(c) $\dfrac{1}{2}$ 　　　　(d) 1

10 If sin α = $\dfrac{1}{2}$, then the value of 3 cos α − 4 cos³ α is

(a) −1 　　　　(b) 0 　　　　(c) 1 　　　　(d) 2

11 The value of $\dfrac{1 - \tan^2 45°}{1 + \tan^2 45°}$ is equal to

(a) tan 60° 　　　　(b) tan 30° 　　　　(c) sin 45° 　　　　(d) tan 0°

12 If sin α = $\dfrac{1}{2}$ and cos β = $\dfrac{1}{2}$, then the value of (α + β) is

(a) 0° 　　　　(b) 30° 　　　　(c) 60° 　　　　(d) 90°

13 If ΔABC is right angled at C, then the value of cos (A + B) is

(a) 0 　　　　(b) 1 　　　　(c) $\dfrac{1}{2}$ 　　　　(d) $\dfrac{\sqrt{3}}{2}$

14 In the adjoining figure, ABC is a right triangle right angled at B. If AB = 10 cm and ∠C = 30°, then the length of the side BC is

(a) $\dfrac{10}{\sqrt{3}}$ cm 　　　　(b) $10\sqrt{3}$ cm

(c) 20 cm 　　　　(d) 5 cm

15 In the adjoining figure, PQR is a right triangle right angled at Q. If PQ = 4 cm and PR = 8 cm then ∠P is equal to

(a) 60° 　　　　(b) 45°

(c) 30° 　　　　(d) 15°

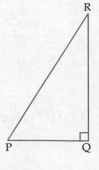

Summary

❏ **Trigonometric ratios of some standard angles**

Trigonometric ratios of 0°, 30°, 45°, 60° and 90° are given in the following table for ready reference:

Angle θ → Ratio ↓	0°	30°	45°	60°	90°
sin θ	0	$\dfrac{1}{2}$	$\dfrac{1}{\sqrt{2}}$	$\dfrac{\sqrt{3}}{2}$	1
cos θ	1	$\dfrac{\sqrt{3}}{2}$	$\dfrac{1}{\sqrt{2}}$	$\dfrac{1}{2}$	0
tan θ	0	$\dfrac{1}{\sqrt{3}}$	1	$\sqrt{3}$	not defined
cot θ	not defined	$\sqrt{3}$	1	$\dfrac{1}{\sqrt{3}}$	0
sec θ	1	$\dfrac{2}{\sqrt{3}}$	$\sqrt{2}$	2	not defined
cosec θ	not defined	2	$\sqrt{2}$	$\dfrac{2}{\sqrt{3}}$	1

• As θ increases from 0° to 90°, the value of sin θ increases whereas the value of cos θ decreases.

❏ **Trigonometrical ratios of complementary angles**

     (*i*) sin (90° − θ) = cos θ   (*ii*) cos (90° − θ) = sin θ

     (*iii*) tan (90° − θ) = cot θ   (*iv*) cot (90° − θ) = tan θ

     (*iv*) sec (90° − θ) = sec θ   (*vi*) cosec (90° − θ) = sec θ.

1   Find the values of:

    (i) $\sin^2 60° - \cos^2 45° + 3\tan^2 30°$
    (ii) $\dfrac{2\cos^2 45° + 3\tan^2 30°}{\sqrt{3}\cos 30° + \sin 30°}$

    (iii) $\sec 30° \tan 60° + \sin 45° \csc 45° + \cos 30° \cot 60°$.

2   Taking A = 30°, verify that

    (i) $\cos^4 A - \sin^4 A = \cos 2A$

    (ii) $4\cos A \cos(60° - A)\cos(60° + A) = \cos 3A$.

3   If A = 45° and B = 30°, verify that $\dfrac{\sin A}{\cos A + \sin A \sin B} = \dfrac{2}{3}$.

4   Taking A = 60° and B = 30°, verify that

    (i) $\dfrac{\sin(A + B)}{\cos A \cos B} = \tan A + \tan B$
    (ii) $\dfrac{\sin(A - B)}{\sin A \sin B} = \cot B - \cot A$.

5   If $\sqrt{2}\tan 2\theta = \sqrt{6}$ and $0° < 2\theta < 90°$, find the value of

               $\sin \theta + \sqrt{3}\cos \theta - 2\tan^2 \theta$.

6   If 3θ is an acute angle, solve the following equation for θ:

            $(\csc 3\theta - 2)(\cot 2\theta - 1) = 0$.

7   If $\tan(A + B) = \sqrt{3}$, $\tan(A - B) = 1$ and A, B (B < A) are acute angles, find the values of A and B.

8   Without using trigonometrical tables, evaluate the following:

    (i) $\sin^2 28° + \sin^2 62° - \tan^2 45°$
    (ii) $\dfrac{2\cos 27°}{\sin 63°} + \dfrac{\tan 27°}{\cot 63°} + \cos 0°$

    (iii) $\cos 18° \sin 72° + \sin 18° \cos 72°$
    (iv) $5\sin 50° \sec 40° - 3\cos 59° \csc 31°$.

9   Prove that: $\dfrac{\cos(90° - \theta)\sec(90° - \theta)\tan \theta}{\csc(90° - \theta)\sin(90° - \theta)\cot(90° - \theta)} + \dfrac{\tan(90° - \theta)}{\cot \theta} = 2$.

10 When $0° < A < 90°$, solve the following equations:

    (i) $\sin 3A = \cos 2A$
    (ii) $\tan 5A = \cot A$.

    Hint.

    (i) $\sin 3A = \cos 2A \Rightarrow \sin 3A = \sin(90° - 2A) \Rightarrow 3A = 90° - 2A$.

11 Find the value of θ if

    (i) $\sin(\theta + 36°) = \cos \theta$, where θ and $\theta + 36°$ are acute angles.

    (ii) $\sec 4\theta = \csc(\theta - 20°)$, where 4θ and $\theta - 20°$ are acute angles.

12 In the adjoining figure, ABC is right-angled triangle at B and ABD is right angled triangle at A. If BD ⊥ AC and BC = $2\sqrt{3}$ cm, find the length of AD.

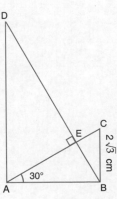

    Hint. In $\triangle ABC$, $\tan 30° = \dfrac{BC}{AB} \Rightarrow \dfrac{1}{\sqrt{3}} = \dfrac{2\sqrt{3}\text{ cm}}{AB}$

    $\Rightarrow$ AB = 6 cm.

    For $\triangle ABE$, $90° = 30° + \angle ABE$

           ($\because$ ext $\angle$ = sum of two opp. int. $\angle$s)

    $\Rightarrow$ $\angle ABE = 60°$.

    In $\triangle ABD$, $\tan 60° = \dfrac{AD}{AB} \Rightarrow \sqrt{3} = \dfrac{AD}{6\text{ cm}}$

19 Coordinate Geometry

INTRODUCTION

Coordinate geometry is that branch of Mathematics which deals with the study of geometry by means of algebra. René Déscartes, a French mathematician, realised around 1637 that a line or a curve in a plane can be represented by an algebraic equation. As a result, a new branch of mathematics called **Coordinate Geometry** came into existence. In coordinate geometry, we represent a point in a plane by an ordered pair of real numbers, called coordinates of the point; and a straight line or a curve by an algebraic equation with real coefficients. Thus, we use algebra advantageously to the study of straight lines and geometric curves.

Recall that there is one and only one point on a number line associated with each real number. A similar situation exists for points in a plane and **ordered pairs** of real numbers.

19.1 ORDERED PAIR

*An **ordered pair** is a pair of objects taken in a specific order.*

An ordered pair is written by listing its two members in a specific order, separating them by a comma and enclosing the pair in parentheses. In the ordered pair (a, b), a is called the *first member* (or *component*) and b is called the *second member* (or *component*).

Equality of ordered pairs. *Two ordered pairs (a, b) and (c, d) are called **equal**, written as $(a, b) = (c, d)$, if and only if $a = c$ and $b = d$.*

Remarks

○ The word 'ordered' implies that the order in which the two elements of the pair occur is meaningful. For example, if we have a sock and a shoe, the order in which they are put on does matter.

○ The ordered pairs (a, b) and (b, a) are different unless $a = b$.

○ The two components of an ordered pair may be equal.

19.2 COORDINATE SYSTEM

When two numbered lines perpendicular to each other (usually horizontal and vertical) are placed together so that the two origins (the points corresponding to zero) coincide then the resulting configuration is called a **cartesian coordinate system** or simply a **coordinate system** or a **cartesian plane**.

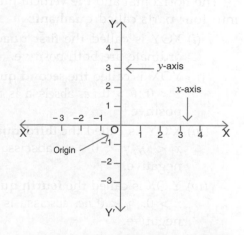

Let X'OX and Y'OY, two number lines perpendicular to each other, meet at the point O (shown in the adjoining figure), then

(*i*) X'OX is called *x*-axis.

(ii) Y'OY is called **y-axis**.

(iii) X'OX and Y'OY taken together are called **coordinate axes**.

(iv) the point O is called the **origin**.

19.2.1 Coordinates of a point

Let P be any point in the coordinate plane. From
P, draw PM perpendicular to X'OX, then

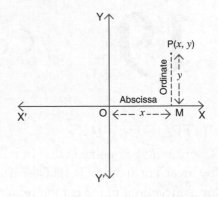

(i) OM is called **x-coordinate** or **abscissa** of P
and is usually denoted by x.

(ii) MP is called **y-coordinate** or **ordinate** of P
and is usually denoted by y.

(iii) x and y taken together are called **cartesian
coordinates** or simply coordinates of P and
are denoted by (x, y).

Remarks

○ To know the position of a point in a plane, we need two independent informations
abscissa and ordinate of the point.

○ The coordinates of a point indicate its position with reference to coordinate axes.

○ In stating the coordinates of a point, the **abscissa** precedes the **ordinate**. The two are
separated by a comma and are enclosed in the bracket (   ). Thus, a point P whose
abscissa is 'x' and ordinate is 'y' is written as (x, y) or P (x, y).

◻ **Convention for signs of coordinates**

(i) The x-coordinate (abscissa) of a point is **positive** if it is measured to the right of O
i.e. along OX and is **negative** if it is measured to the left of O i.e. along OX'.

(ii) The y-coordinate (ordinate) of a point is **positive** if it is measured upwards i.e.
along OY and is **negative** if it is measured downwards i.e. along OY'.

Remarks

○ The coordinates of the origin O are $(0, 0)$.

○ For any point on x-axis, its ordinate is always zero and
so the coordinates of any point P on x-axis are $(x, 0)$.

○ For any point on y-axis, its abscissa is always zero and
so the coordinates of any point Q on y-axis are $(0, y)$.

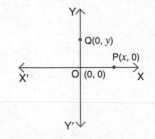

Quadrants

The horizontal and the vertical number lines X'OX and Y'OY divide the coordinate plane
into four parts called **quadrants**.

(i) XOY is called the **first quadrant**. In this quadrant, $x > 0$, $y > 0$ i.e. abscissa and
ordinate are both positive.

(ii) YOX' is called the **second quadrant**. In this quadrant,
$x < 0$, $y > 0$ i.e. abscissa is negative and ordinate is
positive.

(iii) X'OY' is called the **third quadrant**. In this quadrant,
$x < 0$, $y < 0$ i.e. abscissa and ordinate are both
negative.

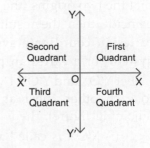

(iv) Y'OX is called the **fourth quadrant**. In this quadrant,
$x > 0$, $y < 0$ i.e. abscissa is positive and ordinate is
negative.

The signs of the coordinates of a point determine the quadrant in which the point lies and conversely, the signs of the coordinates of a point are determined by the quadrant in which it lies. The signs of the coordinates of a point in four quadrants can be remembered with the help of the following table:

Quadrants → Coordinates ↓	1st XOY	2nd YOX'	3rd X'OY'	4th Y'OX
x (abscissa)	+ve	−ve	−ve	+ve
y (ordinate)	+ve	+ve	−ve	−ve

Thus, the points (2, 3), (−2, 3), (−2, −3) and (2, −3) lie in the first, second, third and fourth quadrants respectively.

19.2.2 Plotting of points

When we identify a point in the coordinate plane with a given ordered pair of real numbers, we say that we **plot** the point. For example, to plot the point (2, 3), we adopt two steps:

(i) Start from O (origin) and move 2 units along the x-axis to the right.

(ii) From this place, move 3 units upwards (parallel to y-axis) and mark a *dot* at that place. This point, say A, of the coordinate plane is the point associated with the given ordered pair (2, 3). Label this point as A (2, 3).

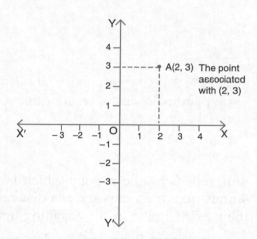

Illustrative Examples

Example 1 (i) What do you mean by abscissa of a point?

(ii) Point P is on x-axis and is at a distance of 4 units from y-axis to its left. Write the coordinates of the point P.

(iii) If the point P(5, a + 3) lies on the x-axis, then find the value of a.

(iv) The point P(a, b) lies in the fourth quadrant. Which of a or b is greater?

Solution. (i) The directed distance of a point from the y-axis is called its abscissa (or x-coordinate).

(ii) As the point P lies on x-axis and is at a distance of 4 units from y-axis to its left, so the coordinates of the point P are (−4, 0).

(iii) As the point P(5, a + 3) lies on the x-axis, its y-coordinate is zero
$\Rightarrow a + 3 = 0 \Rightarrow a = -3.$
Hence, the value of a is −3.

(iv) As the point P(a, b) lies in the fourth quadrant, a > 0 and b < 0.
$\therefore \quad a > b.$
Hence, a is greater.

Example 2 Find the distances of points P(–3, –2) and Q(5, 0) from the *x*-axis and *y*-axis.

Solution. For the point P(–3, –2):

     distance from *x*-axis = 2 and

     distance from *y*-axis = 3.

 For the point Q(5, 0):

     distance from *x*-axis = 0 and

     distance from *y*-axis = 5.

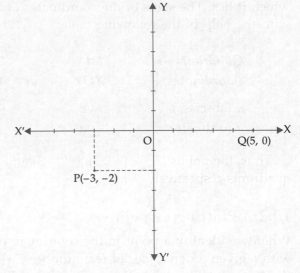

Example 3 The perpendicular distance of a point from the *x*-axis is 4 units and the perpendicular distance from the *y*-axis is 5 units. Write the coordinates of such a point if it lies in the

 (*i*) Ist quadrant   (*ii*) IInd quadrant

 (*iii*) IIIrd quadrant   (*iv*) IV quadrant.

Solution. Let P be a point which is at a distance of 4 units from the *x*-axis and at a distance of 5 units from the *y*-axis (shown in the adjoining figure).

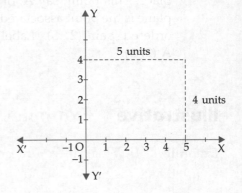

 (*i*) When P lies in the Ist quadrant, then the coordinates of P are (5, 4).

 (*ii*) When P lies in the IInd quadrant, then the coordinates of P are (–5, 4).

 (*iii*) When P lies in the IIIrd quadrant, then the coordinates of P are (–5, –4).

 (*iv*) When P lies in the IVth quadrant, then the coordinates of P are (5, –4).

Example 4 If the coordinates of a point M are (–2, 9) which can also be expressed as $(1 + x, y^2)$ and $y > 0$, then find in which the quadrant do the following points lie:

 $P(y, x)$, $Q(2, x)$, $R(x^2, y – 1)$, $S(2x, –3y)$.

Solution. Given $(–2, 9) = (1 + x, y^2)$, $y > 0$

$\Rightarrow$ $1 + x = –2$ and $y^2 = 9$, $y > 0$

$\Rightarrow$ $x = –3$ and $y = 3$.

$\therefore$ The point $P(y, x)$ is (3, –3), which lies in the IVth quadrant.

The point $Q(2, x)$ is (2, –3), which lies in the IVth quadrant.

The point $R(x^2, y – 1)$ is $((–3)^2, 3 – 1)$ *i.e.* (9, 2), which lies in the Ist quadrant.

The point $S(2x, –3y)$ *i.e.* $(2(–3), –3(3))$ *i.e.* (–6, –9), which lies in the IIIrd quadrant.

Example 5 Plot the points associated with the pairs A(–2, 3), B(–3, –2), C (2, –4), D (–4, 0), E(0, –3) and F(3, 4).

Solution. To plot the point A (–2, 3) in the coordinate plane, start from the point O (origin) and move 2 units along the x-axis to the left, and from here move 3 units upwards. Mark a *dot* at this place, and thus the point A (–2, 3) is plotted.

Similarly, plot the other points in the plane. These points are shown in the adjacent figure.

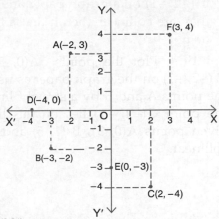

Example 6 Plot the following points on a squared paper:

(i) A $\left(2\frac{1}{2}, 1\frac{1}{2}\right)$ (ii) B $\left(2, -2\frac{1}{3}\right)$ (iii) $\left(1\frac{1}{2}, 1\frac{1}{3}\right)$.

Solution.

(i) To plot the point A $\left(2\frac{1}{2}, 1\frac{1}{2}\right)$ on a squared (graph) paper, mark the two coordinate axes in such a way that the fraction $\frac{1}{2}$ can easily be read. For this, take 2 divisions equal to one unit. The point A $\left(2\frac{1}{2}, 1\frac{1}{2}\right)$ is shown by a dot in the adjacent figure.

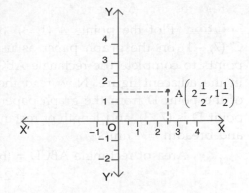

(ii) To plot the point B $\left(2, -2\frac{1}{3}\right)$ on a squared (graph) paper, mark the two coordinate axes in such a way that the fraction $\frac{1}{3}$ can easily be read. For this, take 3 divisions equal to one unit. The point B $\left(2, -2\frac{1}{3}\right)$ is shown by a dot in the adjacent figure.

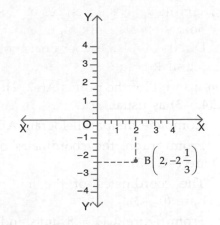

(iii) To plot the point C $\left(1\frac{1}{2}, 1\frac{1}{3}\right)$ on a squared paper, mark the coordinate axes in such a way that the fractions $\frac{1}{2}$ and $\frac{1}{3}$ both can easily be read. For this, take 6 divisions equal to one unit. The point C $\left(1\frac{1}{2}, 1\frac{1}{3}\right)$ is shown by a dot in the adjacent figure.

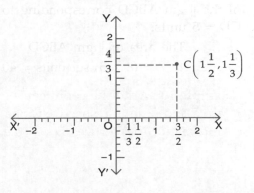

Example 7 Plot the points A (0, 3), B (1, 5) and C (–2, –1) on a graph paper and check whether they are collinear (lie on the same straight line) or not.

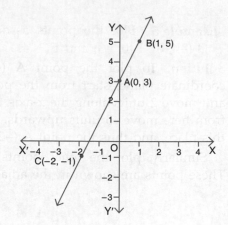

Solution. Plot the points A(0, 3), B(1, 5) and C (–2, –1) on the graph paper as usual. On joining the points A and B by a straight line, we find that the point C(–2, –1) lies on this line. Hence, the given points A(0, 3), B (1, 5) and C (–2, –1) are collinear.

Example 8 Three vertices (corners) of a rectangle are A(1, 3), B(1, –1) and C(7, –1). Plot these points on a graph paper and hence, use it to find the coordinates of the fourth vertex. Also find the area of the rectangle.

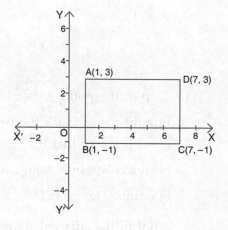

Solution. Plot the points A (1, 3), B (1, –1) and C (7, –1) on the graph paper as usual. Join the points to complete the rectangle ABCD as shown in the adjacent figure. Now read the coordinates of the point D from the graph paper. Clearly, the point D is (7, 3), and length of rectangle = 6 units and breadth = 4 units.

∴   Area of rectangle ABCD = (6 × 4) sq. units
                                        = 24 sq. units.

Example 9 Three vertices of a parallelogram are A(–2, 2), B(6, 2) and C(4, –3). Plot these points on a graph paper and hence, use it to find the coordinates of the fourth vertex D. Also find the coordinates of the mid-point of the side CD. What is the area of the parallelogram?

Solution. Plot the points A(–2, 2), B(6, 2) and C(4, –3) as usual.

Complete the parallelogram ABCD.

From graph, the coordinates of the point D are (–4, –3).

The coordinates of the mid-point M of CD are (0, –3).

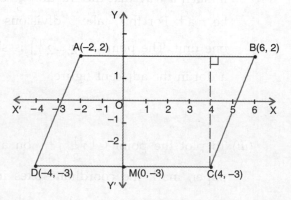

From figure, CD = 8 units and the height of the ‖ gm ABCD corresponding to the side CD = 5 units.

∴   The area of ‖ gm ABCD
        = (8 × 5) sq. units = 40 sq. units.

Example 10 Write the coordinates of the vertices of a rectangle whose length and breadth are 5 and 3 units respectively, one vertex is at the origin, the longer side lies along x-axis and one of the vertices lies in the third quadrant.

Solution. Draw a rectangle OABC on a graph paper with length 5 units and breadth 3 units with one vertex at origin O, the longer side along x-axis and one vertex in the third quadrant as shown in the adjoining figure. The coordinates of its vertices are O(0, 0), A(0, −3), B(−5, −3) and C(−5, 0).

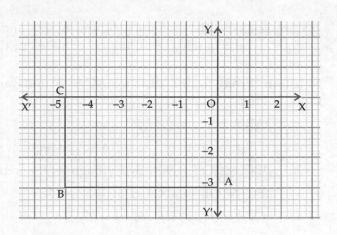

Example 11 The adjoining figure shows an isosceles triangle OAB with sides OA = AB = 13 units and OB = 10 units. Find the coordinates of the vertices.

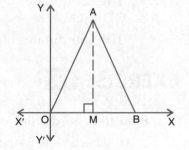

Solution. From A, draw AM ⊥ OB.

Then M is mid-point of OB,

so   OM = MB = 5 units.

In $\triangle$AOM, $\angle$M = 90°. By Pythagoras theorem, we get

$$OA^2 = OM^2 + AM^2 \Rightarrow 13^2 = 5^2 + AM^2$$

$\Rightarrow \quad AM^2 = 169 - 25 = 144$

$\Rightarrow \quad AM = 12$ units.

Clearly, coordinates of O and B are (0, 0) and (10, 0) respectively. As OM = 5 units and AM = 12 units, therefore, coordinates of A are (5, 12).

Example 12 In the adjoining figure, ABC is an equilateral triangle. Find the coordinates of the vertices.

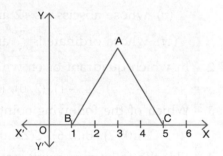

Solution. From figure, BC = 4 units.

As ABC is an equilateral triangle,

AB = AC = 4 units.

From A, draw AM ⊥ BC, then M is mid-point of BC.

So, BM = $\frac{1}{2}$ BC = $\frac{1}{2} \times 4$ units = 2 units.

In $\triangle$ABM, $\angle$M = 90°. By Pythagoras theorem, we get

$$AB^2 = AM^2 + BM^2$$

$\Rightarrow \quad 4^2 = AM^2 + 2^2$

$\Rightarrow \quad AM^2 = 16 - 4 = 12 \Rightarrow AM = 2\sqrt{3}$ units.

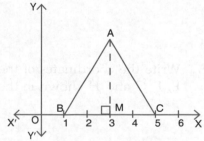

From figure, OM = OB + BM = (1 + 2) units = 3 units.

Clearly, coordinates of B and C are (1, 0) and (5, 0) respectively.

As OM = 3 units and AM = $2\sqrt{3}$ units, therefore, coordinates of A are (3, $2\sqrt{3}$).

Example 13 In the adjoining figure, ΔABC and ΔADB are equilateral triangles. Find the coordinates of the points C and D.

Solution. From figure, distance AO = 3 units and distance OB = 3 units

$\Rightarrow$ AB = 6 units

$\Rightarrow$ BC = 6 units   ($\because$ ΔABC is equilateral)

In ΔOBC, ∠COB = 90°. By Pythagoras theorem,

$$BC^2 = OB^2 + OC^2 \Rightarrow 6^2 = 3^2 + OC^2$$

$\Rightarrow$ $OC^2 = 6^2 + 3^2 = 36 - 9 = 27$

$\Rightarrow$ $OC = \sqrt{27}$ units $= 3\sqrt{3}$ units.

$\therefore$ The coordinates of the point C are $(0, 3\sqrt{3})$.

Also OD = OC.

$\therefore$ The coordinates of the point D are $(0, -3\sqrt{3})$.

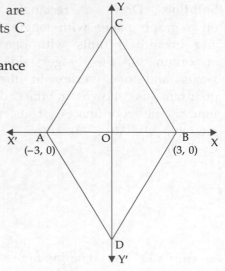

EXERCISE 19.1

1 Find the coordinates of points whose

    (*i*) abscissa is 3 and ordinate −4.

    (*ii*) abscissa is $-\dfrac{3}{2}$ and ordinate 5.

    (*iii*) whose abscissa is $-1\dfrac{2}{3}$ and ordinate $-2\dfrac{1}{4}$.

    (*iv*) whose ordinate is 5 and abscissa is −2.

    (*v*) whose abscissa is −2 and lies on *x*-axis.

    (*vi*) whose ordinate is $\dfrac{3}{2}$ and lies on *y*-axis.

2 In which quadrant or on which axis each of the following points lie?

    (−3, 5), (4, −1), (2, 0), (2, 2), (−3, −6)

3 Which of the following points lie on (*i*) *x*-axis? (*ii*) *y*-axis?

    A(0, 2), B(5, 6), C(23, 0), D(0, 23), E(0, −4), F(−6, 0), G($\sqrt{3}$, 0)

4 Plot the following points on the same graph paper :

    A(3, 4), B(−3, 1), C(1, −2), D(−2, −3), E(0, 5), F(5, 0), G(0, −3), H(−3, 0).

5 Write the coordinates of the points A, B, C, D, E, F, G and H shown in the adjacent figure.

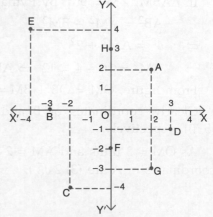

6 In which quadrants are the points A, B, C and D of problem 5 located?

7 Plot the following points on the same graph paper:

$$A\left(2,\frac{5}{2}\right), B\left(-\frac{3}{2},3\right), C\left(\frac{1}{2},-\frac{3}{2}\right) \text{ and } D\left(-\frac{5}{2},-\frac{1}{2}\right).$$

8 Plot the following points on the same graph paper:

$$A\left(\frac{4}{3},-1\right), B\left(\frac{7}{2},\frac{5}{3}\right), C\left(\frac{13}{6},0\right), D\left(-\frac{5}{3},-\frac{5}{2}\right).$$

9 Plot the following points and check whether they are collinear or not:

    (*i*) (1, 3), (–1, –1) and (–2, –3)   (*ii*) (1, 2), (2, –1) and (–1, 4)

    (*iii*) (0, 1), (2, –2) and $\left(\frac{2}{3},0\right)$.

10 Plot the point P(–3, 4). Draw PM and PN perpendiculars to *x*-axis and *y*-axis respectively. State the coordinates of the points M and N.

11 Plot the points A(1, 2), B(–4, 2), C(–4, –1) and D (1, –1). What kind of quadrilateral is ABCD? Also find the area of the quadrilateral ABCD.

12 Plot the points (0, 2), (3, 0), (0, –2) and (–3, 0) on a graph paper. Join these points (in order). Name the figure so obtained and find the area of the figure obtained.

13 Three vertices of a square are A(2, 3), B(–3, 3) and C(–3, –2). Plot these points on a graph paper and hence, use it to find the coordinates of the fourth vertex. Also find the area of the square.

14 Write the coordinates of the vertices of a rectangle which is 6 units long and 4 units wide if the rectangle is in the first quadrant, its longer side lies on the *x*-axis and one vertex is at the origin.

15 In the adjoining figure, ABCD is a rectangle with length 6 units and breadth 3 units. If O is mid-point of AB, find the coordinates of A, B, C and D.

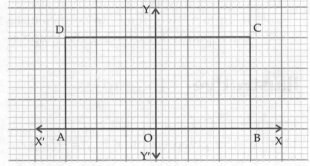

16 The adjoining figure shows an equilateral triangle OAB with each side = 2*a* units. Find the coordinates of the vertices.

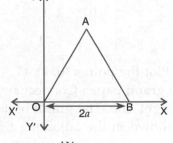

17 In the adjoining figure, ΔPQR is equilateral. If the coordinates of the points Q and R are (0, 2) and (0, –2) respectively, find the coordinates of the point P.

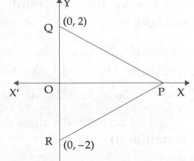

19.3 DEPENDENT AND INDEPENDENT VARIABLES

*If there is a formula between two variables, then the subject of the formula is called **dependent variable** and the other variable is called **independent variable**.*

For example:

(*i*) If A represents the area of a circle of radius R, then we know that A is given by the formula

$$A = \pi R^2.$$

Here, A is dependent variable and R is independent variable.

(*ii*) In the equation/formula $y = 3x + 5$, y is dependent variable and x is independent variable.

By giving different values to the independent variable, we can find the corresponding values of the dependent variable.

19.4 GRAPHS OF LINEAR EQUATIONS IN TWO VARIABLES

The graph of a linear equation in two variables is always a straight line.

To draw graphs of linear equations in two variables x and y, proceed as under:

(*i*) Rewrite the given equation with y as the subject.

(*ii*) Select any three convenient values of x and find the corresponding values of y for each of the selected value of x.

(*iii*) Make table of values.

(*iv*) Draw the axes on the graph paper and choose suitable scale (same on both axes).

(*v*) Plot the points on the graph paper (coordinate plane).

(*vi*) Connect any two points by a straight line and check that the third point lies on it. In fact, two points are sufficient to fix the position of a straight line but we use three points for drawing the graph to check the correctness of the graph.

Illustrative Examples

Example 1 Draw the graph of $y = -2x + 1$.

Solution. The given equation is $y = -2x + 1$.

Table of values

x	0	1	-1
y	1	-1	3

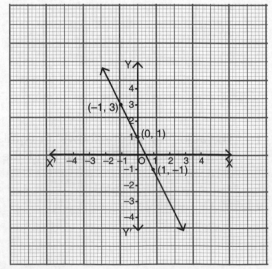

Plot the points $(0, 1)$, $(1, -1)$ and $(-1, 3)$ on the graph paper. Connect any two points by a straight line. The graph of the given equation is shown in the adjoining figure.

Observe that the third point lies on the straight line.

Example 2 Draw the graph of $3x - 2y - 2 = 0$.

Solution. The given equation is $3x - 2y - 2 = 0$, it can be written as

$$2y = 3x - 2 \quad \text{or} \quad y = \frac{3}{2}x - 1 \qquad \qquad ...(i)$$

Select any three values of x, say 0, 2, 4, and find the corresponding values of y by using equation (*i*).

When $x = 0$, $y = \dfrac{3}{2} \cdot 0 - 1 = -1$,

$x = 2$, $y = \dfrac{3}{2} \cdot 2 - 1 = 2$,

$x = 4$, $y = \dfrac{3}{2} \cdot 4 - 1 = 5$.

Table of values

x	0	2	4
y	−1	2	5

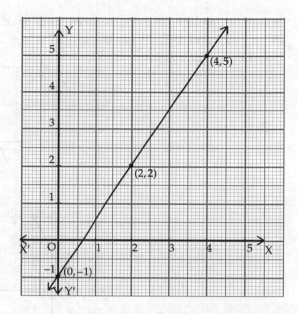

Select coordinate axes and take 1 cm = 1 unit on both the axes.

Plot the points $(0, -1)$, $(2, 2)$ and $(4, 5)$ on the graph paper (coordinate plane). Connect any two points by a straight line. The graph of the given linear equation is shown in the adjoining figure.

Observe that the third point lies on the straight line.

Remark

Select values of x in such a manner that the points to be plotted are not too close.

Example 3 Draw the graph of $2x + 3y = 6$ and use it to find the area of the triangle formed by the line and the coordinate axes. Take 1 cm = 1 unit on both the axes.

Solution. The given equation is $2x + 3y = 6$, it can be written as

$$3y = -2x + 6 \text{ or } y = -\dfrac{2}{3}x + 2 \qquad \ldots(i)$$

Select any three values of x, say 0, 3, − 3 and find the corresponding values of y by using equation (i).

When $x = 0$, $y = -\dfrac{2}{3} \cdot 0 + 2 = 2$,

$x = 3$, $y = -\dfrac{2}{3} \cdot 3 + 2 = 0$,

$x = -3$, $y = -\dfrac{2}{3}(-3) + 2 = 4$.

Table of values

x	0	3	−3
y	2	0	4

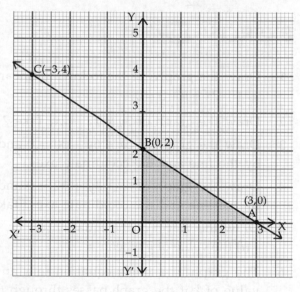

Select coordinate axes and take 1 cm = 1 unit on both the axes. Plot the points A(3, 0), B(0, 2) and C(−3, 4) on the graph paper. Connect any two points by a straight line. The graph of the given equation is shown in the adjoining figure. Observe that the third point lies on the straight line.

Area of the triangle formed by the line and the coordinate axes

$$= \dfrac{1}{2} \times OA \times OB$$

$$= \dfrac{1}{2} \times 3 \times 2 = 3 \text{ sq. units.}$$

Example 4 The graph of a linear equation in x and y passes through A(–1, –1) and B(2, 5). Find the values of h and k if the graph passes through $(h, 4)$ and $\left(\dfrac{1}{2}, k\right)$.

Solution. Select coordinate axes and take 1 cm = 1 unit on both axes. Plot the points A(–1, –1) and B(2, 5) on the graph paper and draw a straight line passing through these points.

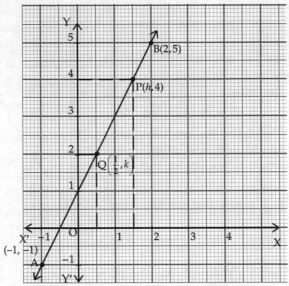

Through $y = 4$, draw a horizontal line to meet the graph of the straight line AB at the point P. Through P, draw a vertical line which meets x-axis at $x = \dfrac{3}{2}$

$\Rightarrow \quad h = \dfrac{3}{2}$.

Similarly, through $x = \dfrac{1}{2}$, draw a vertical line to meet the graph of the straight AB at Q. Through Q, draw a horizontal line which meets y-axis at $y = 2 \Rightarrow k = 2$.

Hence, $h = \dfrac{3}{2}$ and $k = 2$.

EXERCISE 19.2

1. Draw the graphs of the following linear equations:
   (i) $2x + y + 3 = 0$ (ii) $x – 5y – 4 = 0$.

2. Draw the graph of $3y = 12 – 2x$. Take 2 cm = 1 unit on both axes.

3. Draw the graph of $5x + 6y – 30 = 0$ and use it to find the area of the triangle formed by the line and the coordinate axes.

4. Draw the graph of $4x – 3y + 12 = 0$ and use it to find the area of the triangle formed by the line and the coordinate axes. Take 2 cm = 1 unit on both axes.

5. Draw the graph of the equation $y = 3x – 4$. Find graphically
   (i) the value of y when $x = –1$ (ii) the value of x when $y = 5$.

6. The graph of a linear equation in x and y passes through (4, 0) and (0, 3). Find the value of k if the graph passes through $(k, 1·5)$.

7. Use the table given alongside to draw the graph of a straight line. Find, graphically, the values of a and b.

x	1	2	3	a
y	–2	b	4	–5

19.5 GRAPHICAL SOLUTION OF A PAIR OF LINEAR EQUATIONS

To solve graphically a system of two simultaneous linear equations in two variables x and y, proceed as under:

(*i*) Draw graph (straight line) for each of the given linear equation.

(*ii*) Find the coordinates of the point of intersection of the two lines drawn.

(*iii*) The coordinates of the point of intersection of the two lines will be the *common solution* of the given equations.

(*iv*) *Write the values of x and y.*

Note *Check* the above solution by substituting the values of *x* and *y* (obtained above) in both the given equations.

Remarks

- If the two equations have a unique common solution, then the equations are called *consistent* and *independent*. In this case, the lines have one and only one point in common.

- If the two equations have several common solutions, then the equations are called *consistent* and *dependent*. In this case, the two lines will coincide.

- If the two equations have no common solution, then the equations are called *inconsistent*. In this case, the two lines will be parallel.

Illustrative Examples

Example 1 Solve the following system of equations graphically:

$$4x - y = 5, \quad 5y - 4x = 7.$$

Solution. The given equations can be written as

$$y = 4x - 5 \qquad \dots (i) \qquad \text{and} \qquad y = \frac{1}{5}(4x + 7) \qquad \dots (ii)$$

Table of values for equation (*i*)

x	1	0	3
y	−1	−5	7

Table of values for equation (*ii*)

x	−3	$-\frac{1}{2}$	2
y	−1	1	3

Select coordinate axes and take 1 cm = 1 unit on both the axes. Plot the points (1, −1), (0, −5) and (3, 7) on a graph paper. Connect any two points by a straight line.

Plot the points (−3, −1), $\left(-\frac{1}{2}, 1\right)$ and (2, 3) on the same graph paper. Connect any two points by a straight line. The graphs of both the straight lines are shown in the figure given below.

The lines intersect at the point P(2, 3). Therefore, the solution of the given equations is $x = 2, \ y = 3$.

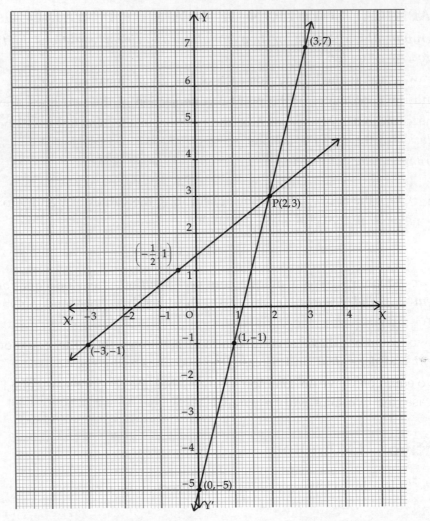

Check. On substituting $x = 2$, $y = 3$ in the given equations, we find that it satisfies both the given equations.

Example 2 Solve graphically the equations $4x - 3y = 0$ and $2x + 3y - 18 = 0$. Also find the ratio of the areas of the triangles formed by these lines and the coordinate axes.

Solution. The given equations can be written as

$$y = \frac{4}{3}x \qquad \ldots(i)$$

and

$$y = \frac{18 - 2x}{3} \qquad \ldots(ii)$$

Table of values for equation (i)

x	0	3	6
y	0	4	8

Table of values for equation (ii)

x	0	3	6
y	6	4	2

Select coordinate axes on the graph paper (as shown) and take 1 cm = 1 unit on both the axes.

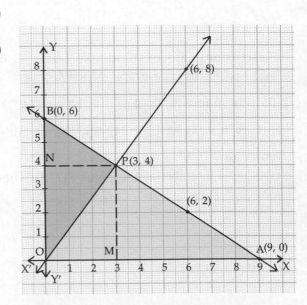

Plot the points (0, 0), (3, 4) and (6, 8) on the graph paper. Connect any two points by a straight line.

Plot the points (0, 6), (3, 4) and (6, 2) on the graph paper. Connect any two points by a straight line. The graphs of both the straight lines are shown in the adjoining figure.

The lines intersect at the point P(3, 4). Therefore, the solution of the given equations is $x = 3$, $y = 4$.

Note that the line $4x - 3y = 0$ passes through origin and the line $2x + 3y - 18 = 0$ meets the x-axis at the point A(9, 0) and the y-axis at the point B(0, 6). There are two triangles *i.e.* $\triangle$POA and $\triangle$OPB formed by these lines and the coordinate axes.

From P, draw PM perpendicular to OA, and PN perpendicular to OB.

$$\text{Area of } \triangle POA = \frac{1}{2} \times \text{base} \times \text{height} = \frac{1}{2} \times OA \times MP$$

$$= \frac{1}{2} \times 9 \times 4 \text{ sq. units} = 18 \text{ sq. units}$$

and   area of $\triangle$OPB $= \frac{1}{2} \times OB \times NP = \frac{1}{2} \times 6 \times 3$ sq. units

$$= 9 \text{ sq. units}$$

$\therefore \quad \dfrac{\text{Area of } \triangle POA}{\text{Area of } \triangle OPB} = \dfrac{18}{9} = \dfrac{2}{1}$

$\Rightarrow$ Area of $\triangle$POA : Area of $\triangle$OPB = 2 : 1.

Example 3 Find graphically the vertices of the triangle whose sides have equations $2y - x = 8$, $5y - x = 14$ and $y - 2x = 1$ respectively. Take 1 cm = 1 unit on both axes.

Solution. The given equations can be written as

$$y = \frac{1}{2}(x + 8) \qquad\qquad\qquad\qquad\qquad\qquad\qquad\qquad \dots(i)$$

$$y = \frac{1}{5}(x + 14) \qquad \dots(ii) \qquad\qquad y = 2x + 1 \qquad\qquad \dots(iii)$$

Select coordinate axes and take 1 cm = 1 unit on both the axes. Plot the points (0, 4), (2, 5) and (−2, 3) on the graph paper (coordinate plane). Connect any two points by a straight line.

Table of values for equation (*i*)

x	0	2	−2
y	4	5	3

Plot the points (− 4, 2), (1, 3) and (6, 4) on the same graph paper and connect any two points by a straight line.

Table of values for equation (*ii*)

x	−4	1	6
y	2	3	4

Plot the points (0, 1), (1, 3) and (2,5) on the same graph paper and connect any two points by a straight line.

Table of values for equation (*iii*)

x	0	1	2
y	1	3	5

The graphs of the three lines are shown in the figure given below.

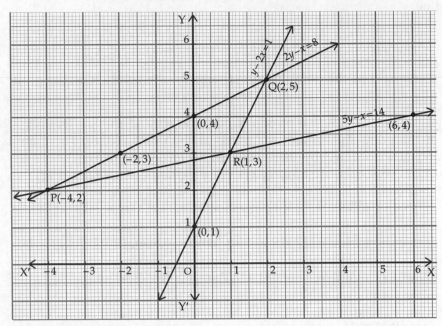

The lines intersect at the points P, Q, R. Therefore, the vertices of the triangle formed by the given lines are (– 4, 2), (2, 5) and (1, 3).

Example 4 A triangle is formed by the lines $x + 2y - 3 = 0$, $3x - 2y + 7 = 0$ and $y + 1 = 0$. Find graphically

(i) the coordinates of the vertices of the triangle.

(ii) the area of the triangle.

Solution. The given equations can be written as

$$y = -\frac{1}{2}(x - 3) \qquad \qquad \qquad \qquad ...(i)$$

$$y = \frac{1}{2}(3x + 7) \qquad \qquad \qquad \qquad ...(ii)$$

$$y = -1 \qquad \qquad \qquad \qquad \qquad ...(iii)$$

Select coordinate axes and take 1 cm = 1 unit on both the axes. Plot the points (3, 0), (1, 1) and (–1, 2) on the graph paper (coordinate plane). Connect any two points by a straight line.

Table of values for equation (i)

x	3	1	–1
y	0	1	2

Plot the points (–1, 2), $\left(-2, \frac{1}{2}\right)$ and (–3, –1) on the same graph paper and connect any two points by a straight line.

Table of values for equation (ii)

x	–1	–2	–3
y	2	$\frac{1}{2}$	–1

Plot the points (0, –1), (2, –1) and (4, –1) on the same graph paper and connect any two points by a straight line.

Table of values for equation (iii)

x	0	2	4
y	–1	–1	–1

The graphs of the three lines are shown in the figure below.

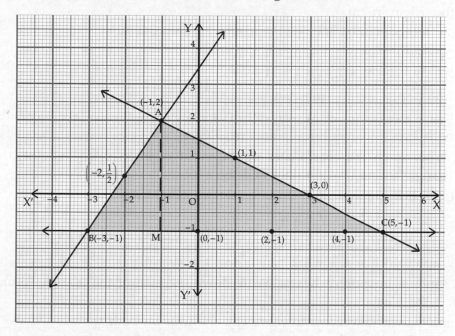

Let the lines intersect at the points A, B and C.

(*i*) The coordinates of the vertices of the triangle formed by the given lines are A(−1, 2), B(− 3, −1) and C(5, −1).

(*ii*) From A, draw AM perpendicular to BC.

Area of ΔABC $= \dfrac{1}{2} \times$ base $\times$ height $= \dfrac{1}{2} \times$ BC $\times$ AM

$$= \dfrac{1}{2} \times 8 \times 3 \text{ sq. units} = 12 \text{ sq. units.}$$

EXERCISE 19.3

1 Solve the following equations graphically: $3x - 2y = 4$, $5x - 2y = 0$.

2 Solve the following pair of equations graphically. Plot atleast 3 points for each straight line.

$$2x - 7y = 6, \quad 5x - 8y = -4.$$

3 Using the same axes of coordinates and the same unit, solve graphically.

$$x + y = 0, 3x - 2y = 10.$$

4 Take 1 cm to represent 1 unit on each axis to draw the graphs of the equations $4x - 5y = -4$ and $3x = 2y - 3$ on the same graph sheet (same axes). Use your graph to find the solution of the above simultaneous equations.

5 Solve the following simultaneous equations graphically:

$$x + 3y = 8, 3x = 2 + 2y.$$

6 Solve graphically the simultaneous equations $3y = 5 - x, 2x = y + 3$.

(Take 2 cm = 1 unit on both axes).

7 Use graph paper for this question. Take 2 cm = 1 unit on both axes.

(*i*) Draw the graphs of $x + y + 3 = 0$ and $3x - 2y + 4 = 0$. Plot three points per line.

(*ii*) Write down the coordinates of the point of intersection of the lines.

(*iii*) Measure and record the distance of the point of intersection of the lines from the origin in cm.

8 Solve the following simultaneous equations, graphically:

$2x - 3y + 2 = 4x + 1 = 3x - y + 2$.

Hint. $2x - 3y + 2 = 4x + 1$, $4x + 1 = 3x - y + 2$.

9 Use graph paper for this question.

(*i*) Draw the graphs of $3x - y - 2 = 0$ and $2x + y - 8 = 0$. Take 1 cm = 1 unit on both axes and plot three points per line.

(*ii*) Write down the coordinates of the point of intersection and the area of the triangle formed by the lines and the *x*-axis.

10 Solve the following system of linear equations graphically:

$2x - y - 4 = 0$, $x + y + 1 = 0$.

Hence, find the area of the triangle formed by these lines and the *y*-axis.

11 Solve graphically the following equations: $x + 2y = 4$, $3x - 2y = 4$.

Take 2 cm = 1 unit on each axis. Write down the area of the triangle formed by the lines and the *x*-axis.

12 On graph paper, take 2 cm to represent one unit on both the axes, draw the lines: $x + 3 = 0$, $y - 2 = 0$, $2x + 3y = 12$.

Write down the coordinates of the vertices of the triangle formed by these lines.

13 Find graphically the coordinates of the vertices of the triangle formed by the lines $y = 0$, $y = x$ and $2x + 3y = 10$. Hence, find the area of the triangle formed by these lines.

19.6 DISTANCE FORMULA

Find the distance between two points whose coordinates are given.

Let P (x_1, y_1) and Q (x_2, y_2) be two given points in the coordinate plane.

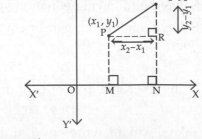

Draw PM, QN perpendiculars on *x*-axis and PR perpendicular on NQ.

From the figure,

$$PR = MN = ON - OM$$
$$= x_2 - x_1 \qquad \dots(i)$$
$$RQ = NQ - NR = NQ - MP$$
$$= y_2 - y_1 \qquad \dots(ii)$$

From right-angled $\triangle PRQ$, by Pythagoras Theorem, we get

$$PQ^2 = PR^2 + RQ^2$$
$$= (x_2 - x_1)^2 + (y_2 - y_1)^2 \qquad \text{(using } (i) \text{ and } (ii))$$

$\therefore \quad PQ = \sqrt{(x_2 - x_1)^2 + (y_2 - y_1)^2}$.

(only positive square root is to be taken because PQ being the distance between two points is positive)

Corollary. The distance of the point (x, y) from the origin $(0, 0)$

$$= \sqrt{(x - 0)^2 + (y - 0)^2} = \sqrt{x^2 + y^2}.$$

Remarks

- We can also write, $PQ = \sqrt{(x_1 - x_2)^2 + (y_1 - y_2)^2}$.
- The formula remains the same if the points $P(x_1, y_1)$ and $Q(x_2, y_2)$ are taken in different quadrants. For convenience, we have taken these points in the first quadrant.
- To prove that a quadrilateral is a
    - **(i)** *parallelogram,* show that opposite sides are equal.
    - **(ii)** *rhombus,* show that all sides are equal.
    - **(iii)** *rectangle,* show that opposite sides are equal and diagonals are also equal

        Or

        show that opposite sides are equal and one angle is 90°.
    - **(iv)** *square,* show that all sides are equal and diagonals are also equal

        Or

        show that all sides are equal and one angle is 90°.

Illustrative Examples

Example 1 Find the distance between the points $P(-5, 7)$ and $Q(-1, 3)$.

Solution. Let $P(-5, 7) \equiv P(x_1, y_1)$ and $Q(-1, 3) \equiv Q(x_2, y_2)$.

The distance between the given points = PQ

$$= \sqrt{(x_2 - x_1)^2 + (y_2 - y_1)^2} = \sqrt{(-1-(-5))^2 + (3-7)^2} = \sqrt{4^2 + (-4)^2}$$
$$= \sqrt{16 + 16} = \sqrt{32} = 4\sqrt{2} \text{ units.}$$

Example 2 Find the values of y for which the distance between the points $P(2, -3)$ and $Q(10, y)$ is 10 units.

Solution. Given $P(2, -3)$, $Q(10, y)$ and $PQ = 10$

$$\Rightarrow \quad \sqrt{(10-2)^2 + (y-(-3))^2} = 10 \Rightarrow 64 + (y + 3)^2 = 100$$
$$\Rightarrow \quad (y + 3)^2 = 100 - 64 = 36$$
$$\Rightarrow \quad y + 3 = 6, -6 \Rightarrow y = 3, -9.$$

Hence, the values of y are 3, −9.

Example 3 Find the points on the x-axis which are at a distance of $2\sqrt{5}$ units from the point $(7, -4)$. How many such points are there?

Solution. Let $(x, 0)$ be any point on the x-axis.

Since the distance between the points $(x, 0)$ and $(7, -4)$ is $2\sqrt{5}$ units,

$$\therefore \quad \sqrt{(x-7)^2 + (0-(-4))^2} = 2\sqrt{5}$$
$$\Rightarrow \quad (x - 7)^2 + 16 = 20 \Rightarrow (x - 7)^2 = 4$$
$$\Rightarrow \quad x - 7 = 2, -2 \Rightarrow x = 9, 5.$$

$\therefore$ The points are $(9, 0)$ and $(5, 0)$.

The number of such points is 2.

Example 4 Find the value of k if the point $P(2, 4)$ is equidistant from the points $A(5, k)$ and $B(k, 7)$.

Solution. Given $P(2, 4)$ is equidistant from the points $A(5, k)$ and $B(k, 7)$, so $AP = BP$

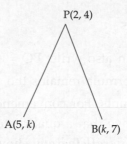

$\Rightarrow \quad \sqrt{(2-5)^2+(4-k)^2} = \sqrt{(2-k)^2+(4-7)^2}$

$\Rightarrow \quad 9+(4-k)^2 = (2-k)^2+9$

$\Rightarrow \quad 9+16-8k+k^2 = 4-4k+k^2+9$

$\Rightarrow \quad -4k = -12 \Rightarrow k = 3.$

Hence, the value of k is 3.

Example 5 Find a point on the y-axis which is equidistant from the points A(6, 5) and B(−4, 3).

Solution. Let P(0, y) be a point on y-axis which is equidistant from points A(6, 5) and B(−4, 3), then

$\quad\quad$ AP = BP

$\Rightarrow \quad \sqrt{(0-6)^2+(y-5)^2} = \sqrt{(0-(-4))^2+(y-3)^2}$

$\Rightarrow \quad 36+(y-5)^2 = 16+(y-3)^2$

$\Rightarrow \quad 36+y^2-10y+25 = 16+y^2-6y+9$

$\Rightarrow \quad -4y+36 = 0 \Rightarrow y = 9.$

Hence, the required point is (0, 9).

Example 6 Find a relation between x and y such that the point (x, y) is equidistant from the points (3, 6) and (−3, 4).

Solution. Let P(x, y) be equidistant from the points A(3, 6) and B(−3, 4).

Then, AP = BP $\Rightarrow$ AP^2 = BP^2

$\Rightarrow \quad (x-3)^2+(y-6)^2 = (x+3)^2+(y-4)^2$

$\Rightarrow \quad x^2-6x+9+y^2-12y+36 = x^2+6x+9+y^2-8y+16$

$\Rightarrow \quad -12x-4y+20 = 0$

$\Rightarrow \quad 3x+y-5 = 0,$ which is the required relation.

Example 7 If the point P(x, y) is equidistant from the points A($a+b$, $b-a$) and B($a-b$, $a+b$), prove that $bx = ay$.

Solution. Given P(x, y) is equidistant from the points A($a+b$, $b-a$) and B($a-b$, $a+b$), so

$\quad\quad$ AP = BP $\Rightarrow$ AP^2 = BP^2

$\Rightarrow \quad (x-(a+b))^2+(y-(b-a))^2 = (x-(a-b))^2+(y-(a+b))^2$

$\Rightarrow \quad (x-a-b)^2-(x-a+b)^2 = (y-a-b)^2-(y-b+a)^2$

$\Rightarrow \quad \overline{(x-a-b+x-a+b)}\,\overline{(x-a-b-x-a+b)} = \overline{(y-a-b+y-b+a)}\,\overline{(y-a-b-y-b+a)}$

$\Rightarrow \quad (2x-2a)(-2b) = (2y-2b)(-2a)$

$\Rightarrow \quad b(x-a) = a(y-b) \Rightarrow bx-ab = ay-ab$

$\Rightarrow \quad bx = ay,$ as required.

Example 8 Find the coordinates of the point Q on the x-axis which lies on the perpendicular bisector of the line joining the points A(−5, −2) and B(4, −2). Name the type of triangle formed by the points Q, A and B.

Solution. As the point Q is on the x-axis, so the point Q is (x, 0).

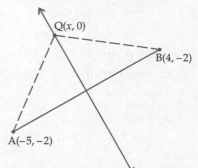

Given, point Q lies on the perpendicular bisector of the line segment joining the points A(−5, −2) and B(4, −2), therefore, Q is equidistant from points A and B *i.e.* AQ = BQ

$\Rightarrow \quad$ AQ^2 = BQ^2

$\Rightarrow \quad (x+5)^2+(0+2)^2 = (x-4)^2+(0+2)^2$

$\Rightarrow \quad x^2 + 10x + 25 + 4 = x^2 - 8x + 16 + 4$

$\Rightarrow \quad 18x = -9 \Rightarrow x = -\dfrac{1}{2}.$

Hence, the point Q is $\left(-\dfrac{1}{2}, 0\right)$.

As AQ = BQ, so the triangle formed by the points Q, A and B is isosceles.

Example 9 If the point A(2, −4) is equidistant from the points P(3, 8) and Q(−10, y), find the values of y. Also find distance PQ.

Solution. As the point A(2, −4) is equidistant from the points P(3, 8) and Q(−10, y), we have

$AQ = AP \Rightarrow AQ^2 = AP^2$

$\Rightarrow \quad (-10 - 2)^2 + (y + 4)^2 = (3 - 2)^2 + (8 + 4)^2$

$\Rightarrow \quad 144 + (y + 4)^2 = 1 + 144 \Rightarrow (y + 4)^2 = 1$

$\Rightarrow \quad y + 4 = 1, -1 \Rightarrow y = -3, -5.$

Hence, the values of y are −3, −5.

Distance PQ = $\sqrt{(-10-3)^2 + (y-8)^2}$

When $y = -3$, PQ = $\sqrt{(-10-3)^2 + (-3-8)^2} = \sqrt{169 + 121} = \sqrt{290}$;

when $y = -5$, PQ = $\sqrt{(-10-3)^2 + (-5-8)^2} = \sqrt{169 + 169} = 13\sqrt{2}$.

Example 10 Find the points on the x-axis whose distances from the points (2, 3) and $\left(\dfrac{3}{2}, -1\right)$ are in the ratio 2 : 1.

Solution. Let P $(x, 0)$ be any point on the x-axis. Let the given points be A (2, 3) and B $\left(\dfrac{3}{2}, -1\right)$, then

$AP = \sqrt{(x-2)^2 + (0-3)^2}$ and $BP = \sqrt{\left(x - \dfrac{3}{2}\right)^2 + (0-(-1))^2}$.

According to given, $\dfrac{AP}{BP} = \dfrac{2}{1} \Rightarrow AP = 2BP$

$\Rightarrow \quad \sqrt{(x-2)^2 + 9} = 2 \cdot \sqrt{\left(x - \dfrac{3}{2}\right)^2 + 1}$

$\Rightarrow \quad (x-2)^2 + 9 = 4\left[\left(x - \dfrac{3}{2}\right)^2 + 1\right]$

$\Rightarrow \quad x^2 - 4x + 4 + 9 = 4\left[x^2 - 3x + \dfrac{9}{4} + 1\right]$

$\Rightarrow \quad x^2 - 4x + 13 = 4x^2 - 12x + 13$

$\Rightarrow \quad -3x^2 + 8x = 0 \Rightarrow x(-3x + 8) = 0$

$\Rightarrow \quad x = 0$ or $-3x + 8 = 0 \Rightarrow x = 0$ or $\dfrac{8}{3}$.

Hence, the required points are (0, 0) or $\left(\dfrac{8}{3}, 0\right)$.

Example 11 The centre of a circle is (2a, a − 7). Find the values of a if the circle passes through the point (11, −9) and has diameter $10\sqrt{2}$ units.

Solution. Radius of circle = $\dfrac{1}{2} \times 10\sqrt{2} = 5\sqrt{2}$.

The centre of the circle is C(2a, a − 7) and it passes through the point P(11, −9), so CP = radius of circle

$\Rightarrow \quad \sqrt{(2a-11)^2 + (a-7+9)^2} = 5\sqrt{2}$

$\Rightarrow \quad (2a - 11)^2 + (a + 2)^2 = (5\sqrt{2})^2$

$\Rightarrow \quad 4a^2 - 44a + 121 + a^2 + 4a + 4 = 50$

$\Rightarrow \quad 5a^2 - 40a + 75 = 0 \Rightarrow a^2 - 8a + 15 = 0$

$\Rightarrow \quad (a - 3)(a - 5) = 0 \Rightarrow a = 3, 5.$

Hence, the values of a are 3, 5.

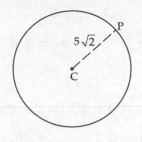

Example 12 Points A(−1, y) and B(5, 7) lie on a circle with centre O(2, −3y). Find the value of y. Hence, find the radius of the circle.

Solution. As points A(−1, y) and B(5, 7) lie on a circle with centre O(2, −3y),

$\qquad$ OA = OB $\hfill$ (each being radius)

$\Rightarrow \quad$ OA^2 = OB^2

$\Rightarrow \quad (-1 - 2)^2 + (y - (-3y))^2 = (5 - 2)^2 + (7 - (-3y))^2$

$\Rightarrow \quad 9 + (4y)^2 = 9 + (7 + 3y)^2$

$\Rightarrow \quad 16y^2 = 49 + 42y + 9y^2 \Rightarrow 7y^2 - 42y - 49 = 0$

$\Rightarrow \quad y^2 - 6y - 7 = 0 \Rightarrow (y - 7)(y + 1) = 0 \Rightarrow y = 7, -1.$

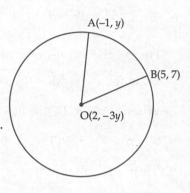

Radius of circle = OA = $\sqrt{(-1-2)^2 + (y-(-3y))^2} = \sqrt{9+16y^2}$.

When $y = 7$, radius = $\sqrt{9+16\times 7^2} = \sqrt{9+784} = \sqrt{793}$ units;

when $y = -1$, radius = $\sqrt{9+16\times(-1)^2} = \sqrt{9+16}$ = 5 units.

Example 13 Do the points P (3, 2), Q (−2, −3) and R (2, 3) form a triangle? If so, name the type of triangle formed.

Solution. PQ = $\sqrt{(-2-3)^2 + (-3-2)^2} = \sqrt{25+25} = \sqrt{50} = 5\sqrt{2}$,

$\qquad$ QR = $\sqrt{(2+2)^2 + (3+3)^2} = \sqrt{16+36} = \sqrt{52} = 2\sqrt{13}$ and

$\qquad$ PR = $\sqrt{(2-3)^2 + (3-2)^2} = \sqrt{1+1} = \sqrt{2}$.

Sum of two smaller distances = $5\sqrt{2} + \sqrt{2} = 6\sqrt{2}$.

Now $6\sqrt{2} > 2\sqrt{13}$ if 72 > 52, which is true.

Therefore, the given points form a triangle.

Also PQ^2 + PR^2 = $(5\sqrt{2})^2 + (\sqrt{2})^2 = 50 + 2 = 52 = $ QR^2

$\Rightarrow \quad$ PQR is a right triangle.

Example 14 By using distance formula, show that the points (4, 2), (7, 5) and (9, 7) are collinear.

Solution. Let the points be A(4, 2), B(7, 5) and C(9, 7), then

$\qquad$ AB = $\sqrt{(7-4)^2 + (5-2)^2} = \sqrt{9+9} = \sqrt{18} = 3\sqrt{2}$,

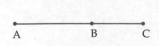

$\qquad$ BC = $\sqrt{(9-7)^2 + (7-5)^2} = \sqrt{4+4} = \sqrt{8} = 2\sqrt{2}$ and

$\qquad$ AC = $\sqrt{(9-4)^2 + (7-2)^2} = \sqrt{25+25} = \sqrt{50} = 5\sqrt{2}$.

$\therefore \qquad$ AB + BC = $3\sqrt{2} + 2\sqrt{2} = 5\sqrt{2}$ = AC.

Hence, the given points are collinear.

Example 15 Show that the points (1, 7), (4, 2), (−1, −1) and (−4, 4) are the vertices of a square.

Solution. Let A(1, 7), B(4, 2), C(−1, −1) and D(−4, 4) be the given points.

$$AB = \sqrt{(4-1)^2 + (2-7)^2} = \sqrt{9+25} = \sqrt{34},$$

$$BC = \sqrt{(-1-4)^2 + (-1-2)^2} = \sqrt{25+9} = \sqrt{34},$$

$$CD = \sqrt{(-4+1)^2 + (4+1)^2} = \sqrt{9+25} = \sqrt{34} \text{ and}$$

$$DA = \sqrt{(-4-1)^2 + (4-7)^2} = \sqrt{25+9} = \sqrt{34}$$

$\Rightarrow$ AB = BC = CD = DA $\Rightarrow$ all the four sides are equal.

Also AC $= \sqrt{(-1-1)^2 + (-1-7)^2} = \sqrt{4+64} = \sqrt{68}$ and

$$BD = \sqrt{(-4-4)^2 + (4-2)^2} = \sqrt{64+4} = \sqrt{68}$$

$\Rightarrow$ AC = BD $\Rightarrow$ both the diagonals are equal.

Hence, the given points are the vertices of a square.

Alternatively

Find all the four sides AB, BC, CD, DA and one diagonal, say AC, as above.

Show that AB = BC = CD = DA.

Here, $AB^2 + BC^2 = 34 + 34 = 68$

$$= AC^2.$$

Therefore, by converse of Pythagoras theorem, $\angle B = 90°$.

Thus, all the four sides are equal and one angle is 90°.

Hence, ABCD is a square.

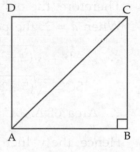

Example 16 Show that the points A(3, 0), B(4, 5), C(−1, 4) and D(−2, −1) taken in order are the vertices of a rhombus. Also find the area of the rhombus.

Solution. AB $= \sqrt{(4-3)^2 + (5-0)^2} = \sqrt{1+25} = \sqrt{26},$

$$BC = \sqrt{(-1-4)^2 + (4-5)^2} = \sqrt{25+1} = \sqrt{26},$$

$$CD = \sqrt{(-2+1)^2 + (-1-4)^2} = \sqrt{1+25} = \sqrt{26} \text{ and}$$

$$DA = \sqrt{(3+2)^2 + (0+1)^2} = \sqrt{25+1} = \sqrt{26}$$

$\Rightarrow$ AB = BC = CD = DA $\Rightarrow$ all the four sides are equal

$\Rightarrow$ ABCD is a rhombus.

Thus, the given points taken in order are the vertices of a rhombus.

Also AC $= \sqrt{(-1-3)^2 + (4-0)^2} = \sqrt{16+16} = \sqrt{32} = 4\sqrt{2}$ and

$$BD = \sqrt{(-2-4)^2 + (-1-5)^2} = \sqrt{36+36} = \sqrt{72} = 6\sqrt{2}.$$

Area of rhombus ABCD $= \dfrac{1}{2}$ (product of diagonals)

$$= \dfrac{1}{2} AC \times BD = \left(\dfrac{1}{2} \times 4\sqrt{2} \times 6\sqrt{2} \right) \text{ sq. units}$$

$$= 24 \text{ sq. units.}$$

Example 17 The points A(2, 9), B(a, 5) and C(5, 5) are the vertices of a triangle ABC right angled at B. Find the value(s) of a and hence find the area of △ABC.

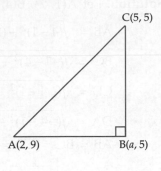

Solution. AB = $\sqrt{(a-2)^2 + (5-9)^2}$ = $\sqrt{(a-2)^2 + 16}$,

BC = $\sqrt{(5-a)^2 + (5-5)^2}$ = $\sqrt{(5-a)^2}$ and

AC = $\sqrt{(5-2)^2 + (5-9)^2}$ = $\sqrt{9+16}$ = 5.

Since ABC is a right angled triangle at B, ∠ABC = 90°.

By Pythagoras Theorem, we have

$AB^2 + BC^2 = AC^2$

$\Rightarrow \quad (a-2)^2 + 16 + (5-a)^2 = 5^2$

$\Rightarrow \quad a^2 - 4a + 4 + 16 + 25 - 10a + a^2 = 25$

$\Rightarrow \quad 2a^2 - 14a + 20 = 0 \Rightarrow a^2 - 7a + 10 = 0$

$\Rightarrow \quad (a - 2)(a - 5) = 0 \Rightarrow a = 2, 5.$

Note that when a = 5, the point B becomes (5, 5), so it becomes the same point as point C, which is not possible.

Therefore, the only admissible value of a is 2.

When a = 2, the point B comes (2, 5).

$\therefore \quad$ AB = $\sqrt{(2-2)^2 + (5-9)^2}$ = $\sqrt{16}$ = 4 and

BC = $\sqrt{(5-2)^2 + (5-5)^2}$ = $\sqrt{9}$ = 3.

$\therefore \quad$ Area of △ABC = $\frac{1}{2}$ base × height = $\frac{1}{2}$ AB × BC = $\left(\frac{1}{2} \times 4 \times 3\right)$ sq. units = 6 sq. units.

Hence, the value of a is 2 and area of △ABC = 6 sq. units.

Example 18 If two vertices of an equilateral triangle are (0, 0) and (3, 0), find the third vertex.

Solution. Given vertices are O (0, 0), A(3, 0) and let third vertex be B (x, y). Then

OA = $\sqrt{(3-0)^2 + (0-0)^2}$ = 3

OB = $\sqrt{(x-0)^2 + (y-0)^2}$ = $\sqrt{x^2 + y^2}$ and

AB = $\sqrt{(x-3)^2 + (y-0)^2}$ = $\sqrt{x^2 - 6x + 9 + y^2}$.

As △OAB is equilateral, OA = OB = AB

$\Rightarrow \quad$ OA = OB and OB = AB

$\Rightarrow \quad \sqrt{x^2 + y^2} = 3 \Rightarrow x^2 + y^2 = 9 \qquad \qquad \qquad \text{...(i)}$

and $\sqrt{x^2 + y^2} = \sqrt{x^2 - 6x + 9 + y^2} \Rightarrow x^2 + y^2 = x^2 - 6x + 9 + y^2$

$\Rightarrow \quad 6x = 9 \Rightarrow x = \frac{3}{2}.$

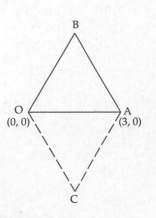

Substituting this value of x in (i), we get

$\left(\frac{3}{2}\right)^2 + y^2 = 9 \Rightarrow y^2 = 9 - \frac{9}{4} = \frac{27}{4} \Rightarrow y = \pm\frac{3\sqrt{3}}{2}$.

$\therefore \quad$ Third vertex of equilateral triangle is $\left(\frac{3}{2}, \frac{3\sqrt{3}}{2}\right)$ or $\left(\frac{3}{2}, -\frac{3\sqrt{3}}{2}\right)$.

Note that there are two equilateral triangles OAB and OAC with the point O(0, 0) and A(3, 0) as two vertices (as shown in the adjoining figure).

Example 19 Find the centre of a circle passing through the points (6, −6), (3, −7) and (3, 3). Also find its radius.

Solution. The given points are A(6, −6), B(3, −7) and C(3, 3).

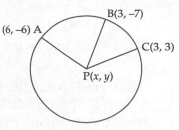

Let P (x, y) be the centre of the circle passing through the points A, B and C, then

$$AP = BP = CP$$

$\Rightarrow$ $\quad AP^2 = BP^2$ and $AP^2 = CP^2$

$\quad AP^2 = BP^2 \Rightarrow (x - 6)^2 + (y + 6)^2 = (x - 3)^2 + (y + 7)^2$

$\Rightarrow$ $\quad x^2 - 12x + 36 + y^2 + 12y + 36 = x^2 - 6x + 9 + y^2 + 14y + 49$

$\Rightarrow$ $\quad -6x - 2y + 14 = 0 \Rightarrow 3x + y - 7 = 0$ $\qquad$ ...(i)

$\quad AP^2 = CP^2 \Rightarrow (x - 6)^2 + (y + 6)^2 = (x - 3)^2 + (y - 3)^2$

$\Rightarrow$ $\quad x^2 - 12x + 36 + y^2 + 12y + 36 = x^2 - 6x + 9 + y^2 - 6y + 9$

$\Rightarrow$ $\quad -6x + 18y + 54 = 0 \Rightarrow x - 3y - 9 = 0$ $\qquad$ ...(ii)

Multiplying (i) by 3, we get

$$9x + 3y - 21 = 0 \qquad \qquad ...(iii)$$

On adding (ii) and (iii), we get

$$10x - 30 = 0 \Rightarrow x = 3.$$

Substituting this value of x in (i), we get

$$3 \times 3 + y - 7 = 0 \Rightarrow 9 + y - 7 = 0 \Rightarrow y = -2.$$

∴ The centre is (3, −2).

Radius = AP = $\sqrt{(3-6)^2 + (-2+6)^2}$ units = $\sqrt{9+16}$ units = 5 units.

Example 20 The two opposite vertices of a square are (−1, 2) and (3, 2). Find the coordinates of the other two vertices.

Solution. Let A (−1, 2) and C (3, 2) be two opposite vertices of the square ABCD and vertex B be (x, y).

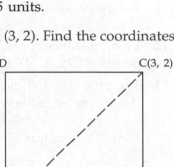

Since ABCD is a square, AB = BC

$\Rightarrow$ $\quad AB^2 = BC^2$

$\Rightarrow$ $\quad (x+1)^2 + (y - 2)^2 = (x - 3)^2 + (y - 2)^2$

$\Rightarrow$ $\quad x^2 + 2x + 1 = x^2 - 6x + 9 \Rightarrow 8x = 8$

$\Rightarrow$ $\quad x = 1.$

Also as ABCD is a square, $\angle B = 90°$

$\Rightarrow$ $\quad AB^2 + BC^2 = AC^2$

$\Rightarrow$ $\quad (x + 1)^2 + (y - 2)^2 + (x - 3)^2 + (y - 2)^2 = (3 + 1)^2 + (2 - 2)^2$

$\Rightarrow$ $\quad 2x^2 - 4x + 10 + 2y^2 - 8y + 8 = 16$

$\Rightarrow$ $\quad 2 \times 1^2 - 4 \times 1 + 2y^2 - 8y + 2 = 0$

$\Rightarrow$ $\quad 2y^2 - 8y = 0 \Rightarrow y (y - 4) = 0 \Rightarrow y = 0, 4.$

Hence, the other two vertices are (1, 0) and (1, 4).

EXERCISE 19.4

1 Find the distance between the following pairs of points:

$\quad$ (i) (2, 3), (4, 1) $\qquad$ (ii) (0, 0), (36, 15) $\qquad$ (iii) (a, b), (−a, −b)

2 A is a point on y-axis whose ordinate is 4 and B is a point on x-axis whose abscissa is −3. Find the length of the line segment AB.

3 Find the value of a, if the distance between the points A(–3, –14) and B(a, –5) is 9 units.

4   (*i*) Find points on the x-axis which are at a distance of 5 units from the point (5, –4).

    (*ii*) Find points on the y-axis which are at a distance of 10 units from the point (8, 8).

    (*iii*) Find point (or points) which are at a distance of $\sqrt{10}$ units from the point (4, 3) given that the ordinate of the point (or points) is twice the abscissa.

Hint. (*iii*) The point (points) are of the form (k, 2k).

5 Find the point on the x-axis which is equidistant from the points (2, –5) and (–2, 9).

6 Find the value of x such that PQ = QR where the coordinates of P, Q and R are (6, –1), (1, 3) and (x, 8) respectively.

7 If Q (0, 1) is equidistant from P (5, –3) and R (x, 6), find the values of x.

8 Find a relation between x and y such that the point (x, y) is equidistant from the points (7, 1) and (3, 5).

9 The x-coordinate of a point P is twice its y-coordinate. If P is equidistant from the points Q(2, –5) and R(–3, 6), then find the coordinates of P.

Hint. The point P is of the form (2k, k).

10 If the points A(4, 3) and B(x, 5) are on a circle with centre C(2, 3), find the value of x.

Hint. AC = BC.

11 If a point A(0, 2) is equidistant from the points B(3, p) and C(p, 5), then find the value of p.

12 Using distance formula, show that (3, 3) is the centre of the circle passing through the points (6, 2), (0, 4) and (4, 6).

13 The centre of a circle is C (2α – 1, 3α + 1) and it passes through the point A (–3, –1). If a diameter of the circle is of length 20 units, find the value (s) of α.

Hint. CA = radius of circle = $\dfrac{1}{2}$ × 20 units = 10 units

$$\Rightarrow \quad \sqrt{(2\alpha-1+3)^2 + (3\alpha+1+1)^2} = 10$$
$$\Rightarrow \quad (2(\alpha+1))^2 + (3\alpha+2)^2 = 100$$
$$\Rightarrow \quad 4(\alpha^2 + 2\alpha + 1) + 9\alpha^2 + 12\alpha + 4 - 100 = 0$$
$$\Rightarrow \quad 13\alpha^2 + 20\alpha - 92 = 0 \Rightarrow (\alpha - 2)(13\alpha + 46) = 0.$$

14 Using distance formula, show that the points A(3, 1), B(6, 4) and C(8, 6) are collinear.

15 Check whether the points (5, –2), (6, 4) and (7, –2) are the vertices of an isosceles triangle.

16 Name the type of triangle formed by the points A(–5, 6), B(–4, –2) and (7, 5).

17 Show that the points A (1, 1), B (–1, –1) and C (–$\sqrt{3}$, $\sqrt{3}$) form an equilateral triangle.

18 Show that the points (7, 10), (–2, 5) and (3, –4) are the vertices of an isosceles right triangle.

19 The points A (0, 3), B (–2, a) and C (–1, 4) are the vertices of a right angled triangle at A, find the value of a.

20 Show that the points (0, –1), (–2, 3), (6, 7) and (8, 3), taken in order, are the vertices of a rectangle. Also find its area.

21 If P(2, −1), Q(3, 4), R(−2, 3) and S(−3, −2) be four points in a plane, show that PQRS is a rhombus but not a square. Find the area of the rhombus.

Hint. Show that PQ = QR = RS = SP and PR ≠ QS.

22 Prove that the points A(2, 3), B(−2, 2), C(−1, −2) and D(3, −1) are the vertices of a square ABCD.

23 Name the type of quadrilateral formed by the following points and give reasons for your answer :

      (*i*) (−1, −2), (1, 0), (−1, 2), (−3, 0)   (*ii*) (4, 5), (7, 6), (4, 3), (1, 2)

24 Find the coordinates of the circumcentre of the triangle whose vertices are (8, 6), (8, −2) and (2, −2). Also, find its circumradius.

Multiple Choice Questions

Choose the correct answer from the given four options (1 to 25):

1 Point (−3, 5) lies in the

    (*a*) first quadrant   (*b*) second quadrant (*c*) third quadrant (*d*) fourth quadrant

2 Point (0, −7) lies

    (*a*) on the *x*-axis   (*b*) in the second quadrant

    (*c*) on the *y*-axis   (*d*) in the fourth quadrant

3 Abscissa of a point is positive in

    (*a*) I and II quadrants   (*b*) I and IV quadrants

    (*c*) I quadrant only   (*d*) II quadrant only

4 The point which lies on *y*-axis at a distance of 5 units in the negative direction of *y*-axis is

    (*a*) (0, 5)   (*b*) (5, 0)   (*c*) (0, −5)   (*d*) (−5, 0)

5 If the perpendicular distance of a point P from the *x*-axis is 5 units and the foot of perpendicular lies on the negative direction of *x*-axis, then the point P has

    (*a*) *x*-coordinate = −5   (*b*) *y*-coordinate = 5 only

    (*c*) *y*-coordinate = −5 only   (*d*) *y*-coordinate = 5 or −5

6 The points whose abscissa and ordinate have different signs will lie in

    (*a*) I and II quadrants   (*b*) II and III quadrants

    (*c*) I and III quadrants   (*d*) II and IV quadrants

7 The points (−5, 2) and (2, −5) lie in

    (*a*) same quadrant   (*b*) II and III quadrants respectively

    (*c*) II and IV quadrants respectively (*d*) IV and II quadrants respectively

8 If P(−1, 1), Q(3, −4), R(1, −1), S(−2, −3) and T(−4, 4) are plotted on the graph paper, then point(s) in the fourth quadrant are

    (*a*) P and T   (*b*) Q and R   (*c*) S only   (*d*) P and R

9 On plotting the points O(0, 0), A(3, 0), B(3, 4), C(0, 4) and joining OA, AB, BC and CO which of the following figure is obtained?

    (*a*) Square   (*b*) Rectangle   (*c*) Trapezium   (*d*) Rhombus

10 Which of the following points lie on the graph of the equation:

    $3x − 5y + 7 = 0$?

    (*a*) (1, −2)   (*b*) (2, 1)   (*c*) (−1, 2)   (*d*) (1, 2)

11 The pair of equation $x = a$ and $y = b$ graphically represents lines which are
   (a) parallel
   (b) intersecting at (b, a)
   (c) coincident
   (d) intersecting at (a, b)

12 The distance of the point P(2, 3) from the x-axis is
   (a) 2 units   (b) 3 units   (c) 1 unit   (d) 5 units

13 The distance of the point P(−4, 3) from the y-axis is
   (a) 5 units   (b) −4 units   (c) 4 units   (d) 3 units

14 The distance of the point P(−6, 8) from the origin is
   (a) 8 units   (b) $2\sqrt{7}$ units   (c) 10 units   (d) 6 units

15 The distance between the points A(0, 6) and B(0, −2) is
   (a) 6 units   (b) 8 units   (c) 4 units   (d) 2 units

16 The distance between the points (0, 5) and (−5, 0) is
   (a) 5 units   (b) $5\sqrt{2}$ units   (c) $2\sqrt{5}$ units   (d) 10 units

17 AOBC is a rectangle whose three vertices are A(0, 3), O(0, 0) and B(5, 0). The length of its diagonal is
   (a) 5 units   (b) 3 units   (c) $\sqrt{34}$ units   (d) 4 units

18 If the distance between the points (2, −2) and (−1, x) is 5 units, then one of the value of x is
   (a) −2   (b) 2   (c) −1   (d) 1

19 The distance between the points (4, p) and (1, 0) is 5 units, then the value of p is
   (a) 4 only   (b) −4 only   (c) ±4   (d) 0

20 The points (−4, 0), (4, 0) and (0, 3) are the vertices of a
   (a) right triangle
   (b) isosceles triangle
   (c) equilateral triangle
   (d) scalene triangle

21 The area of a square whose vertices are A (0, −2), B (3, 1), C (0, 4) and D (−3, 1) is
   (a) 18 sq. units   (b) 15 sq. units   (c) $\sqrt{18}$ sq. units   (d) $\sqrt{15}$ sq. units

22 In the adjoining figure, the area of the triangle ABC is
   (a) 15 sq. units
   (b) 10 sq. units
   (c) 7·5 sq. units
   (d) 2·5 sq. units

23 The perimeter of a triangle with vertices (0, 4), (0, 0) and (3, 0) is
   (a) 5 units   (b) 12 units   (c) 11 units   (d) $7 + \sqrt{5}$ units

24 If A is a point on the y-axis whose ordinate is 5 and B is the point (−3, 1), then the length of AB is
   (a) 8 units   (b) 5 units   (c) 3 units   (d) 25 units

25 The points A(9, 0), B(9, 6), C(−9, 6) and D(−9, 0) are the vertices of a
   (a) rectangle   (b) square   (c) rhombus   (d) trapezium

S ummary

○ An **ordered pair** is a pair of objects taken in a specific order.

○ Two number lines X'OX and Y'OY drawn horizontal and vertical respectively on a graph paper form coordinate system. The point O is called origin. The horizontal line X'OX is called x-axis and vertical line Y'OY is called y-axis. The line X'OX and Y'OY taken together are called coordinate axes.

○ From any point P in the coordinate plane, if we drawn PM perpendicular to X'OX, then

    (i) OM (= x) is called x-coordinate or abscissa of P.

    (ii) MP (= y) is called y-coordinate or ordinate of P.

    (iii) Coordinates of P are written as (x, y) or P(x, y).

○ The x-coordinate is taken positive to the right of origin and negative to the left of origin. The y-coordinate is taken positive above the origin and negative below the origin.

○ Corresponding to every point in the coordinate plane, we get a unique ordered pair (x, y) of real numbers, and conversely, corresponding to every ordered pair (x, y) of real numbers we get a unique point in the coordinate plane.

○ If there is a formula between two variables, then the subject of the formula is called **dependent variable** and the other variable is called independent variable.

○ The graph of a linear equation in two variables is always a straight line.

○ To draw the graph of a linear equation in two variable, proceed as under :

    (i) Rewrite the given equation with y as the subject.

    (ii) Select any three convenient values of x and find the corresponding values of y for each of the selected value of x.

    (iii) Make table of values.

    (iv) Draw the axes on the graph paper and choose suitable scale (same on both axes).

    (v) Plot the points on the graph paper.

    (vi) Connect any points by a straight line and check that the third point lies on it.

❏ **Graphical solution of a pair of linear equation**

To solve graphically a system of two simultaneous linear equations in two variables x and y, proceed as under:

    (i) Draw graph (straight line) for each of the given linear equation.

    (ii) Find the coordinates of the point of intersection of the two lines drawn.

    (iii) The coordinates of the point of intersection of the two lines will be the solution of the given equations.

    (iv) Write the values of x and y.

1. Three vertices of a rectangle are A (2, –1), B (2, 7) and C (4, 7). Plot these points on a graph and hence use it to find the coordinates of the fourth vertex D. Also find the coordinates of

    (i) the mid-point of BC

    (ii) the mid-point of CD

    (iii) the point of intersection of the diagonals.

    What is the area of the rectangle?

2. Three vertices of a parallelogram are A (3, 5), B (3, –1) and C (–1, –3). Plot these points on a graph paper and hence use it to find the coordinates of the fourth vertex D. Also find the coordinates of the mid-point of the side CD. What is the area of the parallelogram?

    Hint. Height of the parallelogram corresponding to the side CD is 4 units.

3. Draw the graphs of the following linear equations :
    (i) $y = 2x - 1$ (ii) $2x + 3y = 6$ (iii) $2x - 3y = 4$.

    Also find slope and y-intercept of these lines.

4. Draw the graph of the equation $3x - 4y = 12$. From the graph, find

    (i) the value of y when $x = -4$

    (ii) the value of x when $y = 3$.

5. Solve graphically, the simultaneous equations: $2x - 3y = 7$; $x + 6y = 11$.

6. Solve the following system of equations graphically: $x - 2y - 4 = 0$, $2x + y - 3 = 0$.

7. Using a scale of 1 cm to 1 unit for both the axes, draw the graphs of the following equations: $6y = 5x + 10$, $y = 5x - 15$. From the graph, find

    (i) the coordinates of the point where the two lines intersect.

    (ii) the area of the triangle between the lines and the x-axis.

8. Find, graphically, the coordinates of the vertices of the triangle formed by the lines:
    $$8y - 3x + 7 = 0, \quad 2x - y + 4 = 0 \text{ and } 5x + 4y = 29.$$

9. Find graphically the coordinates of the vertices of the triangle formed by the lines $y - 2 = 0$, $2y + x = 0$ and $y + 1 = 3 (x - 2)$. Hence, find the area of the triangle formed by these lines.

10. A line segment is of length 10 units and one of its end is (–2, 3). If the ordinate of the other end is 9, find the abscissa of the other end.

11. A(–4, –1), B(–1, 2) and C(α, 5) are the vertices of an isosceles triangle. Find the value of α, given that AB is the unequal side.

12. If A(–3, 2), B(α, β) and C(–1, 4) are the vertices of an isosceles triangle, prove that $\alpha + \beta = 1$, given AB = BC.

13. Prove that the points (3, 0), (6, 4) and (–1, 3) are the vertices of a right angled isosceles triangle.

14. (i) Show that the points (2, 1), (0, 3), (–2, 1) and (0, –1), taken in order, are the vertices of a square. Also find the area of the square.

    (ii) Show that the points (–3, 2), (–5, –5), (2, –3) and (4, 4), taken in order, are the vertices of rhombus. Also find its area. Do the given points form a square?

15 The ends of a diagonal of a square have co-ordinates $(-2, p)$ and $(p, 2)$. Find p if the area of the square is 40 sq. units.

Hint. $\sqrt{2}$ (length of side) = length of diagonal = $\sqrt{(p+2)^2 + (2-p)^2}$

$\Rightarrow$ 2(length of side)^2 = $2p^2 + 8$ $\Rightarrow$ (length of side)^2 = $p^2 + 4$

$\Rightarrow$ area of square = $p^2 + 4 = 40$ (given).

16 What type of quadrilateral do the points A(2, −2), B(7, 3), C(11, −1) and D(6, −6), taken in that order, form?

17 Find the coordinates of the centre of the circle passing through the three given points A (5, 1), B (−3, −7) and C (7, −1).

20 | Statistics

INTRODUCTION

The word 'Statistics' seems to have derived from the Latin word 'status' which means a 'political state'. Originally, statistics was simply the collection of numerical data on some aspects of life of the people useful to the government. However, with the passage of time, its scope broadened. Today, statistics means collection of facts or information concerning almost every aspect of life of the people with a definite purpose in the form of numerical data, organisation, summarisation and presentation of data by tables and graphs (charts), analysing the data and drawing inferences (meaningful predictions) from the data.

20.1 SOME TERMS RELATED TO STATISTICS

☆ **Primary data.** *The information collected by the investigator himself or herself with a definite purpose in his or her mind is called* **primary data**.

☆ **Secondary data.** *The information gathered from a source which already had the information stored is called* **secondary data.**

☆ **Raw data.** *The numerical data recorded in its original form as it is collected by the investigator or received from some source is called* **raw data.**

☆ **Variable.** *A quantity which is being measured in an experiment (or survey) is called a* **variable.** Height, age and weight of people, income and expenditure of people, number of members in a family, number of workers in a factory, marks obtained by students in a test, the number of runs scored in a cricket match etc., are examples of variables.

Variables are of two types:

(*i*) **Continuous variable.** *A variable which can take any value between two given values is called a* **continuous variable.**

For example, height, age and weight of people are continuous variables.

(*ii*) **Discontinuous (discrete) variable.** *A variable which cannot take all possible values between two given values is called a* **discontinuous or discrete variable.**

For example, the number of members in a family and the number of workers in a factory are discrete variables (since the variable cannot take any value between 1 and 2, 2 and 3 etc.)

☆ **Range.** *The difference between the maximum and minimum values of a variable is called its* **range.**

☆ **Variate.** *A particular value of a variable is called* **variate (observation).**

☆ **Frequency.** *The number of times a variate (observation) occurs in a given data is called* **frequency** *of that variate.*

☆ **Frequency distribution.** *A tabular arrangement of given numerical data showing the frequency of different variates is called* **frequency distribution,** *and the table itself is called* **frequency distribution table.**

20.1.1 Tabulation of raw data

Suppose there are 32 students in class IX in a school and in an examination, out of 50 marks, the marks scored by them are as follows :

39, 44, 25, 11, 21, 25, 44, 25, 7, 40, 43, 44, 49, 14, 11, 14, 25, 28, 28, 39, 44, 37, 21, 40, 43, 3, 37, 25, 25, 21, 37, 28.

The data in this form is the **raw (or ungrouped or unclassified) data**. Here, the number of marks obtained is the **variable** and each entry in the above list is an **observation** (or **variate**).

Suppose we wish to analyse the achievement of the students in the examination, the data in the above form does not give much information.

Let us arrange the above data in ascending or descending order. The above data in the ascending order is :

3, 7, 11, 11, 14, 14, 21, 21, 21, 25, 25, 25, 25, 25, 25, 28, 28, 28, 37, 37, 37, 39, 39, 40, 40, 43, 43, 44, 44, 44, 44, 49.

The presentation of data in this form gives better information. The data arranged in this form is called **arrayed data**. However, the presentation of data in this form is quite tedious and time-consuming, particularly when the number of observations is large.

To make it easily understandable, we present the above data in the form of a table called *frequency distribution table (for raw data)*. To prepare table, we take each observation from the data, one at a time, and mark a stroke (|) called **tally mark** in the next column opposite to the variate. For convenience, we write tally marks in bunches of five, the fifth one crossing the four diagonally. The number of *tally marks* opposite to a variate is its **frequency** and it is written in the next column opposite to tally marks of the variate. Note that the sum of all the frequencies is equal to the total number of observations in the given data.

The frequency distribution table for the above raw (ungrouped) data is given below:

Marks obtained	Tally marks	Frequency
3			1
7			1
11				2
14				2
21					3
25							6
28					3
37					3
39				2
40				2
43				2
44						4
49			1
Total		32

The above table is called *simple (or ungrouped) frequency distribution table.*

20.2 MEAN AND MEDIAN OF UNGROUPED DATA

20.2.1 Mean of ungrouped data

Mean (or *arithmetic average*) *of a number of observations is the sum of the values of all the observations divided by the total number of observations.*

The **mean** *of n observations (variates)* $x_1, x_2, x_3, ..., x_n$ *is given by the formula:*

$$\text{Mean} = \frac{x_1 + x_2 + x_3 + ... + x_n}{n} = \frac{\Sigma x_i}{n}$$

where $\Sigma x_i = x_1 + x_2 + x_3 + ... + x_n$.

Thus, $\text{Mean} = \dfrac{\text{sum of all observations}}{\text{total number of observations}}$.

> **Note** The Greek letter Σ (read as sigma) represents the sum.

Illustrative Examples

Example 1 The following are the ages (in years) of 10 teachers in a school :

32, 28, 54, 41, 38, 40, 23, 33, 26, 35.

Find the mean age of these teachers.

Solution. The sum of the ages (in years) of all the 10 teachers

$$= 32 + 28 + 54 + 41 + 38 + 40 + 23 + 33 + 26 + 35$$
$$= 350.$$

$\therefore$ $\text{Mean age} = \dfrac{\text{sum of ages of all the teachers}}{\text{total number of teachers}}$

$$= \frac{350}{10} \text{ years} = 35 \text{ years.}$$

Example 2 The marks obtained (out of 25) by 15 students in a monthly test are :

11, 09, 07, 03, 18, 21, 13, 15, 18, 04, 06, 17, 22, 13, 15.

(*i*) Find the mean of their marks.

(*ii*) Find the mean of their marks when the marks of each student are increased by 2.

Solution. (*i*) The sum of the marks of all the 15 students

$$= 11 + 09 + 07 + 03 + 18 + 21 + 13 + 15 + 18 + 04 + 06 + 17 + 22 + 13 + 15$$
$$= 192.$$

$\therefore$ $\text{Mean of marks} = \dfrac{\text{sum of marks of all the students}}{\text{total number of students}}$

$$= \frac{192}{15} = \frac{64}{5} = 12 \cdot 8$$

(*ii*) When the marks of each students are increased by 2, then the sum of their marks increases by 15×2 *i.e.* by 30.

$\therefore$ The new sum of marks of all the students = 192 + 30 = 222.

$\therefore$ The new mean of their marks $= \dfrac{\text{new sum of marks}}{\text{number of students}}$

$$= \frac{222}{15} = \frac{74}{5} = 14 \cdot 8$$

Note that the new mean of marks also increases by 2.

Example 3 For the given data: 11, 15, 17, $y + 1$, 19, $y - 2$, 3; if the mean is 14, then find the value of y.

Solution. Mean = $\dfrac{\text{sum of the given numbers}}{\text{number of observations}}$

$\Rightarrow \quad \dfrac{11 + 15 + 17 + y + 1 + 19 + y - 2 + 3}{7} = 14$ (given)

$\Rightarrow \quad 64 + 2y = 98 \Rightarrow 2y = 34 \Rightarrow y = 17.$

Hence, the value of y is 17.

Example 4 Find the mean of first seven prime numbers.

Solution. First seven prime numbers are 2, 3, 5, 7, 11, 13, 17.

Sum of these prime numbers = 2 + 3 + 5 + 7 + 11 + 13 + 17 = 58.

$\therefore \quad$ Their mean = $\dfrac{\text{sum of numbers}}{\text{number of numbers}} = \dfrac{58}{7} = 8\dfrac{2}{7}.$

Example 5 Find the mean of the (positive) factors of 24.

Solution. The (positive) factors of 24 are : 1, 2, 3, 4, 6, 8, 12, 24.

Number of these factors = 8 and

the sum of these factors = 1 + 2 + 3 + 4 + 6 + 8 + 12 + 24 = 60.

$\therefore \quad$ Mean = $\dfrac{\text{sum of factors}}{\text{no. of factors}} = \dfrac{60}{8} = \dfrac{15}{2} = 7.5$

Example 6 The mean of 6 observations is 17.5. If five of them are 14, 9, 23, 25 and 10, find the sixth observation.

Solution. Let the sixth observation be x. By def.,

$\therefore \quad$ mean = $\dfrac{\text{sum of all the observations}}{\text{number of observations}}$

$\Rightarrow \quad 17.5 = \dfrac{14 + 9 + 23 + 25 + 10 + x}{6}$

$\Rightarrow \quad 17.5 = \dfrac{81 + x}{6}$

$\Rightarrow \quad 81 + x = 17.5 \times 6$

$\Rightarrow \quad\quad\quad x = 105 - 81 = 24.$

Hence, the sixth observation is 24.

Example 7 The following are the weights (in kg) of 8 students of a class :

50, 44.5, 48.7, 45.1, 50.4, 43, 51, 49.3.

(i) Find the mean weight.

(ii) If a teacher, whose weight is 62 kg, is also included then what will be the mean weight?

Solution. (i) The sum of weights (in kg) of 8 students

$= 50 + 44.5 + 48.7 + 45.1 + 50.4 + 43 + 51 + 49.3$

$= 382.$

$\therefore \quad$ Mean weight = $\dfrac{\text{sum of weights of all students}}{\text{number of students}}$

$= \dfrac{382}{8}$ kg = 47.75 kg.

(*ii*) If the teacher, whose weight is 62 kg, is included then the sum of weights of all observations = sum of weights of students + weight of teacher

$$= 382 \text{ kg} + 62 \text{ kg} = 444 \text{ kg}.$$

Number of observations = 8 + 1 = 9.

$$\therefore \quad \text{Mean weight} = \frac{444}{9} \text{ kg} = \frac{148}{3} \text{ kg} = 49\frac{1}{3} \text{ kg}.$$

Example 8 The mean of 10 numbers is 55. If one number is included, their mean becomes 60. Find the included number.

Solution. The mean of 10 numbers is 55

$\Rightarrow$ the sum of 10 numbers = 55 × 10 = 550.

When one number is included, the mean becomes 60

i.e. the mean of 11 numbers is 60

$\Rightarrow$ sum of 11 numbers = 60 × 11 = 660.

$\therefore$ The included number = sum of 11 numbers – sum of 10 numbers

$$= 660 - 550 = 110.$$

Example 9 The mean height of 10 students is 151·8 cm. Two more students of heights 157·6 cm and 154·4 cm join the group. What is the new mean height?

Solution. $\text{Mean height of 10 students} = \dfrac{\text{sum of heights of 10 students}}{10}$

$\therefore$ $151 \cdot 8 \text{ cm} = \dfrac{\text{sum of heights of 10 students}}{10}$

$\Rightarrow$ sum of heights of 10 students = (151·8 × 10) cm = 1518 cm.

Now two more students of heights 157·6 cm and 154·4 cm join the group.

$\therefore$ Sum of heights of 12 students = (1518 + 157·6 + 154·4) cm = 1830 cm.

$\therefore$ $\text{New mean height} = \dfrac{\text{sum of heights of 12 students}}{12}$

$$= \frac{1830}{12} \text{ cm} = 152 \cdot 5 \text{ cm}.$$

Example 10 There are 50 numbers. If each number is subtracted from 53, then the mean of the numbers so obtained is – 3·5. Find the mean of the given numbers.

Solution. Let the given 50 numbers be $x_1, x_2, x_3, \ldots, x_{50}$.

When each number is subtracted from 53, the numbers so obtained are $53 - x_1, 53 - x_2, 53 - x_3, \ldots, 53 - x_{50}$.

Mean of these numbers $= \dfrac{\sum\limits_{i=1}^{50} (53 - x_i)}{50} = -3 \cdot 5$ (given)

$\Rightarrow$ $53 \times 50 - \sum\limits_{i=1}^{50} x_i = -3 \cdot 5 \times 50$

$\Rightarrow$ $53 \times 50 + 3 \cdot 5 \times 50 = \sum\limits_{i=1}^{50} x_i$

$\Rightarrow$ $56 \cdot 5 \times 50 = \sum\limits_{i=1}^{50} x_i$

$\Rightarrow$ $\dfrac{\sum\limits_{i=1}^{50} x_i}{50} = 56 \cdot 5 \Rightarrow$ mean of given numbers = 56·5

Example 11 The mean marks (out of 100) of boys and girls in an examination are 70 and

73 respectively. If the mean marks of all the students in that examination are 71, find the ratio of number of boys to the number of girls.

Solution. Let the number of boys be x and that of girls be y.

As the mean of marks scored by boys is 70,

$\therefore$ the sum of marks scored by x boys $= 70x$.

Also the mean of marks scored by girls is 73,

$\therefore$ the sum of marks scored by y girls $= 73y$.

$\therefore$ the sum of marks scored by all $(x + y)$ students $= 70x + 73y$.

Since the mean of marks scored by all students is 71,

$\therefore \quad \dfrac{70x + 73y}{x + y} = 71 \Rightarrow 70x + 73y = 71x + 71y$

$\Rightarrow \quad 2y = x \Rightarrow \dfrac{x}{y} = \dfrac{2}{1}$.

Hence, the ratio of number of boys to that of girls $= 2 : 1$.

Example 12 Mean temperature of a city of a certain week was 25°C. If the mean temperature of Monday, Tuesday, Wednesday and Thursday was 23°C and that of Thursday, Friday, Saturday and Sunday was 28°, find the temperature of Thursday.

Solution. Mean temperature of the week $= 25°C$.

$\therefore \quad$ The sum of temperatures of 7 days of the week $= 7 \times 25°C = 175°C$ ...(i)

Sum of temperatures of Monday, Tuesday, Wednesday and Thursday

$$= 4 \times 23°C = 92°C \qquad \qquad \qquad ...(ii)$$

Sum of temperatures of Thursday, Friday, Saturday and Sunday

$$= 4 \times 28°C = 112°C \qquad \qquad \qquad ...(iii)$$

$\therefore \quad$ Sum of temperatures of Monday to Sunday and Thursday

$$= 92°C + 112°C \qquad \qquad \text{[using (ii) and (iii)]}$$

$$= 204°C \qquad \qquad \qquad \qquad ...(iv)$$

$\therefore \quad$ Temperature of Thursday $= 204°C - 175°C \qquad \text{[using (iv) and (i)]}$

$$= 29°C.$$

Example 13 In an examination, the mean of marks scored by a class of 40 students was calculated as 72·5. Later on, it was detected that the marks of one student were wrongly copied as 48 instead of 84. Find the correct mean.

Solution.   Mean of marks $= \dfrac{\text{Incorrect sum of marks of 40 students}}{40}$

$\therefore \qquad \qquad 72 \cdot 5 = \dfrac{\text{Incorrect sum of marks of 40 students}}{40}$

$\Rightarrow \quad$ Incorrect sum of marks of 40 students $= 72 \cdot 5 \times 40 = 2900$.

Since the marks of one student were wrongly copied as 48 instead of 84,

correct sum of marks of 40 students $= 2900 - 48 + 84 = 2936$.

$\therefore \quad$ Correct mean $= \dfrac{2936}{40} = 73 \cdot 4$

20.2.2 Median of ungrouped data

Median is the central value (or middle observation) of a statistical data if it is arranged in ascending or descending order.

Thus, if there are n observations (variates) $x_1, x_2, x_3, ..., x_n$ arranged in ascending or descending order, then

$$\text{Median} = \begin{cases} \dfrac{n+1}{2} \text{th observation, if } n \text{ is odd} \\[2mm] \dfrac{\dfrac{n}{2} \text{th observation} + \left(\dfrac{n}{2}+1\right) \text{th observation}}{2}, \text{if } n \text{ is even.} \end{cases}$$

Illustrative Examples

Example 1 Find the median of the following data:

5, 3, 12, 0, 7, 11, 4, 3, 8.

Solution. Arranging the given data in ascending order, we get

0, 3, 3, 4, 5, 7, 8, 11, 12.

Total number of observations = n = 9, which is odd.

$$\therefore \quad \text{Median} = \frac{n+1}{2} \text{ th observation}$$

$$= \frac{9+1}{2} \text{ th observation}$$

= 5th observation, which is 5.

Hence, median = 5.

Example 2 The number of goals scored by a football team in a series of matches are:

3, 1, 0, 7, 5, 3, 3, 4, 1, 2, 0, 2.

Find the median of this data.

Solution. Arranging the number of goals scored by the team in ascending order, we get

0, 0, 1, 1, 2, 2, 3, 3, 3, 4, 5, 7.

Total number of observations (matches played) = n = 12, which is even.

$$\therefore \quad \text{Median} = \frac{\dfrac{n}{2} \text{th observation} + \left(\dfrac{n}{2}+1\right) \text{th observation}}{2}$$

$$= \frac{6\text{th observation} + 7\text{th observation}}{2} = \frac{2+3}{2} = \frac{5}{2} = 2 \cdot 5$$

Example 3 If the numbers 3, 6, 7, 10, x, 15, 19, 20, 25, 28 are in ascending order and their median is 13, calculate the value of x.

Solution. The numbers 3, 6, 7, 10, x, 15, 19, 20, 25, 28 are in ascending order.

Total number of observations = n = 10, which is even.

$$\therefore \quad \text{Median} = \frac{\dfrac{n}{2} \text{th observation} + \left(\dfrac{n}{2}+1\right) \text{th observation}}{2}$$

$$= \frac{5\text{th observation} + 6\text{th observation}}{2} = \frac{x+15}{2}.$$

According to given, $13 = \dfrac{x+15}{2}$

$\Rightarrow \qquad x + 15 = 26 \Rightarrow x = 11$.

Hence, the value of x is 11.

EXERCISE 20.1

1 Find the mean of 8, 6, 10, 12, 1, 3, 4, 4.

2 5 people were asked about the time in a week they spend in doing social work in their community. They replied 10, 7, 13, 20 and 15 hours, respectively. Find the mean time in a week devoted by them for social work.

3 The enrolment of a school during six consecutive years was as follows:

1620, 2060, 2540, 3250, 3500, 3710.

Find the mean enrolment.

4 Find the mean of the first twelve natural numbers.

5 (i) Find the mean of the first six prime numbers.

(ii) Find the mean of the first seven odd prime numbers.

6 (i) The marks (out of 100) obtained by a group of students in a Mathematics test are 81, 72, 90, 90, 85, 86, 70, 93 and 71. Find the mean marks obtained by the group of students.

(ii) The mean of the age of three students Vijay, Rahul and Rakhi is 15 years. If their ages are in the ratio 4 : 5 : 6 respectively, then find their ages.

7 The mean of 5 numbers is 20. If one number is excluded, mean of the remaining numbers becomes 23. Find the excluded number.

8 The mean of 25 observations is 27. If one observation is included, the mean still remains 27. Find the included observation.

9 The mean of 5 observations is 15. If the mean of first three observations is 14 and that of the last three is 17, find the third observation.

10 The mean of 8 variates is 10·5. If seven of them are 3, 15, 7, 19, 2, 17 and 8, then find the 8th variate.

11 The mean weight of 8 students is 45·5 kg. Two more students having weights 41·7 kg and 53·3 kg join the group. What is the new mean weight?

12 Mean of 9 observations was found to be 35. Later on, it was detected that an observation 81 was misread as 18. Find the correct mean of the observations.

13 A student scored the following marks in 11 questions of a question paper :

7, 3, 4, 1, 5, 8, 2, 2, 5, 7, 6.

Find the median marks.

14 Calculate the mean and the median of the numbers :

2, 3, 4, 3, 0, 5, 1, 1, 3, 2.

15 A group of students was given a special test in Mathematics. The test was completed by the various students in the following time in (minutes) :

24, 30, 28, 17, 22, 36, 30, 19, 32, 18, 20, 24.

Find the mean time and median time taken by the students to complete the test.

16 In a Science test given to a group of students, the marks scored by them (out of 100) are:

41, 39, 52, 48, 54, 62, 46, 52, 40, 96, 42, 40, 98, 60, 52.

Find the mean and median of this data.

17 The points scored by a Kabaddi team in a series of matches are as follows :

7, 17, 2, 5, 27, 15, 8, 14, 10, 48, 10, 7, 24, 8, 28, 18.

Find the mean and the median of the points scored by the Kabaddi team.

18 The following observations have been arranged in ascending order. If the median of the data is 47·5, find the value of x.

   17, 21, 23, 29, 39, 40, x, 50, 51, 54, 59, 67, 91, 93.

19 The following observations have been arranged in ascending order. If the median of the data is 13, find the value of x:

   3, 6, 7, 10, x, $x + 4$, 19, 20, 25, 28.

20.3 GROUPED OR CLASSIFIED DATA

Consider the following examples of grouped frequency distribution :

Example 1 Using class intervals $1 - 5, 6 - 10, 11 - 15, \ldots$ construct the frequency distribution for the following data:

   13, 6, 12, 9, 11, 14, 2, 8, 18, 16, 9, 13, 17, 11, 19, 6, 7, 12, 22, 21, 18, 1, 8, 12, 18.

Solution. The frequency distribution table for the given grouped data is:

Class-intervals	Tally marks	Frequency
1 – 5	‖	2
6 – 10	₦₦ ‖	7
11 – 15	₦₦ ‖‖	8
16 – 20	₦₦ ‖	6
21 – 25	‖	2
Total		25

Example 2 The following is the pocket money survey of 50 students in a school (pocket money in rupees per month):

49, 55, 22, 27, 30, 27, 25, 27, 30, 42, 40, 13, 24, 38, 10, 24, 30, 33, 17, 29, 10, 50, 18, 34, 15, 40, 13, 32, 36, 32, 27, 35, 17, 41, 18, 36, 20, 41, 35, 51, 29, 27, 44, 43, 15, 32, 29, 54, 14, 45.

Form a frequency table with a grouping of $10 - 20, 20 - 30, 30 - 40$ and so on (class $10 - 20$ means including 10 but excluding 20, class $20 - 30$ means including 20 but excluding 30).

Solution. The grouped frequency table for the given data is:

Classes	Tally marks	Frequency
10 – 20	₦₦ ₦₦ ‖	11
20 – 30	₦₦ ₦₦ ‖‖‖	13
30 – 40	₦₦ ₦₦ ‖‖‖	13
40 – 50	₦₦ ‖‖‖‖	9
50 – 60	‖‖‖‖	4
Total		50

Class limits and types of frequency distribution

In example 1, for the class interval 1 – 5, 1 is the **lower limit** and 5 is the **upper limit**.

If x is a member of this class, then $1 \le x \le 5$. Similarly, 6 is the *lower limit* and 10 is the *upper limit* of the class 6 – 10. In this example, the classes are non-overlapping but discontinuous. Such a frequency distribution is called **discrete (or inclusive) distribution**. In this distribution, the upper limit of one class does not coincide with the lower limit of the next class.

In example 2, for the class 1 – 10, 1 is the **lower limit** and 10 is the **upper limit**. If x is a member of this class, then $1 \le x < 10$. Similarly, 10 is the **lower limit** and 20 is the **upper limit** of the class 10 – 20. In this example, the classes are non-overlapping but continuous. Such a frequency distribution is called **continuous (or exclusive) distribution**. In this distribution, the upper limit of one class coincides with the lower limit of the next class.

Converting discrete distribution to continuous distribution

If we measure height, weight and time, there may be fractions of a metre, kilogram and hour respectively, therefore, we need continuous distribution.

To convert discrete classes into continuous classes, we require some *adjustment*.

$$\text{Adjustment factor} = \frac{\text{lower limit of one class} - \text{upper limit of previous class}}{2}.$$

Subtract the adjustment factor from all the lower limits and add the adjustment factor to all the upper limits.

In example 1, adjustment factor $= \frac{6 - 5}{2} = \frac{1}{2} = 0.5$

Continuous frequency distribution table for example 1 is:

Classes before adjustment	Classes after adjustment	Tally marks	Frequency
1 – 5	0·5 – 5·5	II	2
16 – 10	5·5 – 10·5	￞￞￞ II	7
11 – 15	10·5 – 15·5	￞￞￞ III	8
16 – 20	15·5 – 20·5	￞￞￞ I	6
21 – 25	20·5 – 25·5	II	2
Total			25

True class limits

In a continuous distribution, the class limits are called **true** or **actual class limits**. In a discrete distribution, the class limits obtained after adjustment are the *true* or *actual class limits*. The actual class limits are also called *class boundaries*.

In discrete distribution, the original (given) class limits are called the ***stated class limits***.

Class size. *The difference between the actual upper limit and the actual lower limit of a class is called its **class size**.*

In example 2, class size of the class 10 – 20 = 20 – 10 = 10.

In example 1, class size of the class 1 – 5 = 5·5 – 0·5 = 5.

Class mark. *The **class mark** of a class is the value midway between its actual lower limit and actual upper limit.*

In example 2, class mark of the class $10 - 20 = \dfrac{10 + 20}{2} = 15$.

In example 1, class mark of the class $1 - 5 = \dfrac{0 \cdot 5 + 5 \cdot 5}{2} = 3$.

> **Note** In discrete distribution, the class mark of a class is also the value midway between its stated class limits, thus in example 1, the class mark of the class $1 - 5 = \dfrac{1 + 5}{2} = 3$.

Remarks

1. If the classes are of equal size, then class size = difference between two successive class marks.

2. If the classes are of equal size (width) and h is the size of each class and m is mid-value (class mark) of a class, then

   lower limit of the class = its mid-value – half the width of class

   $$= m - \dfrac{h}{2} \text{ and}$$

   upper limit of the class = its mid-value + half the width of class

   $$= m + \dfrac{h}{2}.$$

Cumulative frequency and cumulative frequency table

The sum of frequencies of all the previous classes and that particular class is called the *cumulative frequency* of the class.

The cumulative frequency table for example 2 is:

Classes	Tally marks	Frequency	Cumulative frequency
10 – 20	⣤⣤ ⣤⣤ I	11	11
20 – 30	⣤⣤ ⣤⣤ III	13	24 (11 + 13)
30 – 40	⣤⣤ ⣤⣤ III	13	37 (24 + 13)
40 – 50	⣤⣤ IIII	9	46 (37 + 9)
50 – 60	IIII	4	50 (46 + 4)

20.3.1 Formation of classes from a given raw data

We condense the given raw data into classes (or groups) as follows:

1. Find the *range i.e.* the difference between the maximum and minimum observations. Decide about the number of classes (usually between 5 to 10). In general, the size (width) is a convenient whole number immediately greater than the quotient obtained by dividing the range by the number of classes.

2. Classes should be non-overlapping and continuous.

3. There should be no gaps between classes.

4. As far as possible, classes should be of the same size.

5. Open ended classes such as less than 5 or greater than 9 should be avoided.

6. Limits of each class should be so chosen that there is no ambiguity as to which class a particular observation of the given data belongs to.

We illustrate the above procedure with the help of the following examples.

Illustrative Examples

Example 1 The electricity bills (in rupees) of 40 houses in a locality are given below. Construct a grouped frequency distribution table:

78, 87, 81, 52, 59, 65, 101, 108, 115, 95, 98, 65, 62, 121, 128, 63, 76, 84, 89, 91, 65, 101, 95, 81, 87, 105, 129, 92, 75, 105, 78, 72, 107, 116, 127, 100, 80, 82, 61, 118.

Solution. Here maximum = 129 and minimum = 52,

∴ range = 129 − 52 = 77.

Let us form 8 classes each of size 10.

Since we want to include 129 in the last class, 130 is the upper limit of the last class, so the lower limit of the first class is 50.

The grouped frequency distribution table of the given data is:

Classes	Tally marks	Frequency
50 – 60	II	2
60 – 70	⃓⃓⃓⃓ I	6
70 – 80	⃓⃓⃓⃓	5
80 – 90	⃓⃓⃓⃓ III	8
90 – 100	⃓⃓⃓⃓	5
100 – 110	⃓⃓⃓⃓ II	7
110 – 120	III	3
120 – 130	IIII	4
Total		40

Example 2 The heights of 240 students of a school are measured and tabulated as below:

Height (in cm)	below 100	below 110	below 120	below 130	below 140	below 150
No. of students	12	30	65	180	218	240

Construct a frequency distribution table for the above data. Also answer the following:

(i) How many students have atleast 1 m height but less than 120 cm height?

(ii) How many students have atleast 130 cm height?

Solution. The frequency distribution table for the given data is:

Class intervals (Height in cm)	Frequency (No. of students)	
0 – 100	12	
100 – 110	18	(= 30 – 12)
110 – 120	35	(= 65 – 30)
120 – 130	115	(= 180 – 65)
130 – 140	38	(= 218 – 180)
140 – 150	22	(= 240 – 218)

(i) 53 (= sum of the frequencies of the class intervals 100 – 110 and 110 – 120)

(ii) 60 (= sum of the frequencies of the class intervals 130 – 140 and 140 – 150).

Example 3 If m is the mid-point and l is the upper limit of a class in a continuous frequency distribution, then what is the lower limit of the class?

Solution. As l is the upper limit and m is the mid-point of a class in a continuous frequency distribution,

so half of the width of the class = upper limit – mid-point = $l - m$.

Let x be the lower limit of this class, then

$$x = \text{mid-point} - \frac{1}{2} \text{ of width of this class}$$

$$= m - (l - m) = 2m - l.$$

Example 4 Prepare a continuous grouped frequency distribution from the following data:

Mid-points	5	15	25	35	45
Frequency	4	8	13	12	6

Also find the size of class intervals.

Solution. As the mid-points (class marks) of classes are 5, 15, 25, 35 and 45 which are at equal gaps, so the classes are of equal size.

Therefore, size of class = difference between two consecutive mid-points

$$= 15 - 5 = 10.$$

Half of class size = $\frac{10}{2}$ = 5.

Therefore, the class limits of the first class are : lower limit = mid-point – half of class size and upper limit = mid-point + half of class size *i.e.* 5 – 5 and 5 + 5 *i.e.* 0 and 10. Similarly, we find the class limits for all other classes. Thus, the classes are 0 – 10, 10 – 20, 20 – 30, 30 – 40 and 40 – 50. The continuous distribution of the given data is:

Classes	0 – 10	10 – 20	20 – 30	30 – 40	40 – 50
Frequency	4	8	13	12	6

EXERCISE 20.2

1 State which of the following variables are continuous and which are discrete:
  (i) marks scored (out of 50) in a test.
  (ii) daily temperature of your city.
  (iii) sizes of shoes.
  (iv) distance travelled by a man.
  (v) time.

2 Using class intervals 0 –4, 5 –9, 10 –14, ... construct the frequency distribution for the following data :

  13, 6, 10, 5, 11, 14, 2, 8, 15, 16, 9, 13, 17, 11, 19, 5, 7, 12, 20, 21, 18, 1, 8, 12, 18.

3 Given below are the marks obtained by 27 students in a test :

  21, 3, 28, 38, 6, 40, 20, 26, 9, 8, 14, 18, 20, 16, 17, 10, 8, 5, 22, 27, 34, 2, 35, 31, 16, 28, 37.

(i) Using the class intervals 1 – 10, 11 – 20 etc. construct a frequency table.

(ii) State the range of these marks.

(iii) State the class mark of the third class of your frequency table.

4　Explain the meaning of the following terms :
    (i) variate   (ii) class size   (iii) class mark
    (iv) class limits   (v) true class limits (vi) frequency of a class
    (vii) cumulative frequency of a class.

5　Fill in the blanks :

(i) The number of observations in a particular class is called .... of the class.

(ii) The difference between the class marks of two consecutive classes is the .... of the class.

(iii) The range of the data 16, 19, 23, 13, 11, 25, 18 is ....

(iv) The mid-point of the class interval is called its ....

(v) The class mark of the class 4 – 9 is ....

6　The marks obtained (out of 50) by 40 students in a test are given below:

28, 31, 45, 03, 05, 18, 35, 46, 49, 17, 10, 28, 31, 36, 40, 44, 47, 13, 19, 25, 24, 31, 38, 32, 27, 19, 25, 28, 48, 15, 18, 31, 37, 46, 06, 01, 20, 10, 45, 02.

(i) Taking class intervals 1 – 10, 11 – 20, ..., construct a tally chart and a frequency distribution table.

(ii) Convert the above distribution to continuous distribution.

(iii) State the true class limits of the third class.

(iv) State the class mark of the fourth class.

7　Use the adjoining table to find:

(i) upper and lower limits of fifth class.

(ii) true class limits of the fifth class.

(iii) class boundaries of the third class.

(iv) class mark of the fourth class.

(v) width of sixth class.

Class	Frequency
28 – 32	5
33 – 37	8
38 – 42	13
43 – 47	9
48 – 52	7
53 – 57	5
58 – 62	2

8　The marks of 200 students in a test were recorded as follows:

Marks %	10–19	20–29	30–39	40–49	50–59	60–69	70–79	80–89
No. of students	7	11	20	46	57	37	15	7

Draw the cumulative frequency table.

9　Given below are the marks secured by 35 students in a test:

41, 32, 35, 21, 11, 47, 42, 00, 05, 18, 25, 24, 29, 38, 30, 04, 14, 24, 34, 44, 48, 33, 36, 38, 41, 46, 08, 34, 39, 11, 13, 27, 26, 43, 03.

Taking class intervals 0 – 10, 10 – 20, 20 – 30 ..., construct frequency as well as cumulative frequency distribution table. Find the number of students obtaining below 20 marks.

10 The marks out of 100 of 50 students in a test are given below:

5	35	6	35	18	36	12	36	85	32
20	36	22	38	24	50	22	39	74	31
25	54	25	64	25	70	28	66	58	25
29	72	31	82	31	84	31	82	37	21
32	84	32	92	35	95	34	92	35	5

(*i*) Taking a class interval of size 10, construct a frequency as well as cumulative frequency table for the given data.

(*ii*) Which class has the largest frequency?

(*iii*) How many students score less than 40 marks?

(*iv*) How many students score first division (60% or more) marks?

11 Construct the frequency distribution table from the following data:

Ages (in years)	below 4	below 7	below 10	below 13	below 16
No. of children	7	38	175	248	300

State the number of children in the age group 10 – 13.

12 Rewrite the following cumulative frequency distribution into frequency distribution:

less than or equal to 10	2
less than or equal to 20	7
less than or equal to 30	18
less than or equal to 40	32
less than or equal to 50	43
less than or equal to 60	50

13 The water bills (in rupees) of 32 houses in a locality are given below. Construct a frequency distribution table with a class size of 10.

80, 48, 52, 78, 103, 85, 37, 94, 72, 73, 66, 52, 92, 85, 78, 81, 64, 60, 75, 78, 108, 63, 71, 54, 59, 75, 100, 103, 35, 89, 95, 73.

14 The maximum temperatures (in degree celsius) for Delhi for the month of April, 2014, as reported by the Meteorological Department, are given below:

27·4, 28·3, 23·9, 23·6, 25·4, 27·5, 28·1, 28·4, 30·5, 29·7, 30·6, 31·7, 32·2, 32·6, 33·4, 35·7, 36·1, 37·2, 38·4, 40·1, 40·2, 40·5, 41·1, 42·0, 42·1, 42·3, 42·4, 42·9, 43·1, 43·2.

Construct a frequency distribution table.

15 (*i*) The class marks of a distribution are 94, 104, 114, 124, 134, 144 and 154. Determine the class size and the class limits of the fourth class.

(*ii*) The class marks of a distribution are 9·5, 16·5, 23·5, 30·5, 37·5 and 44·5. Determine the class size and the class limits of the third class.

20.4 GRAPHICAL REPRESENTATION OF STATISTICAL DATA

Since pictures (or graphs) are good visual aids and leave more lasting effect on the mind of an observer, the information contained in a numerical data (or frequency distribution) can be easily understood if we represent it in the form of diagrams (graphs). It is well said that one picture is better than a thousand words. Usually, comparisons among the individual items are best shown by means of graphs.

There are various ways of representing numerical data (or frequency distribution) graphically. In the previous classes, you have learnt:

(i) Bar graphs   (ii) Pie graphs and   (iii) Broken line graphs.

In this section, we shall review bar graphs and shall learn two more ways of representing grouped data (continuous frequency distribution) graphically :

(i) Histogram   (ii) Frequency polygon.

20.4.1 Bar graphs

In bar graphs,

(i) take the width of all bars (rectangles) equal.

(ii) space between consecutive bars should be equal. The bars can touch each other.

(iii) the height (or length) of a bar is equal (or proportional) to the frequency of the corresponding variate (observation).

(iv) the width of bars has no significance. In fact, the width of the bars is shown simply to make the representation more eye-catching.

Illustrative Examples

Example 1 A man with a monthly salary of ₹ 6400 plans his budget for a month as given below:

Item	Food	Clothing	Education	Miscellaneous	Savings
Amount (in ₹)	2100	600	1200	1500	1000

Represent the above data by a bar graph.

Solution. The required bar graph is shown below:

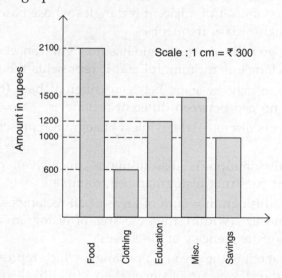

Example 2 Given below is the data of school going students (boys and girls):

Mode of transport	School bus	Walking	Bicycle	Other vehicles
Number of boys	75	120	240	150
Number of girls	135	60	180	90

Draw a bar graph to represent the above data.

Solution. The required bar graph is shown below:

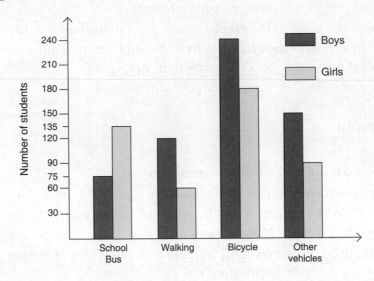

20.4.2 Histogram

A histogram is used to represent continuous grouped data. It consists of adjacent rectangles.

Procedure to draw a histogram:

(*i*) Take the breadth of a rectangle equal to a class size and mark it along *x*-axis, the end points of which correspond to the class limits.

(*ii*) Take the length of a rectangle equal to the frequency of that class and mark it along *y*-axis.

(*iii*) Construct rectangles corresponding to each class with the help of steps (*i*) and (*ii*).

Remarks

○ A histogram consists of a set of adjacent rectangles whose bases are equal to class sizes and heights are equal to class frequencies.

○ In a bar graph, the breadth of a rectangle has no significance ; whereas in a histogram, the breadth of a rectangle is meaningful and it represents the class size.

○ In a bar graph, there may be gaps between different bars (rectangles); whereas in a histogram, there is no gap between different rectangles.

○ A bar graph represents discrete data, while a histogram represents a continuous grouped data.

○ If the frequency distribution is discontinuous (inclusive), change it to continuous (exclusive) and then construct histogram. See example 4.

○ The total area of the histogram = sum of areas of all rectangles. In particular, if the class intervals are of same size (width), then the area of histogram = N*k* where *k* = size of a class and N = sum of frequencies of all classes.

○ In a histogram, in fact, it is the area of a rectangle which represents the frequency of the class. Therefore, if the classes are of unequal size (width) then the heights of rectangles are not equal to the frequencies of the corresponding classes. However, we shall be dealing only with the problems in which class widths are equal.

Illustrative Examples

Example 1 Draw a histogram to represent the following data:

Class intervals	20 – 30	30 – 40	40 – 50	50 – 60	60 – 70
Frequency	3	5	12	9	4

Solution. *Steps:*

   (*i*) Take 1 cm on *x*-axis = 10 units.

   (*ii*) Take 1 cm on *y*-axis = 2 frequency.

   (*iii*) Construct rectangles corresponding to given data.

   The required histogram is shown in the figure given alongside.

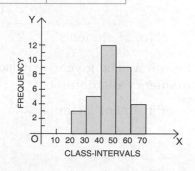

Example 2 Draw a histogram for the following data:

Height (in cm)	150 – 160	160 – 170	170 – 180	180 – 190	190 – 200
No. of students	8	3	4	10	2

Solution. *Steps:*

   (*i*) Since the scale on *x*-axis starts at 150, a break (kink or zig-zag curve) is shown near the origin along *x*-axis to indicate that the graph is drawn to scale beginning at 150 and not at the origin itself.

   (*ii*) Take 1 cm on *x*-axis = 10 cm (height).

   (*iii*) Take 1 cm on *y*-axis = 2 (no. of students).

   (*iv*) Construct rectangles corresponding to the given data.

   The required histogram is shown in the adjoining diagram.

Example 3 Draw a histogram for the following frequency distribution:

Marks obtained	below 15	below 30	below 45	below 60	below 75	below 90
No. of students	15	27	54	72	81	87

Solution. The continuous frequency distribution table is:

Class interval (marks obtained)	Frequency (no. of students)
0 – 15	15
15 – 30	12
30 – 45	27
45 – 60	18
60 – 75	9
75 – 90	6

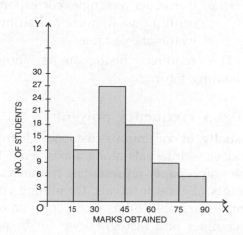

Take 1 cm on x-axis = 15 (marks).

Take 1 cm on y-axis = 6 (students).

Construct the rectangles corresponding to the given data.

The required histogram is shown in the above diagram.

Example 4 Draw a histogram for the following data:

Wt. (in kg)	40 – 44	45 – 49	50 – 54	55 – 59	60 – 64	65 – 69
No. of students	2	8	12	10	6	4

Solution. The given frequency distribution is discontinuous, to convert it into continuous frequency distribution,

$$\text{adjustment factor} = \frac{\text{lower limit of one class} - \text{upper limit of previous class}}{2}$$

$$= \frac{45 - 44}{2} = \frac{1}{2} = 0.5$$

Subtract the adjustment factor (0·5) from all the lower limits and add the adjustment factor (0·5) to all the upper limits.

Continuous frequency distribution for the given data is:

Classes before adjustment	Classes after adjustment	Frequency
40 – 44	39·5 – 44·5	2
45 – 49	44·5 – 49·5	8
50 – 54	49·5 – 54·5	12
55 – 59	54·5 – 59·5	10
60 – 64	59·5 – 64·5	6
65 – 69	64·5 – 69·5	4

To construct histogram:

(*i*) Since the scale on x-axis starts at 39·5, a break (kink) is shown near the origin on x-axis to indicate that the graph is drawn to scale beginning at 39·5.

(*ii*) Take 1 cm along x-axis = 5 kg (weight).

(*iii*) Take 1 cm along y-axis = 2 (no. of students).

(*iv*) Construct rectangles corresponding to the continuous frequency distribution given in the above table.

The required histogram is shown in the adjoining figure.

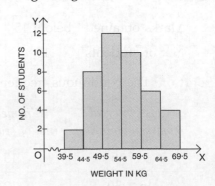

20.4.3 Frequency polygon

Usually, in continuous frequency distributions, the frequencies are represented along y-axis and class intervals along x-axis. Find the mid-points of class intervals. Plot the points on the graph paper representing frequencies of different classes against the corresponding mid-points of class intervals. On joining consecutive points by line segments, we get *frequency graph (curve)*. In other words, on joining the mid-points of the upper bases of the adjacent rectangles of a histogram we get frequency curve. If the end points of *frequency graph* are joined to the mid-points of immediate lower and upper class intervals outside the range with zero frequency, we get a closed figure. The figure so obtained is called a *frequency polygon*.

Thus, a **frequency polygon** is a closed curve representing continuous grouped frequency distribution.

Histogram and frequency polygon can be constructed simultaneously, see example 3.

Illustrative Examples

Example 1 Draw a frequency polygon to represent the following data:

Class interval	20 – 30	30 – 40	40 – 50	50 – 60	60 – 70	70 – 80
Frequency	5	10	19	24	18	6

Solution. *Steps:*

(i) Let 1 cm on x-axis = 10 units and
1 cm on y-axis = 5 frequencies.

(ii) Find mid-points of class intervals.

(iii) Find points corresponding to given frequencies of classes and the mid-points of class intervals, and plot them.

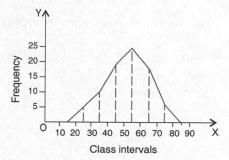

(iv) Join the consecutive points by line segments.

(v) Join the first end-point with mid-point of class 10 – 20 with zero frequency, and join the other end point with the mid-point of class 80 – 90 with zero frequency. The required frequency polygon has been shown above.

Example 2 100 students in a school have heights as tabulated below:

Height (in cm)	121–130	131–140	141–150	151–160	161–170	171–180
No. of students	12	16	30	20	14	8

Draw frequency polygon of the above data.

Solution. The given frequency distribution is discontinuous; to convert it into a continuous distribution,

$$\text{adjustment factor} = \frac{\text{lower limit of one class} - \text{upper limit of previous class}}{2}$$

$$= \frac{131 - 130}{2} = \frac{1}{2} = 0.5$$

Continuous frequency distribution for the given data is:

Classes before adjustment	Classes after adjustment	Frequency
121 – 130	120·5 – 130·5	12
131 – 140	130·5 – 140·5	16
141 – 150	140·5 – 150·5	30
151 – 160	150·5 – 160·5	20
161 – 170	160·5 – 170·5	14
171 – 180	170·5 – 180·5	8

Steps to draw frequency polygon:

(*i*) Since the scale on *x*-axis starts at 110·5, a kink is shown near the origin on *x*-axis to indicate that the graph is drawn to scale beginning at 110·5.

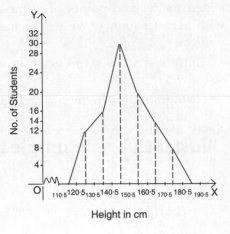

(*ii*) Take 1 cm along *x*-axis = 10 cm (height).

(*iii*) Take 1 cm along *y*-axis = 4 (no. of students).

(*iv*) Find mid-points of class intervals.

(*v*) Find points corresponding to given frequencies of classes and the mid-points of class intervals, and plot them.

(*vi*) Join consecutive points by line segments.

(*vii*) Join first end point with mid-point of class 110·5 – 120·5 with zero frequency and join the other end with mid-point of class 180·5 – 190·5 with zero frequency.

The required frequency polygon is shown alongside.

Example 3 The following is the pocket money survey of 50 students in a school (Pocket money in Rupees per month):

49	55	22	27	30	27	25	27	30	42
40	13	24	38	10	24	30	33	17	29
10	50	18	34	15	40	13	32	36	32
27	35	17	41	18	36	20	41	35	51
29	27	44	43	15	32	29	54	14	45

Form a frequency table with a grouping of 10 – 20, 20 – 30, 30 – 40, and so on.

Construct a combined histogram and frequency polygon for the distribution.

Solution. The frequency distribution table for the given data is:

Classes	Tally Marks	Frequency
10 – 20	ᴺᴸ ᴺᴸ I	11
20 – 30	ᴺᴸ ᴺᴸ III	13
30 – 40	ᴺᴸ ᴺᴸ III	13
40 – 50	ᴺᴸ IIII	9
50 – 60	IIII	4
Total		50

To construct histogram:

(*i*) Take 1 cm along *x*-axis = ₹10.

(*ii*) Take 1 cm along *y*-axis = 2 students.

(*iii*) Construct rectangles corresponding to the above continuous frequency distribution table.

The required histogram is shown in the adjoining diagram.

To construct frequency polygon :

(*i*) Mark mid-points of upper bases of rectangles of the histogram.

(*ii*) Join the consecutive mid-points by line segments.

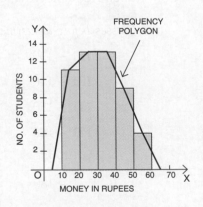

(*iii*) Join the first end point with the mid-point of class 0–10 with zero frequency, and join the other end point with the mid-point of class 60 – 70 with zero frequency.

The required frequency polygon is shown by *thick line segments* in the above diagram.

Example 4 The histogram and the frequency polygon of a frequency distribution is shown alongside.

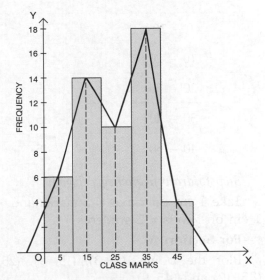

Answer the following about the frequency distribution:

(*i*) What is the class size of each class?

(*ii*) What is the frequency of the class whose class mark is 25?

(*iii*) What is the class whose class mark is 15?

(*iv*) What is the class whose frequency is 18?

(*v*) Construct the frequency table for the given distribution.

Solution. (*i*) As the class marks are 5, 15, 25, 35 and 45 which are at equal gaps, so the classes are of equal size.

∴ Class size of each class = difference between two successive class marks
= 15 – 5 = 10.

(*ii*) 10.

(*iii*) As the size of each class is 10 and the class mark is 15, so the class limits are 15 – 5 and 15 + 5 *i.e.* 10 and 20.

Hence, the class is 10 – 20.

(*iv*) The class whose frequency is 18 is 30 – 40.

(*v*) The frequency distribution table is given below:

Classes	0 – 10	10 – 20	20 – 30	30 – 40	40 – 50
Frequency	6	14	10	18	4

Example 5 The following table gives the distribution of students of two sections according to the marks obtained by them:

Section A		Section B	
Marks	Frequency	Marks	Frequency
0 – 10	3	0 – 10	5
10 – 20	9	10 – 20	19
20 – 30	17	20 – 30	15
30 – 40	12	30 – 40	10
40 – 50	9	40 – 50	1

Represent the marks of the students of both the sections on the same graph by two frequency polygons. From the two polygons compare the performance of the two sections.

Solution. We find the class marks and prepare a new table as under:

Class	Class marks	Section A (No. of students)	Section B (No. of students)
0 – 10	5	3	5
10 – 20	15	9	19
20 – 30	25	17	15
30 – 40	35	12	10
40 – 50	45	9	1

Step to draw frequency polygon:

Take 1 cm on x-axis = 5 marks and 1 cm on y-axis = 2 students

For Section A

Plot the points (5, 3), (15, 9), (25, 17), (35, 12) and (45, 9).

Join the consecutive points by thick line segments.

Join the first end point with the mid-point of class (–10) – 0 with zero frequency, and join the other end point with the mid-point of class 50 – 60 with zero frequency. The required frequency polygon is shown by thick line segments in the adjoining figure.

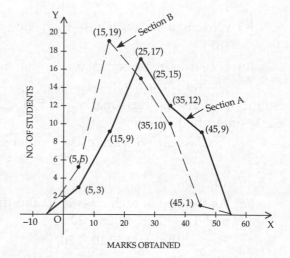

For Section B

Plot the points (5, 5), (15, 19), (25, 15), (35, 10) and (45, 1).

Join the consecutive points with dotted line segments.

Join the first end point with the mid-point of class (–10) – 0 with zero frequency, and join the other end point with the mid-point of class 50 – 60 with zero frequency. The required frequency polygon is shown by dotted line segments in the same figure.

Performance of section A is better than performance of section B.

EXERCISE 20.3

1 The area under wheat cultivation last year in the following states, correct to the nearest lacs hectares was:

State	Punjab	Haryana	U.P.	M.P.	Maharashtra	Rajasthan
Cultivated area	220	120	100	40	80	30

Represent the above information by a bar graph.

2 The number of books sold by a shopkeeper in a certain week was as follows:

Day	Monday	Tuesday	Wednesday	Thursday	Friday	Saturday
No. of books	420	180	230	340	160	120

Draw a bar graph for the above data.

3 Given below is the data of percentage of passes of a certain school in the ICSE for consecutive years:

Year	2000	2001	2002	2003	2004	2005	2006
% of passes	92	80	70	86	54	78	94

Draw a bar graph to represent the above data.

4 Birth rate per thousand of different countries over a certain period is:

Country	India	Pakistan	China	U.S.A.	France
Birth rate	36	45	12	18	20

Draw a horizontal bar graph to represent the above data.

5 Given below is the data of number of students (boys and girls) in class IX of a certain school:

Class	IX A	IX B	IX C	IX D
Boys	28	22	40	15
Girls	18	34	12	25

Draw a bar graph to represent the above data.

6 Draw a histogram to represent the following data:

Marks obtained	0 – 10	10 – 20	20 – 30	30 – 40	40 – 50	50 – 60
No. of students	4	10	6	8	5	9

7 Draw a histogram to represent the following frequency distribution of monthly wages of 255 workers of a factory.

Monthly wages (in rupees)	850 – 950	950 – 1050	1050 – 1150	1150 – 1250	1250 – 1350
No. of workers	35	45	75	60	40

8 Draw a histogram for the following data:

Class marks	12·5	17·5	22·5	27·5	32·5	37·5
Frequency	7	12	20	28	8	11

Hint. Classes are 10 – 15, 15 – 20, 20 – 25, 25 – 30, 30 – 35, 35 – 40.

9 Draw a histogram for the following frequency distribution:

Age (in years)	below 2	below 4	below 6	below 8	below 10	below 12
No. of children	12	15	36	45	72	90

10 Draw a histogram for the following data:

Classes	59 – 65	66 – 72	73 – 79	80 – 86	87 – 93	94 – 100
Frequency	10	5	25	15	30	10

11 Draw a frequency polygon for the following data:

Class intervals	40 – 50	50 – 60	60 – 70	70 – 80	80 – 90	90 – 100
Frequency	15	28	45	32	41	18

12 In a class of 60 students, the marks obtained in a monthly test were as under:

Marks	10 – 20	20 – 30	30 – 40	40 – 50	50 – 60
Students	10	25	12	08	05

Draw a frequency polygon to represent the above data.

13 In a class of 90 students, the marks obtained in a weekly test were as under:

Marks	16 – 20	21 – 25	26 – 30	31 – 35	36 – 40	41 – 45	46 – 50
No. of students	4	12	18	26	14	10	6

Draw a frequency polygon for the above data.

14 In a city, the weekly observations made in a study on the cost of living index are given in the following table:

Cost of living index	140 – 150	150 – 160	160 – 170	170 – 180	180 – 190	190 – 200
Number of weeks	5	10	20	9	6	2

Draw a frequency polygon for the data given above.

15 Construct a combined histogram and frequency polygon for the following data:

Weekly earnings (in rupees)	150–165	165–180	180–195	195–210	210–225	225–240
No. of workers	8	14	22	12	15	6

16 In a study of diabetic patients, the following data was obtained:

Age (in years)	10–20	20–30	30–40	40–50	50–60	60–70	70–80
No. of patients	3	8	30	36	27	15	6

Represent the above data by a histogram and a frequency polygon.

17 The water bills (in rupees) of 32 houses in a locality are given below :

30, 48, 52, 78, 103, 85, 37, 94, 72, 73, 66, 52, 92, 65, 78, 81, 64, 60, 75, 78, 108, 63, 71, 54, 59, 75, 100, 103, 35, 89, 95, 73.

Taking class intervals 30 – 40, 40 – 50, 50 – 60, ..., form frequency distribution table. Construct a combined histogram and frequency polygon.

18 The number of matchsticks in 40 boxes on counting was found as given below:

44, 41, 42, 43, 47, 50, 51, 49, 43, 42, 40, 42, 44, 45, 49, 42, 46, 49, 45, 49, 45, 47, 48, 43, 43, 44, 48, 43, 46, 50, 43, 52, 46, 49, 52, 51, 47, 43, 43, 45.

Taking classes 40 – 42, 42 – 44 ..., construct the frequency distribution table for the above data. Also draw a combined histogram and frequency polygon to represent the distribution.

19 The histogram showing the weekly wages (in rupees) of workers in a factory is given alongside.

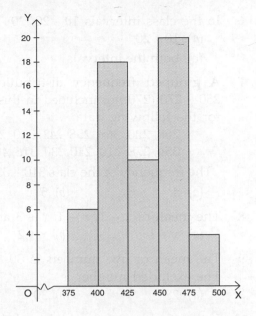

Answer the following about the frequency distribution:

(*i*) What is the frequency of the class 400 – 425?

(*ii*) What is the class having minimum frequency?

(*iii*) What is the cumulative frequency of the class 425 – 450?

(*iv*) Construct a frequency and cumulative frequency table for the given distribution.

20 The runs scored by two teams A and B on the first 42 balls in a cricket match are given below:

No. of balls	1–6	7–12	13–18	19–24	25–30	31–36	37–42
Runs scored by Team A	2	1	8	9	4	5	6
Runs scored by Team B	5	6	2	10	5	6	3

Draw their frequency polygons on the same graph.

Multiple Choice Questions

Choose the correct answer from the given four options (1 to 16):

1 The marks obtained by 17 students in a mathematics test (out of 100) are given below:

91, 82, 100, 100, 96, 65, 82, 76, 79, 90, 46, 64, 72, 66, 68, 48, 49

The range of the data is

(*a*) 46   (*b*) 54   (*c*) 90   (*d*) 100

2 The class mark of the class 90–120 is

(*a*) 90   (*b*) 105   (*c*) 115   (*d*) 120

3 In a frequency distribution, the mid-value of a class is 10 and the width of the class is 6. The lower limit of the class is

(*a*) 6   (*b*) 7   (*c*) 8   (*d*) 12

4 The width of each of 5 continuous classes in a frequency distribution is 5 and the lower limit of the lowest class is 10. The upper limit of the highest class is

(*a*) 15   (*b*) 25   (*c*) 35   (*d*) 40

5 The class marks of a frequency distribution are given as follows:

15, 20, 25, ...

The class corresponding to the class mark 20 is

(*a*) 12·5 – 17·5   (*b*) 17·5 – 22·5   (*c*) 18·5 – 21·5   (*d*) 19·5 – 20·5

6 In the class intervals 10 – 20, 20 – 30, the number 20 is included in
   (*a*) 10 – 20
   (*b*) 20 – 30
   (*c*) both the intervals
   (*d*) none of these intervals

7 A grouped frequency distribution table with class intervals of equal size using 250 – 270 (270 not included in this interval) as one of the class intervals is constructed for the following data:

   268, 220, 368, 258, 242, 310, 272, 342, 310, 290, 300, 320, 319, 304, 402, 318, 406, 292, 354, 278, 210, 240, 330, 316, 406, 215, 258, 236.

   The frequency of the class 310 – 330 is
   (*a*) 4
   (*b*) 5
   (*c*) 6
   (*d*) 7

8 The mean of $x - 1$, $x + 1$, $x + 3$ and $x + 5$ is
   (*a*) $x + 1$
   (*b*) $x + 2$
   (*c*) $x + 3$
   (*d*) $x + 4$

9 The mean of five numbers is 30. If one number is excluded, their mean becomes 28. The excluded number is
   (*a*) 28
   (*b*) 30
   (*c*) 35
   (*d*) 38

10 If the mean of x_1, x_2 is 7.5, and the mean of x_1, x_2, x_3 is 8, then the value of x_3 is
   (*a*) 9
   (*b*) 8
   (*c*) 7·5
   (*d*) 6

11 If each observation of the data is increased by 5, then their mean
   (*a*) remains the same
   (*b*) becomes 5 times the original mean
   (*c*) is decreased by 5
   (*d*) is increased by 5

12 The mean of 100 observations is 50. If one of the observation which was 50 is replaced by 150, the resulting mean will be
   (*a*) 50·5
   (*b*) 51
   (*c*) 51·5
   (*d*) 52

13 For drawing a frequency polygon of a continuous frequency distribution, we plot the points whose ordinates are the frequencies of the respective classes and abscissae are respectively:
   (*a*) upper limits of the classes
   (*b*) lower limits of the classes
   (*c*) class marks of the classes
   (*d*) upper limits of preceding classes

14 Median of the numbers 4, 4, 5, 7, 6, 7, 7, 3, 12 is
   (*a*) 4
   (*b*) 5
   (*c*) 6
   (*d*) 7

15 The median of the data
   78, 56, 22, 34, 45, 54, 39, 68, 54, 84 is
   (*a*) 45
   (*b*) 49·5
   (*c*) 54
   (*d*) 56

16 In a data, 10 numbers are arranged in ascending order. If the 8th entry is increased by 6, then the median increases by
   (*a*) 0
   (*b*) 2
   (*c*) 3
   (*d*) 6

S ummary

....

○ **Statistics** is that branch of mathematics which deals with the collection, presentation, analysis and interpretation of data.

○ Facts and information, collected with a definite purpose, are called **data**.

○ A quantity which is being measured in an experiment (or survey) is called a **variable**.

○ The difference between the maximum and minimum value of a variable is called its **range**.

- A particular value of a variable is called **variate** (or **observation**).
- The number of times a particular observation occurs is called its **frequency**.
- A table showing the frequency of various observations is called **frequency distribution table**.
- **Mean** (or **arithmetic average**) of a number of observations is the sum of the values of all the observations divided by the total number of observations.

  Thus, the mean of n observations $x_1, x_2, x_3, \ldots x_n$ is given by

  $$\text{Mean} = \frac{\Sigma x_i}{n}, \text{ where } \Sigma x_i = x_1 + x_2 + x_3 + \ldots + x_n.$$

- **Median** is the central value of a statistical data if it is arranged in ascending or descending order.

  If there are n observations $x_1, x_2, x_3, \ldots, x_n$ arranged in ascending or descending order, then

  $$\text{Median} = \begin{cases} \dfrac{n+1}{2} \text{ th observation, if } n \text{ is odd} \\[2mm] \dfrac{\dfrac{n}{2}\text{ th observation} + \left(\dfrac{n}{2}+1\right)\text{ th observation}}{2}, \text{ if } n \text{ is even.} \end{cases}$$

- If the number of observations is large, then the grouping of data is done. The classes are formed. Usually, we convert the discrete distribution to continuous distribution. In a continuous distribution, the class limits are called **true** or **actual class limits**.
- The difference between the actual class limits of a class is called its **class size** or **class width**.
- The **class mark** of a class is the value midway between its actual lower limit and actual upper class limit.
- The (numerical) data can be represented graphically.
- In bar graphs, bar of equal width are drawn with equal spacing between them. The height of a bar represents the frequency of the corresponding variate (observation).
- Histograms are used to represent continuous grouped data. Histogram consists of a set of adjacent rectangles. The height of rectangles correspond to the frequency of the class and the breadth of the rectangle corresponds to the class size. There is no gap between different rectangles.
- Continuous frequency distribution can also be represented by **frequency polygons**. In a frequency polygon, we plot points on the graph paper representing frequencies of different classes against the corresponding mid-points of class intervals. On joining consecutive points by line segments, we get **frequency curve** and if the end points of frequency graph are joined to the mid-points of immediate lower and upper class intervals outside the range with zero frequency, we get frequency polygon.

1. Find the mean and the median of the following set of numbers:

   8, 0, 5, 3, 2, 9, 1, 5, 4, 7, 2, 5.

2. Find the mean and the median of all the (positive) factors of 48.

3. The mean weight of 60 students of a class is 52·75 kg. If the mean weight of 35 of them is 54 kg, find the mean weight of the remaining students.

4. The mean age of 18 students of a class is 14·5 years. Two more students of age 15 years and 16 years join the class. What is the new mean age?

5. If the mean of the five observations $x + 1$, $x + 3$, $x + 5$, $2x + 2$, $3x + 3$ is 14, find the mean of first three observations.

6. The mean height of 36 students of a class is 150·5 cm. Later on, it was detected that the height of one student was wrongly copied as 165 cm instead of 156 cm. Find the correct mean height.

7. The mean of 40 items is 35. Later on, it was discovered that two items were misread as 36 and 29 instead of 63 and 22. Find the correct mean.

8. The following observations have been arranged in ascending order. If the median of the data is 63, find the value of x.

   29, 32, 48, 50, x, $x + 2$, 72, 75, 87, 91.

9. Draw a histogram showing marks obtained by the students of a school in a Mathematics paper carrying 60 marks.

Marks	0 – 10	10 – 20	20 – 30	30 – 40	40 – 50	50 – 60
Students	4	5	10	8	30	40

10. In a class of 60 students, the marks obtained in a surprise test were as under:

Marks	14–20	20–26	26–32	32–38	38–44	44–50	50–56	56–62
No. of students	4	10	9	15	12	5	3	2

Represent the above data by a histogram and a frequency polygon.

11. Construct a combined histogram and frequency polygon for the following distribution:

Classes	91–100	101–110	111–120	121–130	131–140	141–150	151–160
Frequency	16	28	44	20	32	12	4

Hint. Take 1 cm along y-axis = 8 (frequency).

12. The electricity bills (in rupees) of 40 houses in a locality are given below:

   78   87   81   52   59   65   101   108   115   95

   98   65   62   121   128   63   76   84   89   91

   65   101   95   81   87   105   129   92   75   105

   78   72   107   116   127   100   80   82   61   118

Form a frequency distribution table with a class size of 10. Also represent the above data with a histogram and frequency polygon.

13 The data given below represent the marks obtained by 35 students:

21	26	21	20	23	24	22	19	24
26	25	23	26	29	21	24	19	25
26	25	22	23	23	27	26	24	25
30	25	23	28	28	24	28	28	

Taking class intervals 19 – 20, 21 – 22 etc., make a frequency distribution for the above data.

Construct a combined histogram and frequency polygon for the distribution.

14 The given histogram and frequency polygon shows the ages of teachers in a school. Answer the following:

   (*i*) What is the class size of each class?

   (*ii*) What is the class whose class mark is 48?

   (*iii*) What is the class whose frequency is maximum?

   (*iv*) Construct a frequency table for the given distribution.

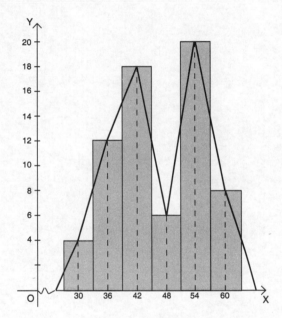

Answers

EXERCISE 1.1

1. $\dfrac{43}{144}; \dfrac{3}{8}, \dfrac{43}{144}, \dfrac{2}{9}$

2. $\dfrac{7}{24}, \dfrac{13}{48}; \dfrac{1}{4}, \dfrac{13}{48}, \dfrac{7}{24}, \dfrac{1}{3}$

3. $-\dfrac{11}{24}, -\dfrac{5}{12}; -\dfrac{1}{2}, -\dfrac{11}{24}, -\dfrac{5}{12}, -\dfrac{1}{3}$

4. $\dfrac{27}{60}, \dfrac{17}{30}, \dfrac{41}{60}; \dfrac{4}{5}, \dfrac{41}{60}, \dfrac{17}{30}, \dfrac{27}{60}, \dfrac{1}{3}$

5. $4\cdot125, 4\cdot25, 4\cdot375$

6. $\dfrac{22}{7}, \dfrac{23}{7}, \dfrac{24}{7}, \dfrac{25}{7}, \dfrac{26}{7}, \dfrac{27}{7}$

7. $\dfrac{19}{30}, \dfrac{2}{3}, \dfrac{7}{10}, \dfrac{11}{15}, \dfrac{23}{30}$

8. $-\dfrac{13}{35}, -\dfrac{12}{35}, -\dfrac{11}{35}, -\dfrac{2}{7}, -\dfrac{9}{35}, -\dfrac{8}{35}, -\dfrac{1}{5}, 0, \dfrac{1}{35}, \dfrac{2}{35}$

9. $\dfrac{11}{21}, \dfrac{23}{42}, \dfrac{4}{7}, \dfrac{25}{42}, \dfrac{13}{21}, \dfrac{9}{14}$

EXERCISE 1.3

2. (i) $0\cdot36$; terminating   (ii) $4\cdot125$; terminating

   (iii) $0\cdot\overline{2}$; non-terminating repeating   (iv) $0\cdot\overline{18}$; non-terminating repeating

   (v) $0\cdot\overline{230769}$; non-terminating repeating   (vi) $0\cdot8225$; terminating

3. (i) terminating   (ii) terminating   (iii) non-terminating repeating
   (iv) terminating   (v) terminating   (vi) non-terminating repeating

4. terminating; because $\dfrac{987}{10500} = \dfrac{47}{500} = \dfrac{47}{2^2 \times 5^3}$, so denominator has only 2 and 5 as prime factors

5. (i) $2\cdot125$ (ii) $0\cdot00416$ (iii) $0\cdot0875$ (iv) $0\cdot4$
   (v) $0\cdot0448$ (vi) $0\cdot158$

6. $5000 = 2^3 \times 5^4; \dfrac{257}{5000} = \dfrac{257}{2^3 \times 5^4} ; 0\cdot0514$

7. $\dfrac{1}{7} = 0\cdot\overline{142857}, \dfrac{2}{7} = 2 \times \dfrac{1}{7} = 0\cdot\overline{285714}, \dfrac{3}{7} = 3 \times \dfrac{1}{7} = 0\cdot\overline{428571},$

   $\dfrac{4}{7} = 4 \times \dfrac{1}{7} = 0\cdot\overline{571428}, \dfrac{5}{7} = 5 \times \dfrac{1}{7} = 0\cdot\overline{714285}, \dfrac{6}{7} = 6 \times \dfrac{1}{7} = 0\cdot\overline{857142}$

8. (i) $\dfrac{1}{3}$ (ii) $\dfrac{47}{9}$ (iii) $\dfrac{40}{99}$ (iv) $\dfrac{43}{90}$ (v) $\dfrac{133}{990}$ (vi) $\dfrac{1}{999}$

9. (i) and (v) are irrational; (ii), (iii), (iv) and (vi) are rational

10. (i) Rational; prime factors of q will be 2 or 5 or both only

   (ii) Rational; prime factors of q will also have a prime factor other than 2 or 5

   (iii) Not rational

   (iv) Rational; prime factors of q will also have a prime factor other than 2 or 5

11. (i) $0\cdot4141141114\ldots$ (ii) $0\cdot151551555\ldots$ (iii) $0\cdot070070007\ldots$

12. $\sqrt{5}, \sqrt{6}$ **13.** 0·5050050005...., 0·6060060006.... **14.** 1·5

15. 3·5, 3·6 **16.** $\sqrt{6}$ **17.** $\sqrt{5}, \sqrt{6}$

EXERCISE 1.4

1. (*i*) $\sqrt{5}$ (*ii*) $\dfrac{34\sqrt{3}}{3}$ (*iii*) 60 (*iv*) $4\sqrt{5}$ (*v*) $\dfrac{7\sqrt{6}}{12}$ (*vi*) $\dfrac{5\sqrt{2}}{4}$

2. (*i*) $10 + 5\sqrt{5} + 2\sqrt{7} + \sqrt{35}$ (*ii*) 20 (*iii*) $7 + 2\sqrt{10}$

(*iv*) $10 - 2\sqrt{21}$ (*v*) $\sqrt{10} + \sqrt{14} + \sqrt{15} + \sqrt{21}$

(*vi*) $4\sqrt{3} - 4\sqrt{7} + \sqrt{15} - \sqrt{35}$

3. (*i*) 28·28 (*ii*) −36·764 **4.** (*i*) 8·66 (*ii*) 121·24

5. (*i*) $\sqrt{\dfrac{7}{25}}, \sqrt{\dfrac{16}{5}}$ (*ii*) $-\sqrt{\dfrac{2}{49}}, \sqrt{\dfrac{25}{3}}$ **6.** (*i*), (*iii*) and (*iv*)

7. (*i*), (*ii*), (*iii*), (*iv*), (*vi*) and (*viii*) **9.** (*i*) $\sqrt{15}; -\sqrt{7}$ (*ii*) $\dfrac{9}{\sqrt{5}}; -3\sqrt{2}$

10. (*i*) $2\sqrt{3}, \sqrt{15}, 4, 3\sqrt{2}$ (*ii*) $4, 3\sqrt{2}, 2\sqrt{8}, 4\sqrt{3}, \sqrt{50}$

11. (*i*) $4\sqrt{3}, \dfrac{9}{\sqrt{2}}, \dfrac{3}{2}\sqrt{5}, 3\sqrt{\dfrac{6}{5}}$ (*ii*) $3\sqrt{5}, 2\sqrt{7}, \dfrac{7}{3}\sqrt{2}, \dfrac{5}{\sqrt{3}}, -\sqrt{3}$

12. $\sqrt[3]{2}, \sqrt[6]{5}, \sqrt{3}$

EXERCISE 1.5

1. (*i*) $\dfrac{3\sqrt{5}}{20}$ (*ii*) $\dfrac{5\sqrt{21}}{3}$ (*iii*) $\dfrac{4 + \sqrt{7}}{3}$ (*iv*) $3\sqrt{2} - 1$ (*v*) $\sqrt{41} + 5$

(*vi*) $\sqrt{7} + \sqrt{6}$ (*vii*) $\dfrac{\sqrt{5} - \sqrt{2}}{3}$ (*viii*) $-5 - 2\sqrt{6}$

2. (*i*) $\dfrac{47 + 21\sqrt{5}}{2}$ (*ii*) $17 - 12\sqrt{2}$ (*iii*) $\dfrac{-119 + 31\sqrt{14}}{7}$

3. 1 **4.** 1

5. (*i*) $a = \dfrac{9}{11}$ (*ii*) $a = 2, b = -\dfrac{5}{6}$ (*iii*) $a = 0, b = 1$

6. $p = 0, q = 1$ **7.** (*i*) 0·414 (*ii*) 0·318 **8.** $2\sqrt{3}$ **9.** 16

10. 98 **11.** (*i*) −18 (*ii*) $8\sqrt{5}$ (*iii*) 322 (*iv*) $-144\sqrt{5}$ **12.** 39

MULTIPLE CHOICE QUESTIONS

1. (*d*) **2.** (*c*) **3.** (*c*) **4.** (*d*) **5.** (*d*) **6.** (*c*) **7.** (*c*)
8. (*b*) **9.** (*d*) **10.** (*d*) **11.** (*c*) **12.** (*c*) **13.** (*b*) **14.** (*b*)
15. (*c*) **16.** (*c*) **17.** (*d*) **18.** (*d*) **19.** (*a*) **20.** (*b*) **21.** (*a*)

CHAPTER TEST

1. (*i*) Recurring decimal (*ii*) recurring decimal (*iii*) terminating decimal; 0·056
(*iv*) terminating decimal; −0·2875 (*v*) recurring decimal

2. (i) $\dfrac{74}{55}$ (ii) $\dfrac{2355}{999}$ **3.** $\dfrac{64}{117}$; $\dfrac{7}{13}$, $\dfrac{64}{117}$, $\dfrac{5}{9}$ **4.** $\dfrac{121}{150}$, $\dfrac{61}{75}$, $\dfrac{123}{150}$, $\dfrac{62}{150}$

9. (i) $2(2\sqrt{2} - \sqrt{3})$ (ii) $\dfrac{57}{15} - \dfrac{41}{30}\sqrt{6}$ (iii) $\dfrac{2 + \sqrt{6} - \sqrt{2}}{4}$

10. $p = 3$, $q = -\dfrac{2}{3}$ **11.** $-4\sqrt{2}$

12. (i) 2207 (ii) $20\dfrac{7}{9}$ (iii) 970

13. $\dfrac{5}{2}\sqrt{3}, 3{\cdot}5, 2\sqrt{2}, \sqrt{10}, -\dfrac{5}{\sqrt{2}}$ **14.** $2; \dfrac{\sqrt{3} + \sqrt{5}}{2}$

15. $\sqrt{13}, \sqrt{15}, 3\sqrt{2}; 2\sqrt{5}, 3\sqrt{2}, \sqrt{15}, \sqrt{13}, 2\sqrt{3}$ **16.** (i) $\sqrt{2}, \sqrt{3}$ (ii) $\sqrt{2}, \sqrt{3}$

17. Take $a = 3\sqrt{2}$, $b = 5\sqrt{2}$

18. q can be expressed as $q = 2^m 5^n$ where m and n are non-negative integers

19. (i) Rational; prime factors of q are 2 or 5 or both only

  (ii) rational; q has a prime factor other than 2 and 5

  (iii) irrational

  (iv) rational; prime factors of q are 2 or 5 or both only

  (v) rational; q has a prime factor other than 2 and 5

  (vi) irrational

EXERCISE 2.1

1. ₹8820; ₹820 **2.** (i) ₹1875 (ii) ₹50700 (iii) ₹2028 **3.** ₹880; ₹10648

4. (i) ₹14080 (ii) ₹1408 (iii) ₹17036·80

5. (i) ₹5750 (ii) ₹710·70 **6.** (i) 12% (ii) ₹12544

7. (i) 6·5% p.a. (ii) ₹5671

8. (i) 12% (ii) ₹672 (iii) ₹7024·64. **9.** ₹2541; ₹541

10. ₹56243·20; ₹6243·20 **11.** ₹5724; ₹724 **12.** ₹23449·80; ₹6449·80

13. (i) ₹10560 (ii) ₹11616 (iii) ₹2016 (iv) ₹1056; ₹105·60 (v) ₹1161·60

14. ₹10648; ₹2648. **15.** ₹410 **16.** ₹4155 **17.** ₹30000 **18.** ₹26450

EXERCISE 2.2

1. ₹5618; ₹618 **2.** ₹11712·80; ₹3712·80 **3.** ₹7774·625

4. ₹5788·12; ₹788·12 **5.** ₹103030·10; ₹3030·10 **6.** ₹12 **7.** ₹6·08

8. ₹2142·40; ₹142·40 **9.** ₹492·25 **10.** ₹8000 **11.** ₹7500 **12.** ₹125000

13. ₹70000 **14.** ₹80 **15.** $4\dfrac{1}{6}$% **16.** 25% **17.** 5% **18.** 10%

19. 40% p.a. **20.** 5%; ₹92610 **21.** 5%; ₹4800 **22.** 10%; ₹600

23. 3 years. **24.** (i) 3 years (ii) 3 years **25.** $1\dfrac{1}{2}$ years **26.** ₹2500

27. (i) $6\dfrac{2}{3}$% (ii) ₹3375 (iii) ₹256 **28.** ₹10000 **29.** ₹6000 **30.** 10%

31. 4% p.a.; ₹1875 **32.** ₹21 **33.** ₹20000 **34.** ₹12000; 10%

EXERCISE 2.3

1. 25300 **2.** 1951 **3.** (i) 7311616 (ii) 6250000 **4.** ₹877·50 **5.** ₹20577

6. 1875 quintals **7.** ₹480000. **8.** 5% p.a. **9.** 5% p.a. **10.** 3 years **11.** 5% p.a.

12. ₹387500   **13.** $95\frac{5}{16}$ %   **14.** Profit ₹80420

MULTIPLE CHOICE QUESTIONS

1. (c)   **2.** (c)   **3.** (b)   **4.** (a)   **5.** (b)   **6.** (d)   **7.** (b)

CHAPTER TEST

1. ₹25   **2.** $6\frac{1}{4}$ %; ₹3468   **3.** ₹25000; ₹3090

4. (i) ₹20000 (each)   (ii) ₹2050; ₹2472   **5.** ₹8000; 8%

6. ₹7500   **7.** (i) 6% p.a. (ii) ₹6000   **8.** 1 year   **9.** 20%   **10.** 397535

11. (i) ₹493125   (ii) ₹161587·20   **12.** ₹43520

EXERCISE 3.1

1. (i) $4x^2 + 28xy + 49y^2$ (ii) $\frac{1}{4}x^2 + \frac{2}{3}xy + \frac{4}{9}y^2$

2. (i) $9x^2 + \frac{1}{4x^2} + 3$ (ii) $9x^4y^2 + 30x^2yz + 25z^2$

3. (i) $9x^2 + \frac{1}{4x^2} - 3$ (ii) $\frac{1}{4}x^2 - \frac{3}{2}xy + \frac{9}{4}y^2$

4. (i) $x^2 + 8x + 15$ (ii) $x^2 - 2x - 15$

(iii) $x^2 + 2x - 63$ (iv) $x^2 - 5xy + 6y^2$

5. (i) $x^2 + 4y^2 + z^2 - 4xy + 4yz - 2zx$

(ii) $4x^2 + 9y^2 + 16z^2 - 12xy - 24yz + 16zx$

6. (i) $4x^2 + \frac{9}{x^2} + 13 - \frac{6}{x} - 4x$ (ii) $\frac{4}{9}x^2 + \frac{9}{4x^2} - 1 - \frac{4}{3}x + \frac{3}{x}$

7. (i) $x^3 + 6x^2 + 12x + 8$ (ii) $8a^3 + b^3 + 12a^2b + 6ab^2$

8. (i) $27x^3 + \frac{1}{x^3} + 27x + \frac{9}{x}$ (ii) $8x^3 - 12x^2 + 6x - 1$

9. (i) $125x^3 - 27y^3 - 225x^2y + 135xy^2$ (ii) $8x^3 - \frac{1}{27y^3} - \frac{4x^2}{y} + \frac{2x}{3y^2}$

10. (i) $2(a^2 + b^2)$ (ii) $4ab$ **11.** (i) $2\left(a^2 + \frac{1}{a^2}\right)$ (ii) 4   **12.** (i) $3 - 3x$ (ii) 0

13. (i) $49p^2 - 81q^2$ (ii) $4x^2 - \frac{9}{x^2}$

14. (i) $4x^2 - 4xy + y^2 - 9$ (ii) $9x^2 - 30x + 25 - y^2$

15. (i) $x^2 - 6x + 9 - \frac{4}{x^2}$ (ii) $625 - 16x^4$

16. (i) $x^2 + 4xy + 4y^2 + 10x + 20y + 21$ (ii) $4x^2 + 4xy + y^2 - 8x - 4y - 45$

(iii) $x^2 - 4xy + 4y^2 - 2x + 4y - 15$ (iv) $9x^2 - 24xy + 16y^2 - 24x + 32y + 12$

17. (i) $8p^3 + 27q^3$ (ii) $x^3 + \frac{1}{x^3}$ **18.** (i) $27p^3 - 64q^3$ (ii) $x^3 - \frac{27}{x^3}$

19. $8x^3 + 27y^3 + 64z^3 - 72xyz$

20. (i) $x^3 + 6x^2 + 11x + 6$ (ii) $x^3 - x^2 - 14x + 24$

21. 0; – 37   **22.** 4

23. (*i*) 10201 (*ii*) 1006009 (*iii*) 104·04
24. (*i*) 9801 (*ii*) 994009 (*iii*) 96·04
25. (*i*) 1092727 (*ii*) 970299 (*iii*) 1030·301
28. 3 **29.** 0 **30.** (*i*) 13770 (*ii*) −16380
31. 100

EXERCISE 3.2

1. 74 **2.** 116 **3.** 25 **4.** 352 **5.** 68 **6.** (*i*) ± 5 (*ii*) ± 1
7. (*i*) ± 8 (*ii*) ± 32 **8.** (*i*) ± 15 (*ii*) ± 135 **9.** (*i*) 26 (*ii*) 5

10. 11 **11.** (*i*) ± 7 (*ii*) $169\frac{1}{2}$ (*iii*) $310\frac{1}{2}$ or $254\frac{1}{2}$ **12.** 123

13. 63 **14.** 135 **15.** (*i*) 14 (*ii*) 194 (*iii*) 52 (*iv*) $\pm 2\sqrt{3}$
16. 727 **17.** (*i*) 7 (*ii*) ±3 (*iii*) ±18

18. (*i*) $\pm 4\sqrt{2}$ (*ii*) $\pm 24\sqrt{2}$ **20.** 45 **23.** ± 5 **24.** ± 445

25. ± 3 **26.** $\pm 22\frac{1}{2}$ **27.** (*i*) 7 (*ii*) 18

28. (*i*) 5 (*ii*) $\pm\sqrt{29}$ (*iii*) $\pm 5\sqrt{29}$ **29.** 0 **30.** $2\sqrt{3}$ **31.** 100
32. 22 **33.** ± 15 **34.** −2 **35.** 721 **36.** 10 **37.** 152

MULTIPLE CHOICE QUESTIONS

1. (*b*) **2.** (*d*) **3.** (*d*) **4.** (*a*) **5.** (*d*) **6.** (*b*) **7.** (*d*)
8. (*c*) **9.** (*d*) **10.** (*c*)

CHAPTER TEST

1. (*i*) $4x^2 + 9y^2 + 12xy - 25$
   (*ii*) $36 + 16a^2 + 49b^2 - 48a + 56ab - 84b$
   (*iii*) $343 - 27x^3y^3 - 441xy + 189x^2y^2$
   (*iv*) $x^3 + y^3 + 3x^2y + 3xy^2 + 6x^2 + 6y^2 + 12xy + 12x + 12y + 8$
2. $x^8 - 256$ **3.** 999996 **5.** 0 **6.** 27 **7.** $p^2 - q^2 = 4$

8. 104 **9.** (*i*) 4 (*ii*) 52 (*iii*) 2702 **10.** $27 + 19\sqrt{2}$ **11.** $\pm 26\frac{26}{27}$

12. $-30\sqrt{3}$ **13.** 85 **14.** (*i*) −10 (*ii*) 29 **15.** 6

EXERCISE 4.1

1. (*i*) $4xy^2(2y + 3x)$ (*ii*) $3ax^2(5x - 3)$
2. (*i*) $7py(3y - 8)$ (*ii*) $2x^2(2x - 3)$
3. (*i*) $2\pi r(r - 2)$ (*ii*) $2(9m + 8n)$
4. (*i*) $5abc(5c - 3ab)$ (*ii*) $14pq^2r(2p - 3r)$
5. (*i*) $2x(4x^2 - 3x + 5)$ (*ii*) $2(7mn + 11m - 31p)$
6. (*i*) $6pq(3pq - 4q + 5p)$ (*ii*) $3a^2b^2(9ab - 6b + 25a)$
7. (*i*) $5(2p - 3q)(3a - 2b)$ (*ii*) $3(x^2 + y^2)(a + 2b)$
8. (*i*) $2(x + 2y)^2(3x + 6y + 4)$ (*ii*) $7(a - 3b)[2(a - 3b)^2 - 3p]$
9. (*i*) $5(2p + q)[2a(2p + q)^2 - 3b(2p + q) + 7]$ (*ii*) $(x^2 + y^2 - z^2)(x - y - z)$

EXERCISE 4.2

1. (i) $(x + y) (x - 1)$
   (ii) $(y - z) (y - 5)$
2. (i) $(x - y) (5y - 7)$
   (ii) $(5p - 8q) (p - 2)$
3. (i) $(a - b) (ab + 3)$
   (ii) $(x - 3) (x^2 + 1)$
4. (i) $(2y - 1) (3xy - 5)$
   (ii) $(x - 2y) (3a + 4b)$
5. (i) $(1 - a) (1 - b)$
   (ii) $(a - 2b) (a - c)$
6. (i) $(x + y) (x + y^2)$
   (ii) $(y - x) (y + x^2)$
7. (i) $(b + 1) (ab - 1)$
   (ii) $(a - 2b) (2 - x)$
8. (i) $(5 + 2r) (ph - 2qk)$
   (ii) $(x - a) (x - 2b)$
9. (i) $(bx - ay) (ax - by)$
   (ii) $(x^2 + y^2) (a^2 + b^2)$
10. (i) $(a - 2b) (a^2 + b)$
    (ii) $3(x - 1) (xy + 4)$
11. $(a + b) (ab - bc + xy)$
12. $(a - b) (x^2 + y^2 + z^2)$
13. $(x - 1) (2 - x + a)$

EXERCISE 4.3

1. (i) $(2x + 5y) (2x - 5y)$
   (ii) $(3x + 1) (3x - 1)$
2. (i) $6(5 + a) (5 - a)$
   (ii) $2(4x + 3y) (4x - 3y)$
3. (i) $(x - y + 3) (x - y - 3)$
   (ii) $(4x + 3y) (2x + 3y)$
4. (i) $5(2x + 3y) (2x - 3y)$
   (ii) $-(7x + 2y) (x + 2y)$
5. (i) $2(x + 3y) (x - 7y)$
   (ii) $2x (8 - x)$
6. (i) $3(6a + b - c) (6a - b + c)$
   (ii) $\pi a (a^2 + \pi b) (a^2 - \pi b)$
7. (i) $8(2x + 1) (3x - 1)$
   (ii) $(x + 1) (x - 1)$
8. (i) $(x - 2y) (1 - x - 2y)$
   (ii) $(2a + b) (2a - b + 1)$
9. (i) $(a - b) (a + b - 2)$
   (ii) $(a - b) (a + b - 1)$
10. (i) $(3 + x - y) (3 - x + y)$
    (ii) $(3x^2 + x + 1) (3x^2 - x - 1)$
11. (i) $(3x^2 + x + 6) (3x^2 - x - 6)$
    (ii) $(x + 1) (x - 1) (x - 5)$
12. (i) $(a^2 + b^2 - 1) (a^2 - b^2 + 1)$
    (ii) $x (x + 5) (x - 5)$
13. (i) $2(x^2 + 4) (x + 2) (x - 2)$
    (ii) $(b + c) (a + b + c) (a - b - c)$
14. (i) $(a + b) (a + b + 1) (a + b - 1)$
    (ii) $(x - y + a + b) (x - y - a - b)$
15. (i) $(ac - bd + bc + ad) (ac - bd - bc - ad)$
    (ii) $(x - y) (4x + y + 2)$
16. (i) $\left(x - \dfrac{1}{x} + 3\right) \left(x - \dfrac{1}{x} - 3\right)$
    (ii) $(x^2 + x + 3) (x^2 - x + 3)$
17. (i) $(a^2 + b^2 + 3ab) (a^2 + b^2 - 3ab)$
    (ii) $(x^2 + 4x + 1) (x^2 - 4x + 1)$
18. (i) $(x^2 + 7)^2 - (5x)^2$
    (ii) $(x^2 - 5x)^2 - 7^2$
    (iii) $x^2 - (5x - 7)^2$
19. (i) 958000
    (ii) 9980

EXERCISE 4.4

1. (i) $(x + 2) (x + 3)$
   (ii) $(x - 1) (x - 7)$
2. (i) $(x + 7) (x - 1)$
   (ii) $(y + 9) (y - 2)$
3. (i) $(y - 9) (y + 2)$
   (ii) $(a + 6) (a - 9)$
4. (i) $(x - 2) (2x - 3)$
   (ii) $(3x - 1) (2x + 5)$
5. (i) $(2x + 5) (3x - 2)$
   (ii) $(3x + 1) (2x - 3)$
6. (i) $(x - 2) (2x + 3)$
   (ii) $(1 - 21y) (1 + 3y)$
7. (i) $(y + 5) (2y - 9)$
   (ii) $(1 - 2x) (5 + 6x)$
8. (i) $(4x + 5) (3x - 2)$
   (ii) $(x - 8) (x - 2)$
9. (i) $10(2x - 3) (3x + 1)$
   (ii) $(x + y) (x - 7y)$

10. (i) $(x + 8y)(2x - 3y)$

11. (i) $(x + 4y)(5x - 3y)$

12. (i) $(ab - 6)(2ab + 5)$

13. (i) $(x - y - 5)(x - y - 1)$

14. (i) $(2a - 5)(2a - 1)$

15. (i) $(1 - 3a - 3b)(3 + 4a + 4b)$

16. (i) $(x + y + 4)(x - 6y + 4)$

17. $(3a - 4)(a - 5)$

(ii) $(2x - 3y)(3x + 2y)$

(ii) $(xy + 4)(xy - 12)$

(ii) $(2a + b)(a - b)$

(ii) $(2x - y - 7)(2x - y - 4)$

(ii) $(1 - 3a - 3b)(1 + a + b)$

(ii) $(a^2 - 10)(a + 1)(a - 1)$

(ii) $(x + 2)(x - 4)(x + 3)(x - 5)$

18. $(x - 1)(2x + 7)(x + 4)(2x - 3)$

EXERCISE 4.5

1. (i) $(2x + y)(4x^2 - 2xy + y^2)$

2. (i) $(4x + 1)(16x^2 - 4x + 1)$

(ii) $(4x - 5y)(16x^2 + 20xy + 25y^2)$

(ii) $7(a + 2b)(a^2 - 2ab + 4b^2)$

3. (i) $\left(\dfrac{x^2}{7} + \dfrac{7}{x^2}\right)\left(\dfrac{x^4}{49} - 1 + \dfrac{49}{x^4}\right)$

(ii) $\left(2x - \dfrac{1}{3y}\right)\left(4x^2 + \dfrac{2x}{3y} + \dfrac{1}{9y^2}\right)$

4. (i) $x^2(1 + x)(1 - x + x^2)$

5. (i) $(3xy - 2)(9x^2y^2 + 6xy + 4)$

6. (i) $(a + b)(a^2 - ab + b^2 + 1)$

7. (i) $(x + 1)(x^2 - x + 2)$

8. (i) $(x + 4)(x^2 + 2x + 4)$

(ii) $4x(2x - 5)(4x^2 + 10x + 25)$

(ii) $(7x + y)(13x^2 - 4xy + 19y^2)$

(ii) $(a - b)(a^2 + ab + b^2 - 1)$

(ii) $(a - 5)(a^2 + 5a + 24)$

(ii) $(a - 2b)(a^2 - ab + b^2)$

9. (i) $(a + 2b)(2a^2 - 4ab + 8b^2 - 5)$

(ii) $\left(a - \dfrac{1}{a}\right)\left(a^2 + \dfrac{1}{a^2} - 1\right)$

10. (i) $(a + b)(a - b)(a^2 + ab + b^2)(a^2 - ab + b^2)$

(ii) $(x + 1)(x - 1)(x^2 + x + 1)(x^2 - x + 1)$

11. (i) $(2x + 3y)(2x - 3y)(4x^2 + 6xy + 9y^2)(4x^2 - 6xy + 9y^2)$

(ii) $\dfrac{1}{x}(x - 2)(x^2 + 2x + 4)$

12. (i) $2(5a - 5b + 1)(25a^2 - 50ab + 25b^2 - 5a + 5b + 1)$

(ii) $(2a + b)(2a - b)(2x - y)(4x^2 + 2xy + y^2)$

13. (i) $(x + y)(x^2 - xy + y^2)(x^6 - x^3y^3 + y^6)$

(ii) $(x - 2)(x^2 + 2x + 4)(x + 1)(x^2 - x + 1)$

MULTIPLE CHOICE QUESTIONS

1. (c)   **2.** (b)   **3.** (c)   **4.** (b)   **5.** (d)   **6.** (c)   **7.** (b)

8. (d)   **9.** (b)   **10.** (a)   **11.** (b)   **12.** (a)   **13.** (c)   **14.** (d)

CHAPTER TEST

1. (i) $5(2x - 3)[3(2x - 3)^2 - 2]$

2. (i) $(x + 1)(2a^2 - b)$

3. (i) $(x - z)(xz + y^2)$

4. (i) $(c - d)(bc - bd - a + 3)$

5. (i) $(x - y)(x + y + z)$

6. (i) $(3x + 2 + 4y)(3x + 2 - 4y)$

7. (i) $(3x - 5y)(7x - 8y)$

8. (i) $(xy - 9)(xy + 8)$

9. (i) $(3a - 2b + 5)(3a - 2b - 2)$

10. (i) $(x + 1)(x - 2)(4x^2 - 4x + 3)$

(ii) $(b - c)[a(b + c) + d]$

(ii) $(p - a)(p - 2b)$

(ii) $5a(a - 1)(a^2 + 6)$

(ii) $(x - 1)(x^2 - y + 1)$

(ii) $a^4x^4(a^4 + x^4)(a^2 + x^2)(a + x)(a - x)$

(ii) $(x^2 + x + 2)(x^2 - x + 2)$

(ii) $4xy(x - 4)(x - 7)$

(ii) $xy(x + 4y)(9x + 5y)$

(ii) $(x^2 - 3x + 5)(x - 1)(x - 2)$

(ii) $(x^2 + 9y^2 + 3xy)(x^2 + 9y^2 - 3xy)$

11. (i) $\left(\dfrac{2}{3}x - \dfrac{1}{2}y\right)\left(\dfrac{4}{9}x^2 + \dfrac{1}{3}xy + \dfrac{1}{4}y^2\right)$ (ii) $(x + 4)(x^2 - 4x + 16)(x - 1)(x^2 + x + 1)$

12. (i) $\left(x + \dfrac{1}{x}\right)\left(x^2 - 1 + \dfrac{1}{x^2} + x - \dfrac{1}{x}\right)$ (ii) $4x(x^2 + 3)(3x^2 + 1)$ **14.** 931

EXERCISE 5.1

1. (i) $x = 9, y = 5$ (ii) $s = 9, t = 6$ (iii) $x = -21, y = 17$ (iv) $x = \dfrac{9}{13}, y = -\dfrac{5}{13}$

2. (i) $a = 2, b = 1$ (ii) $x = 2, y = -\dfrac{3}{2}$

3. (i) $x = 3, y = 4$ (ii) $x = 7\dfrac{27}{31}, y = 2\dfrac{13}{31}$

4. (i) $x = m + n, y = m - n$ (ii) $x = 2a, y = -2b$

5. $x = 15, y = 5; 3$ **6.** $x = \dfrac{16}{5}, y = \dfrac{23}{5}; p = \dfrac{19}{8}$

EXERCISE 5.2

1. (i) $x = 2, y = 1$ (ii) $x = -8, y = -4$

2. (i) $x = 4, y = 3$ (ii) $x = \dfrac{21}{20}, y = -\dfrac{3}{10}$ **3.** (i) $x = 5, y = -3$ (ii) $x = 2, y = 1$

4. (i) $x = 12, y = 8$ (ii) $x = \dfrac{26}{11}, y = \dfrac{5}{11}$

5. (i) $x = \dfrac{26}{3}, y = -\dfrac{8}{3}$ (ii) $x = \dfrac{3}{4}, y = -\dfrac{9}{4}$ **6.** $x = 2, y = -1$

7. (i) $x = 4, y = -4$ (ii) $x = 7, y = 13$ **8.** (i) $x = \dfrac{1}{5}, y = -2$ (ii) $x = 2, y = 1$

9. (i) $x = 1, y = -1$ (ii) $x = a, y = b$

10. $x = 7, y = 9; x - 3y = -20, 5y - 2x = 31$ **11.** $a = 2, b = 3$

12. Yes; $x = 7, y = 2$

EXERCISE 5.3

1. (i) $x = -2, y = 5$ (ii) $x = -1, y = 1$

2. (i) $x = a, y = -b$ (ii) $x = 2a, y = -2b$

EXERCISE 5.4

1. (i) $x = 4, y = -2$ (ii) $x = \dfrac{1}{2}, y = \dfrac{1}{3}$

2. (i) $x = 1, y = 1$ (ii) $x = 0, y = 0; x = \dfrac{1}{2}, y = \dfrac{1}{3}$

3. (i) $x = 0, y = 0; x = 7, y = 1$ (ii) $x = 0, y = 0; x = \dfrac{11}{7}, y = \dfrac{11}{3}$

4. (i) $x = 4, y = 5$ (ii) $x = 2, y = 1$

5. (i) $x = 2, y = 1$ (ii) $x = \dfrac{1}{2}, y = \dfrac{5}{4}$

MULTIPLE CHOICE QUESTIONS

1. (c)   **2.** (b)   **3.** (c)   **4.** (a)   **5.** (d)

CHAPTER TEST
1. (i) $x = 3, y = 4$ (ii) $x = 14, y = 2$ **2.** (i) $x = -2, y = 7$ (ii) $x = 3 \cdot 2, y = 2 \cdot 3$

3. (i) $x = 0, y = 0$; $x = \dfrac{1}{3}, y = \dfrac{1}{4}$ (ii) $x = 8, y = 3$

4. (i) $x = 1, y = -1$ (ii) $x = 2, y = 3$ **5.** $x = 3, y = -1$; $k = 2$

6. $x = 3, y = 2$; 14   **7.** Yes; $x = \dfrac{1}{3}, y = \dfrac{1}{2}$

EXERCISE 6
1. 33, 17   **2.** 11, −9   **3.** 33, 10   **4.** ₹206

5. 16 kg and 20 kg   **6.** 10, 8

7. 20 paise 20 coins, 25 paise 18 coins   **8.** 20 rupee notes = 16, 5 rupee notes = 12

9. 8 and 12   **10.** $\dfrac{2}{15}$ **11.** $\dfrac{8}{15}$ **12.** $\dfrac{6}{8}$ **13.** 43

14. 34   **15.** 72   **16.** 84   **17.** 45   **18.** 842

19. 34 years, 14 years

20. ₹800   **21.** ₹5000 at 12% and ₹7000 at 10%

22. Table ₹600; chair ₹400   **23.** A has ₹500, B has ₹900

24. 60   **25.** 80 g 18-carat, 40 g 12-carat

26. A in 25 days, B in $37\dfrac{1}{2}$ days   **27.** 18 days

28. 360 km   **29.** 15 km/h, 5 km/h   **30.** 8 km/h, 3 km/h

31. 520 km/h, 40 km/h   **32.** ₹1200, ₹70

MULTIPLE CHOICE QUESTIONS
1. (a)   **2.** (b)   **3.** (c)   **4.** (d)   **5.** (d)   **6.** (d)   **7.** (d)

8. (c)

CHAPTER TEST
1. Almonds 400 g, cashew kernel 300 g   **2.** 8

3. ₹8 per regular hour and ₹10 per hour for overtime

4. 16   **5.** Man's age 42 years, his son's age 12 years

6. 113 m^2 **7.** 40 metres   **8.** 19·5 metres

9. Longer candle 27 cm, smaller candle 24 cm

EXERCISE 7
1. (i) 5, 6   (ii) $\dfrac{5}{2}, -\dfrac{5}{2}$ **2.** (i) $0, \dfrac{5}{2}$ (ii) 8, −6

3. (i) 3, −2   (ii) $1, \dfrac{1}{2}$ **4.** (i) $2, -\dfrac{4}{3}$ (ii) $\dfrac{5}{2}, \dfrac{3}{2}$

5. (i) $\dfrac{5}{2}, -5$ (ii) 7, −7   **6.** (i) $\dfrac{9}{2}, -2$ (ii) $0, -\dfrac{11}{6}$

7. (i) $-\dfrac{1}{2}, -\dfrac{1}{2}$ (ii) −8, 16   **8.** (i) $\dfrac{2}{3}, -\dfrac{2}{7}$ (ii) $-1, \dfrac{3}{2}$

9. (i) $-5, \frac{1}{6}$ (ii) $2, \frac{1}{2}$ **10.** (i) $2, -\frac{4}{3}$ (ii) $3, 9$

11. (i) $4, 3$ (ii) $2, -\frac{4}{3}$ **12.** (i) $5, -\frac{1}{2}$ (ii) $2, -3$

MULTIPLE CHOICE QUESTIONS
1. (b)   **2.** (c)   **3.** (a)   **4.** (d)   **5.** (b)

CHAPTER TEST
1. (i) $-3, \frac{1}{2}$ (ii) $2, -\frac{2}{3}$ **2.** (i) $\frac{1}{4}, \frac{1}{4}$ (ii) $-2, -\frac{3}{2}$

3. (i) $5, \frac{5}{2}$ (ii) $3, \frac{4}{3}$

EXERCISE 8
1. (i) $\frac{8}{27}$ (ii) $\frac{16}{25}$ **2.** (i) $8a^{-9}b^6$ (ii) $a + b$ **3.** (i) $\frac{1}{x+y}$ (ii) $3 \times (10)^{-8}$

4. (i) $5ab$ (ii) $2\frac{1}{4}$ **5.** (i) $2\frac{1}{2}$ (ii) $3\frac{1}{3}$ **6.** (i) 9 (ii) $1\frac{11}{16}$

7. (i) 3^{3n} (ii) $\frac{1}{6}$ **8.** (i) $\frac{1}{2}$ (ii) $-12\frac{3}{4}$ **9.** (i) $\frac{1}{27}$ (ii) $2x$

10. (i) 19 (ii) 231 **11.** (i) 12 (ii) 27 **12.** (i) $2\frac{1}{4}$ (ii) 19

13. (i) $\frac{1}{2}$ (ii) 243 **14.** (i) -2 (ii) $\frac{4}{21}$ **15.** (i) 4 (ii) $\frac{1}{25}$

16. (i) -42 (ii) $98 \cdot 25$ **17.** (i) 3 (ii) $x - \frac{1}{x}$ **18.** (i) 1 (ii) 1

19. (i) 1 (ii) 1 (iii) $x^{2(a^3 + b^3 + c^3)}$

20. (i) $\frac{ab}{b-a}$ (ii) 1 **26.** $1, \frac{1}{x^2y^2}, 9a^6$ **27.** (i) $27\frac{1}{4}$ (ii) $-7\frac{8}{9}$

28. 3 **29.** 6 **30.** $x = 2, y = 3, z = 7$ **31.** $x = 2, y = -\frac{2}{3}$

33. 6 **34.** (i) $-\frac{3}{2}$ (ii) 4 (iii) -7 (iv) -4 **35.** (i) $\frac{3}{4}$ (ii) $\frac{5}{7}$

36. $x = 1, y = -3$ **38.** 1 **39.** 64 **40.** (i) $x = 3$ (ii) $x = 1, \ y = -1$

MULTIPLE CHOICE QUESTIONS
1. (d)   **2.** (c)   **3.** (b)   **4.** (a)   **5.** (a)   **6.** (c)

CHAPTER TEST
1. $x = 4, y = 3, z = 1; 2\frac{1}{40}$ **2.** (i) $3\frac{26}{27}$ (ii) $9\frac{1}{8}$ **6.** (i) 1 (ii) 1 (iii) 1

9. (i) $x = 6$ (ii) $x = \frac{3}{4}, y = -\frac{8}{3}$ (iii) $x = 3, y = \frac{5}{2}$ (iv) $x = 3, y = 1$

EXERCISE 9.1

1. (i) $\log_5 25 = 2$ (ii) $\log_a 64 = 5$ (iii) $\log_7 100 = x$ (iv) $\log_9 1 = 0$

    (v) $\log_6 6 = 1$ (vi) $\log_3 \dfrac{1}{9} = -2$ (vii) $\log_{10} 0.01 = -2$ (viii) $\log_{81} 27 = \dfrac{3}{4}$

2. (i) $2^5 = 32$ (ii) $3^4 = 81$ (iii) $3^{-1} = \dfrac{1}{3}$ (iv) $(8)^{\frac{2}{3}} = 4$

    (v) $(8)^{\frac{5}{3}} = 32$ (vi) $10^{-3} = 0.001$ (vii) $2^{-2} = 0.25$ (viii) $a^{-1} = \dfrac{1}{a}$

3. (i) 4 (ii) 3 (iii) $\dfrac{3}{2}$ (iv) $\dfrac{3}{2}$ (v) -2 (vi) -1 (vii) -8 (viii) -2

4. (i) 9 (ii) 5 (iii) 0.01 (iv) 2 (v) 11 (vi) 4 (vii) 729 (viii) 243

    (ix) $\dfrac{1}{8}$ (x) 5 (xi) 10 (xii) 2 (xiii) $\dfrac{5}{2}$ (xiv) 2 (xv) ± 3 (xvi) $\dfrac{1}{10}$

    (xvii) $6\dfrac{1}{2}$ (xviii) $\dfrac{1}{100}$, $1, \sqrt[3]{10}$

5. $\dfrac{a^2}{1000}$ **6.** (i) $\dfrac{x^2}{1000}$ (ii) $\dfrac{y^3}{10}$ (iii) $\dfrac{x^2 \sqrt{y}}{z^3}$ **7.** 10^{a+b}

8. 10^{3m-2n} **9.** (i) $\sqrt{x}$ (ii) $10y^4$ (iii) $\dfrac{x^{\frac{3}{2}}}{y^4}$ **10.** $y^3 z^2$ **11.** $\dfrac{x^4 y^4}{100}$

EXERCISE 9.2

1. (i) $\log a$ (ii) $\dfrac{3}{2}$ (iii) 2 (iv) $\log 4$ (v) 6 (vi) $\dfrac{1}{3}$

2. (i) $\dfrac{2}{3}$ (ii) $\dfrac{1}{2}$ (iii) 2 (iv) 1 (v) 2 (vi) 0 (vii) 1 (viii) 2

3. (i) $\log 27$ (ii) $\log_{10} 8000$ (iii) $\log 256$ (iv) $\log \dfrac{50}{9}$ (v) $\log \dfrac{9}{100}$

5. $1 - 4a + 2b - 3c$ **6.** (i) 10^a (ii) $\dfrac{2}{5}a$ **7.** (i) 0 (ii) 1

8. (i) 0 (ii) 1 **9.** (i) 1 (ii) 7 **10.** $\dfrac{4}{3}\pi r^3$ **11.** 3 **12.** $\dfrac{100}{x^2}$

13. $\log_{10} 20$ **14.** $\dfrac{\sqrt{x}}{\sqrt[3]{y}}$ **15.** $3x + y$ **16.** $1 - m + 3n$ **17.** 1

18. (i) $\dfrac{9}{5}$ (ii) 6 (iii) $\dfrac{3}{2}$ (iv) 1000 **19.** (i) 5 (ii) 1 **20.** $x = \dfrac{1}{25}, y = \dfrac{1}{2}$

22. (i) 2 (ii) 5 (iii) 4.5 (iv) 3 (v) 1 (vi) 14 (vii) 2

23. $1\dfrac{1}{40}$ **24.** 10 **27.** 3 **30.** $\dfrac{1}{\alpha + \beta + \gamma}$ **31.** (i) 3 (ii) 2

MULTIPLE CHOICE QUESTIONS

1. (c)   **2.** (d)   **3.** (b)   **4.** (a)   **5.** (c)   **6.** (d)   **7.** (a)

CHAPTER TEST

1. $\dfrac{7}{3}\log_a x + \dfrac{8}{3}\log_a y - \dfrac{1}{12}\log_a z$ **2.** 5

7. (i) 7   (ii) $\sqrt{2}$ (iii) $\dfrac{1}{\sqrt{3}}$ (iv) $6\dfrac{1}{2}$ (v) 5, –5   (vi) 11, –11   (vii) 3, –4

(viii) 3   (ix) 10   **8.** $x = 1000$, $y = 100$

EXERCISE 10.1

1. No; because BC and QR are not corresponding sides. In fact, BC = PQ.

2. No; angles must be included angles.

12. $x = 15$, $y = 41$

EXERCISE 10.2

1. AB = QR, then $\triangle ABC \cong \triangle QRP$ by ASA congruence rule.

2. BC = RP, then $\triangle ABC \cong \triangle QRP$ by AAS congruence rule.

3. No; sides must be corresponding sides.

14. (i) $x = 13$, $y = 11$ (ii) $x = 8$, $y = 4$

EXERCISE 10.3

1. $\angle B = 45°$, $\angle B = 45°$

4. (i) 115   (ii) 68   (iii) 72°   **5.** (i) 42   (ii) 40   (iii) 93

6. (a) 95°   (b) 74°   (c) $x = 127°$, $y = 38°$ **7.** 100°

8. (a) $\angle ACE = 120°$, $\angle AEC = 30°$ (c) $x = 42°$, $y = 66°$, $z = 48°$

EXERCISE 10.4

1. PR; because $\angle Q = 80°$ and the side opposite the greatest angle is longest   **3.** $\angle P$

4. (i) $\angle C$ (ii) $\angle A$ **5.** BC, CA, AB   **7.** AB, DC, BD

10. (i) No; sum of the lengths of two sides = length of third side.

     (ii) No; sum of the lengths of two sides is less than the length of third side.

     (iii) Yes; because in each case the sum of lengths of two sides is greater than the length of third side.

MULTIPLE CHOICE QUESTIONS

1. (c)   **2.** (a)   **3.** (b)   **4.** (c)   **5.** (c)   **6.** (d)   **7.** (b)

8. (b)   **9.** (c)   **10.** (a)   **11.** (a)   **12.** (d)   **13.** (d)   **14.** (c)

15. (b)   **16.** (d)   **17.** (a)   **18.** (b)

CHAPTER TEST

1. Two triangles need not be congruent, because AB and EF are not corresponding sides in two triangles.

9. 72°

11. (a) 108° (b) (i) 34   (ii) 70   (iii) 44°   (c) $x = 46°$, $y = 26°$, $z = 72°$

EXERCISE 11

1. (a) (i) 13 cm (ii) 8·2 cm   (b) (i) 2·8 cm   (ii) 72°   (c) 5·2 cm

10. (c) (i) 5 cm (ii) 10 cm

12. (i) 3 cm   (ii) 4·6 cm   (iii) 2·4 cm   (iv) 2·2 cm

MULTIPLE CHOICE QUESTIONS

1. (c)   **2.** (b)   **3.** (d)   **4.** (c)   **5.** (c)   **6.** (d)

EXERCISE 12

1. (i) No   (ii) Yes; 13 cm   (iii) Yes; 5 cm   **2.** 8 m   **3.** $6\sqrt{7}$ m

4. 13 m   **5.** 16 cm, 12 cm   **7.** 8 km   **8.** 10 m, 24 m, 26 m

12. $8\sqrt{2}$ cm; $32\sqrt{2}$ cm^2 **13.** 50 cm^2; $20\sqrt{2}$ cm

14. (a) 4 cm   (b) $5\sqrt{2}$ cm; 25 cm^2

15. (a) 13 cm   (b) 17 cm   (c) $3\frac{1}{6}$ cm   **16.** (a) 4 cm, 8 cm, 20 cm, $5\sqrt{17}$ cm

17. 13 cm   **18.** 100 cm   **19.** (a) 12 cm   (b) 26 cm   (c) (ii) 24 cm^2; $14\sqrt{2}$ cm

MULTIPLE CHOICE QUESTIONS

1. (b)   **2.** (a)   **3.** (b)   **4.** (b)   **5.** (c)   **6.** (b)   **7.** (c)

CHAPTER TEST

1. (a) 28 cm   (b) (i) 10 cm   (ii) 24 cm   (iii) 96 cm^2 (c) (i) 12 cm   (ii) 13·5 cm^2

6. $\dfrac{bc}{\sqrt{b^2 + c^2}}$ **7.** $36\sqrt{2}$ cm

EXERCISE 13.1

1. 90°, 120°   **3.** 72°, 108°, 72°, 108°

4. (a) ∠CDB = 30°, ∠ADB = 80°

(b) ∠OAD = 35°, ∠AOD = 68°, ∠ADO = 77°   (c) 54

5. (a) $x = 4, y = 5$ (b) $x = 30°, y = 95°$ (c) $x = 6, y = 21$ **6.** 80°

7. (a) 45°   (b) ∠OAB = ∠OBA = 34°, ∠AOB = 112°

(c) ∠OAD = 54°, ∠ADO = 36°, ∠AOD = 90°

8. (a) $x = 50°, y = 88°$ (b) $x = 36°, y = 108°$ (c) ∠ODC = 58°, ∠OBA = 34°

23. $\sqrt{3} : 1$

EXERCISE 13.2

1. 63°   **9.** 7·2 cm   **10.** 5·6 cm   **11.** 6·1 cm   **12.** 3·1 cm

13. 61°   **17.** 3·5 cm   **18.** 106°   **19.** 78°

MULTIPLE CHOICE QUESTIONS

1. (d)   **2.** (d)   **3.** (c)   **4.** (b)   **5.** (c)   **6.** (c)   **7.** (d)

8. (a)   **9.** (c)   **10.** (d)   **11.** (c)   **12.** (d)

CHAPTER TEST

4. (i) $x = 29°$ (ii) $x = 39°, y = 111°$ (iii) $x = 64°, y = 96°$

5. (i) $x = 37°, y = 106°, z = 37°$ (ii) $x = 110°$ (iii) $x = 70°, y = 120°, z = 85°$

6. (i) 17°   (ii) 73°   (iii) 45°   (iv) 73°   **7.** 8 cm, $8\sqrt{3}$ cm

EXERCISE 14

9. (b) 5 : 9   (c) (i) 2 : 1   (ii) 1 : 6

10. (a) 5 cm   (b) 6 units   (c) (i) 18 cm^2 (ii) AEFD

15. (a) AB = 12 cm, BC = 9 cm   (b) BC = 12 cm, CA = 10 cm, AB = 15 cm
    (c) (i) 80 cm^2 (ii) 5 : 3   16. 25 sq. units

MULTIPLE CHOICE QUESTIONS

1. (a)   2. (b)   3. (b)   4. (a)   5. (c)   6. (a)   7. (b)
8. (c)

CHAPTER TEST

1. (a) (i) 24 cm^2 (ii) 12 cm^2 6. 12 cm^2

EXERCISE 15.1

1. 10 cm   2. 7 cm   3. 5 cm   4. 16 cm   5. 12 cm

6. (i) 1 cm (ii) 7 cm   7. (a) (i) 13 cm (ii) 10 cm   (b) $4\frac{1}{6}$ cm

8. 21 cm   9. $2\sqrt{29}$ cm   10. 15 cm   11. $2\sqrt{3}$ cm
12. 24 cm   13. 12 cm^2 14. 28 cm

MULTIPLE CHOICE QUESTIONS

1. (c)   2. (d)   3. (a)   4. (d)   5. (c)   6. (a)

CHAPTER TEST

1.   (i) 24 cm   (ii) $12\sqrt{5}$ cm   (iii) $6\sqrt{5}$ cm
2. 9 cm   3. 24 cm   4. (a) 6.65 cm

EXERCISE 16.1

1. 12 cm^2 2. (i) 6 cm^2 (ii) 210 cm^2 (iii) 34·56 cm^2

3. 336 cm^2; 33·6 cm   4. ₹ 47250   5. 30 cm^2, 30 cm   6. 27·71 m^2

7. 54 cm   8. 62·4 cm^2; 10·4 cm   9. (i) 96 cm^2 (ii) 2598 m^2

10. 8 cm^2; 2·83 cm   11. 34·86 cm^2 12. 12 cm^2 13. 17 cm

14. 40 cm   15. 150 cm^2 16. Base = 16 cm, each of other sides = 12 cm

17. 24 cm or 10 cm   18. 1200 m, 400 m   19. $375\sqrt{15}$ m^2; ₹4940

20. $1000\sqrt{6}$ cm^2; $1000\sqrt{6}$ cm^2 21. (a) 19·3 cm^2 (b) 12·5 cm^2

EXERCISE 16.2

1. (i) 240 cm^2 (ii) 108 cm^2 2. 306 m^2 3. 92·35 cm^2 4. 84 cm^2

5. 30 cm, 540 cm^2 6. 98 m   7. (a) 400 m^2 (b) 28 cm^2

8. 160 m^2 9. (i) 26 m, 10 m   (ii) 100 m^2 10. 3 m

11. 8000 m^2 12. 960; $\frac{7}{20}$ 13. 16 x = 5y; 60 m^2

14. $x^2 + 13x - 30 = 0$, $x = 2$ metres   **15.** 75·6 m^2 **16.** 278 m^2

17. (a) 23 m, 17 m^2 (b) 50 m, 51 m^2 (c) 50 cm^2, 54 cm

18. 8 cm   **19.** 22 m, 31·11 m   **20.** 196 m^2, 19·80 m

21. (i) 81 cm^2 (ii) 80 cm^2 **22.** 120 cm^2, 12 cm

23. 119·8 cm^2, 11·98 cm   **24.** 18 cm^2 **25.** 96 cm^2

26. $\dfrac{pq}{p+q}$ cm   **27.** 96 cm^2 **28.** 14 cm   **29.** 90 cm^2

30. 7·5 cm^2 **31.** 20 cm   **32.** (i) 6 cm (ii) 24 cm^2

33. (a) 5 cm, 26 cm^2 (b) 8 units, 40 sq. units (c) 2·4 m   **34.** 216 cm^2

35. 35 cm, 25 cm   **36.** 40 cm   **37.** Base = 14 cm, altitude = 7 cm

38. 24 m, 12 m   **39.** 240 m^2 **40.** 96 cm   **41.** 48 cm

42. $(130 + 32\sqrt{3})$ cm^2, $4(8 + 5\sqrt{2})$ cm   **43.** (a) 51·59 cm^2 (b) 32 cm^2 (c) 192 cm^2

44. (a) 4·5 m^2 (b) 1087·5 m^2 (c) 72 cm^2 **45.** 40 metres

46. 12 cm   **47.** $\dfrac{105}{x}$ cm, $44 = 2\left(x + \dfrac{105}{x}\right)$; 15 cm, 7 cm

48. $(90 - x)$ m ; $x(90 - x) = 1800$; 60 m, 30 m

EXERCISE 16.3

1. 14 cm   **2.** 9 cm; $254\frac{4}{7}$ cm^2 **3.** 19·8 cm   **4.** 12 cm; $75\frac{3}{7}$ cm

5. 88   **6.** 36 cm   **7.** (a) (i) 28 cm (ii) 88 cm (b) 100·48 cm^2 ; 57·12 cm

8. 40   **9.** 48 km/h   **10.** (i) 19·6 cm (ii) 1207 cm^2 (iii) 4 times

11. (a) 14 cm (b) 17·5 cm   **12.** ₹9625   **13.** 26 cm, 18 cm

14. 44 cm   **15.** 154 cm^2 **16.** 346·5 cm^2 **17.** (a) 88 cm (b) 19·35 cm^2

18. 567 cm^2

19. (a) 42 cm^2; 72 cm (b) 42 cm^2 (c) 98 cm^2 **20.** (a) 231 cm^2; 80 cm (b) 283·969 cm^2

21. (a) 29 m^2 (b) 24·5 cm^2 **22.** 346·5 cm^2 ; 283·5 cm^2

23. 12 cm^2 **24.** (a) 72·75 cm^2 (b) 14 cm^2

25. 22050 m^2 **26.** (i) $1 : \sqrt{2}$ (ii) 1 : 2

27. (a) (i) 17850 m^2 (ii) 664 m (b) $636\frac{4}{7}$ m^2

28. (a) 122·57 cm^2 (b) 42 cm^2 **29.** (a) 4032 m^2 (b) 228 cm^2

30. (a) 59·5 cm^2 (b) 66·5 cm^2 **31.** (a) 504 cm^2 (b) (i) 31·4 cm (ii) 39·25 cm^2

32. (a) 31·4 cm; 31·4 cm^2 (b) 9·72 cm^2

33. (a) 41·25 cm^2 (b) 1404 cm^2 **34.** (a) (i) 44 cm (ii) 86·625 cm^2 (b) 6·125 cm^2

35. (a) 428·75 cm^2 (b) 2·58 cm^2 **36.** (i) $\dfrac{132}{7}$ cm (ii) $\dfrac{198}{7}$ cm^2

37. 78·5 cm^2; 285·5 cm^2

EXERCISE 16.4

1. 294 cm^2, 343 cm^3 **2.** 94 m^2; 60 m^3; 7·07 m   **3.** 14 cm

4. 40 ; 6   **5.** (a) 12 cm   (b) 150 cm^2, 125 cm^3 **6.** 7

7. 70 cm   **8.** 486 cm^2, 15·57 cm   **9.** 9 cm

10. 504000 cm^3; 38200 cm^2 **11.** 120   **12.** 60

13. 0·729 m³; 0·9 m   14. 7·39 cm   15. 38 cm³

16. 1440 cm²   17. 3 cm   18. ₹12480

19. 13·95   20. $\dfrac{8}{13}$ metre   21. ₹1350   22. ₹2596·80

23. 75   24. 6   25. 8·4 litres

26. (a) 80 cm³   (b) (i) 16·5 m²   (ii) 6600 m³   (c) 1000 m³   27. 2250 m³

MULTIPLE CHOICE QUESTIONS

1. (b)   2. (c)   3. (a)   4. (c)   5. (d)   6. (b)   7. (c)

8. (c)   9. (a)   10. (c)   11. (a)   12. (b)   13. (d)   14. (d)

15. (b)   16. (c)   17. (d)   18. (a)   19. (c)   20. (a)   21. (a)

22. (b)   23. (c)   24. (b)

CHAPTER TEST

1. (a) 54 cm²   (b) 32 cm   2. (a) 51 cm²   (b) 144 cm²   (c) 54 m²

3. 19·3 cm²   4. 31·4 cm   5. 196 cm²   6. (a) 300; 6450 cm² (b) 36 cm

7. ₹ 20790   8. 1480·5 m²   9. 59·4 cm; 61·1 cm²

10. (a) 12·5 cm (b) (i) $\sqrt{10}$ cm (ii) 11·4 cm²   11. (a) 32·5 cm²; 23 cm   (b) 5 cm

13. 154 cm²   14. 7 cm; 38·5 cm²   15. 1008 cm²   16. No

17. 378 km   18. 75 cm   19. (i) 8 cm   (ii) 448 cm³   21. 152000 cm³; 16800 cm²

22. (i) 564000 cm³   (ii) 69864 cm³   (iii) 55·9 kg

23. (i) 450   (ii) ₹54000   24. ₹756

EXERCISE 17

1. (a) (i) $\dfrac{3}{5}$ (ii) $\dfrac{4}{5}$ (iii) $\dfrac{3}{4}$ (iv) $\dfrac{4}{3}$ (v) $\dfrac{5}{4}$ (vi) $\dfrac{5}{3}$

   (b) (i) $\dfrac{5}{13}$ (ii) $\dfrac{12}{13}$ (iii) 1   (iv) 1

2. (a) (i) $\dfrac{4}{5}$ (ii) $\dfrac{4}{5}$ (iii) $\dfrac{7}{5}$ (iv) 1   (b) (i) $\dfrac{5}{12}$ (ii) $\dfrac{4}{5}$ (iii) 1   (iv) 14

3. (a) $\dfrac{5}{4}$ (b) (i) $\dfrac{4}{5}$ (ii) $\dfrac{3}{4}$ (iii) −1   (iv) $\dfrac{3}{2\sqrt{2}}$ (v) −1

4. (a) (i) $\dfrac{2}{5}$ (ii) $\dfrac{2}{5}$ (iii) $\dfrac{6}{5}$ (iv) $\dfrac{14}{5}$ (b) (i) $\dfrac{3}{5}$ (ii) 4 units

5. (i) $\dfrac{12}{13}$ (ii) $\dfrac{1}{5}$ 6. (a) (i) $\dfrac{7}{25}$ (ii) $\dfrac{24}{7}$ (b) (i) $\dfrac{9}{41}$ (ii) $\dfrac{40}{41}$ (iii) $\dfrac{40}{9}$

7. (i) $\dfrac{3}{5}$ (ii) $\dfrac{4}{5}$

8. (a) (i) $\dfrac{4}{5}$ (ii) $\dfrac{4}{3}$ (iii) $\dfrac{7}{12}$ (b) $4\dfrac{4}{5}$

   (c) (i) AD = 20 cm, AB = 25 cm, DC = 20 cm, AC = $20\sqrt{2}$ cm

9. (i) $\dfrac{4}{5}$ (ii) $\dfrac{3}{4}$ 10. $\dfrac{5}{13}; \dfrac{12}{13}$ 11. $1\dfrac{11}{20}$ 12. $1\dfrac{2}{5}$

13. $\dfrac{2(\sqrt{5}-1)}{\sqrt{5}}$ 14. $\dfrac{p+\sqrt{q^2-p^2}}{q}$ 15. $3\dfrac{31}{120}$ 16. $\dfrac{12}{65}$ 17. 8

18. $\dfrac{3}{5}$ **19.** $2\dfrac{3}{7}$ **20.** $\dfrac{17}{19}$ **21.** $\dfrac{p^2 - q^2}{p^2 + q^2}$ **22.** $\dfrac{1}{9}$

23. (i) $\dfrac{17}{19}$ (ii) 3   **24.** $\dfrac{1}{4}$ **25.** $\dfrac{3}{2}$

28. (a) (i) $\dfrac{6}{5}$ (ii) $\dfrac{5}{13}$ (b) (i) $\dfrac{12}{13}$ (ii) $\dfrac{5}{12}$ **29.** $\dfrac{150}{\sqrt{13}}$ cm ; $103\dfrac{11}{13}$ cm^2

30. (a) (i) $\dfrac{5}{13}$ (ii) $\dfrac{4}{3}$ (b) $\dfrac{12}{\sin \theta}$ or $\dfrac{9}{\cos \theta}$ **32.** cot θ   **33.** 2

MULTIPLE CHOICE QUESTIONS

1. (b)   **2.** (c)   **3.** (a)   **4.** (d)   **5.** (a)   **6.** (a)   **7.** (b)

8. (a)   **9.** (b)   **10.** (a)   **11.** (a)   **12.** (b)   **13.** (c)

CHAPTER TEST

1. (a) $\sin A = \dfrac{2}{3}$, $\cos A = \dfrac{\sqrt{5}}{3}$, $\tan A = \dfrac{2}{\sqrt{5}}$, $\cot A = \dfrac{\sqrt{5}}{2}$, $\sec A = \dfrac{3}{\sqrt{5}}$,

     $\operatorname{cosec} A = \dfrac{3}{2}$; $\sin C = \dfrac{\sqrt{5}}{3}$, $\cos C = \dfrac{2}{3}$, $\tan C = \dfrac{\sqrt{5}}{2}$, $\cot C = \dfrac{2}{\sqrt{5}}$,

     $\sec C = \dfrac{3}{2}$, $\operatorname{cosec} C = \dfrac{3}{\sqrt{5}}$

     (b) $x = 10 \cot \theta$, $y = 10 \operatorname{cosec} \theta$

2. (a) (i) $\dfrac{4}{5}$ (ii) $3\dfrac{2}{15}$ (b) (i) 3   (ii) $5\dfrac{1}{4}$ (iii) $-4\dfrac{3}{4}$ **3.** $\dfrac{q^2 - 2p^2}{p\sqrt{q^2 - p^2}}$

4. (i) $\dfrac{3}{5}$ (ii) $\dfrac{4}{5}$ (iii) -1 **6.** $\dfrac{3}{5}$ **7.** $9\dfrac{1}{9}$ **8.** $12\dfrac{8}{15}$ m

EXERCISE 18.1

1. (i) $\dfrac{7}{4}$ (ii) 2   (iii) $\dfrac{3}{2}$ (iv) $\dfrac{1}{4}$ **2.** (i) $\dfrac{1}{3}$ (ii) $\dfrac{3}{2}$ (iii) $\dfrac{25}{36}$

3. (i) 0   (ii) 3   (iii) $-5\dfrac{17}{20}$ **6.** (i) $\dfrac{1}{\sqrt{3}}$ (ii) $\dfrac{1}{3}$ **8.** $2 : \sqrt{3}$

11. (i) 30° (ii) 10° (iii) 60°   **12.** 45°; $\dfrac{3}{2}$

13. (i) $\sqrt{3}$ (ii) 60   (iii) $\dfrac{1}{2}$ (iv) 2   **14.** (i) 20° (ii) 15°   **15.** 15°

16. (i) 60   (ii) 1   (iii) $-\dfrac{1}{2}$ **17.** (i) 45°   (ii) 45°

18. (i) $\dfrac{1}{2}$ (ii) $\dfrac{1}{2}$ (iii) -1 **19.** $\dfrac{1}{2}$ **20.** 60°

21. A = 45°, B = 15°   **22.** 8 cm, $8\sqrt{3}$ cm   **23.** BC = $2\sqrt{3}$ cm, AB = $4\sqrt{3}$ cm

24. $12\sqrt{3}$ m   **25.** $4(3 - \sqrt{3})$ m

EXERCISE 18.2

1. (i) 1   (ii) 1   (iii) 1   **2.** (i) $\dfrac{1}{2}$ (ii) 2   (iii) 0   (iv) 1   (v) 1

3. (i) 0   (ii) 0   **4.** (i) 2   (ii) 3   **5.** (i) 5   (ii) 0

6. (i) cot 9° + sin 18°   (ii) tan 41° + sec 3°   **12.** (i) 0   (ii) 1   (iii) 0

15. (i) sin^2 θ   (ii) 2   **17.** (i) 24° (ii) 36° (iii) 39°   **18.** (i) 27°   (ii) 55°

MULTIPLE CHOICE QUESTIONS
1. (*d*)   **2.** (*b*)   **3.** (*c*)   **4.** (*b*)   **5.** (*b*)   **6.** (*a*)   **7.** (*d*)
8. (*c*)   **9.** (*d*)   **10.** (*b*)   **11.** (*d*)   **12.** (*d*)   **13.** (*a*)   **14.** (*b*)
15. (*a*)

CHAPTER TEST
1. (*i*) $1\dfrac{1}{4}$ (*ii*) 1   (*iii*) $3\dfrac{1}{2}$ **5.** $\dfrac{4}{3}$ **6.** $10°, 22\dfrac{1}{2}°$

7. $A = 52\dfrac{1}{2}°$, $B = 7\dfrac{1}{2}°$ **8.** (*i*) 0   (*ii*) 4   (*iii*) 1   (*iv*) 2

10. (*i*) 18°   (*ii*) 15°   **11.** (*i*) 27°   (*ii*) 22°   **12.** $6\sqrt{3}$ cm

EXERCISE 19.1
1. (*i*) $(3, -4)$ (*ii*) $\left(-\dfrac{3}{2}, 5\right)$ (*iii*) $\left(-1\dfrac{2}{3}, -2\dfrac{1}{4}\right)$ (*iv*) $(-2, 5)$

    (*v*) $(-2, 0)$ (*vi*) $\left(0, \dfrac{3}{2}\right)$

2. II, IV, *x*-axis, I, III respectively   **3.** (*i*) C, F, G   (*ii*) A, D, E

5. A(2, 2), B(−3, 0), C(−2, −4), D(3, −1), E(−4, 4), F(0, −2), G(2, −3), H(0, 3)

6. A lies in the first quadrant, B lies on *x*-axis, C lies in the third quadrant and D in the fourth quadrant

9. (*i*) collinear   (*ii*) non-collinear   (*iii*) collinear

10. M (−3, 0) and N (0, 4)   **11.** Rectangle; 15 sq. units

12. Rhombus; 12 sq. units   **13.** (2, −2); 25 square units

14. (0, 0), (6, 0), (6, 4), (0, 4)   **15.** A(−3, 0), B(3, 0), C(3, 3), D(−3, 3)

16. O(0, 0), A(a, $\sqrt{3}\,a$), B($2a$, 0)   **17.** ($2\sqrt{3}$, 0)

EXERCISE 19.2
3. 15 sq. units   **4.** 6 sq. units   **5.** (*i*) −7   (*ii*) 3   **6.** 2   **7.** $a = 0$, $b = 1$

EXERCISE 19.3
1. $x = -2, y = -5$ **2.** $x = -4, y = -2$ **3.** $x = 2, y = -2$ **4.** $x = -1, y = 0$
5. $x = 2, y = 2$ **6.** $x = 2, y = 1$ **7.** (*ii*) $(-2, -1)$ (*iii*) 4·5 cm

8. $x = 2, y = -1$ **9.** (*ii*) (2, 4) ; $6\dfrac{2}{3}$ sq. units

10. $x = 1, y = -2$; $\dfrac{3}{2}$ sq. units   **11.** $x = 2, y = 1$; $\dfrac{4}{3}$ sq. units

12. (−3, 2), (−3, 6), (3, 2)   **13.** (0, 0), (5, 0), (2, 2) ; 5 sq. units

EXERCISE 19.4
1. (*i*) $2\sqrt{2}$ units   (*ii*) 39 units   (*iii*) $2\sqrt{a^2 + b^2}$ units   **2.** 5 units   **3.** −3

4. (*i*) (2, 0) or (8, 0)   (*ii*) (0, 2) or (0, 14)   (*iii*) (1, 2) or (3, 6)   **5.** (−7, 0)

6. 5 or −3   **7.** 4 or −4   **8.** $x - y = 2$ **9.** (16, 8)   **10.** 2   **11.** 1

13. $2, -\dfrac{46}{13}$ **15.** Yes   **16.** Scalene triangle   **19.** 1   **20.** 40 sq. units

21. 24 sq. units   **23.** (*i*) square (*ii*) parallelogram   **24.** (5, 2); 5 units

MULTIPLE CHOICE QUESTIONS

1. (*b*)	**2.** (*c*)	**3.** (*b*)	**4.** (*c*)	**5.** (*d*)	**6.** (*d*)	**7.** (*c*)
8. (*b*)	**9.** (*b*)	**10.** (*d*)	**11.** (*d*)	**12.** (*b*)	**13.** (*c*)	**14.** (*c*)
15. (*b*)	**16.** (*b*)	**17.** (*c*)	**18.** (*b*)	**19.** (*c*)	**20.** (*b*)	**21.** (*a*)
22. (*c*)	**23.** (*b*)	**24.** (*b*)	**25.** (*a*)			

CHAPTER TEST

1. (4, −1); (*i*) (3, 7)   (*ii*) (4, 3)   (*iii*) (3, 3); 16 sq. units

2. (−1, 3); (−1, 0); 24 sq. units   **4.** (*i*) −6   (*ii*) 8   **5.** $x = 5, y = 1$

6. $x = 2, y = -1$ **7.** (4, 5); 12·5 sq. units   **8.** (−3, −2), (5, 1), (1, 6)

9. (2, −1), (3, 2), (−4, 2); 10·5 sq. units   **10.** 6 or −10

11. −7   **14.** (*i*) 8 sq. units   (*ii*) 45 sq. units; No   **15.** 6 or −6

16. Rectangle   **17.** (2, −4)

EXERCISE 20.1

1. 6   **2.** 13 hours   **3.** 2780   **4.** 6·5   **5.** (*i*) $\frac{41}{6}$ (*ii*) $10\frac{5}{7}$

6. (*i*) 82 (*ii*) Vijay : 12 years, Rahul : 15 years; Rakhi : 18 years   **7.** 8   **8.** 27

9. 18   **10.** 13   **11.** 45·9 kg   **12.** 42   **13.** 5

14. Mean = 2·4, median = 2·5

15. Mean time = 25 minutes, median time = 24 minutes

16. Mean = 54·8, median = 52   **17.** Mean = 15·5 points, median = 12 points

18. 45   **19.** 11

EXERCISE 20.2

1. (*i*) Discrete   (*ii*) continuous   (*iii*) discrete   (*iv*) continuous   (*v*) continuous

2.

Classes	0 – 4	5 – 9	10 – 14	15 – 19	20 – 24
Frequency	2	7	8	6	2

3. (*i*)

Classes	1 – 10	11 – 20	21 – 30	31 – 40
Frequency	8	7	6	6

(*ii*) Range = 38   (*iii*) 25·5

5. (*i*) frequency   (*ii*) size   (*iii*) 14   (*iv*) class mark   (*v*) 6·5

6. (*i*)

Classes	1 – 10	11 – 20	21 – 30	31 – 40	41 – 50
Frequency	7	8	7	10	8

(*ii*)

Classes	0·5 – 10·5	10·5 – 20·5	20·5 – 30·5	30·5 – 40·5	40·5 – 50·5
Frequency	7	8	7	10	8

(*iii*) lower limit = 20·5; upper limit = 30·5   (*iv*) 35·5

7. (*i*) upper limit = 52;   lower limit = 48
   (*ii*) upper limit = 52·5; lower limit = 47·5
   (*iii*) 37·5 and 42·5   (*iv*) 45   (*v*) 5

8.

Marks % (classes)	10 – 19	20 – 29	30 – 39	40 – 49	50 – 59	60 – 69	70 – 79	80 – 89
Frequency	7	11	20	46	57	37	15	7
C. frequency	7	18	38	84	141	178	193	200

9.

Classes	0 – 10	10 – 20	20 – 30	30 – 40	40 – 50
Frequency	5	5	7	10	8
C. frequency	5	10	17	27	35

Number of students obtaining below 20 marks = 10

10. (*i*)

Classes	Tally marks	Frequency	Cumulative frequency
0 – 10	III	3	3
10 – 20	II	2	5
20 – 30	NI NI I	11	16
30 – 40	NI NI NI III	18	34
40 – 50	–	–	34
50 – 60	III	3	37
60 – 70	II	2	39
70 – 80	III	3	42
80 – 90	NI	5	47
90 – 100	III	3	50

(*ii*) 30 – 40   (*iii*) 34   (*iv*) 13.

11.

Classes	0 – 4	4 – 7	7 – 10	10 – 13	13 – 16
Frequency	7	31	137	73	52

Number of children in the age group 10 – 13 = 73

12.

Classes	0 – 10	11 – 20	21 – 30	31 – 40	41 – 50	51 – 60
Frequency	2	5	11	14	11	7

13.

Classes	30 – 40	40 – 50	50 – 60	60 – 70	70 – 80	80 – 90	90 – 100	100 – 110
Frequency	2	1	4	4	9	5	3	4

14.

Classes	23·5 – 27·5	27·5 – 31·5	31·5 – 35·5	35·5 – 39·5	39·5 – 43·5
Frequency	4	7	4	4	11

15. (*i*) 10; lower limit = 119;   upper limit = 129
    (*ii*) 7; lower limit = 20;   upper limit = 27

EXERCISE 20.3

17.

Class intervals	30–40	40–50	50–60	60–70	70–80	80–90	90–100	100–110
No. of houses	3	1	4	5	9	3	3	4

18.

Class intervals	40–42	42–44	44–46	46–48	48–50	50–52	52–54
Frequency	2	12	7	6	7	4	2

19. (*i*) 18   (*ii*) 475 – 500   (*iii*) 34

(*iv*)

Classes	Frequency	Cumulative frequency
375 – 400	6	6
400 – 425	18	24
425 – 450	10	34
450 – 475	20	54
475 – 500	4	58

MULTIPLE CHOICE QUESTIONS

1. (*b*)   **2.** (*b*)   **3.** (*b*)   **4.** (*c*)   **5.** (*b*)   **6.** (*b*)   **7.** (*c*)

8. (*b*)   **9.** (*d*)   **10.** (*a*)   **11.** (*d*)   **12.** (*b*)   **13.** (*c*)   **14.** (*c*)

15. (*c*)   **16.** (*a*)

CHAPTER TEST

1. Mean = 4·25, median = 4·5   **2.** Mean = 12·4, median = 7

3. 51 kg   **4.** 14·6 years   **5.** 10   **6.** 150·25 cm

7. 35·5   **8.** 62

12.

Class intervals	50–60	60–70	70–80	80–90	90–100	100–110	110–120	120–130
No. of houses	2	6	5	8	5	7	3	4

13.

Class intervals	19 – 20	21 – 22	23 – 24	25 – 26	27 – 28	29 – 30
No. of students	3	5	10	10	5	2

14.   (*i*) 6   (*ii*) 45 – 51   (*iii*) 51 – 57

Classes	27 – 33	33 – 39	39 – 45	45 – 51	51 – 57	57 – 63
Frequency	4	12	18	6	20	8